ANATOMY OF THE MONOCOTYLEDONS

EDITED BY C. R. METCALFE

Keeper of the Jodrell Laboratory,
Royal Botanic Gardens, Kew

III

COMMELINALES–ZINGIBERALES

BY

P. B. TOMLINSON

Research Scientist, Fairchild Tropical Garden,
Miami, Florida; and
Lecturer in Forest Anatomy, Cabot Foundation,
Harvard University, Cambridge, Massachusetts,
U.S.A.

OXFORD

AT THE CLARENDON PRESS

1969

Oxford University Press, Ely House, London W. I

GLASGOW NEW YORK TORONTO MELBOURNE WELLINGTON
CAPE TOWN SALISBURY IBADAN NAIROBI LUSAKA ADDIS ABABA
BOMBAY CALCUTTA MADRAS KARACHI LAHORE DACCA
KUALA LUMPUR SINGAPORE HONG KONG TOKYO

PRINTED IN GREAT BRITAIN

FOREWORD

IN the foreword to the first volume of this series in 1960 I remarked that anatomical research had been conducted in the Jodrell Laboratory from 1876. Since that was written a new laboratory has replaced the older one, with modern facilities, a much-increased staff, and scope for wider research on the living collections. Anatomical investigations, of which this present volume is a very significant product, will continue to be a major interest and with better accommodation and more assistance it is hoped more rapid progress with the succeeding volumes of *Anatomy of the Monocotyledons* will result.

Much is owed to the ready help and collaboration of external colleagues working in concert with Dr. Metcalfe and to none is gratitude more unreservedly given than to Dr. P. B. Tomlinson, author of Volume II (Palmae) and now of Volume III, which deals with the orders Commelinales–Zingiberales, following the arrangement in Hutchinson's *Families of Flowering Plants*.

For some years Dr. Tomlinson has worked at the Fairchild Tropical Garden in Florida with excellent resources for the pursuit of his specialized studies and the continued support and ready understanding of the Director, Dr. John Popenoe, is warmly appreciated. On several occasions Tomlinson has visited Kew but he has also been fortunate to travel extensively to collect in various tropical and subtropical regions so that his anatomical investigations are in many instances supported by first-hand field knowledge.

Dr. Sherwin Carlquist of the Rancho Santa Ana Botanic Garden, California, has contributed the section on Rapateaceae in this volume and this help is greatly appreciated and also that of Dr. Bassett Maguire of the New York Botanical Garden who specially collected material of this family.

In his work on the Bromeliaceae Dr. Tomlinson has been guided through the systematic complexities of the family by Dr. Lyman Smith of the Smithsonian Institution, Washington, the acknowledged authority on this difficult taxonomic group. Furthermore the rich collections of bromeliads of Mr. Mulford Foster at Orlando, Florida, have been made freely available to Dr. Tomlinson and this privilege has been of great value in ensuring a wide treatment of the family. The collaboration of Professor R. A. Howard and Professor R. C. Rollins of Harvard University is also gratefully acknowledged.

The coverage of families in this volume, while not by any means complete, is sufficiently comprehensive to give a wide survey of their salient anatomical features. Clearly it assembles a great deal of matter already published, but Dr. Tomlinson's own observations add very considerably to our knowledge of these families. By using modern laboratory methods and by drawing on his field experience of the plants the author has been able to direct attention to some errors of interpretation made by previous investigators. I believe the volume will be accepted as a notable contribution to the systematic anatomy of the Monocotyledons.

GEORGE TAYLOR

EDITOR'S PREFACE

WE are already indebted to Dr. P. B. Tomlinson for Volume II of *Anatomy of the Monocotyledons* in which he briefly surveys the external morphology and describes in greater detail the histology of the palms. Even while the writing of the palm volume was in progress, Tomlinson had investigated the anatomy of the Zingiberaceae and Costaceae. Later, spurred on by his boundless energy and stimulated by direct contact with tropical and subtropical vegetation in three widely separated regions, he has turned his attention to no less than sixteen families of monocotyledons forming the second half of the Calyciferae in Hutchinson's *Families of Flowering Plants*.

Although the plants now described are herbaceous rather than arboreal, many of the herbs are very tall in stature compared with most of those that are encountered in temperate regions. This is partly due to the evolution of the pseudostem, which we encounter, for example, in the banana family (Musaceae) and consists of tightly overlapping leaf bases which collectively form a structure resembling a stem in appearance when viewed externally. The pseudostem, in the moist conditions of the tropics, provides sufficient mechanical support for the very large, petiolate leaves of the bananas and Heliconias. The large size of these plants has thus been achieved along a very different evolutionary pathway from that of the palms, where the great stature that is reached by many of them depends on the possession of a massive trunk which is morphologically a true stem but in which there is no true cambium as in the dicotyledons. At the other end of the scale the plants described by Dr. Tomlinson include the humble Pipe-wort (*Eriocaulon septangulare*). Although widely distributed in North America, this species has an interesting extension to the British Isles where it is, however, confined to the Scottish Hebrides and the west coast of Ireland. This volume also covers the distinctive family Bromeliaceae, with its terrestrial and epiphytic plants confined to the New World, but of which a few members are becoming more familiar as house plants in temperate regions. The Commelinaceae are made familiar to every student of botany who has been called upon to watch the 'streaming of protoplasm' in the staminal hairs of *Tradescantia*, but other families such as the Xyridaceae are relatively unknown, in spite of the attractive flowers of some of them, except to those botanists who have had the good fortune to visit the warmer parts of the world. The fascinating family Rapateaceae is mainly confined to parts of tropical South America but with an interesting small extension into Africa. For the anatomical description of this family which is presented here we are indebted to Dr. Sherwin Carlquist of the Rancho Santa Ana Botanic Garden, Claremont, California, whose collaboration is greatly appreciated.

It is by no means easy to provide an account of the systematic anatomy of such a varied assortment of plants in a manner that makes for easy reference. Indeed it has been found by experience that there is no single method of description that is equally satisfactory for dealing with monocotyledons in general. This is, firstly, because some families show more histological diversity than others. Secondly, the anatomy of some families is incompletely known compared with that of others. Thirdly, there are some families such as the Marantaceae where diversity of external form conceals a relative uniformity of internal structure. Uniformity of structure makes detailed descriptions of individual genera and species appear highly repetitive and dull. This applies also where our present knowledge is too scrappy to enable genera and species to be easily differentiated. Both of these considerations have played a part in making both the author and editor decide that we are not at present in a position to justify an attempt to draw up descriptions for individual genera, and still less for species, for members of the families covered in the present volume. The mode of presentation is, therefore, rather different from that which was adopted in Volume I dealing with the Gramineae and in Volume II which covers the Palmae. The style is, in fact, more like that used by Metcalfe and Chalk in *Anatomy of the Dicotyledons*. Although this change makes for lack of uniformity, it has seemed wiser to present the information in whatever way is most appropriate for the plants to be described than to be bound too rigidly by a universal plan which is unsuitable for some families. In two forthcoming volumes, where the story of the Glumiflorae will be completed, a return has been made to the style for the Gramineae in Volume I.

Both the editor and author have, in earlier writings, stressed that, contrary to common belief, our knowledge of the histology of the vegetative organs of the families of flowering plants is still very restricted. This applies particularly to families that occur in tropical and subtropical areas. Indeed, the editor knows from first-hand experience that it is quite easy to make new discoveries in a tropical country by examining the vegetative organs of even quite common plants with the aid of such simple devices as a good hand lens and some safety-razor blades. If we go a stage further and use a compound microscope as well, our discoveries can be all the more interesting and enlightening. It may be that in dealing with some of the larger tropical species we shall sometimes need saws and machetes as supplementary tools in our investigations. The main point to be stressed is, however, that in the relatively unexplored regions of the world it is still possible to make worthwhile additions to anatomical knowledge without expensive equipment provided one knows how to set about the task.

It cannot be too strongly emphasized that the subject-matter of this volume must in no sense be accepted as the final word on the topics discussed. It is hoped rather that the summary of our present knowledge provided here will serve as a stimulus to further investigation.

C. R. METCALFE

Keeper of the Jodrell Laboratory

Royal Botanic Gardens, Kew
February 1967

AUTHOR'S PREFACE

T H I S volume continues the series dealing with the anatomy of the vegetative organs of monocotyledonous families initiated in 1960 with Volume I dealing with the Gramineae and continued with Volume II dealing with the Palmae. This present volume covers a sequence of families to be found in Hutchinson's *Families of Flowering Plants*, Vol. II, *Monocotyledons*. In writing *Anatomy of the Monocotyledons* Hutchinson's system has been used as a taxonomic guide especially to the sequence and composition of the families and for these purposes it has proved to be very useful. It is well known, however, that opinions concerning the taxonomic and phylogenetic affinities of monocotyledonous families are still far from unanimous and this state of affairs seems likely to persist until our views can rest more firmly on established fact rather than on speculative considerations. It will therefore come as no surprise that, in this volume, the author has found that occasional departures from Hutchinson's system have made it possible to conform more closely to the taxonomic pattern that is suggested by the anatomical evidence. For example, the author, unlike Hutchinson, has treated the Costaceae and Heliconiaceae as families rather than tribes.

The sixteen families dealt with are included by Hutchinson in 5 orders, Commelinales, Xyridales, Eriocaulales, Bromeliales, and Zingiberales (orders 90–94). It may seem rather arbitrary to have selected these orders for treatment in a self-contained volume until it is appreciated that these orders include all the families of his Calyciferae except the predominantly aquatic groups Butomales – Najadales (orders 83–89). This division of the Calyciferae is therefore convenient since it permits a future volume of this series to be devoted solely to those families of monocotyledons which are predominantly aquatic. Other volumes will deal with major assemblages from Hutchinson's system in the same way.

For purposes of description and discussion these 16 families fall conveniently into two sections. The first 8 families were all originally members of the order Farinosae erected by Engler to include 13 families. The 5 families of Engler's Farinosae not included in this present volume are variously dispersed by Hutchinson throughout other orders. This rearrangement by Hutchinson is one example of the way in which the Farinosae have been dismembered by successive generations of taxonomists and suggests that the Farinosae are not a natural group. Information presented in this volume allows a limited discussion of the classification of these 8 families in the light of their anatomy.

On the other hand, the last 8 families in this volume constitute the very natural order Zingiberales (the Scitamineae of most earlier authorities). Accounts of these families are largely based on a series of detailed papers already published by the author in the *Journal of the Linnean Society* (Botany). The scitaminean families are dealt with less exhaustively than the others and the literature relating to them is surveyed less completely than for the farinosean families.

The families included in this volume are all described in Solereder and Meyer's *Systematische Anatomie der Monokotyledonen* (1929–33). The present volume complements rather than supersedes Solereder and Meyer's pioneer work. Indeed, Solereder and Meyer's treatise summarizes the older literature more completely and for this reason will continue to be an invaluable reference work.

Obvious differences in the layout of this volume compared with its predecessors may call for comment. However, differences between Volumes I and II themselves have already established a precedent for treating the monocotyledonous groups in diverse ways rather than adopting a rigid system. Volume III, to a large extent, returns to the style of presentation in Metcalfe and Chalk's *Anatomy of the Dicotyledons*. For each family a summarized synthesis of new and old information is presented rather than a separate description of each genus or species. Each summary account thus provides a general description of the whole family. Features of special interest, and their distribution, are pointed out where appropriate. There are several reasons for adopting this approach. One is that, in general, examination of species that have been investigated by previous anatomists tends to confirm older observations. To present the original and the confirmatory evidence twice over would involve meaningless duplication. A second reason is that in most families the general anatomical facies for large numbers of species or even genera is very constant. To describe each taxon separately would involve so much repetition that special observations would be obscured. The reader who wishes to gain an over-all view of the anatomy of each family together with some idea of their anatomical features which are of systematic value will therefore find this volume of most immediate value. The reader who wishes to find a precise and detailed description of that particular genus or species which is his immediate concern may be disappointed, until it is realized that an attempt has been made to guide him into anatomical literature in such a way that this information may be sought.

Because these summaries are syntheses of old and new information it may not be clear to what extent they are based on original observations. For this reason at the end of each family description I have included a list of material specially examined, with an indication of its source. An additional appendix to each family indicates the extent to which I have surveyed the literature. In these appendixes I have, as far as possible, not only given the names of the species examined by each author, but have also indicated which particular organs or tissues have received attention. A separate bibliography is given for each family. Although this leads to some duplication in citation this disadvantage is outweighed by the convenience of allowing the reader to look up separately the literature referring to each family.

The families dealt with in this volume are predominantly, if not wholly, tropical in their distribution. Representatives of some of the families are to be found in almost any tropical country, but others have a more limited distribution. This poses special problems if one wishes to gain an equally thorough understanding of all families. Who, for example, can comprehend the variety and complexity of the Bromeliaceae without seeing them in their diverse habitats, both epiphytic and terrestrial, in the New World tropics, to which they are virtually confined? The Zingiberaceae are a widespread family but show most diversification in the Indo-Malayan region. The systematic anatomist (or any other specialist) may believe he appreciates the special problems posed by the Marantaceae when he has seen the diversity of their growth forms as encountered at first hand in West African forests—until he further widens his experience of the family as he travels in the American tropics.

Although I am primarily an anatomist rather than a collector or field-botanist I have been fortunate enough to have had an opportunity to study many of the plants on which I have worked in their natural environments and I have personally collected a fair proportion of the material used in my anatomical investigations. It has been a special privilege to have undergone these broadening experiences at a time when biology is becoming so increasingly preoccupied with the uniformity of organelles that we are becoming decreasingly aware of the diversity of organisms. The need for an equally over-all view of diversity as well as uniformity is important in biology. Too few of us have the opportunity to catch a glimpse of both panoramas.

For historical reasons the largest herbaria and most comprehensive botanical libraries are situated in temperate countries. It is equally obvious to the plant geographer that the greatest wealth of botanical materials is in tropical countries remote from these large collections and libraries. A survey of the kind attempted in this volume requires reference books, collections of dried specimens, living plants, and the necessary facilities for microscopical investigation. Inevitably these are not all available in one place. A compromise has to be sought. It is to be hoped that there is not too much evidence in these pages of this compromise, of the fact that the work which has enabled them to be written has been undertaken during periods when I have worked in three important and widely separated centres of tropical vegetation, that furthermore it has taken more than eight years to study the plants and write the volume. During this period my research interests have widened and deepened with constant access to a living tropical flora and, moreover, concepts which initially governed the scope of this work have changed with the lapse of time.

Because many organizations and individuals have contributed to this book, a list of acknowledgements must be lengthy and therefore runs the great risk of failing to recognize adequately all the help received. Financial support has come largely from research grants (GB 506 and 2991) awarded by the National Science Foundation, supplemented by others from the American Philosophical Society. The Director, Dr. John Popenoe, and Board of Trustees of Fairchild Tropical Garden have provided me not only with laboratory facilities, but with a freedom of movement which has made an undertaking centred somewhere in mid-Atlantic entirely feasible.

In the United States I am indebted to Dr. R. A. Howard and Dr. R. C. Rollins of the Arnold Arboretum and Gray Herbarium respectively for library and other facilities in Cambridge, Massachusetts. The help of Dr. Lyman B. Smith, Curator of Phanerogams at the U.S. National Museum,

Smithsonian Institution, Washington, D.C., is greatly appreciated. Dr.
Sherwin Carlquist of the Rancho Santa Ana Botanic Gardens, Claremont,
California, has contributed the whole of the account of the Rapateaceae.

On the other side of the Atlantic I have, through the kindness of the
Director, Sir George Taylor, been permitted to work in the Library, Her-
barium, and Jodrell Laboratories (both new and old) at the Royal Botanic
Gardens, Kew, and, above all, to enjoy close collaboration with Dr. C. R.
Metcalfe, the guiding hand in the preparation of the *Anatomy of the Mono-
cotyledons*. Dr. Metcalfe's assistance at all stages ensured the success of this
Anglo-American undertaking.

For help with the collection or donation of the material examined during
the course of this survey I am indebted to a great number of people. These
include C. D. Adams, D. W. Bierhorst, J. P. M. Brenan, L. J. Brass, Sherwin
Carlquist, R. K. Godfrey, J. B. Hall, R. E. Holttum, Keith Jones, R. J. Kral,
Bassett Maguire, J. K. Morton, G. R. Proctor, R. W. Read, N. Y. Sandwith,
N. W. Simmonds, and D. B. Ward. I reserve for special mention the following:
Mulford B. Foster, who gave me access to his collection of living Bromeliaceae; Harold E. Moore Jr., who supplied a great deal of material
of Commelinaceae; Lyman B. Smith, who gave me so much help with
Bromeliaceae, Eriocaulaceae, and Xyridaceae; Vernon I. Cheadle, who
supplied much material from his Australian and South African collections.

For taxonomic and nomenclatural discussion about certain families I am
further indebted to Lyman B. Smith (Bromeliaceae), John Lewis (Xyridaceae),
and J. P. M. Brenan (Commelinaceae). These specialists will be relieved to
know that I take full responsibility for any taxonomic opinions that are expressed in this work and for its numerous nomenclatural deficiencies, especially
wherever it is evident to them I have disregarded their suggestions. Their
consolation must be that without their assistance these deficiencies would have
been so much greater.

Preparation of microscopical sections in the later stages of the work has
been to a large extent the responsibility of Miss Lesley Jackson. Without her
patience in dealing with the large series of samples which have been available
for study I could not have accomplished more than a fraction of this work.
For additional technical assistance I must thank G. A. Vargo and R. V.
Osgood. Miss E. Long (Kew) and Miss A. Bellenger (Miami) have tackled
the typing and retyping of manuscripts with great thoroughness. Miss Mary
Gregory, Bibliographer at the Jodrell Laboratory, has devoted a good deal
of her energy to checking numerous bibliographic details, arranging figures,
revising proofs and preparing the index.

Illustrations rearranged as Figs. 1–6; 8–11; 31; 67–68; 70–86 are reproduced
by permission of the Council of the Linnean Society from the *Journal of the
Linnean Society* (Botany), Volumes 55 (1953–8); 56 (1958–61); 58 (1961–4);
59 (1964–6). I am grateful to the Editors of the *Journal of the Arnold Arboretum*
and of the *Kew Bulletin* for permission to reproduce Fig. 73 G–J and Figs. 14
and 15 respectively.

I make no apologies for the inevitable omissions and errors that the methods
of presentation adopted in this book must introduce. I prefer to assume that
most readers will find travelling hopefully is of more consequence than failing

to arrive. Despite common belief to the contrary, descriptive plant anatomy is still only an embryonic discipline. Temporary pauses on the road towards further completeness are most useful in showing the great distance which still has to be travelled.

P. B. TOMLINSON

Fairchild Tropical Garden, Miami, Florida, U.S.A.
November 1966

CONTENTS

NOTE

Table 1 is on p. xviii, Table 2 is on p. 2, Table 3 is on p. 296. Tables included in the family descriptions are lettered A (p. 15), B (p. 143), C (p. 195), D (p.217).

ABBREVIATIONS USED IN THE TEXT

vascular bundle	vb (plural vb's)
outer (parenchymatous) sheath	O.S.
inner (sclerotic) sheath	I.S.
transverse section	T.S.
longitudinal section	L.S.
very	v.
species	sp. (plural spp.)

A NOTE ON NOMENCLATURE

THROUGHOUT the text authorities for scientific names have not been quoted. They are cited with the names included either in the list of 'Material examined by the author' or under 'Genera and species referred to in the literature' at the end of each family description.

The attempt to list under each 'Literature' section the names of plants studied by authors cited in the bibliographies raises the problem of synonomy. The name used by an earlier worker may have been changed subsequently. To correct this, even if the newer names were known, would involve loss of contact with the original reference. In a few instances a newer name is indicated with the old one, but the task of creating a complete synonomy is beyond my capabilities. Otherwise names are repeated as quoted by original authors with the exception of a few minor spelling changes (e.g. *Vriesia* to *Vriesea*) to eliminate apparent inconsistencies.

SIZE OF FAMILIES

THESE estimates are largely my own but serve to show the great range in size of families, in terms of numbers of constituent species, dealt with in this volume. The estimates are likely to be no more than approximations but they are arranged so that by adjusting them one column to the left or right they can be readily corrected. It must be remembered that these families are all tropical and some of them are poorly known. In some, new taxa are being described at a rapid rate so that the known size of a family is rapidly increasing. The best example is Rapateaceae which increased in size from 25 species in 9 genera to 80 species in 16 genera within 28 years, entirely as a result of recent exploration.

TABLE 1

Estimated family size

Family	Number of species						
	1–10	10–50	50–100	100–500	500–1000	1000–1500	1500+
Commelinaceae						x	
Cartonemataceae	x						
Flagellariaceae		x					
Mayacaceae		x					
Xyridaceae				x			
Rapateaceae			x				
Eriocaulaceae					x		
Bromeliaceae							x
Musaceae			x				
Heliconiaceae			x				
Strelitziaceae		x					
Lowiaceae	x						
Zingiberaceae					x		
Costaceae			x				
Cannaceae			x				
Marantaceae					x		

DESCRIPTIVE TERMS

(Explanatory note by C. R. METCALFE)

IN the course of the history of botany there has been a tendency for technical terms to be used in slightly different senses by different authors. There is also the difficulty that quite different morphological and histological terms have sometimes been used to denote the same type of form and cellular organization. Indeed the language of descriptive botany is in a state of slow but continuous flux in which certain evolutionary tendencies may perhaps be discerned. This is not the place in which to discuss anatomical terminology in detail, except to point out that a rather wider range of carefully defined descriptive terms than is at present available would lend precision to written descriptions. Nevertheless it is equally undesirable to magnify obscurity by introducing numerous fresh terms which are not generally familiar to more than a handful of botanical specialists. It is, therefore, our aim in these volumes to present the information as far as circumstances permit in language that is in general use amongst botanists.

It does so happen, however, as is perhaps only natural when members of a team are working in widely separated localities, that one or other of the team members will start using rather different terms, or will employ identical terms with rather different shades of meaning to suit his own purposes. It is therefore important to draw attention to a few differences in Dr. Tomlinson's descriptive vocabulary compared with terms that have been used in other volumes in this series. At the same time the reader can be introduced to a few terms that are used here with which he may not already be familiar. The terms are as follows.

Buttress

Term used when vascular bundles are seen in transverse sections, especially of a leaf, to be connected to either or both leaf surfaces by girder-like columns of cells. Buttresses may consist of translucent parenchymatous cells, or fibres or of a mixture of both. In Vol. I buttresses have been termed girders (see Vol. I, pp. xxix and xlvii).

Costa (and hence costal)

Strictly a rib, and generally used with reference to the midrib, or to the midrib and principal veins of a leaf. Hence used with reference to ribs on surface of the leaves of grasses and other monocotyledonous leaves. In this and the two previous volumes of this series used in the adjectival form 'costal' which is applied to bands or zones of cells of the leaf epidermis lying above the larger veins (cf. intercostal).

Expansion cells

These are longitudinal bands of inflated translucent cells especially of the leaf epidermis and subjacent cell layers. Often held to be concerned with rolling or folding of leaves. Equivalent to bulliform cells in Vol. I.

Hapaxanthic

Adjectival term applied to shoots of which the growth is terminated with flowering (cf. pleonanthic).

Helophytic

Swamp dwelling.

Intercostal

Adjectival term used with reference to bands or zones of cells of leaf epidermis lying between the larger veins (cf. costa and costal).

Micro-hairs

Term first used with reference to small, mostly 2-celled, hairs on grass leaves (see Vol. I, pp. xxii and xliii). Used in this volume with reference to hairs, especially of Commelinaceae, which are similar morphologically to micro-hairs of grasses, although rather larger in size.

Pleonanthic

Term applied to shoots of which the growth is not terminated by flowering (cf. hapaxanthic).

Spiromonistichous

Adjectival term used to denote leaves arranged on the stem in a low spiral.

PART I

CLASSIFICATION OF THE 'FARINOSAE'

THE Farinosae were established by Adolph Engler in 1886 as one of his major orders (*Reihe*) of monocotyledons on the basis of a presumed common characteristic in the endosperm of the seed. This was regarded as 'mealy' (farinaceous or starch-rich) in contrast to the 'fleshy' or 'oily' (respectively protein- or oil-rich) endosperm of the allied order Liliiflorae. The naturalness or otherwise of this order is much disputed and we are indebted to Hamann (1961, 1962b) for a lengthy discussion of this subject.

Endosperm alone is unreliable as an indicator of major taxonomic categories in the monocotyledons. This is suggested even in Engler's system itself. Three families, Haemodoraceae, Juncaceae, Velloziaceae, with starchy endosperm are included in the Liliiflorae, not the Farinosae. The Philydraceae, on the other hand, are included within the Farinosae although they are described as having 'fleshy' seeds. It now seems that seeds of this family include both oil and starch (Hamann 1962a). The Cyanastraceae have a reduced endosperm largely replaced by a 'chalazosperm' but are included in the Farinosae, presumably because this unique reserve tissue includes starch. Further indication that the character of the endosperm is not fundamental is found in Engler's Pandanales since these include families whose seeds may be farinaceous (Sparganiaceae), fleshy (Typhaceae, but according to Bentham and Hooker starch-rich, almost fleshy), or oily (Pandanaceae).

It is also clear that Engler himself did not wish his Farinosae to be regarded as a particularly closely knit assemblage. He distributes the 13 families included within the order amongst no less than 6 suborders (Table 2). These in turn were regarded as somewhat remote from each other. Indeed in some characters certain farinosean families show a closer relation to liliiflorean families than to other families of their own order.

That Engler's Farinosae are unnatural is also reflected in their subsequent treatment by systematists. Very few authors have kept them together as a group. Fewer still have retained the name of the order. The majority have distributed the member families among as few as 2 to as many as 7 orders and in a great variety of ways and with little common agreement. Hamann has summarized this redistribution, tabulating classification systems of no less than 23 authors in such a way that their diversity is clearly displayed. Just about all possible combinations of farinosean families have been proposed in attempts to express their natural affinities.

Although newer systems have tended to reject the endosperm as a feature of major taxonomic importance, attempts to recognize other basic features

B

seem to lead to no more generally acceptable groupings. Thus the position of the ovule (often as expressed by the later position of the embryo) has been accorded major importance by some authorities (e.g. Wettstein). Whether or

TABLE 2

Families of Engler's Farinosae *as redistributed by Hutchinson (1959) and Hamann (1961)*

Engler	Hutchinson	Hamann
Suborder and family	Division and order	Order and suborder
Flagellariineae		
1. **Flagellariaceae***	Calyciferae Commelinales	Commelinales
Enantioblastae		
2. Restionaceae	Glumiflorae	Commelinales (Restionineae)
3. Centrolepidaceae	Glumiflorae	Commelinales (Restionineae)
4. **Mayacaceae**	Calyciferae (Commelinales)	Commelinales (Commelinineae)
5. **Xyridaceae**	Calyciferae (Xyridales)	Commelinales (Commelinineae)
6. **Eriocaulaceae**	Calyciferae (Eriocaulales)	Commelinales (Eriocaulineae)
Bromeliineae		
7. Thurniaceae	Glumiflorae	Juncales
8. **Rapateaceae**	Calyciferae (Xyridales)	Commelinales (Commelinineae)
9. **Bromeliaceae**	Calyciferae (Bromeliales)	Bromeliales
Commelinineae		
10. **Commelinaceae**	Calyciferae (Commelinales)	Commelinales (Commelinineae)
(including *Cartonema*)	Calyciferae as **Cartonemataceae** (Commelinales)	
Pontederiineae		
11. Pontederiaceae	Corolliferae	Liliales
12. Cyanastraceae	Corolliferae	Liliales
Philydrineae		
13. Philydraceae	Corolliferae	Liliales

* Families in **bold type** are dealt with in this volume.

not the flower is provided with a distinct calyx and corolla is another frequently emphasized pair of alternatives. This distinction, for example, is made the basis for recognizing 3 major groups by Hutchinson—Calyciferae, Corolliferae, and Glumiflorae.

The tendency to use 'key' characters to express major sub-divisions is somewhat contrary to contemporary taxonomic thought, however, and Hamann has adopted a more modern approach by assessing evidence from a number of separate disciplines on a quantitative basis in an attempt to elucidate the interrelationships of the farinosean families. Their relative affinity is then expressed on a numerical basis as a 'similarity quotient' (*Ähnlichkeitsquotient*). This must not be confused with the 'advancement index' of Sporne and his co-workers (e.g. Lowe 1961). The former expression refers to phenetic, the latter to phyletic affinity. Subsequently Hamann proposes, on the basis of his very thorough analysis, to distribute the farinosean families amongst four orders (Table 2). While these mathematical aids to the expression of taxonomic opinions are often very revealing they are subject to a number of weaknesses. One of these, as Hamann himself points out, is that information is not equally available for all families and for all characters. Thus in the Farinosae, an order which probably includes more than 5000 species, in about 180 genera, information about embryology is available for only 23 genera and then usually only for 1 species in each genus (Hamann 1964). In addition, information about many features is incomplete or simply inaccurate.

Hamann has made the observation that in the years following the establishment of Engler's scheme, the creation of new orders, by other taxonomists either by the elevation of existing suborders to ordinal rank or by some other process of taxonomic inflation, has been much more pronounced in the monocotyledons than in the dicotyledons. Thus if the arrangement of the families as found in Engler and Diels's *Syllabus der Pflanzenfamilien* (1936) is compared with more recent systems, as exemplified by Takhtajan (1959) and Hutchinson (1959), this process becomes evident. Engler's original 11 orders (with 45 families) are split into 21 (76 families) by Takhtajan and 29 (69 families) by Hutchinson. Hutchinson's system shows an almost threefold increase over Engler's in number of monocotyledonous orders (29 compared with 11), but his number of dicotyledonous orders is less than double that of Engler (82 compared with 44). The Farinosae have been involved to a marked degree in this rearrangement. Takhtajan distributes Engler's farinosean families throughout 6 orders, Hutchinson throughout 7 (see Table 2). These facts all suggest that the Farinosae are not a very natural group and the members show no close interrelationships.

It is worth while at this point to comment on the Scitamineae, another of Engler's orders (previously a family in Bentham and Hooker's scheme). No subsequent author has attempted to split the Scitamineae although some have felt the need to associate them with other monocotyledonous families with inferior ovaries, which in its turn merely reflects a continuation of the tradition established by Bentham and Hooker, who included most of such families in their second series, Epigynae. This points to the great naturalness of the group and this is an area of mutual agreement by taxonomists. Since the Scitamineae are dealt with in this volume (as the Zingiberales) we have an example of a truly natural monocotyledonous order to serve as a model in our discussion of the Farinosae.

Does the redistribution of the farinosean families in the manners suggested in Table 2 at all reflect a more natural subdivision? Is the tendency to divide the Farinosae into smaller groups and to elevate these groups to ordinal rank more expressive of their interrelationships and relative isolation? Or is this process simply one of taxonomic 'inflation' of the kind to be discouraged because it serves no useful purpose (Harris 1964)? Information about the anatomy of the vegetative parts of a number of farinosean families in the following pages of this volume permits a limited discussion of these questions. The discussion is limited because these volumes are arranged according to Hutchinson's system of classification (in order to establish consistency, not necessarily because we are agreed that this system is superior to any other), consequently Engler's farinosean families are dealt with only in part. A fuller discussion will only be possible when information about the remaining families is available. In addition the discussion is based on information from only one discipline and therefore lacks the comprehensiveness which modern systematics requires. Despite these deficiencies the comparison is worth attempting especially with the Zingiberales as a base for reference.

APPLICATION OF ANATOMICAL
INFORMATION TO THE CLASSIFICATION OF
THE 'FARINOSAE'

Is the 'Farinosae' a natural assemblage?

No combination of anatomical (or morphological) features closely delimits the Farinosae, in so far as they have been studied for the purpose of this volume. They cannot be recognized as a coherent order comparable to the Zingiberales. In fact in anatomical features the constituent families differ from each other almost to the same degree as the whole of the order Zingiberales differs from other groups of monocotyledons. Therefore anatomical evidence fully substantiates the modern tendency, exemplified in Hutchinson's system, to redistribute the original farinosean families amongst a large number of small orders. Each of these would then have a rank comparable to the Zingiberales. This modern tendency is not taxonomic inflation but more accurately expresses interrelationships since it stresses real differences at the expense of imaginary similarities. A few examples will serve to illustrate the anatomical heterogeneity of the Farinosae which is set out in further detail in the Appendix.

There is no constant arrangement of the leaf in the bud as in the Zingiberales. One may recall the unique rolling of the leaf blade in Commelinaceae and that the entire order Zingiberales has a constant and distinctive vernation. In respect of leaf rolling, therefore, the Commelinaceae differ from other Farinosae to a degree which elsewhere in the monocotyledons isolates an order. Hairs in the Farinosae are very diverse but show no obvious common characteristics. Certain families have very distinctive hairs. Notable are the glandular hairs in Commelinaceae and Eriocaulaceae. The peltate scales of the Bromeliaceae are so unlike the hairs of any other monocotyledon that they at once suggest an isolated position for the family. Closer examination of development of hairs might indicate common characteristics which are lost as hairs mature. This still remains to be done.

The range in structure of adult stomata and particularly of guard cells is very wide, much greater than that in the Zingiberales. We still have insufficient information about stomatal ontogeny to make lengthy comparisons worth while, as is discussed on p. 390, but the little available evidence suggests great heterogeneity. Stomata in all the families have at least 2 thin-walled lateral subsidiary cells. These are known to develop in at least two distinct ways. The Commelinaceae almost invariably have additional subsidiary cells which are produced in a well-ordered fashion. No other farinosean family appears to have this same regular sequence. Unfortunately we have no information about stomatal development in Zingiberales to indicate how constant stomatal ontogeny is in an order which we can accept as natural. Nevertheless, stomatal features suggest diverse rather than uniform origins for the Farinosae.

Variation in shape of epidermal cells is at least as great as in the Zingiberales and, as in that order, includes families (e.g. Bromeliaceae) with sinuous as well as families (most others) with non-sinuous epidermal walls. The Heliconiaceae and Marantaceae contrast in the same way with most remaining families in the Zingiberales. Variation in thickness of epidermal walls is more pronounced than in Zingiberales since it ranges from the distinctive type of Bromeliaceae with shallow cells thickened on their inner walls, to uniformly thin-walled cells, as, for example, in many Commelinaceae and Eriocaulaceae. The range of hypodermal structures is much greater in Farinosae than in Zingiberales. Families with or without colourless hypodermal layers or with sclerenchymatous in addition to colourless hypodermal layers are included. In the remaining mesophyll layers differentiation is too diverse to allow a common facies to be discerned. Most families, as in the Zingiberales, do not produce well-developed fibrous systems independent of the veins but Bromeliaceae and Rapateaceae are to a certain extent exceptional.

Vascular bundle construction does not suggest a common origin for the farinosean families. This may be contrasted with the Zingiberales where the large bundles of the leaf axis are markedly constant in their structure as seen in transverse section. Speculation about the relative primitiveness or advancement of vascular bundles which depends on a comparison of their appearance in transverse section must remain largely meaningless until a great deal more is known about the way in which they develop. Vascular bundles in some families (e.g. Commelinaceae, Eriocaulaceae, Xyridaceae) are often described as 'similar to those in grasses' but this statement need not imply any close relationship either amongst these families or between them and the Gramineae.

General stem morphology is so diverse that meaningful comparisons are impossible to make. The application of stem anatomy to taxonomy must await a detailed understanding of development of the monocotyledonous shoot. However, it is known that shoot construction may be very constant in a family, the Commelinaceae being a well-known example recently reinvestigated by Rohweder (1963). Nevertheless, some interesting parallels in shoot construction may be seen between Commelinaceae and Costaceae, although these families can scarcely be regarded as close relatives.

Silica is universally present in Zingiberales, its distribution and appearance being diagnostic for each family. Silica is not a uniform feature of the Farinosae and occurs in only a few families. Range of vessel specialization in the Farinosae exceeds that in the Zingiberales. Tracheal elements in some families, such as Commelinaceae and Xyridaceae, reach a much higher degree of specialization than in any family in the Zingiberales. On the other hand, vessels in many Bromeliaceae remain at the same low degree of specialization found in many zingiberalean families. Roots are not a source of obvious features whereby the Farinosae might be characterized. The tendency to develop short-cells in the cortical parenchyma has been noted in some families with the further observation that these short-cells may become aggregated into horizontal tiers, notably in the Eriocaulaceae. Nevertheless, a similar tendency is found in the Alismataceae (Stant 1964) and Hydrocharitaceae. One suspects that, rather than being a feature indicative of genetic relationships, this peculiar differentiation is correlated with hydrophytism. Biochemical diversification in Farinosae is not less than in Zingiberales as far as microscopic inspection reveals. Raphide-sacs may or may not be present; mucilage is secreted by a few members of both groups.

The conclusion from anatomical evidence must be that these 8 families have had no recent common ancestor. Otherwise, if they are genetically related each must have had an extremely long period of independent evolution.

Are the farinosean families equally isolated from each other?

Further discussion of the taxonomic status of these 8 families requires an assessment of their interrelationships. Can one detect affinities between pairs or groups of families?

It is tempting to subject the information in the Appendix to this volume to the simple mathematical analysis carried out by Hamann (1961) in the hope of creating some 'index of affinity' whereby interrelationships would be expressed numerically. I have tried this only to discover that it would be quite misleading. For example, a simple assessment of the relative isolation of each family according to the number of unique features found in each suggests that Commelinaceae are very isolated (13 unique features). However, this figure appears largely because they develop a wide variety of hairs which can be subdivided into several distinct categories. With regard to type of hair Commelinaceae are therefore often listed in isolation. Whether, in fact, the ability to develop a wide structural range of hairs does indicate genetic isolation is not known. In contrast the Bromeliaceae possess one major and unique type of hair, the peltate scale. This distinguishes the family immediately but since I have not subdivided scales into further categories Bromeliaceae are listed in isolation but once with respect to hairs. A numerical assessment would inevitably favour Commelinaceae at the expense of Bromeliaceae, although the hairs in the latter family are much more unusual than those in the former. In the same way some families lack silica and are automatically excluded from further numerical assessment whereas those which possess silica may do so in such a variety of ways that a dozen categories are available for analysis. Silica is clearly of diagnostic systematic value in the Farinosae, but a direct numerical analysis would distort its value.

The difficulties of making an objective assessment may be further exemplified. It is easy to distinguish between families with or without silica, the distinction is clear cut. To do the same for presence or absence of palisade layers in the mesophyll is impossible because the recognition of palisade layers can be largely subjective. Again, some features may be more fundamentally significant than others. The presence or absence of raphide-sacs implies a greater degree of biochemical differentiation, less dependent on a direct environmental influence, than the presence or absence of thick epidermal walls.

For these reasons I prefer to discuss the possible interrelationships of these families on more traditional lines in the following paragraphs, emphasizing those features diagnostic for each family. It may be stated at the outset that, with the exception of the relationship between Cartonemataceae and Commelinaceae, the families are largely isolated from each other and there is no obvious way of grouping them.

Bromeliaceae

Within this family there are marked trends from mesomorphic or xeromorphic forms towards unspecialized and ultimately to highly specialized epiphytic forms. The rosette habit and intracauline roots seem essentially associated with these trends. The association between xerophytism and epiphytism seems obvious, although as the epiphytic habit has been perfected, certain xeromorphic features have disappeared. Structural features which are obviously correlated with these ecological trends include the unique peltate scales; elaboration of the stomatal apparatus (especially in xerophytes); development of colourless water-storage mesophyll layers; development of sclerenchyma, either as hypodermal layers, or in marginal spines, or as isolated fibrous strands, or as bundle-sheath extensions. The epidermis in Bromeliaceae is highly specialized; anticlinal walls are sinuous; the inner wall of each cell is usually thickened and encloses a solitary silica-body in such a way that the body appears to be embedded in the wall. Obvious biochemical specialization includes the universal development of raphide-sacs. The biochemistry of Bromeliaceae otherwise remains largely unknown. When investigated fully it is certain to be profoundly illuminating.

The anatomy of Bromeliaceae, in so far as it has been investigated, so clearly expresses the peculiar ecological specialization of the family that more conservative features which might express phyletic affinity seem to be obscured. Intracauline roots characteristic of this family are otherwise found only in the Velloziaceae. Rapateaceae are frequently regarded as having a close affinity with Bromeliaceae, their similar geographical distribution supporting this. It may be significant that Rapateaceae often have silica-bodies which recall those of Bromeliaceae; a similar tendency to develop a sclerotic hypodermis and mucilage cavities is found in both families. Nevertheless, differences between them are considerable.

Clearly the Bromeliaceae have had a long independent line of evolution. Continued anatomical investigation might reveal something of their origin. For example, peltate scales in the family are so distinctive that at first sight it seems impossible to compare them with hairs in other families. Nevertheless, bromeliaceous hairs are briefly uniseriate during development, may persist as uniseriate capitate hairs on seedlings, whilst a few genera permanently retain uniseriate hairs and do not develop scales. Uniseriate hairs are otherwise common in other farinosean families. How significant is this?

Cartonemataceae and Commelinaceae

These families may be discussed together since their close relationship is not in dispute. The separation of *Cartonema* from Commelinaceae is largely unfamiliar to taxonomists. Anatomical evidence for this separation is presented fully elsewhere (p. 66). *Cartonema* is still in need of further investigation.

Commelinaceae are a very natural and isolated group. Shoot construction (q.v.) is unlike that in any other monocotyledon and involves a regular pattern of growth which includes the development of nodal vascular plexi. The following anatomical features characterize the family: unique leaf vernation; 3-celled glandular hairs; stomata with (2)–4–6 subsidiary cells; fleshy leaves with the surface layers commonly specialized as 'water-storage' tissue; peripheral collenchyma in the stem; articulate raphide-canals; highly specialized vessel elements. A tendency to develop silica has been noted.

It is difficult, on an anatomical basis, to suggest affinities between Commelinaceae and any other farinosean family. Three-celled glandular hairs in Eriocaulaceae might suggest a connexion were it not for the fact that this remains largely unsupported by other anatomical evidence. These hairs in the 2 families can be distinguished readily and may simply be parallel forms. Flagellariaceae have been associated traditionally with the Commelinaceae although the evidence for this is obscure. The Flagellariaceae themselves are an unnatural assemblage. None of the special anatomical features which characterize Commelinaceae occurs in the Flagellariaceae. Silica is present in Flagellariaceae, but not in the special way in which it is deposited in the Commelinaceae. Placing these 2 families close together in schemes of classification seems unnatural and should be discontinued.

Eriocaulaceae

The range of growth forms in this family is considerable but has been little investigated. Comparative studies are therefore difficult. There appears to be a reduction from large, erect, even woody forms to rosette and decumbent plants. Specialized anatomical features are not marked but the family can be diagnosed as follows. Hairs always with a short basal collar cell, the distal part of the hair either glandular (sometimes T-shaped) or otherwise filamentous. Epidermis commonly large-celled and thin-walled, but sometimes thick-walled. Stomata paracytic with markedly asymmetrical guard cells with one conspicuous outer ledge. Outer sheath of vascular bundles well developed, often extending vertically to each epidermis, these buttresses sometimes being continuous laterally with colourless hypodermal layers. Amphivasal vascular bundles common in both aerial and underground axes. Leafless scape of inflorescence axis with characteristic anatomy (see p. 170). Root including paired or clustered root-hairs. Root cortex commonly with short-cells (often in regular horizontal tiers). Vessels usually highly specialized in all parts. Specialized secretory structures absent.

Eriocaulaceae have a number of features in common with other farinosean families but these do not make affinities obvious. For example, rhizome structure shows similar trends to that found in Xyridaceae and to a lesser extent in Rapateaceae. It may be equally significant that the 3 families have similar congested inflorescences on the ends of naked or almost naked scapes and indeed this is one reason why they are placed close together in Hutchinson's system. Root structure in Eriocaulaceae, Mayacaceae, Rapateaceae, and Xyridaceae shows certain parallels which have already been discussed on p. 6. A connexion between Eriocaulaceae and Mayacaceae may be sought via *Tonina* on the basis of general habit. There is less similarity between Commelinaceae and Eriocaulaceae, except in the matter of glandular hairs. There seems little basis for comparison with Bromeliaceae.

Flagellariaceae

Anatomically (and morphologically) this family is so heterogeneous that the disposition of its 3 constituent genera is problematical. It is equally problematical to define the family on an anatomical basis. The separation of *Hanguana* as a monotypic family (see p. 81) only partially solves the problem because *Joinvillea* and *Flagellaria* remain together as a no more natural unit. The epidermis of *Joinvillea* has been likened to that of the grasses, largely because it is differentiated into long- and short-cells. It should be noted, however, that a similar differentiation of the epidermis occurs in a few palms (Tomlinson 1961).

We must conclude then that, despite a recent survey, the anatomy of this group is still insufficiently known to make comment about its natural position worthwhile. As has been mentioned, there is no anatomical justification for associating the genera of Flagellariaceae with Commelinaceae.

Mayacaceae

Any information which might be gleaned about the affinities of this family from a study of its vegetative anatomy is largely obscured by modifications associated with its aquatic or amphibious existence. These include well-developed septate air-canals in leaf, stem, and root; reduced vascular tissues surrounded by an endodermis; the narrow leaf with a single median vein. Axillary hairs and paracytic stomata recall Eriocaulaceae. The general habit of *Tonina* (Eriocaulaceae) is similar to that of *Mayaca* and further comparison of these two would be worthwhile. Hutchinson's suggestion that *Mayaca* may be merely a reduced member of the Commelinaceae is based on presumed similarities in the reproductive parts and is not supported by anatomical evidence. Until we have more information about these plants it is probably better to acknowledge the isolated position of Mayacaceae rather than to associate them artificially with other families.

Rapateaceae

The possible relationship between this family and the Bromeliaceae has already been mentioned briefly on p. 8. Otherwise Rapateaceae are an isolated group distinguished by a combination of features which includes peculiar leaf morphology; axillary, slime-producing hairs; paracytic stomata; well-developed sclerenchyma; mesophyll cells with infolded walls; distribution of silica and vessels; absence of calcium oxalate crystals. Hutchinson suggests a relationship between Rapateaceae and Xyridaceae based on floral morphology, emphasizing this by placing them together in the tribe Xyridales. *Achlyphila* and *Xyris* of Xyridaceae do have a distinctive leaf morphology which might be interpreted as similar to that of Rapateaceae. *Xyris* also has axillary hairs which may secrete mucilage. Other anatomical evidence does not suggest any close relationship between the 2 families.

Xyridaceae

This is a more heterogeneous assemblage than all other farinosean families except Flagellariaceae. There is some justification for dividing the Xyridaceae into 2 families. The problems which would result if this were done are mentioned on p. 123 and it is concluded that the arguments for keeping all genera of Xyridaceae in one family are more compelling than those which would separate them. This relative heterogeneity makes it difficult both to diagnose Xyridaceae and to assess their relationships with other families. For example, the suggested similarity between Rapateaceae and Xyridaceae on the basis of leaf morphology (which may be entirely due to parallelism) is determined by *Achlyphila* and *Xyris* alone. *Abolboda* and *Orectanthe* do not resemble Rapateaceae since their leaves are lanceolate and unspecialized like those in Bromeliaceae and Eriocaulaceae.

General conclusions

The taxonomist who seeks, on the basis of systematic anatomy, a clearcut resolution of the problems involved in creating a natural classification for the families included in the Farinosae will be disappointed by the above comments. My conclusions may appear entirely negative but are of value because they focus attention on the salient anatomical characters of the families under consideration. No further progress towards a more complete understanding of their taxonomy or phylogeny will be possible without taking anatomical data into consideration. A botanist with access to the pages which follow may also hope to test the affinities of non-flowering material more accurately than was previously possible. The value of this form of exercise is becoming increasingly recognized in the advancement of taxonomy. Identification of non-flowering material may sometimes also have practical application.

Speculation about taxonomic and evolutionary matters based on inadequate factual data can so easily lead to erroneous conclusions. Additional data on which taxonomy can make real advances are one of our greatest needs today. It is hoped that the pages which follow will be viewed in this light.

LITERATURE CITED

BENTHAM, G., and HOOKER, J. D. (1883) *Genera plantarum*, Vol. 3, Pt. 2. London.

ENGLER, A., and DIELS, L. (1936) *Syllabus der Pflanzenfamilien*, edn 11. Berlin.

HAMANN, U. (1961) Merkmalsbestand und Verwandtschaftsbeziehungen der Farinosae. *Willdenowia* **2**, 639–768.

—— (1962a) Über Bau und Entwicklung des Endosperms der Philydraceae und über die Begriffe 'mehliges Nährgewebe' und 'Farinosae'. *Bot. Jb.* **81**, 397–407.

—— (1962b) Weiteres über Merkmalsbestand und Verwandtschaftsbeziehungen der 'Farinosae'. *Willdenowia* **3**, 169–207.

—— (1964) Embryologie und Systematik am Beispiel der Farinosae. *Ber. dt. bot. Ges.* **77**, (45)–(54).

HARRIS, T. (1964) The inflation of taxonomy. *Proc. Linn. Soc.* **175**, 1–7.

HUTCHINSON, J. (1959) *Families of flowering plants*, Vol. II, *Monocotyledons*, edn 2. Oxford.

LOWE, J. (1961) The phylogeny of monocotyledons. *New Phytol.* **60**, 355–87.

ROHWEDER, O. (1963) Anatomische und histogenetische Untersuchungen an Laubsprossen und Blüten der Commelinaceen. *Bot. Jb.* **82**, 1–99.

STANT, M. Y. (1964) Anatomy of the Alismataceae. *J. Linn. Soc.* (Bot.) **59**, 1–42.

TAKHTAJAN, A. (1959) *Die Evolution der Angiospermen*. Jena.

TOMLINSON, P. B. (1961) *Anatomy of monocotyledons* (ed. C. R. METCALFE), Vol. II, *Palmae*. Oxford.

FAMILY DESCRIPTIONS

COMMELINACEAE[1]
(Figs. 1–12)

SUMMARY

THIS large family of some 40 genera and 1000 species is pantropical in its distribution, although a few species occur in warm temperate regions. It consists mostly of perennial herbs which are commonly rhizomatous and typically succulent. *Tinantia* and some species of *Commelina* are annuals. Although the shoot morphology varies, the underlying principles of construction appear to be very constant. The main types of habit which were recognized by Clark (1904) are said to indicate a trend from more primitive, radially symmetrical to specialized dorsiventral shoots. However, the difference between radial and dorsiventral symmetry seems rather to reflect a difference between adult and juvenile stages of the same axis. Thus the main, seedling axis initially has a distichous leaf insertion, representing the juvenile phase, but the leaf insertion becomes spiral in the adult phase. Lateral branches initially repeat the juvenile distichous phase before reaching the adult spiral phase. Protraction or contraction of these phases, associated with variation in length of internodes, largely determines the habit. Thus ontogenetic sequences which are characteristic of primitive members of the family may be extended or abbreviated and fixed in advanced members. In addition there is a tendency for the main, seedling axis to be eliminated early and to be replaced by lateral shoots.

Recognizing these principles, the following trends may be evident: (i) Shoots with main, radially symmetrical axis dominant, whilst the internodes are suppressed and unbranched except for lateral inflorescences, e.g. in *Cochliostema odoratissimum*. (ii) Axis similarly monopodial, but bearing frequent radially symmetrical (i.e. soon adult) vegetative as well as reproductive lateral axes, as in *Rhoeo*. (iii) Erect shoots sometimes tall, owing to internodal elongation, and woody as in *Palisota* spp. (iv) Plants similar but smaller, herbaceous, unbranched, and usually annual in *Tinantia*. (v) In *Hadrodemas* radially symmetrical erect shoots with congested internodes, apparently monopodial but actually sympodial, via a lateral branch, owing to the presence of an inflorescence which terminates each growth segment.

The main axis is radially symmetrical, but the branches are dorsiventrally symmetrical, i.e. persistently juvenile and contrasting markedly with main axis, as in *Cyanotis* and *Callisia* spp. In *Callisia fragrans* the juvenile stage in each lateral branch is protracted to produce a long stolon which eventually gives rise to a distal, erect rosette.

[1] This corresponds to the Commelinaceae of Hutchinson, from which *Cartonema* has been excluded as a distinct family (see p. 66). *Triceratella* is discussed separately (see p. 56) because it shows several anomalous features.

The most specialized types include those in which all axes are distichous and the juvenile condition dominant. The axes are sometimes erect with long internodes, e.g. in *Campelia* and *Dichorisandra*, or decumbent, e.g. in *Commelina* and *Tripogandra* spp. Radial symmetry may be regained in terminal inflorescences. An intermediate condition is shown by spp. of *Callisia* and *Cyanotis* with rudimentary radially symmetrical erect shoots which are soon replaced by dominant dorsiventral branches. Dorsiventral symmetry may or may not be alterable. As Clark demonstrated experimentally, the species that are thought to be most highly evolved are those with fixed dorsiventral symmetry. Replacement of the erect axis, which appears to have occurred phylogenetically, may also occur ontogenetically, as in *Tradescantia virginica* (Gravis 1898). Two main types of branching in dorsiventral shoots are distinguished by Holm (1906), according to the way in which the foliage leaves are arranged on the branch after the bicarinate, adaxial ('adossierte') prophyll has arisen:

(a) leaves inserted in same plane of distichy as the prophyll, e.g. in *Commelina virginica*,
(b) leaves inserted in a plane of distichy at right angles to that of prophyll, e.g. in *C. nudiflora*.

The first leaf above the prophyll is sometimes reduced to a scale leaf as in *Tradescantia floridana* according to Holm (1906).

Seedling stems are sometimes erect, annual, and monocarpic as in *Tinantia*, or somewhat diffusely creeping and annual as in some *Commelina* spp. The seedling axis is more usually replaced by creeping or somewhat decumbent stems arising from renewal buds at a lower node, the continued production of buds producing perennials, e.g. *Tradescantia virginica* as described by Gravis (1898). The early growth of renewal buds is often horizontal and produces rhizome segments bearing scale leaves. Rhizome segments in *Commelina virginica* are reduced to 1 internode according to Holm. Rhizomes are usually sympodially branched, as in *Commelina hirtella*, but indistinctly monopodial in *Tradescantia rosea* according to Holm. Erect shoots of perennial spp. occupying dry habitats are sometimes very ephemeral as indicated by Trochain (1932). Prophyllar buds are sometimes present, as in *Tinantia*, and these occasionally give rise to 2 branches apparently from a single node.

Special growth forms include that of *Weldenia candida* described by Holm and also observed in spp. of *Tradescantia* where there is a terminal leaf rosette at the soil surface, borne at the end of a long, erect, scale-bearing subterranean stem. *Cyanotis bulbifera* has a well-developed bulb, *Cyanotis caespitosa* a short corm-like axis, and in *Hadrodemas* the habit is sympodial and sub-arborescent. *Spatholirion* and *Streptolirion* have scandent, twining stems. *Cochliostema* is epiphytic (Troll 1961). Many spp., especially of *Callisia*, *Cyanotis*, and *Tradescantia*, are succulent. *Floscopa* is somewhat amphibious.

The naturalness of this family is emphasized by its uniform construction (e.g. Rohweder 1963) and a number of anatomical features is common to all members. Hair structure, however, is v. diverse. Leaves in bud typically have opposite halves of the blade rolled separately against the midrib, with the abaxial surface outermost. The leaf lamina includes relatively few longitudinal veins connected by a v. dense system of transverse veins. **Hairs** are either (i) 3-celled glandular micro-hairs each with a delicate clavate terminal cell, found in almost all spp., or (ii) uniseriate unbranched macro-hairs showing a great range in size and number of constituent cells, occasionally with special differentiation of some cells. Most extreme variants include: short, 2-celled spines, which are common, especially on the leaf margins; hooked-hairs, which are common in certain genera; and branched hairs, restricted to *Palisota*. The cell layers near the surface are always thin-walled and characteristically enlarged. These constitute the greater part of the leaf tissue and are said to have a water-storage function. The epidermis alone frequently serves for water-storage, but this function is often taken over or supplemented by colourless hypodermal tissues in certain genera. **Stomata** have large guard cells and 4–6 shallow subsidiary cells, the latter developing in a characteristic way from cells adjacent to stomatal mother cells (see p. 33). The veins in the lamina are typically independent of the surface layers and without well-developed fibrous supporting tissues.

The stem has a distinctive basic construction, differing from that of other monocotyledons. It exhibits hypodermal strands of **collenchyma,** a narrow cortex without vascular tissue, a central cylinder wholly ensheathed by a distinct endodermoid layer and often by sclerenchyma. There is a system of longitudinal vb's arranged in a characteristic manner and interconnected only at the nodes. Each central vb in an internode usually has a well-developed protoxylem lacuna. Calcium oxalate crystals are abundant in elongated raphide-sacs arranged in long series to form conspicuous **raphide-canals** resembling articulate laticifers in leaf and stem. Large rhombohedral crystals are otherwise common, especially in the hypodermis and epidermis of the lamina. **Silica** is restricted to a few genera and occurs as small spinulose bodies either embedded in the thickened outer wall of the epidermis, or in special shallow, thick-walled epidermal cells. **Vessels** with simple perforation plates and sieve-tubes with simple, more or less transverse sieve-plates occur in all parts.

Hairs

Polymorphic and v. plastic; plasticity not wholly obscuring considerable diagnostic value of hairs at specific and commonly at generic level as well. Many spp. with several distinct kinds of hair on the same individual. Hairs of 2 main, scarcely intergrading genetic types: (1) Three-celled **glandular micro-hairs,** usually inconspicuous to the naked eye. (These micro-hairs are v. much larger than the micro-hairs of grasses. See Vol. I of this series, pp. xxii and xliii.) (2) **Macro-hairs,** v. variable, often visible to the naked eye; subdivisible into several categories (5 according to Staudermann 1924), different categories connected by more or less continuous series of intermediate forms; continuous series may be regarded as one of increasing elaboration beginning with simple papillae.

1. *Glandular micro-hairs* (Figs. 1 and 2). (*Schleimhaare* of Staudermann)

Uniseriate, unbranched, probably always 3-celled (Fig. 1. A) but commonly described as 2-celled by older workers (e.g. Caro 1903) apparently due to failure to observe lowest septum. Each hair derived by oblique division from one end of a protodermal mother cell (Möbius 1908), the smallest daughter cell dividing twice by successive transverse walls to become 3-celled. **Basal cell** remaining wedged into epidermis in varying degrees, but rarely sunken, e.g. in *Cochliostema*. **Middle cell** slightly thick-walled, cutinized, sometimes tanniniferous or with other specialized inclusions which often accumulate beneath distal septum. Shape and size of middle cell constant and diagnostic for each sp., e.g. wide in *Rhoeo* (Fig. 1. O), narrow in *Pollia* (Fig. 1. Q). Position of first septum diagnostic, i.e. either at same level as outer epidermal wall and so often obscure in surface view as in *Cyanotis* (Fig. 2. E–L), *Murdannia* (Fig. 9. A–D), *Polyspatha*, or some distance above outer epidermal wall and conspicuous e.g. especially *Tinantia* (Fig. 1. G). **Distal cell** inflated, obtuse, usually wider than middle cell; delicate-walled, ephemeral because readily shrivelling or becoming detached, especially from herbarium material. Size of distal cell, especially in relation to middle cell, relatively constant and diagnostic for each sp. and often each genus. Length of distal cell varying considerably throughout family, from over 400 μm in *Cochliostema* (Fig. 1. Ab) to less than 40 μm in *Aneilema, Ballya, Murdannia* (Fig. 9. A–J). Table A indicates range in length of distal cells from abaxial surface of lamina, based only on average for one or v. few samples.

TABLE A

Length of distal cells in micro-hairs

More than 400 μm	*Cochliostema* (Fig. 1. Ab)
300–400 μm	*Athyrocarpus*
150–300 μm	*Geogenanthus* (Fig. 1. Z); *Palisota* spp. (e.g. *P. thyrsiflora*, Fig. 2. N); *Stanfieldiella* (Fig. 1. Y).
100–150 μm	*Callisia* spp. (e.g. *C. elegans*, Fig. 2. S); *Coleotrype* (Fig. 1. X); *Commelina* spp. (e.g. *C. graminifolia*); *Cuthbertia* (Fig. 1. J); *Cyanotis* spp. (e.g. *C. obtusa*); *Dichorisandra* (Fig. 1. W); *Hadrodemas* (Fig. 1. V); *Pollia* spp. (e.g. *P. condensata*, Fig. 2. D); *Tripogandra* spp. (e.g. *T. grandiflora*, Fig. 1. T).
80–100 μm	*Aploleia* (Fig. 1. N.); most *Callisia* spp. (Fig. 2. P–U); most *Commelina* spp. (Fig. 1. S); *Forrestia*; *Palisota* spp. (e.g. *P. barteri*, Fig. 2. M); *Pollia* spp. (e.g. *P. mannii*); *Polyspatha* spp. (e.g. *P. hirsuta*); *Siderasis* (Fig. 1. I); *Tradescantia* spp.; *Zebrina*.
60–80 μm	*Belosynapsis*; most *Cyanotis* spp. (Fig. 2. E–L); *Gibasis* (Fig. 1. P); *Pollia* spp. (e.g. *P. sorzogonensis*); *Rhoeo* (Fig. 1. O; 2. O); *Tripogandra* spp. (e.g. *T. cumanensis*).
50–60 μm	*Aneilema* spp. (e.g. *A. peniniense*); *Campelia* (Fig. 1. H); *Floscopa* spp. (e.g. *F. rivularis*); *Murdannia* spp. (e.g. *M. graminea*); *Tinantia* (Fig. 1. G).
Less than 50 μm	*Aneilema* spp. (e.g. *A. hockii*, Fig. 9. F–J); *Ballya* (Fig. 9. E); *Cyanotis* spp. (e.g. *C. axillaris*); *Floscopa* spp. (e.g. *F. flavida*, Fig. 1. D); *Murdannia* spp. (Fig. 9. A–D) (e.g. *M. spiratum*).

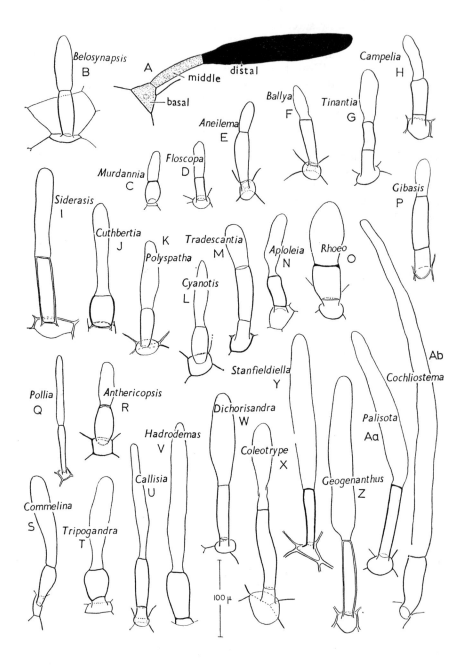

FIG. 1. COMMELINACEAE. Glandular micro-hairs (×233). All from abaxial surface of lamina, except Y (adaxial surface) (after Tomlinson 1966).

A. *Geogenanthus undatus*. Micro-hair in L.S. to show essential construction.

B–Ab. Micro-hairs in surface view.

B. *Belosynapsis vivipara*. C. *Murdannia nudiflora*. D. *Floscopa flavida*. E. *Aneilema hockii*. F. *Ballya zebrina*. G. *Tinantia erecta*. H. *Campelia zanonia*. I. *Siderasis fuscata*. J. *Cuthbertia graminea*. K. *Polyspatha hirsuta*. L. *Cyanotis longifolia*. M. *Tradescantia commelinoides*. N. *Aploleia monandra*. O. *Rhoeo spathacea*. P. *Gibasis karwinskyana*. Q. *Pollia macrophylla*. R. *Anthericopsis sepalosa*. S. *Commelina* sp. (B. H. 60–952). T. *Tripogandra grandiflora*. U. *Callisia elegans*. V. *Hadrodemas warszewicziana*. W. *Dichorisandra reginae*. X. *Coleotrype natalensis*. Y. *Stanfieldiella imperforata* (adaxial). Z. *Geogenanthus undatus*. Aa. *Palisota barteri*. Ab. *Cochliostema odoratissimum*.

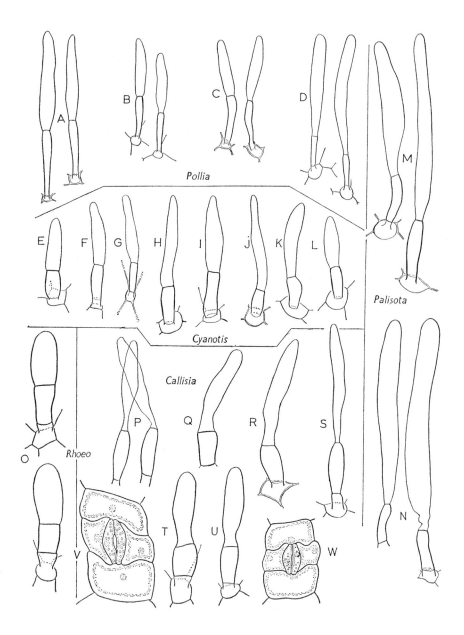

Pollia

Cyanotis

Callisia

Palisota

Rhoeo

18

FIG. 2. COMMELINACEAE (after Tomlinson 1966).

A–U. Glandular micro-hairs from abaxial surface of lamina ($\times$ 233).

A–D. *Pollia.*

  A. *P. crispata.* B. *P. mannii.* C. *P. macrophylla.* D. *P. condensata.*

E–L. *Cyanotis.*

  E. *C. bulbifera.* F. *C. kewensis.* G. *C. arachnoidea.* H. *C. lanata.*
I. *C. lapidosa.* J. *C. somaliensis.* K. *C. cristata.* L. *C. caespitosa.*

M, N. *Palisota.*

  M. *P. barteri.* N. *P. thyrsiflora.*

O. *Rhoeo spathacea.* Seedling; micro-hairs from first plumular leaf.

P–U. *Callisia.*

  P. *C. macdougallii.* Q. *C. soconuscensis.* R. *C. fragrans.* S. *C. elegans.*
T. *C. repens* (4n). U. *C. repens* (2n) (cf. next two figs.).

V, W. Stomata from abaxial surface of lamina, surface view ($\times$ 233).

  V. *C. repens* (4n). W. *C. repens* (2n) (cf. previous two figs.).

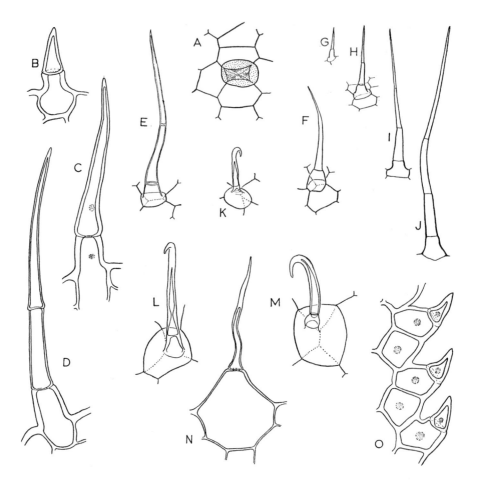

FIG. 3. COMMELINACEAE. Macro-hairs from lamina (after Tomlinson 1966).

A. *Floscopa rivularis*. Epidermal papilla, surface view ($\times 250$).

B–D. *Hadrodemas warzcewicziana*. Marginal hairs showing transition from 2-celled prickle-hairs (Fig. B) to 2- (Fig. C) and 3- (Fig. D) celled uniseriate hairs ($\times 233$).

E. *Campelia zanonia*. Adaxial uniseriate hair, surface view ($\times 150$).

F. *Tinantia erecta*. Adaxial uniseriate hair, surface view ($\times 60$).

G–J. *Tradescantia commelinoides*. Adaxial uniseriate hairs, surface view illustrating range in size ($\times 46$).

K–M. Hook-hairs ($\times 250$).

K. *Pollia condensata* (abaxial). L. *P. sorzogonensis* (abaxial). M. *Polyspatha hirsuta* (adaxial).

N. *Callisia elegans*. Adaxial prickle-hair in T.S. ($\times 233$).

O. *Callisia soconuscensis*. Uniform prickle-hairs from leaf margin ($\times 233$).

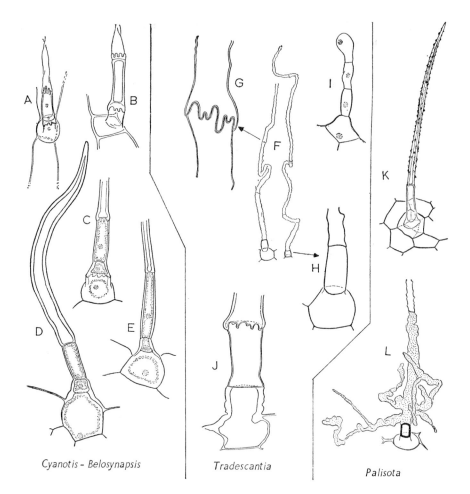

A B C D E
Cyanotis - Belosynapsis

F G H I J
Tradescantia

K L
Palisota

22

Fɪɢ. 4. COMMELINACEAE. Macro-hairs from lamina (cont.) (after Tomlinson 1966).

A–E. *Cyanotis* and *Belosynapsis*. 4-celled uniseriate and flagelliform hairs, distal cell incomplete except in D (×233).

A. *Cyanotis arachnoidea*. Abaxial flagelliform hair, surface view. B. *C. lanata*. Abaxial flagelliform hair, surface view. C. *C. villosa*. Abaxial flagelliform hair, surface view; distal cell rigid. D. *Belosynapsis vivipara*. Abaxial 4-celled hair in T.S. E. Same, surface view of adaxial epidermis.

F–J. *Tradescantia*.

F–I. *T. sillamontana*.

F. Uniseriate hairs (incomplete distally) surface view (×66). G. Detail of distal septum (×500). H. Detail of hair base (×233). I. 4-celled capitate hair, abaxial surface (×233). J. *T. crassula*. Base of marginal hair, recalling flagelliform hairs of *Cyanotis* (×200).

K, L. *Palisota*.

K. *P. hirsuta*. Abaxial rugose hair in surface view (×133). L. *P. barteri*. Abaxial branched hair, surface view, distal cell incomplete (×233).

Range of variation in length of distal cell within a single sp. still unexplored. Range within a genus slight, e.g. in *Cyanotis*, mostly 60–80 μm long (Fig. 2. E–L), but much longer in *C. obtusa*, shorter in *C. axillaris*; range restricted in *Aneilema* (Fig. 9. F–J), *Murdannia* (Fig. 9. A–D). Range v. unrestricted, however, in e.g. *Palisota, Pollia, Polyspatha*. Further indication of variety in appearance of micro-hairs shown in Fig. 1 and 2.

Basal and middle cells densely cytoplasmic at maturity, usually nucleate; distal cell at maturity enucleate, contents densely staining (e.g. with aqueous methylene blue); said to be mucilaginous by Staudermann; special chemical properties indicated by distinctive response to stains (Drawert 1941).

Micro-hairs probably present and abundant in all members of family, rarely infrequent or apparently absent, e.g. from spp. of *Setcreasea* and *Tradescantia*. Usually uniformly distributed over both surfaces of lamina, outer surface of sheath and stem; often less frequent on adaxial than abaxial surface, e.g. in *Murdannia* (cf. Fig. 9. M, N), sometimes restricted adaxially to a few hairs close to margin. Adaxial micro-hairs of blade commonly somewhat larger (but never by more than about 25 per cent) than abaxial. Hairs of sheath and stem often more variable in size than those of blade. Micro-hairs almost invariably sharply differentiated from macro-hairs, but somewhat intermediate hairs observed on stems of *Geogenanthus*.

(Although the size of micro-hairs is evidently under genetic control it is interesting to note in diploid and tetraploid forms of *Callisia repens* that their micro-hairs are indistinguishable in contradistinction to the size of the guard cells and other epidermal cells, which varies according to the degree of ploidy (Fig. 2. T–W).)

2. *Macro-hairs* (Figs. 3 and 4).

Complete transition shown throughout family from small papillae to long, often specialized, uniseriate hairs but several distinct categories recognizable. Large series of transitional forms often shown by single sp. Distribution of macro-hairs characteristic for the family, common on one or both surfaces of lamina; often otherwise restricted to margin of lamina, and those at margin becoming more obvious towards leaf base; usually prominent on mouth of leaf sheath; those on sheath either uniformly distributed on outer surface or most commonly forming a distinct vertical series on the ventral side of the sheath, continuing down stem to next node below. Other features of hair distribution probably of more restricted diagnostic value, e.g. the adaxial series of macro-hairs above mid-vein of lamina of *Tripogandra* spp. Transitions between one type of macro-hair and another commonly observed on a single leaf, e.g. the series papillae – prickle-hairs – hook-hairs or uniseriate hairs in spp. of *Aneilema* and *Commelina*. Further work on possible influence of environment on indumentum in Commelinaceae much needed.

The following arbitrary categories of macro-hairs recognizable (cf. Staudermann 1924).

A. *Unbranched hairs*

(*a*) **Papillae** (Fig. 3. A). Superficial cells each with a prominent thick-walled protuberance; representing either an undivided epidermal cell or an epidermal cell divided once periclinally producing a shallow, superficial papilla, as in *Pollia* according to Holm (1906) and in *Aneilema, Commelina, Tinantia*. Papillae of first type also recorded in *Commelina, Floscopa* (Fig. 3. A), *Murdannia, Pollia, Polyspatha, Tradescantia*. Papillae sometimes diagnostically restricted to leaf margin, notably in *Commelina*. Papillae in *Pollia* apparently silicified. Papillae with a late periclinal division cutting off a short, often pointed, distal cell and then transitional to the following type.

(b) Two-celled **prickle-hairs** (Figs. 3. B, N, O; 10. G, K–L) (*Stacheln* of Staudermann). Distal pointed cell long or short, usually thick-walled; septum between basal and distal cell often resembling 'ball and socket' joint. Marginal prickle-hairs often resembling and showing transitions to papillae. Surface prickle-hairs either with enlarged basal cell more or less equal to or exceeding epidermis in depth, or basal cell much shallower than epidermis, circular in surface view, and evidently derived from protodermal cell by unequal periclinal division, prickle-hairs then sometimes forming a more or less continuous layer above the true epidermis as in *Ballya* (Fig. 10. B, D–E), *Callisia* spp. Marginal prickle-hairs observed in *Aneilema, Aploleia, Ballya, Callisia* spp. (e.g. in *C. soconuscensis*, forming a regular, continuous marginal series (Fig. 3. O); in *C. fragrans*, forming an irregular, discontinuous series), *Coleotrype, Floscopa, Forrestia, Polyspatha*. Marginal hairs either forming a single series in 1 plane (e.g. *Callisia* spp.) or multiseriate, extending in several planes (e.g. *Coleotrype*). Surface prickle-hairs with a shallow basal cell observed in *Aneilema, Ballya, Pollia*, and *Callisia* spp. (e.g. *C. elegans*); with an inflated basal cell and often transitional to large uniseriate hairs as in *Coleotrype, Forrestia, Geogenanthus, Gibasis, Polyspatha*.

(c) Two-celled **hook-hairs** (Figs. 3. K–M; 10. F). (*Hakenborsten* of Staudermann; *Klimm*- or *Hakenhaare* of Solereder and Meyer). Resembling prickle-hairs with a shallow basal cell but with distal cell bent just below apex forming a hook; distal cell possibly silicified. Restricted to *Aneilema, Ballya* (Fig. 10. F), *Commelina* spp., *Pollia* (Fig. 3. K, L), *Polyspatha* (Fig. 3. M). Hairs of this kind confined to surface of lamina, sheath, and stem, never present on leaf margin. Distribution of these hairs variable but possibly of diagnostic value; commonly intermixed with prickle-hairs as in *Aneilema, Ballya, Pollia*. Hairs of two distinct sizes sometimes developed on a single plant.

(d) **Uniseriate hairs** (Figs. 3. C–J; 4. F–H) (including *Borsten* and *Randhaare* of Staudermann; *Borsten* distinguished from *Stacheln* by relative lengths of distal and basal cell). Up to 10 cells long and essentially elongated prickle-hairs with frequent septa (cf. Fig. 3. B–D, G–J); basal cell usually enlarged, often bell-shaped (Staudermann). Marginal hairs (*Randhaare* of Staudermann) usually longest, length increasing towards base of lamina and greatest on mouth of sheath. Hairs at first adpressed but erected by unequal growth of inflated basal cell, as observed by Renner (1909) in *Forrestia bicolor*; unequal expansion often indicated by wrinkled cuticle on one side of basal cell. Uniseriate hairs stiff, with a long pointed distal cell; often staining intensely with safranin. Distribution and size v. variable even within a single sp., rarely uniformly and densely scattered as in *Siderasis*; often restricted to one surface of lamina; commonly found on leaf margin and then towards base; longest hairs typically well developed on mouth of tubular sheath (occasionally restricted to this position), continuous as a vertical band down ventral side of leaf sheath and internode below. Uniseriate hairs observed in most genera but more characteristic of some than others, e.g. relatively feebly developed in *Anthericopsis, Cuthbertia, Rhoeo, Setcreasea, Zebrina*. Sometimes well developed in one sp. of a genus (e.g. *Cochliostema velutina*) but not in others (e.g. *C. odoratissimum*). Abundance of uniseriate hairs perhaps largely conditioned by environment.

Following types (e–g) may be regarded as elaborated uniseriate hairs.

(*e*) **Flagelliform hairs** (Fig. 4. A–E) (*Peitschenhaare* of Staudermann). Essentially a 4-celled uniseriate hair with specialization of two most distal cells; restricted to *Belosynapsis* and *Cyanotis*, except for somewhat similar hairs in a few *Tradescantia* spp. Each hair consisting of (i) an enlarged basal cell, usually as deep as rest of epidermis but shallower in *C. kewensis*; (ii) a short cell; (iii) an elongated middle cell; (iv) a distal cell. Distal cell rarely with additional septa. Hairs varying in length and amount of wall thickening of distal cell from sp. to sp. and size and degree of specialization of middle cell. Distal cell commonly v. long with delicate walls as in *Cyanotis arachnoidea* (Fig. 4. A), *C. djurensis, fasciculata, lanata* (Fig. 4. B), *obtusa*; often producing conspicuous woolly indumentum; or distal cell short, rigid with thick walls as in *Belosynapsis* spp. (Fig. 4. D–E), *Cyanotis longifolia, somaliensis, villosa* (Fig. 4. C), *zeylanica*. Middle cell characteristically thick-walled, staining intensely with safranin, often with conspicuous 'dove-tailing' of septa between cells on either side, the middle cell forming distinct 'socket' to receive proximal cell. Dove-tailing less pronounced in or even absent from some spp. e.g. *Belosynapsis, Cyanotis kewensis*, hairs then corresponding to uniseriate hairs but largely distinguished by additional basal short-cell. Somewhat similar dove-tailing of adjacent cells observed in *Tradescantia crassula* (Fig. 4. J), *T. sillamontana*, but without *Cyanotis*-type of cell sequence.

(*f*) **Rugose hairs** (Fig. 4. K) restricted to *Palisota*. Uniseriate hairs with long pointed distal cell; wall of distal cell with numerous spicular thickenings. Superficially similar hairs in *Tradescantia sillamontana* (Fig. 4. F–H) with irregular spicule-like papillae on distal cell as outgrowths of whole cell and not thickenings of wall as in *Palisota*.

(*g*) **Capitate hairs** (Fig. 4. I). Four-celled uniseriate hairs with a terminal clavate cell observed in *Tradescantia sillamontana*; distal cell nucleate and not with specialized contents as in glandular micro-hairs. Similar capitate hairs perhaps common on reproductive parts of other genera e.g. *Tinantia*.

B. *Branched hairs* (Fig. 4. L) (*Rhizoid-haare* of Staudermann)

Restricted to *Palisota*. Usually 4-celled with (i) a basal cell much shallower than rest of epidermis and apparently cut off by unequal division of protodermal cell; (ii) a short cell, collar-like, thick-walled, cutinized and staining intensely with safranin; (iii) a branched cell with delicate walls, inflated and usually elaborately lobed in an irregular stellate manner; (iv) a distal cell, thin or thick-walled, usually rugosely spiculate and resembling the distal cell of rugose hairs in this genus. Distal cell readily detached. Branched hairs sometimes showing transitions to rugose hairs, suggesting a genetic affinity between the two types.

Leaf

Simple, blade lanceolate but varying from ovate (e.g. *Dichorisandra*) to linear and narrowly grass-like as in some *Commelina* spp.; sub-terete in *Cuthbertia* spp.; rarely cordate at the base as in *Geogenanthus, Streptolirion*. Texture usually somewhat succulent. Large, spirally arranged leaves on more primitive stout shoots with an indistinct shortly sheathing base present, e.g. in *Cochliostema, Rhoeo*. Leaves in smaller, and in all distichous shoots each, with a long tubular eligulate sheathing base, commonly with long hairs at mouth of tube. Lamina more or less articulate to sheath, less commonly with distinct petiole as in *Athyrocarpus, Coleotrype, Forrestia, Geogenanthus, Pollia, Siderasis, Streptolirion,* and especially in *Palisota*. Leaf blade commonly secondarily orientated by twisting of petiole or base of blade. Tubular sheath sometimes perforated dorsally either by emerging vegetative branch or by inflorescence, e.g. in *Buforrestia, Campelia, Coleotrype, Forrestia, Tinantia*. Leaf blade rolled in bud, each half usually rolled separately with adaxial surface innermost, 2 rolled halves folded together above midrib; expanded halves of blade often unequal. Presence or absence of a thickened midrib region, extending throughout length of blade, a diagnostic feature.

(i) *Lamina*

Dorsiventral. **Cuticle** always thin, smooth or conforming to outer contour of epidermis; conspicuous waxy deposit rarely developed except in *Setcreasea*. **Epidermis** often deep and constituting a large part of total volume of leaf tissue (e.g. Fig. 8. I, J). Outer epidermal wall always thin but sometimes bearing slight localized thickenings (except on lateral subsidiary cells of stomata). Outer epidermal wall sometimes with numerous, uniformly scattered, **lenticular thickenings,** v. conspicuous in surface view in well-stained preparations, e.g. in *Aploleia* (Fig. 5. N), *Callisia* (Fig. 5. I, L–M), *Dichorisandra, Hadrodemas, Tripogandra* and in *Tradescantia navicularis*. Thickened cells of this kind closely resembling and intermixed with silica-cells in *Callisia* (e.g. Fig. 5. I), *Hadrodemas, Tripogandra*. **Striate thickenings** noted, e.g. in *Cuthbertia* (Fig. 7. B) and *Tradescantia crassifolia*, but most characteristic of and apparently diagnostic for *Murdannia* (Fig. 9. M–U). Striae present either as parallel and rarely connected longitudinal ridges, e.g. in spp. with elongated epidermal cells (*M. graminea*, Fig. 9. S–U; *M. nudiflora*) or forming a distinct reticulum in spp. with more isodiametric epidermal cells (*M. zeylanica*, Fig. 9. M–N). Striae characteristically modified on cells of stomatal apparatus.

Epidermal thickenings of all kinds most readily visible on upper and lower surface of blade. Lenticular thickenings at leaf margin becoming continuous and resembling striate thickenings (cf. Fig. 5. N and O); similar parallel striations observed in epidermal cells of sheath and blade in all above-mentioned genera.

Epidermal cells typically enlarged and often, together with similar colourless enlarged hypodermal cells (e.g. Figs. 8. A–B; 11. F–M), forming succulent surface layers said by Solereder and Meyer to function as water-storage tissue (cf. also Metzler 1924). Anticlinal walls of storage cells thus frequently appearing wrinkled or plicated in T.S. of preserved leaves apparently due to cell

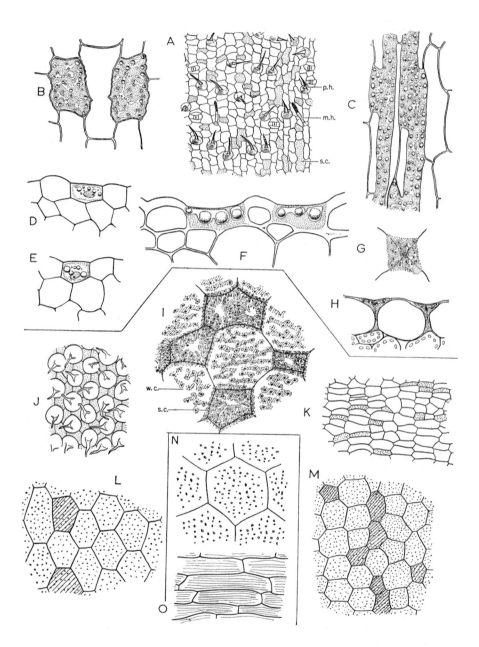

Fɪɢ. 5. COMMELINACEAE. Silica and other epidermal features (after Tomlinson 1966).

A–F. *Coleotrype natalensis*. Silica-cells of first type.

A. Outer surface of leaf sheath, surface view ($\times 42$). B. Intercostal silica-cells, surface view ($\times 183$). C. Costal silica-cells, surface view ($\times 183$). D–F. Silica-cells from stem in T.S. ($\times 460$). D, E. Immature cells from base of internode. F. Mature cells.

G, H. *Forrestia marginata*. Silica-cells from intercostal region of lamina ($\times 183$).

G. Surface view. H. in T.S.

I–M. Silica-cells of second type.

I. *Callisia soconuscensis*. Abaxial epidermis, surface view; silica and warted epidermal cells ($\times 183$). J. *Callisia elegans*. Adaxial epidermis, surface view ($\times 52$). K. *Hadrodemas warszewicziana*. Adaxial epidermis, surface view ($\times 52$). L. *Callisia repens*. Adaxial epidermis, surface view with occasional silica-cells ($\times 60$). M. *Callisia soconuscensis*. Adaxial epidermis, surface view ($\times 52$).

N, O. *Aploleia monandra*. Warted adaxial epidermal cells without silica, surface view ($\times 183$).

N. From centre of lamina. O. Marginal cells.

p.h.—prickle-hair; m.h.—micro-hair; s.c.—silica-cell; w.c.—warted cell. Silica-cells hatched in L and M.

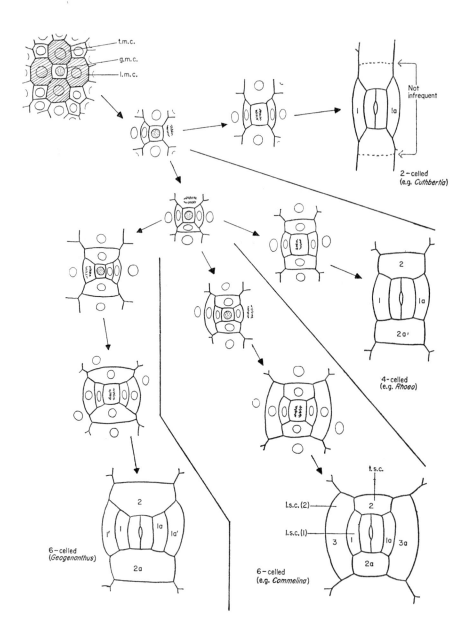

t.m.c.
g.m.c.
l.m.c.

Not infrequent

2-celled
(e.g. *Cuthbertia*)

1 1a

2
1 1a
2a'

4-celled
(e.g. *Rhoeo*)

6-celled
(*Geogenanthus*)

2
1' 1 1a 1a'
2a

t.s.c.
l.s.c.(2)
l.s.c.(1)
2
3 1 1a 3a
2a

6-celled
(e.g. *Commelina*)

Fɪɢ. 6. COMMELINACEAE. Diagrammatic representation of types of stomatal development in Commelinaceae, not to scale (after Tomlinson 1966).

Sequence of divisions is variable, those represented are the most commonly observed (see Stebbins and Jain 1960).

t.m.c.—terminal subsidiary cell mother cell; g.m.c.—guard cell mother cell; l.m.c.—lateral subsidiary cell mother cell; t.s.c.—terminal subsidiary cell; l.s.c.(1)—innermost lateral subsidiary cell; l.s.c.(2)—outermost lateral subsidiary cell.

deflation but cells never appearing sinuous-walled in surface view. Unrolling of young leaves brought about by enlargement of adaxial epidermal cells according to Löv (1926), possibly also by colourless hypodermal cells.

Adaxial epidermis uniform, rarely with costal bands of small elongated cells differentiated above larger veins (e.g. *Floscopa, Stanfieldiella*); stomata occasionally developed above larger veins as in *Anthericopsis*. Shape and arrangement of epidermal cells in surface view somewhat diagnostic as shown by the following examples. (i) Cells not arranged in well-defined longitudinal files and polygonal in outline in *Anthericopsis, Campelia, Cochliostema, Geogenanthus, Hadrodemas* (Fig. 5. K), *Siderasis*. (ii) Cells in well-defined longitudinal files. This type subdivided as follows. (*a*) Hexagonal, especially in *Callisia* (Fig. 5. L–M) and *Tripogandra*. (*b*) Hexagonal but transversely extended in *Palisota* and *Pollia*. (*c*) Rectangular-hexagonal but somewhat longitudinally extended as in most genera. (*d*) Rectangular and distinctly longitudinally extended as in *Cyanotis* (Fig. 11. D) and *Cuthbertia*. Depth of epidermis apparently influenced by environment but fairly constant for each sp. Shallowest epidermal cells typically situated above well-developed hypodermal layers as in *Cyanotis* (Fig. 11. F–K). Adaxial epidermal cells enlarged but more or less cubical as in *Dichorisandra, Geogenanthus* (Fig. 8. J), *Gibasis, Stanfieldiella, Zebrina*, adaxial then either much deeper than abaxial epidermis as in *Gibasis* and *Zebrina* or epidermis of each surface more or less equally deep as in *Coleotrype, Forrestia, Geogenanthus, Stanfieldiella*. Adaxial (and sometimes also abaxial) epidermal cells much enlarged in anticlinal direction in *Ballya* (Fig. 10. B) and *Callisia* spp.

Abaxial similar to adaxial epidermis but cells usually shallower (often much shallower as in *Gibasis* and *Zebrina*) and more irregular in surface view. Costal bands of narrow elongated cells more often developed below larger veins as in *Coleotrype, Cuthbertia, Floscopa, Forrestia, Gibasis*, some *Tradescantia* spp. or below bands of elongated hypodermal cells as in spp. of *Cyanotis* (Fig. 11. B) (e.g. *C. lanata*).

Other specialized epidermal cells, including marginal and silica-cells, described below and on p. 55.

Stomata (Figs. 6 and 7) mostly restricted to abaxial surface, infrequent or absent adaxially; equally numerous on both surfaces in *Floscopa*; adaxial stomata sometimes in distinct longitudinal bands above large veins as in *Anthericopsis* and *Ballya*. Abaxial stomata diffuse, rarely in distinct longitudinal files as sometimes in *Cyanotis* (Fig. 11. A). Stomatal apparatus v. distinctive due to a constant arrangement of 2 or more shallow subsidiary cells bearing a special developmental relationship to the guard cells (Campbell 1881, Strasburger 1886, Benecke 1892, Porsch 1905, Drawert 1941, Stebbins and Jain 1960, Stebbins and Khush 1961). This is illustrated diagrammatically in Fig. 6.

Stomata and subsidiary cells exhibiting one or other of the following arrangements: (*a*) 2-celled, with 2 lateral subsidiary cells (l.s.c.) alone (Fig. 7. B); (*b*) 4-celled, with 4 subsidiary cells, 2 l.s.c., and 2 terminal subsidiary cells (t.s.c.) (Fig. 2. V–W); (*c*) 6-celled, with 2 small lateral (l.s.c. 1), 2 additional lateral (l.s.c. 2) as long as entire stomatal complex, and 2 terminal subsidiary cells (Fig. 9. P). Six-celled stomata in *Geogenanthus* (Fig. 7. J) distinctive because provided with larger terminal and smaller second pair of lateral subsidiary cells. Type of stomatal apparatus constant and characteristic for each genus:

2-celled stomata

    Cuthbertia (Fig. 7. A–B)   (*Triceratella*)

4-celled stomata

Aploleia	*Hadrodemas*
Belosynapsis (Fig. 11. N)	*Palisota*
Callisia (Fig. 2. V–W)	*Rhoeo*
Campelia	*Setcreasea*
Cochliostema	*Siderasis*
Coleotrype	*Tinantia*
Cyanotis (Figs. 7. I; 11. A–B)	*Tradescantia*
Dichorisandra	*Tripogandra*
Forrestia	*Zebrina*
Gibasis	

6-celled stomata

Aneilema	*Geogenanthus*[1] (Fig. 7. J–K)
Anthericopsis	*Murdannia* (Figs. 7. H; 9. M, P–Q, T–U)
Athyrocarpus	*Pollia*
Ballya (Fig. 10. D)	*Polyspatha*
Commelina	*Stanfieldiella* (Fig. 7. C)
Floscopa	

Development of stomatal apparatus (Fig. 6 and legend)

Development normally proceeds in the following manner. The guard mother cell (g.m.c.) is cut off, usually from one end of a protodermal cell by unequal division. The first pair of l.s.c.'s is formed by unequal divisions in cells belonging to each file lateral to that containing the g.m.c. There are no further divisions except those in the g.m.c. in 2-celled stomata. T.s.c.'s are formed by unequal division of polar cells in same file as the g.m.c. There are no further divisions except in the g.m.c. in 4-celled stomata. The second pair of l.s.c.'s is produced by a second unequal division in cells lateral to the g.m.c. in 6-celled stomata. The final division in the formation of the stomatal apparatus, no matter of what kind it may be, takes place when the g.m.c. divides longitudinally to produce the guard cells. *Geogenanthus* is unusual because the l.s.c. divides a second time to produce a 6-celled stomatal apparatus of a distinctive type. Rearrangement of subsidiary cells gives rise to a characteristic appearance of the leaf surface in which each stomatal complex appears to be derived from one file of cells only. The subsidiary are always shallower than the normal epidermal cells; the second pair of lateral subsidiary cells is often the deepest (Figs. 7. K; 9. Q). Because the stomatal complex is shallow and the cells of the epidermis are frequently enlarged, well-developed substomatal chambers are often present, especially in *Ballya* and *Callisia* spp. where the epidermal cells are extended in an anticlinal direction (Fig. 10. B). The depth of the chambers is often enhanced by the deep layer of hypodermal

[1] See Fig. 6.

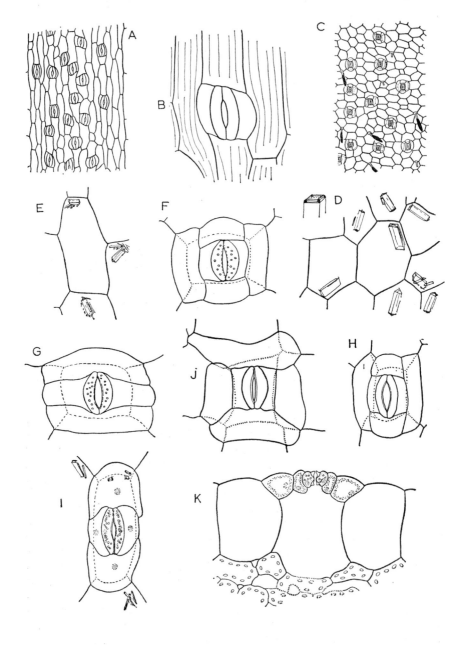

FIG. 7. COMMELINACEAE. Epidermal features of lamina.

A, B. *Cuthbertia ornata.*

A. Abaxial epidermis, surface view ($\times$50). B. Stoma, surface view ($\times$233).

C, D. *Stanfieldiella imperforata.*

C. Abaxial epidermis, surface view ($\times$125). D. Details of crystal-bearing cells ($\times$233); inset detail of crystal.

E. *Cyanotis arachnoidea.* Crystal-bearing epidermal cells, surface view ($\times$233).

F–J. Abaxial stoma, surface view ($\times$233).

F. *Stanfieldiella imperforata.* G. *Tradescantia blossfeldiana.* H. *Murdannia simplex.* I. *Cyanotis arachnoidea.* J. *Geogenanthus undatus.*

K. *Geogenanthus undatus.* T.S. abaxial stoma ($\times$233).

35

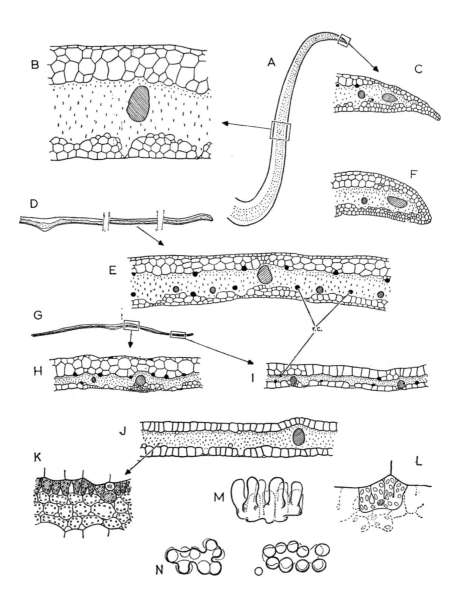

Fɪɢ. 8. COMMELINACEAE. Anatomy of leaf (after Tomlinson 1966).

A–C. *Rhoeo spathacea*. T.S. lamina.

A. (×3). B. Enlargement of part of Fig. A (×25). C. Leaf margin (×25).

D–F. *Cochliostema odoratissimum*. T.S. lamina.

D. (×3). E. Enlargement of part of Fig. D (×25). F. Leaf margin (×25).

G–I. *Coleotrype natalensis*. T.S. lamina.

G. (×3). H. Enlargement of part of Fig. G towards midrib (×25). I. Same, towards margin (×25).

J, K. *Geogenanthus undatus*.

J. T.S. lamina, half-way between base and apex, and between margin and midrib (×25). K. Enlargement of mesophyll with tanniniferous palisade cross-hatched (×100).

L–O. *Palisota barteri*. Palisade cells.

L. Single palisade cell *in situ* from T.S. of lamina (×293).

M–O. Diagrammatic representation of isolated cells.

M. In perspective. N. Viewed from within leaf. O. Viewed from without leaf.

r.c.—raphide-canals in solid black.

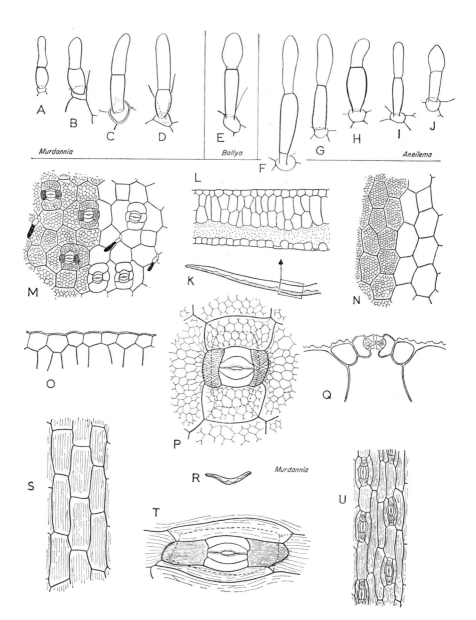

Fɪɢ. 9. COMMELINACEAE. *Aneilema, Ballya, Murdannia,* comparative leaf anatomy (after Tomlinson 1966).

A–J. Glandular micro-hairs from abaxial surface of lamina, surface view ($\times 233$).

A–D. *Murdannia.*

A. *M. nudiflora.* B. *M. simplex.* C. *M. graminea.* D. *M. zeylanica.*

E. *Ballya zebrina.*

F–J. *Aneilema.*

F. *A. aequinoctiale.* G. *A. hockii.* H. *A. lanceolatum.* I. *A. beniniense.* J. *A. setiferum.*

K–U. *Murdannia.*

K–Q. *M. zeylanica.*

K. T.S. lamina ($\times 3$). L. Enlarged part of Fig. K ($\times 25$). M. Abaxial epidermis, surface view ($\times 65$). N. Adaxial epidermis, surface view ($\times 65$). O. Adaxial epidermis in T.S. ($\times 65$). P. Stoma from abaxial epidermis, surface view ($\times 233$). Q. Abaxial stoma in T.S. ($\times 233$).

R–U. *M. graminea.*

R. T.S. lamina ($\times 3$). S. Adaxial epidermis, surface view ($\times 65$). T. Abaxial stoma, surface view ($\times 233$). U. Abaxial epidermis, surface view ($\times 65$).

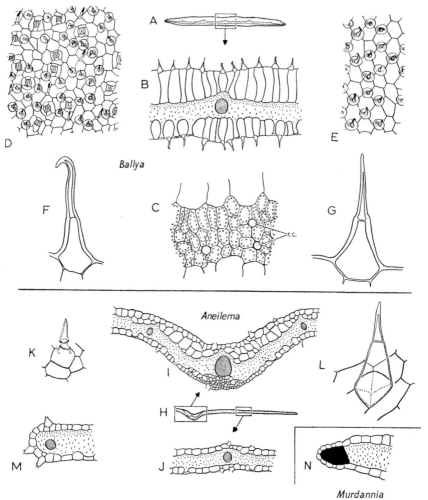

A

B

D

E

Ballya

F

C — r.c.

G

Aneilema

K

I

L

H

M

J

N

Murdannia

Fɪɢ. 10. COMMELINACEAE. *Aneilema, Ballya, Murdannia*, comparative leaf anatomy (cont.) (after Tomlinson 1966).

A–G. *Ballya zebrina.*

A. T.S. lamina (×3). B. Enlarged part of Fig. A (×25). C. Mesophyll in T.S. (×103). D. Abaxial epidermis, surface view (×42). E. Adaxial epidermis, surface view (×42). F. T.S. hook-hair from abaxial surface of lamina (×233). G. T.S. prickle-hair from abaxial surface of lamina (×233).

H–M. *Aneilema.*

H. *A. aequinoctiale.* T.S. lamina (×3). I. Enlarged part of midrib region of Fig. H (×25). J. Enlarged part of lamina region of Fig. H (×25). K. *A. subnudum.* Abaxial prickle-hair (distal cell partially detached) (×150). L. *A. hockii.* Adaxial prickle-hair, costal region (×150). M. *A. protensum.* T.S. lamina margin (×65).

N. *Murdannia zeylanica.* T.S. leaf margin (×65) for comparison with Fig. M. Marginal sclerenchyma solid black.

r.c.—raphide-canals.

cells. Because the subsidiary cells in *Cochliostema* are scarcely shallower than those of the epidermis, the substomatal chamber then becomes largely surrounded by hypodermal layers.

Guard cells always large, conspicuous, up to 69 μm long in *Tradescantia virginiana* according to Solereder and Meyer. Each with 2 cutinized ledges above slight wall thickenings; outer ledge always conspicuous, inner small, insignificant, or even absent; ledges more or less equal in some *Tripogandra* spp. Stomatal apparatus commonly elevated slightly above leaf surface, never sunken. Holden (1913) observed partial occlusion of substomatal chamber in *Tradescantia pulchella* by enlargement of mesophyll cells, experimentally shown to be an effect of low temperature. Irregularities in arrangement of subsidiary cells common, described by Drawert (1941) in relation to possible causal mechanism of cell division. Special staining properties of subsidiary and guard cells described by Drawert; some of apparent staining reactions observed in surface view perhaps caused by shallowness of these cells.

Hypodermis of colourless, usually enlarged cells often developed as a continuous (sometimes discontinuous) adaxial layer, less commonly as an abaxial layer and then always interrupted by substomatal chambers. Presence of adaxial hypodermis constant and diagnostic in a few genera, but in others often v. variable and distribution possibly determined by environment. Adaxial hypodermis in many leaves associated with mid-vein (Fig. 10. H–I), becoming less pronounced distally and marginally (cf. Fig. 8. H and I). Hypodermis best developed in large leaves, e.g. *Cochliostema* (multiseriate adaxial hypodermis up to 5 cells deep in midrib region, abaxial hypodermis multiseriate but shallower (Fig. 8. D–E)), *Rhoeo* (multiseriate adaxial hypodermis mostly 2 cells deep, abaxial hypodermis shallower and more frequently uniseriate (Fig. 8. A–C)), *Hadrodemas* (adaxial hypodermis of 1–2 layers of enlarged cells, abaxial hypodermis of 3–4 layers of shallow cells). Adaxial hypodermis in semi-terete leaves of *Cuthbertia* multiseriate, up to 5 cells deep; discontinuous and represented by broad bands 1–2 cells deep, interrupted by mesophyll in *Anthericopsis* and *Tradescantia* spp. (e.g. *T. virginiana*). Adaxial hypodermis otherwise more or less continuously uniseriate (Fig. 11. F–I) but biseriate in midrib region as in *Campelia, Cyanotis, Murdannia* (Fig. 9. K–L), *Setcreasea, Tradescantia* spp. (e.g. *T. navicularis*). Abaxial hypodermis in these genera mostly absent or represented by occasional bands of elongated cells as in *Belosynapsis* (Fig. 11. M), *Cyanotis* spp. (Fig. 11. K) (e.g. *C. obtusa*). Hypodermis mostly absent from remaining majority of genera except for layers commonly developed in thickened midrib either as a continuous band, or sometimes as 2 separate adaxial bands as in *Aneilema* spp. (Fig. 10. I); abaxial midrib hypodermis less common. Midrib hypodermis often extending into lamina and so transitional to spp. with continuous adaxial epidermis, especially in *Coleotrype* (Fig. 8. G–I), *Gibasis*. Hypodermis in some genera a constant feature, notably in *Cyanotis, Murdannia*, but v. variable in *Tradescantia*, e.g. absent from *T. commelinoides*, discontinuous in *T. virginiana*, continuous in *T. navicularis*, multiseriate in a broad band across midrib in *T. crassifolia*.

Adaxial (rarely abaxial) hypodermal cells large, cubical, colourless, inflated, often including conspicuous crystalline deposits; commonly hexagonal in surface view (Fig. 11. C); anticlinal walls often plicate in preserved material, indicating deflation of cells. Massive water tissue sometimes formed by considerable anticlinal expansion of hypodermal cells in *Cyanotis* (e.g. *C. cristata*, Fig. 11. F; *C. lapidosa*). Epidermis above well-developed hypodermis usually shallow compared with enlarged epidermis where colourless hypodermal layers are absent, indicating reciprocal function of surface layers. Hypodermal cells when restricted to midrib region probably functioning solely as expansion cells, according to Löv (1926). Hypodermal cell shape in *Rhoeo* studied in detail by Hulbary (1948). **Development of hypodermis** probably occurring in two ways either (*a*) from mesophyll cells as observed by Pfitzer (1870), Gravis (1898*b*), Caro (1903), Metzler (1924) and probably most usual condition, or (*b*) by occasional periclinal divisions of epidermal cells as observed by Caro in *Tradescantia navicularis* and by myself occasionally in spp. of *Murdannia, Callisia, Coleotrype*. Abnormal development of a massive abaxial hypodermis of anticlinally extended cells observed in sun- but not in shade-plants of *Cyanotis zeylanica* by Holtermann (1902).

Chlorenchyma often v. shallow and representing only a small fraction of total volume of leaf tissue. Palisade of 1(–3) layers usually developed but cells often shallow and somewhat conical (Fig. 8. K). Abaxial mesophyll composed of loose, often much-lobed cells. Mesophyll cells in *Dichorisandra* and some *Tradescantia* spp. (e.g. *T. virginiana*) elongated and lobed in a characteristic manner. Abaxial mesophyll cells somewhat palisade-like in sub-terete leaves of *Cuthbertia*. Palisade of *Palisota* v. distinctive, composed of lobed cells, more or less V-, Y-, U-, or W-shaped in T.S. with several vertical infoldings (Fig. 8. L–O). Somewhat similar invaginated palisade cells recorded or occasionally observed in spp. of *Cuthbertia, Cyanotis, Forrestia, Rhoeo, Tinantia, Zebrina*. Tannin sometimes localized in palisade tissue. Crystals sometimes present in mesophyll. Raphide-canals abundant and conspicuous in mesophyll of all spp. (see p. 54).

Veins rather diffuse, independent of surface layers in most spp., sometimes interrupting hypodermis or situated above and below bands of shallow costal epidermal cells. Larger veins sometimes attached to abaxial surface as in spp. of *Coleotrype, Commelina, Forrestia, Gibasis, Tradescantia*; larger veins rarely attached to both surfaces as in spp. of *Commelina* and *Tradescantia*. Bundle sheaths not usually composed of 2 distinct layers; veins mostly with a complete parenchymatous sheath of elongated cells containing a few chloroplasts, the sheath often completed either both above and below or only below by thick-walled, collenchymatous or even fibrous cells. Massive fibrous buttresses never developed except for distinct buttresses of thin-walled fibres below, rarely both above and below, veins in *Gibasis*. Sheath cells in *Floscopa rivularis* lobed, the lobes extending into the surrounding mesophyll. Vascular tissues of large veins including several files of metaxylem elements and, frequently, extended protoxylem. Xylem tissues in *Tinantia* sometimes replaced by lacunae as in the vb's of the stem. **Transverse veins** abundant, forming a dense system in longitudinal intercostal areas, always independent of surface layers; usually narrow, inconspicuous; sheathed by thin-walled elongated cells containing numerous small chloroplasts. Rarely in more robust leaves of *Dichorisandra, Geogenanthus, Gibasis, Palisota, Siderasis* transverse veins

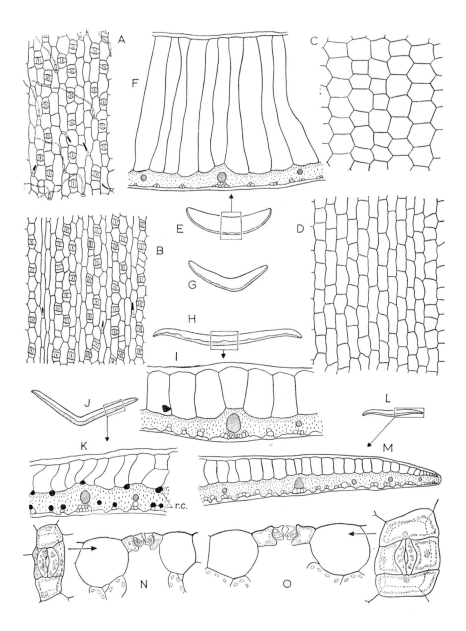

F I G. 11. C O M M E L I N A C E A E. *Cyanotis* and *Belosynapsis*, comparative leaf anatomy (after Tomlinson 1966).

A. *Cyanotis arachnoidea*. Abaxial epidermis, surface view ($\times$42).

B–D. *Cyanotis axillaris*. Surface layers in surface view ($\times$42).
   B. Abaxial epidermis. C. Adaxial hypodermis. D. Adaxial epidermis.

E–F. *Cyanotis cristata*. T.S. lamina.
   E. ($\times$3). F. Enlarged part of Fig. E ($\times$25).

G. *Cyanotis somaliensis*. T.S. lamina ($\times$3).

H–I. *Cyanotis arachnoidea* T.S. lamina.
   H. ($\times$3). I. Enlarged part of Fig. H ($\times$25).

J, K. *Cyanotis djurensis*. T.S. lamina.
   J. ($\times$3). K. Enlarged part of Fig. J ($\times$25).

L, M. *Belosynapsis vivipara*. T.S. lamina.
   L. ($\times$3). M. Enlarged part of Fig. L ($\times$25).

N, O. Stomata in surface view and T.S. ($\times$233).
   N. *Belosynapsis vivipara*. O. *Cyanotis longifolia*.

   r.c.—raphide-canals. Cells of epidermis not drawn in Figs. F, I, K, and M.

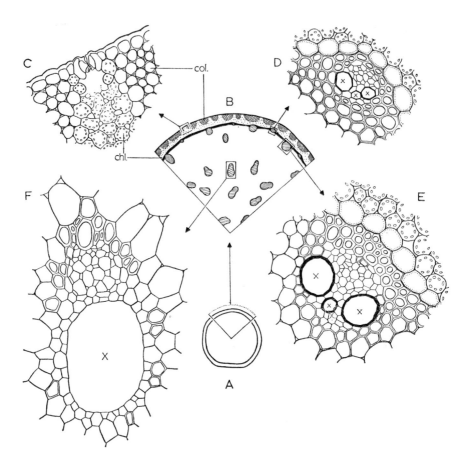

F<small>IG</small>. 12. COMMELINACEAE. Stem anatomy of *Commelina imberbis*.

A. T.S. stem (× 3). B. T.S. sector of stem (× 10).

C–F. T.S. enlarged parts of Fig. B (× 180).

    C. Surface layers. D. 'Cortical' bundle. E. 'Peripheral' bundle.
F. 'Medullary' bundle. (Nomenclature after Scott and Priestley 1925.)
chl.—chlorenchyma; col.—collenchyma.

congested, sheathed partly by thick-walled cells, and conspicuously connecting few longitudinal veins. Lamina usually including a thickened **midrib region,** but midrib rarely v. prominent except in large-leaved spp. such as *Cochliostema, Dichorisandra, Geogenanthus, Palisota*; including several scattered vb's, often in 2 distinct series. Veins independent of surface layers, more or less embedded in a chlorenchymatous band continuous with that of lamina. Hypodermal ground tissue colourless, often well developed and sometimes collenchymatous, especially those cells adjacent to adaxial surface, as in some *Commelina* spp. Sheath of midrib veins well developed and often colourless. **Leaf margin** often including a diagnostically useful strand of collenchymatous or fibrous elements (Fig. 10. N), as in spp. of *Callisia, Cuthbertia, Cyanotis, Gibasis, Murdannia, Tripogandra*; otherwise including a conspicuous marginal or sub-marginal vein (Figs. 8. C, F; 10. M). Marginal fibrous strand sometimes generically diagnostic as in *Murdannia* and serving to distinguish it from *Aneilema* without marginal fibres. Marginal fibres in other genera often less constant. Epidermal cells of leaf margin often conspicuously different from those elsewhere, sometimes forming distinct papillae.

Fleshy leaves aggregated to form bulbs in *Cyanotis bulbifera*, essentially like foliage leaves of other spp. but colourless and with an enlarged mesophyll, the hypodermal cells massive, the central mesophyll cells smaller and functioning as starch-storage cells.

(ii) *Petiole*

Occasionally developed as a short fleshy organ at the base of the lamina as in *Athyrocarpus, Coleotrype, Dichorisandra, Forrestia, Geogenanthus, Pollia, Siderasis*; apparently functioning as a pulvinus in orientating leaf blade. Petiole long and well developed in *Palisota*. Hypodermal ground tissues colourless, well developed, sometimes collenchymatous, especially at the margin and close to each surface. Central band of chlorenchyma enclosing the usually single arc of veins. Median usually somewhat larger than lateral veins. Vascular bundles in petiole of *Palisota* scattered and not restricted to a single arc. Vascular bundles usually without well-differentiated mechanical sheaths and resembling larger veins of leaf.

(iii) *Leaf sheath*

Usually long, especially on leaves of dorsiventral shoots with long internodes; tubular, eligulate; mouth of tube commonly conspicuously hairy and hairs often forming a conspicuous band on the surface of the leaf sheath opposite the insertion of the blade. Sheath sometimes perforated by emerging axillary, vegetative or floral, bud. **Epidermis** usually shallow, never differentiated like that of lamina but resembling that of stem. Epidermal cells usually longitudinally extended, rectangular in surface view, but transversely extended in *Buforrestia*, sometimes slightly thick-walled, outer wall usually slightly thicker than remaining walls. Outer epidermal wall bearing numerous minute longitudinal ridges in *Aploleia, Callisia, Cuthbertia, Murdannia, Tripogandra* spp., a condition usually correlated with the presence of lenticular or striate thickenings on the epidermis of the lamina. Abaxial costal cells, external to veins, usually longer and narrower than those elsewhere. Cells of adaxial epidermis v. uniform and without costal bands.

Stomata frequent, more or less restricted to abaxial bands in intercostal regions, resembling those of lamina or sometimes with a less regular arrangement of subsidiary cells. **Chlorenchyma** always present distally as outermost 2–3 layers of ground parenchyma, forming either a continuous cylinder or interrupted by bands of colourless bundle sheath tissue. Inner ground parenchyma cells colourless, large; adaxial cells sometimes somewhat radially compressed; ground parenchyma cells partly collapsed to form air-canals in leaf sheath of *Aneilema hockii*. **Veins** arranged in a single cylinder, rather uniform in size except for a few small veins; sometimes with a large conspicuous median vein, as in *Athyrocarpus*. Vascular bundles each with a colourless sheath of narrow cells continuous abaxially with a strand of collenchymatous or rarely fibrous cells. Mechanical tissues sometimes absent, but thick-walled cells occasionally developed adjacent to vascular tissues as in *Aneilema*, *Buforrestia*, *Pollia*. Metaxylem of large veins including 1 or more wide vessels and commonly with extended protoxylem.

STEM

(i) Aerial internodes

Anatomy v. constant and characteristic throughout the family apart from qualitative differences between internodes in different parts of a single shoot and between different levels in a single internode. **Cuticle** usually thin and inconspicuous, but occasionally ribbed like the epidermis of the sheath, as in *Callisia*, *Murdannia*, *Tripogandra* spp., and in *Tradescantia navicularis* according to Holm. **Epidermis** shallow, slightly thick-walled and like that on abaxial surface of sheath. **Stomata** frequent, not in obvious files but sometimes restricted to bands of epidermal cells separated by wider or narrower nonstomatal regions. Distribution of stomatal bands in *Tradescantia fluminensis* described by Lück (1958) and said to reflect a periodicity in mitotic activity in protodermal cells, the periodicity continuous as a spiral from one internode to the next. Stomatal apparatus as in leaf; guard cells sometimes with 2 more or less equal ledges as in *Aneilema*. **Cortex** distinct but always v. narrow and without vb's (Fig. 12. A–B). **Hypodermis** almost always differentiated as 1–3 layers of conspicuous collenchyma (Ambronn 1881, Grevillius 1887), the collenchymatous cylinder interrupted by chlorenchyma below the stomata (Fig. 12. B–C). Interruptions visible in surface view either as vertical bands below stomatal files or as narrow elliptical islands below scattered stomata. Stem occasionally with shallow ribs representing raised bands as in *Commelina capitata*. Ground parenchyma internal to collenchyma often only 2–3 cells wide, composed wholly of loose **chlorenchyma** with well-developed intercellular spaces. Chlorenchyma somewhat lacunose in *Floscopa*. Raphide-sacs conspicuous. Inner limit of cortex represented by a distinct compact **uniseriate parenchyma sheath** (Fig. 12. D), commonly described as an endodermis (e.g. by Scott and Priestley) but lignified Casparian strip not visible and records in literature of its appearance often somewhat conflicting. This endodermoid layer at immature base of internode always thin-walled and conspicuous as a starch sheath (Eberhard 1900, Hämmerle 1901) with many small grains.

Same layer in upper part of same internode commonly with unevenly thickened walls appearing U-shaped in T.S. and so markedly endodermoid. Variation in appearance of endodermoid layer with age and level in internode probably accounting for conflicting statements in the literature. **Central cylinder** limited externally by a conspicuous 1–4-layered sclerotic cylinder (Fig. 12. B, D–E) immediately within the endodermoid layer, of narrow, compact, usually thick-walled and lignified cells, mostly with truncate end walls. Cylinder always completing sclerosis first in upper part of internode and otherwise v. variable in appearance in different spp., occasionally indistinct or represented by thin-walled cells. **Vascular bundles** of stem restricted to central cylinder and with a v. characteristic distribution related to method of development (see below). Following types of bundle recognized in *Tradescantia fluminensis* by Scott and Priestley (1925), but in other spp. differences between different categories of central vb's sometimes less obvious.

(1) '*Peripheral*' *vascular bundles* (Fig. 12. E), almost always adjacent to or embedded in sclerotic cylinder but rarely in periphery of central cylinder. Each vb usually with a continuous sheath of mechanical cells resembling cells of the confluent sclerotic cylinder. Metaxylem usually including 2 wide vessels; rarely with more wide vessels as in *Polyspatha*; xylem usually somewhat V-shaped in T.S., rarely becoming amphivasal. Xylem lacunae rarely developed, except in *Tinantia*.

(2) '*Cortical*' *vascular bundles* situated in the central cylinder close to but independent of the sclerotic sheath. These vb's wrongly named because not situated in the cortex. Cortical vb's narrow, with reduced vascular tissues, often only visible in upper part of internode and dying out towards base. Cortical bundle in Fig. 12. D embedded in sclerotic cylinder, a less usual condition.

(3) *Perimedullary* and (4) *Medullary vascular bundles*, the 2 types v. similar in appearance (Fig. 12. F) and chiefly distinguished by position. Large vb's sometimes with a fibrous bundle sheath adjacent to xylem and phloem, or to xylem alone. Xylem usually represented by a conspicuous xylem lacuna, thickening rings of original xylem elements often visible against wall of lacuna.

Ground parenchyma of central cylinder uniform except for frequent narrow raphide-sacs. Starch often abundant, especially in lower parts of stem, distribution described in detail by Eberhard (1900). Basic construction of shoot, as described above for narrow stems, fundamentally similar in wider stems as in *Dichorisandra* and *Palisota*.

(ii) *Nodal anatomy, course and development of vascular bundles*

Vascular bundles of all types connected at nodes by a **nodal plexus.** Medullary and perimedullary vb's fused to form a central vascular plate, peripheral bundles forming a peripheral ring, these 2 nodal plates connected by frequent radially horizontal vascular strands. Root traces connected internally to a distinct plate of short tracheids at the periphery of the node above the foliar plexus (Mangin 1882, Gravis 1898*a*, Haga 1922), independent of the inner radial anastomoses. (The report by De Bary (1884) that the radial anastomoses are root traces has been shown by subsequent authors (e.g.

Haga 1922) to be incorrect.) Branch traces connected by 2 tangential strands to peripheral part of nodal ring (Gravis 1898a).

The following account of the **construction of the stem** in the Commelinaceae is largely based on the excellent analysis by Gravis (1898a, b) and Scott and Priestley (1925).

The Commelinaceae-type of stem had been described by early workers, notably Falkenberg (1876) and De Bary (1884), as differing in the arrangement of its vascular bundles from all other monocotyledons. According to these authors the essential features of this type were: (a) a peripheral *cauline* system of vascular bundles never entering the leaf and only indirectly in contact with the leaf traces at the nodes; (b) a *foliar* system of vascular bundles situated in the central cylinder, each bundle being inserted more or less horizontally into the stem at the node, then proceeding vertically through one internode in a perimedullary and in the second internode in a medullary position. These central bundles never bend outwards to the periphery of the stem as in the 'Palm-type' of foliar trace said to be characteristic of other monocotyledons. The individuality of each trace is lost at the base of the second node by fusion with the nodal plexus. Guillaud (1878) also noted the same two systems in the rhizome of *Tradescantia virginica* but suggested that they were not entirely independent. Gravis (1898a) made very careful and detailed studies of *Tradescantia virginica* and *fluminensis*. He concluded that there was no vascular system restricted to the stem. The bundles of the peripheral system (*faisceaux anastomotiques*) anastomose in a sympodial manner but are connected by vascular strands to the central system (*faisceaux foliaires*) at the nodes. The bundles of the central system are more obviously continuous into the leaf as leaf traces. In his extensive observations Gravis emphasized the following features which were overlooked by earlier workers and which, indeed, tend to be overlooked by all who reconstruct leaf-trace systems. (a) The bundles which enter the stem from a single leaf are not all alike. Gravis distinguished 4 main types according to size and position: median, lateral, intermediary, and marginal veins, and used a formula to represent the numbers of such veins. (b) The arrangement of the vb's varies somewhat according to the diameter of the stem, although the fundamental construction is not altered. (c) The vascular arrangement varies at different levels along a single shoot and this was illustrated by Gravis throughout the length of several different shoots, including those with seedling axes.

Scott and Priestley (1925) analysed shoot construction in *Tradescantia fluminensis*, a diminutive sp., from the developmental aspect and were able to account for the variation in structure of bundles of the different systems, (1)–(4) described on p. 50, on a simple mechanical basis.

The vb's originate as procambial strands, the course of which undergoes little change as the stem matures so that their arrangement is essentially the same in the procambial state as when they are fully differentiated, this arrangement being easily determined from serial sections of a single internode. Traced upwards the bundles at the centre of the stem first become identifiable at the node and proceed through the length of 1 internode in a medullary position. At the first node above their origin they move into a perimedullary position, which they occupy for the length of a further internode. In a transverse section of a single internode medullary and perimedullary bundles of 2 successive leaves usually lie on alternate radii, except for the median bundle which usually occupies the same radius throughout 2 internodes. The perimedullary bundles pass into the leaf inserted at the second node above that of their origin. The bundles are not always restricted to 2 internodes in the stem, since Gravis (1909) observed that the bundles may remain distinct for as many as 5 inter nodes. The peripheral bundles originate independently, and their differentia- tion is always completed much later than that of the central bundles.

Xylem differentiation in the 2 systems, (1)–(2); (3)–(4), is closely correlated and is related to leaf development. In the leaf-trace system of any one leaf, xylem differentiation proceeds acropetally in the medullary and perimedullary bundles in the stem and continues into the main veins of the leaf, which them- selves originate in an acropetal direction. Xylem differentiation in the leaf is most advanced in the median vein and proceeds in this and the main lateral veins to the apex of the leaf primordium. When this 'xylem-forming tendency' in the procambial strands of the leaf reaches the leaf apex it is reversed and xylem differentiates in the basipetal direction, not only in the existing veins but also in smaller longitudinal veins and in the transverse veins. Differentia- tion proceeds to the base of the leaf and, at its insertion, forms the central nodal plate in the stem. Since the central bundles have lost their ability to differentiate xylem, no basipetal xylem is formed in perimedullary (3) and medullary (4) bundles. Xylem differentiation continues, however, in the 'cortical' bundles (2) but rather feebly and often extends only part of the way down the internode in these small bundles. The basipetal differentiation of xylem is, on the other hand, able to continue in the 'peripheral' bundles (1) since these still retain their meristematic properties and so it continues to the base of the internode but ceases at the node below where it produces the peri- pheral part of the nodal plate. Thus, the nodal plate is formed where the 'xylem-forming tendency' of immature tissues impinges on mature tissues of a lower internode. Since xylem formed by the basifugal differentiation in the central bundles is matured before elongation growth of the stem as a whole has ceased, it is passively ruptured and replaced by a wide lacuna in each bundle. On the other hand, xylem differentiation in the peripheral bundles is not usually completed until after elongation of the internodes has ceased, so that rupture of the tracheal elements does not usually occur and xylem lacunae are infrequent.

The efficiency of the xylem lacunae as water-conductors in the Commeli- naceae has been tested by several workers. Scott and Priestley suggested that they are not effective, but Buchholz (1921) considered that they may be the only channels for water conduction to certain parts of the plant during their development. This is certainly true for *Tinantia* (cf. Gravis 1909) in which the xylem throughout many parts of the plant is represented solely by lacunae. Tyloses may occur in the lacunae, as recorded by Gravis (1898a).

More recently shoot development in Commelinaceae has been examined by Rohweder (1963) on a comparative basis. Peripheral and central systems can be distinguished but the central system is much less regular than Scott and Priestley indicate. Peripheral strands cannot be traced with certainty across the nodal complex.

(iii) *Rhizome or subterranean stems*

Underground parts of erect shoots not markedly different from aerial stems but commonly bearing scale leaves separated by short internodes. Sympodial and irregular monopodial branching described by Holm in several spp. of *Tradescantia*. Short corm-like axis developed in *Cyanotis caespitosa* and *bulbifera*. Rhizome-like features induced by Bloch (1935) by burying aerial stems of *Tradescantia fluminensis*. Short erect axis of *Rhoeo* with rhizome-like anatomy.

The anatomy of the rhizome not fundamentally different from that of aerial stem, but typically differing from it in the following features. **Periderm** commonly developed from 'etagen'-meristem. Collenchyma often and chlorenchyma always absent. **Cortex** usually wider than that of aerial stem. **Sclerotic cylinder** often absent or represented by an indistinct parenchymatous cylinder, cortex and central cylinder consequently indistinctly separated. **Endodermoid layer** rarely developed, sometimes present as a discontinuous layer at inner limit of cortex. **Vascular plexus** occasionally developed at periphery of central cylinder, as in spp. of *Cyanotis*, *Murdannia*, *Palisota*, *Rhoeo*. Vascular bundles resembling those of aerial stems, but usually without wide xylem lacunae; xylem of central bundles sometimes irregular, rarely amphivasal as in *Murdannia* and in peripheral bundles of *Palisota*. **Starch** common, often abundant.

ROOT

Roots arising adventitiously at the nodes. Root initials differentiated early, in fixed numbers, arising from the parenchyma external to the peripheral vb's (Gravis 1898a, Schubert 1913, Scott and Priestley 1925), remaining dormant until subjected to a suitable external growth-stimulating influence. Root-traces inserted on an independent peripheral plexus immediately above nodal vascular plexus (Mangin 1882, Gravis 1898a, Haga 1922). Roots on a single individual commonly showing functional specialization either as storage, feeding, or supporting roots; commonly fleshy (cf. Drobnig 1893), locally tuberous in *Anthericopsis* and *Dichorisandra*; sometimes rigid and stilt-like as in *Coleotrype*. Contractile roots recorded by Holm (1906). **Piliferous layer** conspicuous, usually persistent; root-hairs developing from short trichoblasts. **Exodermis** immediately beneath piliferous layer always developed as 1(–2) layers of compact thin-walled cells, more or less radially extended and hexagonal in T.S.; commonly suberized, outer wall sometimes slightly thickened. Radial walls commonly exhibiting conspicuous transverse wrinkles, suggested by Holm to be a result of root contraction. **Sclerotic cylinder** of 1–4 layers of narrow, compact cells, mostly with thickened walls, differentiated immediately within exodermis. Cylinders most strongly developed in rigid supporting roots, as in *Coleotrype*, but appearance varying considerably in roots of a single individual; usually absent from fleshy storage roots. **Periderm** occasionally developed in outer cortex, with occasional etagen-like divisions in peripheral layers, especially in older and more fleshy roots. **Cortex** wide, usually uniformly parenchymatous, radial air-canals rarely formed by collapse of tangential files of cells, as in *Floscopa* and *Murdannia*, or by irregular enlargement of wide intercellular spaces as in *Dichorisandra*. Files of narrow, elongated raphide-sacs often conspicuous. Starch common, sometimes abundant in fleshy roots. Inner cortical cells arranged in regular radial and concentric files. **Endodermis** consisting of thin-walled cells in young roots but more conspicuous and commonly developing U-shaped wall thickenings in mature roots. **Pericycle** 1-layered, usually thin-walled, but occasionally developing thick pitted walls. Pericycle often absent from narrow branch roots. Stele with polyarch vascular arrangement, number of xylem poles often rather constant for a single sp. Anomalous stelar structure with medullary phloem strands and occasional isolated vessels observed in *Dichorisandra*. Ground tissue of stele somewhat thick-walled and fibrous but that of wider steles usually including a medulla of thin-walled cells. Centre of stele in narrow roots often occupied by 1–2 wide vessels as in *Commelina, Murdannia, Tinantia*. Branch roots arising in pericycle opposite protoxylem poles (Rywosch 1909). Bistelic root described in *Tradescantia virginica* by Fourcroy (1956), but probably one stele representing a buried lateral root, as suggested by Rivière (1956). Physiological aspects of root formation discussed by Dorfmüller and Mevius (1937).

Seedling Anatomy

Vascular transition between root and stem in hypocotyl described by Gérard (1881), Gravis (1898*a*), Schlickum (1896), Messeri (1925), Boyd (1932).

Secretory, Storage, and Conducting Elements

Crystals. Calcium oxalate abundant as rhombohedral or tabular crystals in all parts, often v. abundant and conspicuous in epidermis (Fig. 7. D–E) and hypodermis of lamina. Crystals often large and solitary, but mostly in clusters or as coarse sand, the amount of crystalline material being v. variable for a single sp. Bundles of needle- or rod-like raphide crystals abundant in specialized raphide-sacs forming **articulated raphide-canals** and probably present in all parts, but often inconspicuous or easily overlooked in root. Cells differentiating early in longitudinal files, each cell including a single bundle of raphides or more rarely a single rod-like crystal. Cells not undergoing further division and so becoming markedly extended by over-all elongation of adjacent tissues. Raphide-cells visible in mature organs as long elements resembling articulated, unbranched laticifers. Contents becoming mucilaginous (Fuchs 1898, Onken 1922) but end walls not naturally breaking down to form continuous tubes, although such cells (*Schlauchgefässe*) often mistakenly described as continuous tubes by earlier workers (see Gravis 1898*a*). Sphaerocrystals observed in dried-out mucilage obtained from raphide-sacs of *Dichorisandra albomarginata* by Caro (1903). Raphide-sacs scattered in mesophyll of leaf, most commonly adjacent to surface layers (Figs. 8. E–I; 11. K); usually conspicuous in T.S. of stem and leaf sheath and sometimes also in root as small apparently angular cells with refractive contents, scattered throughout ground parenchyma, but especially conspicuous in peripheral chlorenchyma of stem and leaf sheath. Raphide-sacs in peripheral ground tissue of stem shorter than those at centre, as observed by Gravis in *Tradescantia virginica*, and indicating later cessation of cell division in peripheral tissues as compared with central tissue, in accordance with process of shoot development as described by Scott and Priestley (1925). Raphide-sacs dimorphic in leaves of *Geogenanthus*, with wide cells in files adjacent to adaxial epidermis each including a single rod-shaped crystal; narrow cells in files adjacent to abaxial epidermis each including a cluster of more needle-like crystals.

Silica in specialized epidermal silica-cells (Fig. 5) (Möbius 1908) restricted to *Callisia, Coleotrype, Forrestia, Gibasis, Hadrodemas, Tripogandra*, but not in *Campelia* as recorded by Molisch (1918). Silica-cells said by Caro (1903) to be widely distributed but this information unreliable as indicated by Solereder and Meyer. Following notes refer largely to my own observations. Silica often abundant, irregularly distributed in epidermis of leaf and stem but never in stomatal subsidiary cells. Silica-cells of 2 distinct types.

(*a*) Silica in early-differentiated protodermal cells, these cells ceasing to enlarge and remaining much shallower (except in *Forrestia*, Fig. 5. G–H) than remaining epidermal cells at maturity (Fig. 5. D–F). Alternatively silica-cell sometimes derived by unequal periclinal division of protodermal cell. Silica as small spinulose spherical bodies varying in size up to 10 μm in diameter, appearing early in silica-cell; cell lumen typically becoming occluded at maturity by thickenings of inner walls except for elaborately labyrinthiform spaces including the silica-bodies (Fig. 5. B–C). Wall thickening usually so complete that shallow silica-cells readily mistaken for thickened wall of undivided cell. Immature silica-cells in *Callisia* observed by Molisch to have 2–3 amoeboid nuclei. Silica-cells of this type in all above genera except *Forrestia* typically restricted to costal regions of lamina, sheath (Fig. 5. A–C); more diffuse in stem; commonly associated with marginal fibrous strand of blade. Sometimes more diffusely distributed and not associated with costal regions in *Coleotrype* and *Gibasis*. In *Forrestia* silica-cells scattered over both blade surfaces as well as in costal regions, cells narrow but almost as deep as normal epidermal cells (Fig. 5. G–H).

(*b*) Silica in *Callisia, Hadrodemas, Tripogandra* as minute bodies rarely more than 1–2 μm in diameter deposited abundantly in outer wall of otherwise unmodified epidermal cells in leaf and stem (Fig. 5. I–M). Silica-cells of this type readily confused with epidermal cells with lenticular wall thickenings normally associated with them in the above genera (e.g. Fig. 5. I).

Silica-cells of diagnostic value and suggesting 2 groups of genera: *Callisia, Hadrodemas, Tripogandra* with both type (*a*) and (*b*) silica-cells; *Coleotrype, Forrestia, Gibasis* with only type (*a*) silica-cells.

Silica incrustation of distal cells of hook- and prickle-hairs not uncommon. Idioblastic papillae of epidermis in *Pollia* sometimes silicified.

Tannin often common, in unspecialized ground tissue cells in all parts, conspicuous in mesophyll of some *Pollia* spp. Distribution in *Dichorisandra ovata* discussed in detail by Hämmerle (1901).

Starch common as storage grains in ground parenchyma of root and stem, sometimes abundant in the mesophyll of the leaf. Grains smooth, more or less spherical or slightly ellipsoidal, slightly eccentric, never flattened; sometimes with a small incision at one end; usually simple but storage cells commonly including a few compound grains. Starch always present in transitory form in 'starch sheath' surrounding central cylinder in immature internodes.

Anthocyanin commonly present in surface tissues in spp. of *Cyanotis*,

Dichorisandra, Tradescantia but especially in *Rhoeo* and *Zebrina*. Silvery appearance of leaves in some spp. apparently due to air-filled intercellular spaces.

Xylem. Vessels probably present in all parts. Elements in stem and root, if unextended, usually with simple perforation plates on more or less oblique end walls. Xylem of each vb in centre of stem commonly replaced by a wide lacuna; annular or spiral remains of wall thickenings commonly persistent at the edge of lacuna.

Phloem. Sieve-tubes with simple sieve-plates on more or less transverse walls probably in all parts.

TRICERATELLA (after Tomlinson 1964)

Somewhat anomalous and differing from rest of family in the following ways: absence of glandular micro-hairs; hairs otherwise 6-celled with a clavate distal cell; stomata 2-celled; elongated mesophyll cells lobed; thick-walled mechanical cells absent from lamina; raphide-sacs apparently next to veins in lamina; collenchyma absent from stem; vessels restricted to root and stem with unspecialized scalariform perforation plates resembling end walls of tracheids.

TAXONOMIC NOTES

The value of anatomical data in the classification of Commelinaceae has been reviewed by Tomlinson (1966) in relation to a tentative subdivision of the family into 15 groups by Brenan (1966). *Cartonema* is regarded by Brenan as one of these groups, but anatomical evidence which supports the isolation of this genus and therefore the creation of the family Cartonemataceae is summarized in the separate account of that family on p. 66.

Of the remaining genera, *Triceratella* can be distinguished by a number of anatomical features as indicated above. *Triceratella* is treated as a separate group by Brenan, but without any special emphasis on its isolation. Tomlinson suggests that its isolation should be emphasized by creating a separate sub-family for it, distinct from a second subfamily which would include all remaining genera of Commelinaceae (*sensu stricto*).

With the removal of *Cartonema* and *Triceratella* the remaining genera form a natural unit, at least anatomically. Brenan and Tomlinson both agree that no further major subdivision is possible, contrary to the artificial attempt of earlier systematists to make major subdivisions.

The distribution of anatomical features throughout Brenan's groups is discussed by Tomlinson with the conclusion that it is difficult to find combinations of anatomical features by which these groups can be typified. This is not to imply that they are not natural, but merely suggests that divergence has not proceeded to the anatomical level. On the other hand, some smaller groups of genera within Brenan's larger groups may possess common anatomical features suggestive of a close affinity. Sometimes these anatomical groupings cut across Brenan's subdivision. *Callisia, Hadrodemas, Tripogandra* have the same type of silica-cell, although *Hadrodemas* is not included by Brenan in the same group as the remaining two genera. Silica of a different type is otherwise restricted to *Coleotrype, Forrestia, Gibasis* and silica may have appeared independently at least twice in the Commelinaceae. Despite this difficulty of recognizing Brenan's groupings on an anatomical basis, many genera in Commelinaceae apparently can be recognized anatomically, e.g. *Cochliostema, Cyanotis, Palisota*. Anatomical features may also differentiate closely related genera such as *Aneilema, Ballya, Murdannia* which have hitherto been much confused.

Tomlinson's conclusion is that anatomical information may be very helpful in generic diagnoses but the whole subject still needs much more detailed investigation.

GENERA AND SPECIES REPORTED ON IN THE LITERATURE

Ambronn (1881) *Tradescantia erecta, T. sellowi, T. virginica*; stem.

Bary (1884) *Tradescantia albiflora*; stem.

Benecke (1892) *Tradescantia* sp.; stomatal apparatus.

Bloch (1935) *Tradescantia fluminensis* Vell.; stem.

Boyd (1932) *Commelina coelestis, C. dianthifolia, C. graminifolia, Cyanotis cristata, Palisota pynaertii, Rhoeo discolor, Tinantia fugax, Tradescantia geniculata* var. *kunthiana*; seedling anatomy.

Buchholz (1921) *Tinantia viridis*; stem.

Campbell (1881) *Tradescantia vulgaris*; stomatal apparatus.

Caro (1903) *Aneilema japonicum* Kunth, *Buforrestia imperforata* C. B. Clarke, *Callisia (Spironema) fragrans* Lindl., *C. repens* L., *Campelia zanonia* H. B. K., *Coleotrype natalensis* C. B. Clarke, *Commelina coelestis* Willd., *Cyanotis kewensis* as *Erythrotis beddomei* Hook., *Dichorisandra albomarginata* Linden, *D. chysiana* Hort. Lindl., *D. vittata* Hort., *Forrestia preussii* K. Schum., *Palisota ambigua* C. B. Clarke, *P. barteri* Hook., *Pollia sorzogonensis* Steud., *Rhoeo spathacea* as *R. discolor* Swartz, *Tinantia fugax* Scheidw., *Tradescantia fuscata* Lodd., *T. navicularis* Ortgeis., *T. subaspera* Ker.-Gawl., *Zebrina pendula* Schnizl.; all parts.

Drawert (1941) *Tradescantia virginica* L.; scale-leaves.

Drobnig (1893) *Tradescantia crassifolia* Cav.; root.

Eberhard (1901) *Callisia (Spironema) fragrans* Lindl., *Campelia zanonia* H. B. K., *Dichorisandra ovata* Hort., *D. thyrsiflora* Mik., *D. undulata* C. Koch and Lindl., *Tradescantia crassula* Link and Otto, *T. zebrina* Hort.; all parts.

Falkenberg (1876) *Commelina africana, Tradescantia argentea, T. crassula*; stem.

Fourcroy (1944, 1956) *Tradescantia virginica*; root.

Fuchs (1898) *Tradescantia* spp.; raphide-sacs.

Gérard (1881) *Commelina tuberosa*; seedling anatomy.

Gravis (1898a, b) *Tradescantia fluminensis* Vell., *T. virginica* L.; all parts.

Gravis (1911) *Dichorisandra* sp., *Tinantia* sp.; all parts.

Grevillius (1887) *Callisia (Spironema) fragrans, Tradescantia albiflora*; stem.

Guillaud (1878) *Tradescantia virginica* L.; rhizome.

Haga (1922) *Tradescantia repens*; nodal anatomy.

Hämmerle (1901) *Dichorisandra ovata*; leaf, stem.

Holden (1913) *Tradescantia pulchella*; leaf.

Holm (1906) *Aneilema nudiflorum* R. Br., *Commelina dianthifolia* DC., *C. erecta, C. hirtella* Vahl, *C. nudiflora* L., *C. virginica* L., *Tinantia anomola* (Torr.) Clarke, *Tradescantia crassifolia* Cav., *T. floridana* Wats., *T. micrantha* Torr., *T. pinetorum* Greene, *T. rosea* Vent., *T. scopulorum* Rosc., *T. virginica* L., *T. warscewicsiana* Kunth & Bouche, *Tradescantia* sp., *Weldenia candida* Schult. f.; all parts.

Holtermann (1902) *Cyanotis zeylanica* C. B. Clarke; leaf.

Hulbary (1948) *Rhoeo spathacea* as *R. discolor*; leaf.

Kny (1889) *Tradescantia crassifolia*; root.

Laubert (1910) *Tradescantia cumanensis*; leaf.

Löv (1926) *Commelina coelestis, Cyanotis zebrina, Tinantia fugax*; leaf.

Lück (1958) *Tradescantia fluminensis* Vell.; stomata on stem.

Mangin (1882) *Callisia (Spironema) fragrans, Cyanotis villosa, Tradescantia virginica, Zebrina discolor*; stem.

Messeri (1925) *Commelina coelestis* Willd., *Tradescantia pilosa* Lehm.; seedling anatomy.

Metzler (1924) *Callisia (Spironema) fragrans, C. montevidensis, C. repens, Dichorisandra* sp., *Rhoeo spathacea* as *R. discolor, Tradescantia gruinensis, T. navicularis, T. zebrina*; leaf.

Möbius (1908) *Callisia repens*; leaf.

Molisch (1918) *Campelia zanonia* Rich.; leaf.

Onken (1922) *Commelina coelestis* Willd., *Tradescantia erecta* Jacq., *T. virginica* L.; raphide-canals.

Porsch (1905) *Campelia zanonia* (L.) H. B. K., *Cochliostema odoratissimum* Lem., *Commelina coelestis* Willd., *Commelina* sp., *Dichorisandra cuprea* Hort., *D. siebertii* Hort., *D. thyrsiflora* Mik., *Palisota barteri* Hook. f., *Palisota* sp., *Tradescantia discolor* Rafin., *T. virginica* L., *T. viridis* Hort., *Zebrina pendula* Schnizl.; stomatal apparatus.

Preston (1898) *Commelina* sp.; all parts.

Renner (1909) *Forrestia bicolor*; hairs on leaf sheath.

Rivière (1956) *Tradescantia virginica*; root.

Rohweder (1963) studied stem development in the following spp.: *Aneilema beniniense* (Beauv.) Kunth, *Callisia fragrans* (Lindl.) Woods., *C. repens* L., *Coleotrype natalensis* C. B. Clarke, *Commelina benghalensis* L., *Cyanotis kewensis* C. B. Clarke, *Gibasis geniculata* (Jacq.) Rohw., *Palisota barteri* Hook. f., *Rhoeo spathacea* (Sw.) Stearn, *Tinantia erecta* (Jacq.) Schlecht., *Tradescantia albiflora* Kunth var. *albovittata, T. x andersoniana* Ludw. and Rohw., *T. fluminensis* Vell., *Tripogandra pflanzii* (Brückn.) Rohw., *Zebrina pendula* Schnizl.

Rywosch (1909) *Tradescantia albiflora*; root.

Sabnis (1921) *Commelina albescens*; stem, leaf.

Schlickum (1896) *Commelina coelestis* Willd.; seedling anatomy.

Scott and Priestley (1925) *Tradescantia fluminensis* Vell.; stem development.

Siedler (1892) *Tradescantia virginica*; root.

Snow (1951) *Rhoeo spathacea* as *R. discolor*; experimental morphology of shoot apex.

Solereder and Meyer (1929) *Aneilema spiratum* R. Br., *Commelina tuberosa* L., *Cyanotis kewensis* C. B. Clarke, *Forrestia marginata* Hassk., *Palisota barteri* Hook. f., *Pollia sorzogonensis* Endl., *Rhoeo spathacea* as *R. discolor* Hance, *Tinantia fugax* Scheidw. β *erecta, Tradescantia virginica* L., *Zebrina pendula* Schnizl.; all parts.

Staudermann (1924) *Aneilema aequinoctiale* Kunth, *A. spiratum* R. Br., *A. versicolor* Dalz., *Callisia (Spironema) fragrans, C. insignis* C. B. Clarke, *C. umbellata* Lam., *Campelia zanonia* H. B. K., *Commelina benghalensis* L., *C. coelestis* Willd., *C. forskalaei* Vahl, *C. subulata* Roth., *C. virginica* L., *Cyanotis cephalotes* Schult., *C. fasciculata* Schult., *C. nodiflorum* Kunth, *C. villosa* Schult., *Dichorisandra aubletiana* Schult., *Floscopa scandens* Lour., *Forrestia mollis* Hassk., *Palisota barteri, Pollia sorzogonensis* Steud., *Tinantia fugax* Scheidw., *Tradescantia fluminensis* Vell., *T. hypophaea, T. mertensiana, T. nana* Mart. et Gal., *T. rosea* Vent., *T. virginica* L., *T. viridis*; hairs.

Strasburger (1886) *Commelina communis, Tradescantia zebrina*; stomatal apparatus.
Tomlinson (1964, 1966) see Material Examined by the Author.
Trochain (1932) *Commelina benghalensis* L., *C. forskalaei* Vahl; all parts.

MATERIAL EXAMINED BY THE AUTHOR
(All parts examined unless otherwise stated)

From living material cultivated at the Bailey Hortorium, Cornell University (BH, with collection number if available), otherwise either from collection of Dr. V. I. Cheadle (V. I. C., with collection number), collected by myself (P. B. T., with collection number), in spirit collection of the Jodrell Laboratory (Jodrell), cultivated at Kew, or cultivated at Fairchild Tropical Garden (FTG, with collection number if available).

Aneilema acuminata R. Br.; cultivated at Kew.
A. aequinoctiale Kunth; V. I. C. CA 680; Natal.
A. beniniense Kunth; P. B. T. 25.x.57; Ghana.
A. hockii De Wild.; cultivated at Kew.
A. lanceolatum Benth.; P. B. T. 15.i.58; Ghana.
A. setiferum A. Chev.; P. B. T. 25.iv.58; Ghana.
A. subnudum A. Chev.; P. B. T. 9.iv.58; Ghana.
A. umbrosum Kunth; P. B. T. 15.i.58; Ghana.
Anthericopsis sepalosa Engl.; cultivated at Kew. Leaf.
Aploleia monandra (Swartz) H. E. Moore; (BH) Moore 8045.
Ballya zebrina Brenan; cultivated at Kew.
Belosynapsis capitata Fischer; cultivated at Kew.
B. vivipara Fischer; cultivated at Kew.
Callisia elegans Alex.; (BH). Leaf, stem.
C. fragrans (Lindl.) Woodson; cultivated at Kew.
C. macdougallii Miranda; (BH).
C. repens L.; Jodrell.
C. soconuscensis Matuda; (BH).
C. tehuantepecana Matuda; (BH) Moore 8179.
Campelia zanonia H. B. K.; (BH) Moore 8051.
Cochliostema odoratissimum Lem.; (BH). Leaf.
C. velutina R. W. Read; (FTG) Read 1246. Leaf.
Coleotrype natalensis C. B. Clarke; (BH).
Commelina africana L.; P. B. T. 25.xi.57; Ghana.
C. capitata Benth.; P. B. T. 25.ii.57; Ghana.
C. coelestis Willd.; cultivated at Kew.
C. communis Engelm.; cultivated at Kew.
C. cyanea R. Br.; V. I. C. CA 138; Brisbane.
C. diffusa Burm.; P. B. T. 28.viii.61; Hawaii.
C. elliptica H. B. K.; P. B. T. 15.ix.59A; Mexico.
C. erecta var. *angustifolia* (Michx.) Fern.; P. B. T. 8.v.61A; Florida.
C. gerrardi C. B. Clarke; P. B. T. 22.i.58. Rhizome, root.
C. imberbis Ehrenb.; Jodrell. Leaf, stem.
Cuthbertia (*Phyodina*) *graminea* Small; P. B. T. 10.vi.63A; Florida.

C. ornata Small; P. B. T. 8.v.61B; Florida.

Cyanotis arachnoidea C. B. Clarke; cultivated at Kew.

C. axillaris D. Don; cultivated at Kew.

C. bulbifera Hutchinson; P. B. T. 29.iv.58; Ghana.

C. caespitosa Kotschy and Peyr.; P. B. T. 25.iv.58; Ghana.

C. cristata D. Don; (BH) L.G. 5862. Leaf, stem.

C. djurensis C. B. Clarke; P. B. T. 9.iv.58; Ghana.

C. fasciculata Wall.; cultivated at Kew.

C. kewensis C. B. Clarke; cultivated at Kew.

C. lanata Benth.; (BH).

C. lapidosa Phillips; V. I. C. CA 560; Pretoria.

C. longifolia Benth.; cultivated at Kew.

C. obtusa Trin.; cultivated at Kew.

C. pilosa Schult.; cultivated at Kew.

C. 'somaliensis'; cultivated at Kew.

C. villosa Schult.; cultivated at Kew.

C. zeylanica C. B. Clarke; cultivated at Kew.

Dichorisandra hexandra Standley; (BH) Moore 8221*a*.

D. reginae (Linden and Rodiges) H. E. Moore; (BH).

Floscopa flavida C. B. Clarke; cultivated at Kew. Leaf, stem.

F. rivularis C. B. Clarke; P. B. T. 25.iv.58; Ghana.

Forrestia marginata Hassk.; cultivated at Kew.

Geogenanthus undatus (C. Koch and Linden) Milbraed and Strauss; (BH). Leaf, stem.

Gibasis geniculata (Jacq.) Rohw.; cultivated at Kew.

G. karwinskyana (Roem. and Schult.) Rohw.; (BH) Moore 8002. Leaf, stem.

Hadrodemas warszewicziana (Kunth and Bouche) H. E. Moore; (BH). Leaf.

Murdannia graminea (L.) Bruckn.; V. I. C. CA 137; Brisbane.

M. nudiflora (L.) Brenan; (BH). Leaf, stem.

M. simplex (Vahl) Brenan; P. B. T. 15.xi.56; Ghana.

M. spiratum (L.) Bruckn.; cultivated at Kew.

M. zeylanica (C. B. Clarke) Bruckn.; cultivated at Kew.

Palisota barteri Hook.; P. B. T. 25.xi.57; Ghana.

P. elizabethae (L.) Gentil.; cultivated at Kew.

P. hirsuta K. Schum.; P. B. T. 20.xii.57; Ghana.

P. thyrsiflora Benth.; (BH) L.G. 58–107.

Phaeosphaerion (*Athyrocarpus*) *persicarifolia* Hemsl.; cultivated at Kew. Leaf, stem.

Pollia condensata C. B. Clarke; P. B. T. 28.xi.57A; Ghana.

P. crispata Benth.; V. I. C. CA 158; Brisbane.

P. macrophylla Benth.; V. I. C. CA 223; Cairns.

P. mannii C. B. Clarke; P. B. T. 28.xi.57B; Ghana.

P. sorzogonensis Miq.; P. B. T. 8.iii.56; Malaya.

Polyspatha hirsuta Mildbr.; P. B. T. 25.xi.57; Ghana.

P. paniculata Benth.; P. B. T. 25.xi.57; Ghana.

Rhoeo spathacea (Swartz) Stearn; cultivated at Fairchild Tropical Garden.

Setcreasea pallida Rose; (BH) Moore 8012.

Siderasis fuscata (Loddiges) H. E. Moore; (BH). Leaf.

Stanfieldiella imperforata Brenan; P. B. T. 25.xi.57; Ghana.

Tinantia erecta Schlecht.; (BH). Leaf.

Tradescantia blossfeldiana Mildbr.; (BH). Leaf, stem.

T. brevicaulis Rafin.; cultivated at Kew.

T. commelinoides Schult.; cultivated at Kew.

T. congesta Mart. and Gal.; cultivated at Kew.

T. crassula Link and Otto; (BH).

T.? fluminensis Vell.; (BH). Leaf, stem.

T. guatemalensis C. B. Clarke; cultivated at Kew.

T. iridescens Lindl.; P. B. T. 15.x.59B; Mexico.

T. multiflora Sw.; P. B. T. 12.vii.62c; Jamaica.

T. navicularis Ortgies; (BH).

T. sillamontana Matuda; (BH). Leaf, stem.

T. virginiana L.; P. B. T. 16.iv.61; Florida.

Triceratella drummondii Brenan; R. B. Drummond 5780; Kew Herbarium.

Tripogandra cumanensis (Kunth) Woodson; (BH) Moore 8239. Leaf, stem.

T. grandiflora (Donn. Smith) Woodson; (BH). Leaf, stem.

T. 'radiata'; cultivated at Kew.

Zebrina pendula Schnizl.; cultivated at Fairchild Tropical Garden.

BIBLIOGRAPHY FOR COMMELINACEAE

AMBRONN, H. (1881) Ueber die Entwickelungsgeschichte und die mechanischen Eigenschaften des Collenchyms. *Jb. wiss. Bot.* **12**, 473–541.

BARY, A. DE (1884) *Comparative anatomy of the vegetative organs of the Phanerogams and Ferns.* Oxford.

BENECKE, W. (1892) Die Nebenzellen der Spaltöffnungen. *Bot. Ztg.* **50**, 521–9; 537–46; 553–62; 569–78; 585–93; 601–7.

BLOCH, R. (1935) Wound healing in *Tradescantia fluminensis* Vell. *Ann. Bot.* **49**, 651–70.

BOYD, L. (1932) Monocotylous seedlings. *Trans. Proc. bot. Soc. Edinb.* **31**, 5–224.

BRENAN, J. P. M. (1966) The classification of Commelinaceae. *J. Linn. Soc.* (Bot.) **59**, 349–70.

BUCHHOLZ, M. (1921) Über die Wasserleitungsbahnen in den interkalaren Wachstumszonen monokotyler Sprosse. *Flora, Jena* **114**, 119–86.

CAMPBELL, D. H. (1881) On the development of the stomata of *Tradescantia* and Indian Corn. *Am. Nat.* **15**, 761–6.

CARO, (1903) Beiträge zur Anatomie der Commelinaceae. Diss. Heidelberg. pp. 36.

CLARK, J. (1904) Beiträge zur Morphologie der Commelinaceen. Diss. Munchen. pp. 33. See *Flora, Jena* **93**, 483–513 (1904).

DORFMÜLLER, W., and MEVIUS, W. (1937) Der Einfluß des Lichtes bei der normalen und „Künstlichen" Wurzelbildung an Commelinaceen-Stecklingen. *Ber. dt. bot. Ges.* **55**, 131–41.

DRAWERT, H. (1941) Beobachtungen an den Spaltöffnungen und der Blatthaaren von *Tradescantia virginica* L. *Flora, Jena* **135**, 303–18.

DROBNIG, M. (1893) Beiträge zur Kenntnis der Wurzelknollen. Diss. Rostock. pp. 80, 1892. See *Bot. Zbl.* **56**, 89–92 (1893).

EBERHARD, C. (1900) Beiträge zur Anatomie und Entwickelung der Commelynaceen. Diss. Göttingen. Hanover. pp. 102, 1900. See *Bot. Zbl.* **87**, 16–19 (1901).

FALKENBERG, P. (1876) *Vergleichende Untersuchungen über den Bau der Vegetationsorgane der Monocotyledonen.* Stuttgart. pp. 202.

FOURCROY, M. (1944) L'arc extra-ligneux dans la racine du *Tradescantia virginica.* *Bull. Soc. bot. Fr.* **91**, 86–88.

—— (1956) Nouvel exemple de racine bistélique: *Tradescantia virginica.* Ibid. **103**, 590–5.

FUCHS, P. C. A. (1898) Untersuchungen über den Bau der Raphidenzelle. *Öst. bot. Z.* **48**, 324–32.

Gérard, R. (1881) Recherche sur le passage de la racine à la tige. *Annls Sci. nat.* bot. ser. 6, 11, 279–430.

Gravis, A. (1898a) Recherches anatomiques et physiologiques sur la *Tradescantia virginica* L. *Mém. Acad. r. Belg.* pp. 304.

—— (1898b) Anatomie comparée du *Chlorophytum elatum* (Ait.) et du *Tradescantia virginica* L. *Bull. Soc. r. Bot. Belg.* **87**, 92–95.

—— (1909) Contributions à l'anatomie des Commélinées. *Assoc. Fr. adv. Sci. Congr. Lille.* 507–25; See *Bot. Zbl.* **116**, 162. (1911).

Grevillius, A. Y. (1887) Undersökningar öfver det mekaniska systemet hos hängande växtdelar. *Bot. Notiser* 135–41.

Guillaud, A. J. (1878) Recherches sur l'anatomie comparée et le développement des tissus de la tige dans les Monocotylédones. *Annls Sci. nat.* bot. ser. 6, 5, 5–176.

Haga, A. (1922) Über den Bau der Leitungsbahnen im Knoten der Monokotylen. *Recl. Trav. bot. néerl.* **19**, 207–18.

Hämmerle, J. (1901) Ueber einige bemerkenswerthe anatomische Verhältnisse bei *Dichorisandra ovata. Ber. dt. bot. Ges.* **19**, 129–38.

Holden, H. S. (1913) On the occlusion of the stomata in *Tradescantia pulchella. Ann. Bot.* **27**, 369–70.

Holm, T. (1906) Commelinaceae. Morphological and anatomical studies of the vegetative organs of some N. and C. American species. *Mem. natn. Acad. Sci.* Wash. **10**, 159–92.

Holtermann, C. (1902) Anatomisch-physiologische Untersuchungen in den Tropen. *Sber. preuß. Akad. Wiss.* **30**, 656–74.

Hulbary, R. L. (1948) Three-dimensional cell shape in the tuberous roots of asparagus and in the leaf of *Rhoeo. Am. J. Bot.* **35**, 558–66.

Kny, L. (1889) Ueber die Bildung des Wundperiderms an Knollen in ihrer Abhängigkeit von äusseren Einflüssen. *Ber. dt. bot. Ges.* **7**, 154–68.

Laubert, R. (1910) Über die Panaschöre Buntblätterigkeit der *Tradescantia cumanensis.* In *Just's bot. Jber.* **88** (2), sec. 21, no. 167.

Löv, L. (1926) Zur Kenntnis der Entfaltungszellen monokotyler Blätter. *Flora, Jena* **20**, 283–343.

Lück, H. B. (1958) Recherches sur la mécanique du développement des cellules épidermiques II. Structure de l'épiderme et répartition des stomates sur les entre-nœuds de *Tradescantia fluminensis* Vell. *Naturalia monspel.* ser. bot. **10**, 33–42.

Mangin, L. (1882) Origine et insertion des racines adventives et modifications corrélatives de la tige chez les Monocotyledones. *Annls Sci. nat.* bot. sér. 6, **14**, 216–363.

Messeri, E. (1925) Richerche sullo sviluppo del sistema vascolare in alcune Monocotiledoni. *Nuovo G. bot. ital.* **32**, 317–62.

Metzler, W. (1924) Beiträge zur vergleichenden Anatomie blattsukkulenter Pflanzen. *Bot. Arch.* **6**, 50–83.

Möbius, M. (1908) Über ein eigentümliches Vorkommen von Kieselkörpern in der Epidermis und den Bau des Blattes von *Callisia repens. Wiesner-Festschr.,* Wien 80–91. See *Just's bot. Jber.* **36** (1), sec. 6, no. 164 (1908).

Molisch, H. (1918) Beiträge zur Mikrochemie der Pflanzen 10. Ueber Kieselkörper in der Epidermis von *Campelia zanonia* Rich. *Ber. dt. bot. Ges.* **36**, 277–81.

Onken, A. (1922) Über die Bedeutung des Milch- und Schleimsaftes für Beseitigung des überschüssigen Calziums. Ein Beitrag zur Exkretphysiologie der höheren Pflanzen. *Bot. Arch.* **2**, 281–333.

Pfitzer, E. (1870) Beiträge zur Kenntnis der Hautgewebe der Pflanzen. *Jb. wiss. Bot.* **7**, 532–87.

Porsch, O. (1905) *Der Spaltöffnungsapparat im Lichte der Phylogenie.* Jena. pp. 196.

Preston, G. K. (1898) A species of *Commelina. Am. J. Pharm.* **70**, 321–35.

Renner, O. (1909) Zur Morphologie und Ökologie der pflanzlichen Behaarung. *Flora, Jena* **99**, 127–55.

Rivière, S. (1956) Une fausse bistélie de la racine de *Tradescantia virginica. Bull. Soc. bot. Fr.* **103**, 596–8.

Rohweder, O. (1963) Anatomische und histogenetische Untersuchungen an Laubsprossen und Blüten der Commelinaceen. *Bot. Jb.* **82**, 1–99.

Rywosch, S. (1909) Untersuchungen über die Entwicklungsgeschichte der Seitenwurzeln der Monocotylen. *Z. Bot.* **1**, 253–83.

SABNIS, T. S. (1921) The physiological anatomy of the plants of the Indian desert. *J. Indian bot. Soc.* **2**, 157–67, 217–27, 271–99.

SCHLICKUM, A. (1896) Morphologischer und anatomischer Vergleich der Kotyledonen und ersten Laubblätter der Keimpflanzen der Monokotylen. *Bibl. bot.*, Stuttgart **6**, Heft 35, pp. 88.

SCHUBERT, O. (1913) Bedingungen zur Stecklingsbildung und Pfropfung von Monocotylen. *Zentbl. Bakt. ParasitKde* Abt. 2, **38**, 309–443. See *Just's bot. Jber.* **41** (2), sec. 20, no. 405 (1913).

SCOTT, L. I., and PRIESTLEY, J. H. (1925) Leaf and stem anatomy of *Tradescantia fluminensis*, Vell. *J. Linn. Soc.* (Bot.) **47**, 1–28.

SIEDLER, P. (1892) Über den radialen Saftstrom in den Wurzeln. *Beitr. Biol. Pfl.* **5**, 407–42.

SNOW, N. (1951) Experiments on spirodistichous shoot apices I. *Phil. Trans. R. Soc.* B **235**, 131–62.

SOLEREDER, H., and MEYER, F. J. (1929) Commelinaceae in *Systematische Anatomie der Monokotyledonen*, Heft IV, 129–55.

STAUDERMANN, W. (1924) Die Haare der Monokotylen. *Bot. Arch.* **8**, 105–84.

STEBBINS, G. L., and JAIN, S. K. (1960) Developmental studies of cell differentiation in the epidermis of Monocotyledons I. *Allium, Rhoeo* and *Commelina. Devl. Biol.* **2**, 409–26.

—— and KHUSH, G. S. (1961) Variation in the organization of the stomatal complex in the leaf epidermis of monocotyledons and its bearing on their phylogeny. *Am. J. Bot.* **48**, 51–59.

STRASBURGER, E. (1886) Ein Beitrag zur Entwicklungsgeschichte der Spaltöffnungen. *Jb. wiss. Bot.* **5**, 297–342.

TOMLINSON, P. B. (1964) Notes on the anatomy of *Triceratella* (Commelinaceae). *Kirkia* **4**, 207–12.

—— (1966) Anatomical data in the classification of Commelinaceae. *J. Linn. Soc.* (Bot.) **59**, 371–95.

TROCHAIN, J. (1932) Sur la biologie de deux Commelinacées (*Commelina forskalaei* Vahl et *C. benghalensis* Linn.) *C. r. hebd. Séanc. Acad. Sci., Paris* **194**, 743–5.

TROLL, W. (1961) *Cochliostema odoratissimum* Lem. Organisation und Lebensweise. *Beitr. Biol. Pfl.* **36**, 325–89.

VAN FLEET, D. S. (1942) The development and distribution of the endodermis and an associated oxidase system in monocotyledonous plants. *Am. J. Bot.* **29**, 1–15.

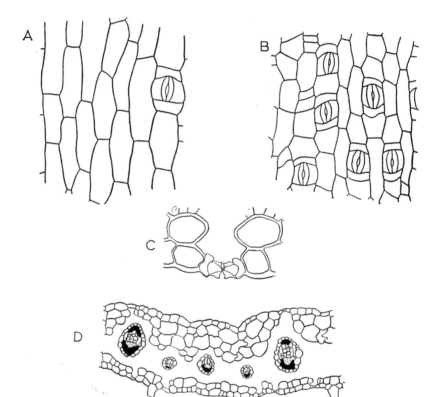

64

FIG. 13. CARTONEMATACEAE. Leaf.

A–B. *Cartonema parviflorum*. Epidermis of lamina, surface view (× 130).
  A. Adaxial. B. Abaxial.

C. *C. spicatum*. T.S. stoma from abaxial surface of leaf (× 330).

D. *C. parviflorum*. T.S. lamina in median part (× 11).

CARTONEMATACEAE

(Fig. 13)

SUMMARY

A NORTH Australian family of 6 species belonging to the genus *Cartonema*; formerly included within the Commelinaceae. Perennial herbs with slender, simple, conspicuously pubescent, erect stems arising from a congested rhizome. Leaves with a tubular sheath extending into a long narrow blade. *Cartonema* differs from the Commelinaceae in the following important anatomical features: **hairs** of 1 type only, each uniseriate, long and terminating in an ellipsoidal glandular cell; cells of **epidermis** longitudinally extended and not so voluminous as in most Commelinaceae; **chlorenchyma** cells of lamina commonly arranged in a radiate manner around veins; **veins** of lamina with a complete, thin-walled outer sheath, inner sheath conspicuously fibrous above and below many veins; **stem** without peripheral collenchyma, central vb's without wide protoxylem lacunae; **raphide-sacs** absent. (According to Pichon, calcium oxalate is absent and cortical vb's occur in the stem, both features separating *Cartonema* from all Commelinaceae; these observations need confirming.)

LEAF (Fig. 13. A–D)

Hairs abundant and conspicuous on aerial parts, but sometimes restricted to abaxial surface of lamina (*C. parviflorum*) or to leaf margin alone (*C. spicatum*). Each hair thin-walled, uniseriate, with a large, rather short basal cell, 2–3 narrow stalk cells and a small, ellipsoidal glandular terminal cell with finely granular dark brown contents. (These hairs cannot be confused with the glandular micro-hairs of Commelinaceae.)

Lamina dorsiventral. **Epidermis** with a thin, inconspicuous, cutinized layer; outer wall slightly thicker than remaining thin walls. Cell size rather variable. Adaxial epidermis (Fig. 13. A) not v. uniform, usually including irregular stomatal series above largest veins, as in *C. parviflorum*, and towards margin. Cells rather irregular, longitudinally extended, usually rectangular but sometimes somewhat spindle-shaped. Abaxial epidermis (Fig. 13. B) uniform; cells rather irregular, rectangular but never as long as adaxial cells, somewhat thicker-walled than adaxial cells. **Stomata** usually present on adaxial surface in distinct costal bands above largest veins; uniformly scattered on abaxial surface but not in regular files. Guard cells (Fig. 13. C) each surrounded by 4 shallow subsidiary cells; lateral subsidiary cells narrow, thin-walled; terminal subsidiary cells short, wide, and shallow but not recognized by Solereder and Meyer in *C. philydroides*. Guard cells 40–60 μm long, each with 2 conspicuous ledges above wall thickenings, outer ledge usually more conspicuous than inner. **Hypodermis** (Fig. 13. D) present below both surfaces but rather discontinuous. Adaxial hypodermis most fully developed, in median region often 3–4-layered although interrupted by mesophyll above largest veins; in *C. spicatum* forming 2 bands up to 6 layers deep on either side of the median vein;

always 1-layered at leaf margin. Abaxial hypodermis 1-layered and interrupted by wide substomatal chambers, the chambers elliptical in surface view and often surrounded by somewhat lobed but not uniformly arranged cells. Hypodermal cells usually somewhat longitudinally extended and rectangular in surface view; innermost cells small and more or less cubical; abaxial cells always small. **Chlorenchyma** rather distinctive, cells mostly vertically extended or arranged radiately around veins, least conspicuously so in *C. spicatum*. Central mesophyll cells less anticlinally extended or even isodiametric. Large isodiametric cells, possibly tannin-cells but contents not preserved, seen next to adaxial hypodermis in *C. parviflorum*. **Veins** equidistant from and independent of surface layers; including several large veins, each pair pectinating with several smaller veins. O.S. of veins conspicuous and well developed, usually complete but sometimes incomplete above some large veins; sheath cells considerably longitudinally extended. I.S. represented by conspicuous fibrous strands above and below most veins but always absent laterally; fibres often absent from adaxial part of small veins, absent adaxially from most veins in *C. spicatum*. Xylem including several files of wide tracheal elements. **Transverse commissures** infrequent, inconspicuous, each consisting of a short, narrow vascular strand sheathed by thin-walled cells, the strands connecting the longitudinal veins at irregular intervals. Leaf **margin** occupied by 1–2 layers of small, colourless, slightly thick-walled cells; marginal vein absent.

INFLORESCENCE AXIS (*C. spicatum*)

Structure similar to stem of Commelinaceae. **Hairs** frequent, similar to those on the lamina. **Stomata,** resembling those of the lamina, frequent. Single-layered colourless **hypodermis** conspicuous, but hypodermal tissues not collenchymatous. **Chlorenchyma** conspicuous as a fairly wide layer of small cells. Inner limit of cortex represented by a colourless 'endodermoid' layer immediately surrounding a wide **sclerotic cylinder** of long, thick-walled cells with truncated ends. Sclerotic cylinder including a series of v. narrow vb's adjacent to the endodermoid layer, each vb with reduced vascular tissues, the tracheal elements often abutting directly on to sheath cells. Central **vascular bundles** scattered, each with a fibrous phloem sheath, xylem sheathed by prosenchyma; xylem including many files of wide tracheal elements, often V-shaped in T.S. Extended protoxylem elements common but protoxylem lacunae never formed.

(According to Pichon the cortex of *Cartonema* contains vb's. This may refer to a different part of the axis from that described above.)

ROOT (*C. spicatum*)

Piliferous layer persistent. Compact, 1–2 hypodermal layers becoming suberized. Outermost 2–3 cortical layers, within the suberized zone, consisting of small, compact cells; most of cortex occupied by wide, radial **air-lacunae** separated one from another by narrow diaphragms mostly 1 cell wide. **Endodermis** v. conspicuous, consisting of wide cells with massive U-shaped wall thickenings. **Stele** narrow, polyarch; protoxylem poles inconspicuous, phloem strands narrow. Central ground tissue consisting wholly of thick-walled elements.

SECRETORY, STORAGE, AND CONDUCTING ELEMENTS

Crystals of calcium oxalate probably present, but never in distinct raphide-sacs as in the Commelinaceae.

Silica absent.

Tannin frequent, usually in unmodified cells.

Xylem. Vessels observed in root of *C. spicatum*; elements 180–230 μm long, 18–23 μm wide with simple perforation plates on slightly oblique or more or less transverse end walls, rarely scalariform with v. few thickening bars.

TAXONOMIC NOTES

Cartonema was formerly included within the Commelinaceae but was placed in a separate family, the Cartonemataceae, by Pichon (1946), a conclusion accepted by Hutchinson (1959) but with which Brenan (1966) does not agree. Anatomical differences between *Cartonema* and the rest of the Commelinaceae which support this opinion are outlined in the summary on p. 66. This support is only tentative, being based on dried material only. However, it should be pointed out that the general construction of the leaf and stem in *Cartonema* is very similar to that of the Commelinaceae so that although it is probably correct to regard the genus as an isolated taxon, it is closely related to the Commelinaceae. The anatomy of *Cartonema* in relation to that of the Commelinaceae is discussed further in Tomlinson (1966).

SPECIES REPORTED ON IN THE LITERATURE

Solereder and Meyer (1929) Notes on leaf and stem of *C. spicatum* R. Br. as *C. philydroides* F. v. Mull. in account of Commelinaceae.

Staudermann (1924) *C. spicatum* R. Br. Hairs.

MATERIAL EXAMINED BY THE AUTHOR

Cartonema parviflorum Hassk.; Specht 1253; N.T. Australia. Kew Herbarium. Leaf. *C. spicatum* R. Br.; Allen 152; Darwin, N. Australia. Kew Herbarium. All parts.

BIBLIOGRAPHY FOR CARTONEMATACEAE

BRENAN, J. P. M. (1966) The classification of Commelinaceae. *J. Linn. Soc.* (Bot.) **59**, 349–70.

HUTCHINSON, J. (1959) *Families of flowering plants*, Vol. II, *Monocotyledons*, edn 2. Oxford.

PICHON, M. (1946) Sur les Commélinacées. *Phanérogamie* **12**, 217–42.

SOLEREDER, H., and MEYER, F. J. (1929) Commelinaceae. In *Systematische Anatomie der Monokotyledonen*, Heft IV, 129–55.

STAUDERMANN, W. (1924) Die Haare der Monokotyledonen. *Bot. Arch.* **8**, 105–84.

TOMLINSON, P. B. (1966) Anatomical data in the classification of Commelinaceae. *J. Linn. Soc.* (Bot.) **59**, 371–95.

FLAGELLARIACEAE
(Figs. 14, 15)

A SMALL family of 3 very dissimilar genera which probably do not constitute a natural assemblage. Anatomical differences between them are so great that it is most convenient to consider each genus separately.

1. FLAGELLARIA
(Figs. 14. B, G; 15. A, K, L)

SUMMARY

A tropical genus of some 13 species, widely distributed from West Africa to Malaysia, Polynesia, and north Australia. **Scandent** herbs with solid, slender stems supported by leaf tendrils. Leaf with a tubular sheathing base articulated to the indistinct petiole; lamina lanceolate, rolled in bud, the thickened midrib commonly extending into a long **tendril** coiled like a watch-spring. Anatomical characteristics include the thick-walled **guard cells** with dumbbell-shaped lumina, resembling those of grasses; a colourless **hypodermis** below each surface of the lamina; **vascular bundles** in stem and leaf each with 2 wide metaxylem vessels; long **secretory cells** with refractive contents in leaf; **silica** as inconspicuous granular bodies in vb sheath cells; **vessels** in all parts, but rather variable.

LEAF

(i) *Lamina*

Isolateral. **Hairs** absent. Cutinized layer thin. **Epidermis** similar on each surface, cells thin-walled or with slight thickening of inner wall; anticlinal walls not sinuous. Epidermis (Fig. 15. A) including indistinct costal bands 4–5 cells wide above and below veins, and much wider intercostal bands. Costal cells longitudinally extended, rectangular in surface view or with oblique end walls; intercostal cells similar but shorter and more irregular, often somewhat spindle-shaped. **Stomata** uniformly scattered on both surfaces, not in regular files. Each stoma with 2 narrow, deep, lateral subsidiary cells; terminal subsidiary cells not differentiated although cells in this position somewhat shorter than those elsewhere. Guard cells described as 'grass-like', with median wall thickenings constricting the lumen into the shape of a dumbbell; outer cutinized ledge prominent, inner ledge inconspicuous. **Hypodermis** indistinct, 1-layered below each surface, of colourless, compact, more or less cubical cells, occasionally including a few chloroplasts. Cells surrounding substomatal chambers not uniformly arranged, most often containing chloroplasts. Outer wall of hypodermal cells in midrib region commonly becoming slightly sclerotic. **Chlorenchyma** without distinct palisade layers, cells nearest each surface somewhat larger than hypodermal cells but not as large as central mesophyll cells with fewer chloroplasts (Fig. 14. G). **Veins** consisting of alternately large and small vb's. Large veins (Fig. 14. G) attached to each

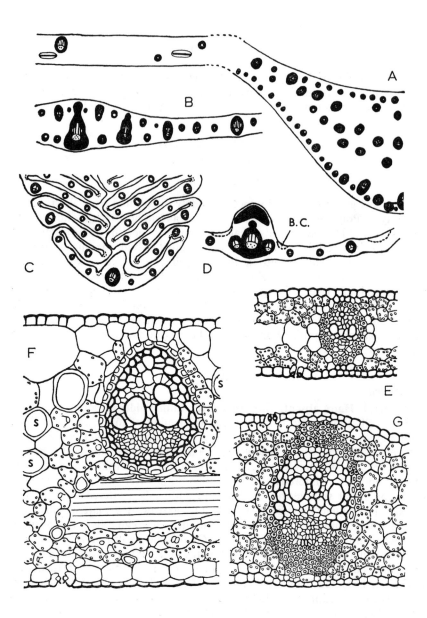

Fig. 14. FLAGELLARIACEAE. Lamina T.S. (after Smithson 1956).

A. *Hanguana* (×10). B. *Flagellaria* (×22). C. *Joinvillea borneensis* (×37). D. *J. gaudichaudiana* (×22). E. *J. borneensis* (×185). F. *Hanguana* (×185). G. *Flagellaria* (×185).

B.C.—bulliform cells, S—secretory cell. In A and F the horizontal lines indicate bundles cut longitudinally.

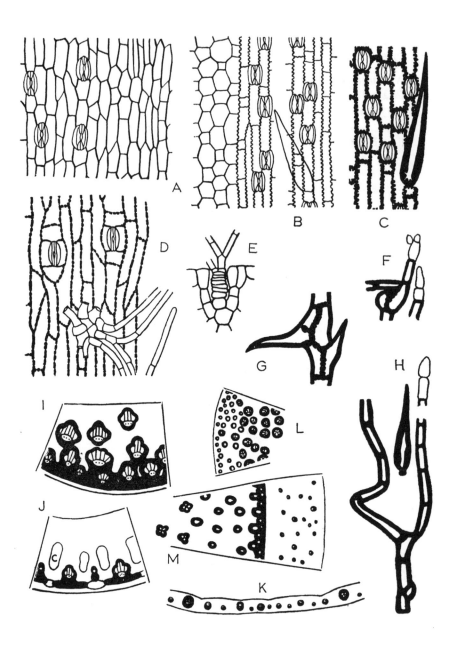

Fig. 15. FLAGELLARIACEAE. Leaf and stem (after Smithson 1956).

A–D. Epidermis of lamina in surface view (×185).

A. *Flagellaria*. B. *Joinvillea borneensis*. C. *J. gaudichaudiana*. D. *Hanguana*.

E–H. Epidermal hairs (×185).

E. L.S. base of hair of *Hanguana*. F–H. Portions of hairs of *Joinvillea gaudichaudiana*.

I–K. T.S. leaf sheath (×22).

I. *Joinvillea gaudichaudiana*. J. *J. borneensis*. K. *Flagellaria*.

L–M. T.S. stem (×10).

L. Aerial stem of *Flagellaria*. M. Main stem of *Hanguana*.

C—lysigenous cavity

hypodermis by massive fibrous extensions of bundle sheath, abaxial usually more strongly developed than adaxial part of sheath. Smaller veins situated in adaxial mesophyll, independent of surface layers or occasionally in contact with adaxial hypodermis. O.S. consisting of an inconspicuous chlorenchymatous sheath of longitudinally extended cells, scarcely distinguishable from mesophyll cells in T.S. Sclerotic I.S. complete around large veins, fibrous above and below veins but completed laterally by sclerotic parenchyma; fibres present either both above and below or only below small veins and sheath then completed by thin-walled cells. Xylem of large veins including 2 wide, lateral metaxylem vessels and often extended protoxylem (Fig. 14. G). Phloem strand undivided. **Transverse veins** inconspicuous, sheathed by thin-walled cells. **Midrib** region (Fig. 14. B) thickened, including a massive central vb attached to each hypodermis, its abaxial buttress massive and fibrous; adaxial buttress composed mostly of wide sclerotic cells and only capped by fibres, sometimes including isolated phloem strands. Smaller vb's of midrib arranged in 2 series, one series close to each surface, each vb with a well-developed external fibrous sheath sometimes in contact with hypodermis but internal part of sheath always thin-walled.

(ii) *Sheath* (Fig. 15. K)

Epidermis of abaxial surface similar to that of lamina except for more obvious costal bands and greater uniformity of cells. Adaxial epidermis v. uniform, composed of long, rectangular cells with slightly lignified, thickened and pitted walls. **Hypodermis** of abaxial surface 1–2-layered, slightly sclerotic except below stomata. Adaxial hypodermis slightly sclerotic, cells flattened and conspicuously pitted, cells below stomata thin-walled, lobed, and somewhat chlorenchymatous. **Stomata** of abaxial surface resembling those of lamina, but those of adaxial surface each situated in a slight depression. Guard cells of adaxial stomata with unthickened walls except for slight thickening below the 2 equally conspicuous ledges. Hypodermal cells below stomata always thin-walled. **Chlorenchyma** differentiated in ground parenchyma towards abaxial surface. **Vascular bundles** arranged in a cylinder, consisting of few large veins alternating with many smaller veins (Fig. 15. K). Fibres usually restricted to abaxial part of each vb except for occasional adaxial fibres with wide lumina. Vascular tissues of large vb's like those in the large veins of the lamina, but reduced in smaller veins, often to phloem alone or even absent and bundle represented by a fibrous strand.

(iii) *Tendril*

All leaves potentially capable of bearing tendrils but only those leaf tips finding support become coiled into tendrils. Leaf tip otherwise abscissed and lamina maturing without a tendril (du Sablon 1887). Tendril including an adaxial fibrous band separated from epidermis by 2–3 hypodermal layers and including several reduced vb's with complete fibrous sheaths. Fibrous band somewhat discontinuous in proximal part of tendril. Abaxial tissue composed of several layers of colourless, much elongated parenchyma cells.

(Du Sablon records that the tendril of *Flagellaria*, unlike that of other tendril-bearing plants, is sensitive on the adaxial and not the abaxial surface, in spite of the adaxial fibrous zone which lignifies v. early. Stimulation of the adaxial surface by contact with a potential support causes the abaxial cells to expand considerably whereas the rigid adaxial surface cannot elongate. Consequently the tendril becomes curved.)

STEM (Fig. 15. L)

Narrow, solid, cane-like, with long internodes. **Epidermis** wholly cutinized, outer wall slightly thickened. Cells longitudinally extended, mostly rectangular in surface view but rather irregular; often with several rather short cells adjacent to each stoma. **Stomata** frequent, guard cells intermediate in wall thickness between those of lamina and adaxial surface of sheath. **Hypodermis** 1–2-layered, colourless, slightly sclerotic, interrupted below stomata. **Cortex** narrow, without an independent vascular system, including an irregular peripheral layer of chlorenchyma. Periphery of **central cylinder** delimited from cortex by a zone of congested vb's surrounded by sclerotic ground tissue, the whole forming a rigid peripheral mechanical zone. Peripheral vb's each with a massive fibrous sheath adjacent to phloem; vascular tissues reduced, xylem occasionally absent or represented by a single vessel; extended protoxylem not developed. Structure of vb's showing a gradual transition towards less congested central **vascular bundles,** each sheathed by thin-walled fibres; xylem including 2 wide vessels and extended protoxylem, phloem strand undivided. Central vb's often with an irregular or even inverse orientation. Most recently entered **leaf traces** recognized by absence of a sclerotic sheath around xylem, presence of many small vessels and well-developed protoxylem. Many intermediate types of bundle structure exist.

ROOT

No detailed anatomical information available. Root stele of *F. indica* recorded by van Tieghem (1887) as having normal structure, the lateral roots originating opposite the xylem poles.

SECRETORY, STORAGE, AND CONDUCTING ELEMENTS

Crystals. Calcium oxalate present as small druse-like bodies in the assimilating cells of the lamina.

Silica present as small irregular bodies occurring singly in small cells above and below the fibrous sheaths of the veins in the lamina. Silica-cells usually in longitudinal files but never situated in the epidermis.

Secretory cells present in leaf and stem as v. long thin-walled elements with refractive contents. Cells of same diameter as ordinary mesophyll cells and so not obvious in T.S.

Xylem. Vessels probably in all parts; metaxylem elements in stem short and wide, mostly with simple perforation plates on more or less transverse end walls but sometimes with oblique scalariform perforation plates; elements in leaf with scalariform-reticulate perforation plates on oblique or slightly oblique end walls, often with few thickening bars. Elements sometimes with simple perforation plates, especially in the leaf sheath. According to the data given by Fahn (1954) and Smithson (1956) the tracheal elements in *Flagellaria* are much more variable in the type of perforation plate than is usual amongst monocotyledons.

Phloem. Sieve-tubes in leaf and stem with compound sieve-plates on oblique or v. oblique end walls.

2. JOINVILLEA

(Figs 14. C–E; 15. B, C, F–J)

SUMMARY

A small genus of some 6 species extending from Malaya to the Philippines and New Caledonia. Plants reed-like with slender, erect, hollow stems. Leaves with a lanceolate, markedly plicate lamina abruptly narrowed at the base and articulated to the tubular leaf sheath; mouth of the sheath more or less ligulate. Anatomical features include the inflated, unicellular, spine-like, sometimes much branched **hairs**; the **epidermis,** with markedly sinuous walls, including short **silica-cells**; the **stomata** with thick-walled guard cells resembling those of the grasses; the mesophyll of the lamina with a central colourless tissue; **vascular bundles** with 2 wide metaxylem vessels; **air-canals** in the leaf sheath; silica present internally in short **stegmata** adjacent to the veins as well as in the epidermal short-cells. **Vessels** probably present in all parts, perforations of the end walls rather variable.

LEAF

(i) *Lamina*

Closely folded in bud, the two plicate halves folded together against the thickened midrib region (Fig. 14. C). Isolateral, or somewhat dorsiventral with 2 surfaces slightly different.

Hairs. Unicellular, inflated spines with thickened walls (Fig. 15. B, C) distributed irregularly on the leaf, often opposite the bands of expansion cells in the folds of the lamina; base sometimes surrounded by slightly enlarged epidermal cells. Multicellular, irregularly branched hairs with thick-walled pitted cells, the branches terminating in small, thin-walled cells, recorded for *J. gaudichaudiana* (Fig. 15. F–H). **Epidermis** uniform except for bands of enlarged **expansion cells** (Fig. 15. B) on each side of the midrib and within the angle of each fold of the lamina, the bands abruptly demarcated from the adjacent epidermis. Expansion cells thin-walled, square in surface view, walls not sinuous; bringing about unfolding of the lamina by their marked anticlinal expansion and becoming considerably enlarged in mature leaves. Epidermis elsewhere rather uniform, that of each surface differing mainly in the density of stomata. Walls thickened, markedly sinuous (Fig. 15. B, C) in surface view owing to presence of finely sutured cuticle on the anticlinal walls; cell lumen of abaxial surface almost occluded in *J. gaudichaudiana.* Epidermis composed of files of longitudinally extended, rectangular **long-cells** including and often alternating with cubical **short-cells.** Each short-cell containing a more or less cubical **silica-body** almost filling the cell lumen. Narrow bands of fairly conspicuous costal cells differentiated above and below veins, the costal long-cells somewhat longer and narrower than similar cells elsewhere. **Stomata** uniformly scattered in intercostal bands, not in regular files, less frequent on adaxial than on abaxial surface. Each stoma with a pair of narrow, deep, lateral subsidiary cells with thin, non-sinuous walls. Terminal subsidiary cells not differentiated although short-cells sometimes situated in polar position. Guard cells somewhat elevated above the subsidiary cells, each with a thickened wall constricting the cell lumen into a dumb-bell shape as in the stomata of grasses; outer cutinized ledge v. conspicuous but inner probably absent. **Hypodermis** absent except for a band of more or less colourless cells below the bands of epidermal expansion cells. Mesophyll isolateral. **Chlorenchyma** composed of 2–3 layers of almost isodiametric cells below each surface; substomatal chambers v. small. Central layer of mesophyll forming a sheet of large, cubical, more or less colourless cells (Fig. 14. E) provided with interlocking papillae, the cells often containing tannin and sometimes becoming silicified. **Veins** frequent, usually attached to each surface by fibrous buttress or buttresses completed by sclerotic hypodermal cells. Smallest veins occasionally independent of surface layers. O.S. well developed and conspicuous on each side of all veins. Sheath cells longitudinally extended, containing chloroplasts but in T.S. often appearing colourless. I.S. always well developed, completely fibrous. Larger veins (Fig. 14. E) including 2 wide metaxylem vessels and extended protoxylem. Phloem strand not sclerotic. Vascular tissues of smaller veins reduced. **Transverse veins** infrequent but conspicuous, equidistant from each surface and situated within the central colourless mesophyll layer; vascular tissues sheathed by irregular interlocking, thick-walled, lignified cells. **Midrib** region (Fig. 14. D) including a single large abaxial vb with a well-developed sheath and 2 small vb's, the prominent adaxial part of the rib occupied by fibrous tissue.

(ii) *Sheath*

Hairs recorded for abaxial surface of sheath in *J. gaudichaudiana*. **Epidermis** of adaxial surface without short-cells, cells v. uniform, rather short; walls scarcely thickened, not sinuous. Abaxial epidermis including long- and short-cells as in the lamina, but walls thickened, pitted, and not sinuous; long-cells rather irregular and often with oblique end walls. **Stomata** resembling those of lamina; infrequent adaxially. **Chlorenchyma** restricted to a narrow, 2-layered, peripheral abaxial band, the cells becoming sclerotic with age except near the stomata. **Peripheral mechanical zone** formed either by the ring of congested vb's with massive fibrous sheaths embedded in sclerotic ground parenchyma (*J. borneensis*, Fig. 15. J), or by a continuous fibrous zone including small vascular or phloem strands (*J. gaudichaudiana*, Fig. 15. I). Main vascular system in *J. gaudichaudiana* internal to mechanical zone and consisting of 2–3 irregular arcs of independent vb's without fibrous sheaths. **Vascular bundles** in *J. borneensis* with massive abaxial fibrous sheaths forming part of the mechanical zone except for occasional smaller veins independent of zone. Each vb with 2 wide metaxylem vessels and often with extended protoxylem. **Air-canals,** developing lysigenously according to Smithson, pectinating with vb's in *J. borneensis* (Fig. 15. J); each separated from its neighbours by a radial partition of somewhat sclerotic ground tissue opposite a vb; air-canals less obvious and more irregular in *J. gaudichaudiana*. Adaxial ground parenchyma cells tangentially extended and somewhat sclerotic.

STEM AND ROOT

No information about the anatomy of these organs is available, apart from the observations on the tracheal elements by Fahn (1954).

SECRETORY, STORAGE, AND CONDUCTING ELEMENTS

Crystals of calcium oxalate occur in the mesophyll cells.

Silica present in the leaf either (i) in epidermal short-cells as more or less cubical, smooth bodies filling the cell lumen, or (ii) as irregular but smooth silica-bodies almost filling the lumen of unevenly thickened, stegmata-like cells; these silica-cells in files adjacent to fibres of longitudinal veins and sometimes adjacent to transverse veins. Silicification of the central mesophyll cells common, especially in *J. gaudichaudiana*.

Tannin common as deposits in unspecialized cells.

Xylem. Vessels in leaf with scalariform perforation plates on oblique or v. oblique end walls, number of thickening bars varying considerably. Simple perforation plates not infrequent, especially in the leaf sheath according to Fahn. Simple perforation plates recorded in stem by Fahn, but oblique, scalariform perforation plates also common.

3. HANGUANA (SUSUM)

(Figs. 14. A, F; 15. D, E, M)

SUMMARY

A single species in Ceylon, Indo-china, and Malaysia, inhabiting damp situations in humid forests, or aquatic. Rhizomatous perennial herb with long runners arising from the base of the erect stems and forming dense colonies. Leaves crowded spirally on the short stems; stiff, lanceolate with a sheathing base, the basal leaves with distinct petioles. The aquatic variety sometimes regarded as a distinct species, *H. anthelminticum* Bl. *Hanguana* is anatomically v. different from *Flagellaria* and *Joinvillea*, notably in the following features: **hairs** common on the aerial parts, sunken, branched; **stomata** with thin-walled, not grass-like guard cells; an indistinct colourless **hypodermis** present in the leaf; longitudinal **veins** of the lamina arranged in two distinct systems, **transverse veins** conspicuous; **vascular bundles** of all parts enclosed within a continuous, thick-walled **endodermis,** and always including several files of tracheids, never two as in the other genera. Conspicuous **tannin-cells** present. **Silica** occurs as granular deposits in the bundle-sheath cells and sometimes also in the hypodermis of the lamina. **Vessels** absent from aerial parts.

LEAF

Lanceolate, with a thickened midrib passing gradually into the open sheathing base.

(i) *Lamina*

Dorsiventral. **Hairs** common on leaf and stem, each with a deeply sunken uniseriate base (Fig. 15. E) arising from a slightly enlarged epidermal cell, the base situated in a conical depression in the surface lined with small epidermal cells. Hairs branched at the leaf surface into long uniseriate filaments (Fig. 15. D), each filament ending in a long, pointed cell. Distal filamentous cells lost from lamina but on leaf base often persisting as a fan-shaped weft and forming a complete indumentum. **Epidermis**; cells with thickened outer wall and a conspicuous cutinized layer deeply penetrating the anticlinal walls. Walls conspicuously pitted. Adaxial epidermis fairly uniform but with occasional narrow costal bands of rather short cells above largest veins. Intercostal cells longitudinally extended, rectangular in surface view, or with somewhat oblique end walls. Abaxial epidermis (Fig. 15. D) without costal bands, cells shallower and with thinner walls than, but otherwise similar to, cells of adaxial surface. **Stomata** almost restricted to abaxial surface, diffuse and not in regular files. Each stoma with a pair of thin-walled, rather wide, deep, lateral subsidiary cells; terminal subsidiary cells short but not otherwise different from other epidermal cells. Guard cells each with 2 almost equivalent ledges, the walls beneath the ledges scarcely thickened and not occluding the cell lumen as in *Flagellaria* and *Joinvillea*. **Hypodermis** (Fig. 14. F) of colourless, thin-walled cells usually present as a single layer below each surface but generally interrupted above largest veins. Adaxial hypodermis 1(–2)-layered, cells transversely extended and more or less hexagonal in surface view; costal cells often almost cubical. Abaxial hypodermis shallow, always 1-layered, cells longitudinally extended, rectangular in surface view; cells adjacent to the substomatal chambers small, irregular, and not uniformly arranged. **Chlorenchyma.** Adaxial cells somewhat more compact than those elsewhere but scarcely palisade-like; mesophyll cells arranged in longitudinal files, each tabular, longitudinally extended and markedly papillose, the papillae enclosing large intercellular spaces. Mesophyll including large **tannin-cells.**

Veins arranged in 3 distinct systems (Fig. 14. A): (i) Adaxial longitudinal system of wide veins situated in adaxial mesophyll, independent of surface layers but larger veins usually interrupting continuity of hypodermis. Each vein with a continuous, conspicuous **endodermal sheath** (Fig. 14. F) of cells with unevenly thickened walls appearing U-shaped in T.S., the cell lumen including small granular silica-bodies. Endodermoid cells elongated with truncate ends and resembling the endodermal cells of mature monocotyledonous roots. I.S. composed of a single fibrous layer, above the xylem sometimes represented by sclerotic cells with wide lumina. Xylem of large veins including several files of wide tracheal elements and extended protoxylem. Phloem strand undivided. Smaller veins with reduced vascular tissues. (ii) Abaxial longitudinal system of uniformly small vb's situated in abaxial mesophyll but independent of surface layers. O.S. composed of a few abaxial files of endodermoid cells and completed adaxially by thin-walled, colourless elongated cells without silica contents. Vascular tissues reduced, xylem usually absent. (iii) **Transverse veins** numerous, wide and conspicuous, more or less equidistant from each surface and often extending below the adaxial and above the abaxial longitudinal veins. Each bundle with a continuous endodermoid layer outside the massive fibrous sheath. Vascular tissues including a single file of wide metaxylem elements and a strand of narrow phloem cells; phloem sometimes irregularly distributed. **Midrib** region (Fig. 14. A) thickened, gradually confluent with lamina on either side and with sheath below. Chlorenchyma continuous with that of lamina but restricted to surface layers, cells small and not papillose. Central ground parenchyma consisting of colourless, isodiametric cells forming a v. lacunose tissue. Vb's near both surfaces each with a massive fibrous sheath; central tissue including many scattered bundles with less conspicuous sheaths. Vascular tissues as in the veins of the lamina, those of adaxial bundles sometimes irregularly or even inversely orientated. Endodermoid sheath continuous around all veins, rarely becoming thin-walled around xylem of smaller veins.

(ii) *Sheath*

Hairs common, like those of the lamina, except for more permanent distal cells; often forming a superficial, mycelial-like weft. **Epidermis** somewhat different on the 2 surfaces. Abaxial epidermis more or less like that of the lamina, but with fewer stomata. Adaxial epidermis composed of thick-walled pitted cells, more or less rectangular in surface view, shorter than the cells of the lamina. Anatomy of the sheath essentially like that of the midrib region of the lamina. Ground parenchyma more spongy. Chlorenchyma developed below each surface.

STEM (Fig. 15. M)

Described as a **rhizome** by Smithson. Developing long runners according to Backer (1951). **Hairs** occasional, resembling those of the leaf. **Epidermis** composed of more or less isolateral cells, irregularly polygonal in surface view. **Stomata** absent. Surface layers suberized but without periderm divisions. **Cortex** narrow, composed of uniform ground parenchyma cells, each including few starch grains. Cortical vb's scattered, each with a complete endodermoid sheath surrounding the massive fibrous sheath. Vascular tissues sometimes absent and the bundle then represented by a purely fibrous strand. **Central cylinder** delimited from cortex by a conspicuous **endodermis,** the endodermal cells thick-walled, like those sheathing the individual vb's. Outer layer of central cylinder, immediately within endodermis, distinguishable as an irregular, 1–2-layered **pericyclic layer** of thick-walled cells surrounding a vascular plexus of many congested vb's, embedded in a continuous fibrous tissue, the vascular tissues of these bundles resembling those of the central vb's. Central **vascular bundles** each with a complete endodermoid sheath of rather thin-walled cells enclosing a massive fibrous sheath, xylem strand somewhat V-shaped in T.S. with many files of tracheids. Protoxylem sometimes developed. Gradual transition between peripheral vb's and those of the centre of the stem. Ground tissue of central cylinder including abundant starch.

(Brief notes by Solereder and Meyer on the anatomy of the **inflorescence axis** suggest that it is identical in structure with the organ described above.)

ROOT

No anatomical information available.

Secretory, Storage, and Conducting Elements

Silica present as irregular granular deposits in endodermoid cells around all vb's. Solereder and Meyer record large silica-bodies in adaxial hypodermis of lamina and sometimes also in abaxial hypodermis and adaxial mesophyll cells.

Tannin common as brownish deposits in most tissues, in mesophyll of lamina included within enlarged tannin-cells.

Starch present in ground parenchyma cells adjacent to vb's in leaf sheath; abundant in central ground parenchyma of stem. Starch grains smooth, not flattened, somewhat ellipsoidal and slightly eccentric.

Xylem. Vessels absent from stem and leaf, according to Smithson.

Taxonomic Notes

Smithson (1956) has already shown that these 3 genera are anatomically as well as morphologically distinct. These anatomical differences are outlined above in the summaries for each genus. *Flagellaria* and *Joinvillea* show some affinity with each other since they have the same type of guard cell and the same type of vascular bundle. Both have vessels in the aerial parts, although the structure of the vessel end walls within a single organ is more diverse than is usual amongst monocotyledons. *Hanguana* differs from these 2 genera in many important respects and Smithson questions whether it should rightly be included within the Flagellariaceae, pointing out that the anatomical evidence is supported by evidence from palynology (Erdtman 1952). Shaw (1965) recognizes this isolation in creating the family Hanguanaceae.

Apart from the grass-like guard cells in *Flagellaria* and *Joinvillea*, the epidermis of *Joinvillea* has been likened to that of the grasses. This is discussed by Chadefaud (1955) in view of the fact that in these 2 genera the pollen grains also recall those of the grasses.

Genera and Species reported on in the Literature

Chadefaud (1955) *Flagellaria guineensis*; stomata.
Sablon (1887) *Flagellaria indica*; tendril anatomy.
Smithson (1956) see Material Examined by the Author.
Solereder and Meyer (1929) *Flagellaria indica* L.; stem, leaf; *Hanguana malayanum* var. *anthelminticum* as *Susum anthelminticum* Bl.; stem, leaf.
Tieghem (1887) *Flagellaria indica*; lateral roots.
Worgitzky (1887) *Flagellaria indica*; tendril anatomy.

Material Examined by the Author

The above account is based on that of Smithson (1956) together with a re-examination of the material which she studied, i.e.

Flagellaria indica L.; Singapore. Leaf, stem.
Hanguana malayanum (Jack.) Merr.; Bukit Timah, Singapore. Leaf, stem.
Joinvillea borneensis Becc.; Taiping Hill, Malaya. Leaf.
J. gaudichaudiana Brongn. and Gris.; Kew Herbarium, Christopherson 1286; Oahu. Leaf.

Bibliography for Flagellariaceae

BACKER, C. A. (1951) Flagellariaceae in *Flora Malesiana* ser. 1, **4**, 245.

CHADEFAUD, M. (1955) Remarques sur quelques pollens de plantes tropicales, particulière-ment intéressants des points de vue palynologique ou systématique. *Revue gén. Bot.* **62**, 641–60.

ERDTMAN, G. (1952) *Pollen morphology and plant taxonomy*. Uppsala.

FAHN, A. (1954) Metaxylem elements in some families of the Monocotyledoneae. *New Phytol.* **53**, 530–40.

SABLON, LECLERC DU (1887) Recherches sur l'enroulement des vrilles. *Annls Sci. nat.* bot. ser. 7, **5**, 1–50.

SHAW, H. K. AIRY (1965) Diagnoses of new families, new names, etc. for the seventh edition of Willis's 'Dictionary'. *Kew Bull.* **18**, 249–73.

SMITHSON, E. (1956). The comparative anatomy of the Flagellariaceae. *Kew Bull.* 491–501.

SOLEREDER, H., and MEYER, F. J. (1929) Flagellariaceae. In *Systematische Anatomie der Monokotyledonen*, Heft IV, 3–6.

TIEGHEM, P. VAN (1887) Structure de la racine et disposition des radicelles dans les Centro-lépidées, Eriocaulées, Joncées, Mayacées et Xyridées. *J. Bot., Paris* **1**, 305–15.

WORGITZKY, G. (1887) Vergleichende Anatomie der Ranken. *Flora, Jena* **70**, 73.

MAYACACEAE

(Figs. 16, 17)

SUMMARY

A FAMILY of one genus, *Mayaca*, including about 15 species in tropical and subtropical America with a centre of development in the Amazonian basin, together with one species in Portuguese West Africa. Small, perennial herbs with a *Lycopodium*-like habit, growing in swampy situations or even wholly aquatic. Stem v. slender, creeping or ascending, sparingly branched; buds only occasional and at distant intervals but always forming a branch. Roots few, filiform. Flowers usually solitary at the ends of long naked or basally leafy peduncles. Growth habit sympodial by eviction of terminal flower; lateral renewal bud growing out early or late in relation to flower development. Leaves closely inserted in a dense spiral; short, lanceolate or thread-like, each including a single median vein extending to the apex which is often bidentate. Leaf base not sheathing, with a narrow insertion. Anatomical features largely conditioned by the hydrophytic habit and include: the absence of hairs except in the leaf axils; longitudinal **air-canals** in root, stem, and leaf segmented by **transverse diaphragms** of stellate cells; absence of mechanical tissues; reduced stelar tissues sheathed throughout stem and root by an **endodermis**; stem endodermis becoming thickened and possibly of mechanical significance. Secretory elements absent.

LEAF (Fig. 16)

Short, lanceolate or linear with a single median vein extending almost to the apex. **Apex** commonly described as bifid (Fig. 16. L) but not consistently so. Isolateral or with slight dorsiventral symmetry. **Hairs** (Fig. 16. M) restricted to short, uniseriate, filamentous trichomes, 2–5 cells long in the leaf axils; sub-proximal cell always short, cutinized.

(These hairs originate v. early and become mature before the axillant leaf shows procambium. The dense indumentum which they form thus serves to protect the shoot apex and leaf primordia. The hairs are ephemeral and mostly lost from old shoots. Hairs of this kind were previously recorded only by Poulsen in *M. lagoensis* until the present writer found them in *M. aubletii*, *fluviatilis*, *sellowiana*. They were either overlooked by previous authors or dismissed as filamentous micro-organisms which are commonly caught up in the leaf axils.)

Cuticle absent. **Epidermis** of each surface similar; cells colourless, thin-walled, longitudinally extended and more or less rectangular in surface view but rather irregular. Costal cells above and below mid-vein somewhat longer and narrower than cells elsewhere. **Stomata** (Fig. 16. A–B) few, v. diffuse, either equally numerous on each surface or least common on adaxial surface; restricted to narrow region on either side of mid-vein above and below air-canals, frequently situated above or below **transverse**

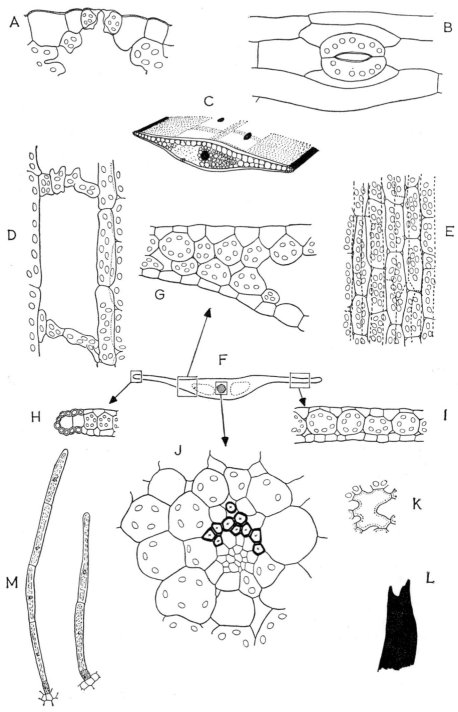

Fig. 16. MAYACACEAE. Leaf anatomy.

A–L. *Mayaca aubletii*, lamina.

A. T.S. abaxial stoma (×460). B. Stoma surface view (×460). C. Construction of lamina (diagrammatic, not to scale). D. Septate air-lacuna, seen through abaxial surface (×290). E. Lamina wing, seen through abaxial surface to show uniseriate mesophyll; outline of epidermal cells dotted (×290). F. T.S. lamina, outline (×42). G. T.S. midrib region, marginal boundary of lacuna (×290). H. T.S. lamina margin (×290). I. T.S. lamina wing (×290). J. T.S. vein (×290). K. Colourless central diaphragm cell, as seen in T.S. lamina (×290). L. Leaf apex, outline (×65).

M. *M. fluviatilis*. Axillary hairs (×230).

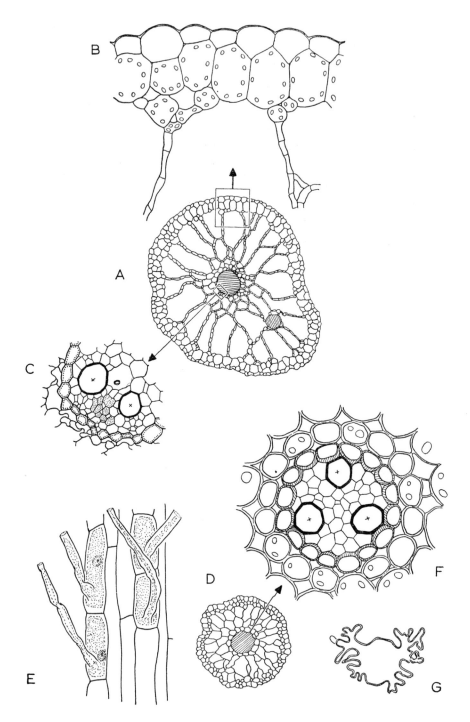

F<small>IG</small>. 17. MAYACACEAE (*Mayaca fluviatilis*).

A–C. Stem.

A. T.S. (×42). B. T.S. stem periphery (×230). C. T.S. periphery of stele including one vb; endodermis stippled (×290).

D–G. Root.

D. T.S. (×100). E. Piliferous layer, surface view with root-hairs (×230). F. T.S. stele (×500). G. Short-cell, isolated from cortical root diaphragm (×460).

diaphragms. Each stoma with two narrow, irregular, lateral subsidiary cells (Fig. 16. B). Guard cells uniformly thin-walled, with cutinized ledges (Fig. 16. A). **Chlorenchyma** consisting of cubical or longitudinally extended cells with rounded corners enclosing small intercellular spaces (Fig. 16. E); 1-layered at leaf margin (Fig. 16. H–I) but commonly 2-layered towards mid-vein (Fig. 16. G). Mesophyll on each side of mid-vein including a longitudinal air-canal, extending almost whole length of leaf (Fig. 16. C, G). Chloren-chyma more or less continuous above but absent below canal. Air-canals segmented at regular intervals by frequent 1-layered **transverse septa** (Fig. 16. D) of small, fairly compact but lobed cells with abundant chloroplasts in peripheral cells, central cells thin-walled and colourless (Fig. 16. K). **Vein** (Fig. 16. J) enclosed within chlorenchyma, sheathed by a continuous layer sometimes becoming thick-walled; sheath described as endodermis by earlier workers but Casparian strip not observed. Vascular tissues reduced but including narrow adaxial tracheal elements (× in Fig. 16. J) with spiral or scalari-form wall pitting. Mechanical tissues otherwise absent except for colourless, narrow, but thin-walled prosenchymatous marginal cells (Fig. 16. H). Vein at the bifid leaf apex ending in a group of swollen terminal tracheids lying immediately beneath an apical opening according to Solereder and Meyer but not observed in material examined.

STEM (Fig. 17. A–C)

Slender, bearing buds only at distant intervals, the buds always growing out as vegetative or floral branches; lateral buds commonly displacing ter-minal flower and continuing growth of axis in a sympodial manner. **Epidermis** colourless, without stomata; cells uniformly rectangular and longitudinally extended. **Cortex** without a separate vascular system except for leaf traces passing into the stele. **Hypodermal tissues** (Fig. 17. B) represented by 1–2 layers of cubical, chlorenchymatous cells with numerous chloroplasts and some-times starch grains. Cortex mostly occupied by longitudinal **air-lacunae** (Fig. 17. A) originating schizogenously by enlargement of intercellular spaces be-tween the reticulum of cortical cells, the 1-layered longitudinal partitions of the reticulum commonly becoming mere plates of cell-wall material by col-lapse of constituent cells in mature stems. Air-canals segmented at frequent and regular intervals by **transverse plates** of stellate cells including numerous chloroplasts. Innermost 2–3 cortical layers adjacent to stele compact, chloren-chymatous and not collapsed. **Stele** (Fig. 17. C) narrow, cylindrical or slightly fluted, often distinctly triangular in T.S., enclosed by a continuous **endodermis** of elongated cells with truncate end walls. Endodermis in young stems with thin walls and conspicuously lignified Casparian strips on the radial walls but becoming unevenly thickened and lignified in old stems, the cells then con-spicuously U-shaped in T.S. and said by Poulsen to be of considerable mechanical significance. Vascular tissues usually arranged in 3 (rarely fewer or more) distinct, collateral **vascular bundles** (Fig. 17. C); outermost tissue of vb's separated from endodermis by a single, indistinct pericyclic layer. Each vb including a few narrow phloem elements between two lateral files of wide, scalariformly pitted tracheal elements; inner protoxylem lacuna sometimes developed. Phloem strand narrow and inconspicuous. Central ground tissues of stele scarcely thick-walled. **Leaf traces** entering stele fairly abruptly, enclosed in a plate of stellate cells during their brief passage across the cortex. **Endodermis** of leaf trace and stem continuous.

Inflorescence Axis

Recorded as resembling the vegetative stem except for 6 small cortical vb's, sometimes each enclosed within an endodermis. Six stelar vb's enclosed by common endodermis with U-shaped wall thickenings; 2 pairs of vb's closely juxtaposed. Vascular tissues sometimes reduced to phloem alone (Poulsen).

Root (Fig. 17. D–G)

Adventitious roots arising endogenously, commonly but not exclusively associated with the development of buds. Root cap present but inconspicuous. **Piliferous layer** compact, cells longitudinally extended, commonly bearing long, unbranched root-hairs arising as outgrowths from one end of a superficial cell (Fig. 17. E). **Cortex** wide (Fig. 17. D), with a compact hypodermal layer, middle cortex including large long cells readily mistaken for air-canals. **Transverse septa** developed at v. regular intervals, each composed of a single layer of stellate, short, colourless cells (Fig. 17. G) with much longer arms than the diaphragm cells of stem and leaf; septal cells often including starch grains. **Stele** (Fig. 17. F) narrow; endodermis conspicuous, cells becoming unevenly thickened and appearing U-shaped in T.S. Pericycle 1-layered but commonly interrupted by the xylem. Vascular tissues usually triarch, sometimes 2- or 4-arch. Each xylem pole represented by a single file of scalariformly-pitted tracheal elements (× in Fig. 17. F), commonly replacing pericyclic cell and situated immediately adjacent to the endodermis. Phloem v. reduced. **Lateral roots,** according to van Tieghem, originating in the pericycle opposite the phloem and not opposite the xylem as is the normal condition. This abnormal feature, shared with a number of related families, is a result of the common absence of a pericyclic layer between the xylem and endodermis.

Storage and Conducting Elements

Crystalline and other specialized secretory deposits not developed.

Starch sometimes abundant in peripheral layers of stem and leaf base as conspicuous, spherical grains.

Xylem. Vessel elements in root and stem with long, scalariform, indistinctly perforate end walls; perforations not seen in leaf in material examined but recorded by Cheadle (1953).

Taxonomic Notes

Mayaca has attracted the attention of several anatomists because of its peculiar habit and morphology, but although there is quite an extensive literature on the genus its anatomy is still only imperfectly known. This account makes no attempt to remedy these deficiencies and still leaves much to be desired. In particular the causal factors bringing about branch and root production would be worthy of investigation and a detailed developmental study would be desirable.

Different species of *Mayaca* appear to be almost identical in their anatomy. Thus Horn af Rantzien (1946) found no anatomical variation of taxonomic importance in leaf and stem of material he studied. Uphof compared the structure of land and water forms of *M. fluviatilis* but differences were slight and entirely quantitative. The peculiar anatomy of *Mayaca* is largely an outcome of its aquatic habit so that information relating to its systematic position and possible phylogeny is wholly obscured. Consequently there is not much information to shed further light on the suggestion by Hutchinson that *Mayaca* is merely a reduced member of the Commelinaceae and might well be regarded as a member of that family. It may be noted, however, that the vascular bundles in the stem of *Mayaca* closely resemble those at the periphery of the stele in the Commelinaceae. Vessels in Commelinaceae, however, have simple perforation plates, perforations in *Mayaca* are always scalariform. The hairs in the leaf axils, with a proximal short cutinized cell, recall those of Eriocaulaceae. The general habit strongly recalls that of *Tonina*. The roots of *Mayaca* strongly resemble those of the Eriocaulaceae. It is probable that *Mayaca* originated from the same stock that has produced Eriocaulaceae, Commelinaceae, and Xyridaceae.

Species reported on in the Literature

Boubier (1895) *M. longipes* Mart., *M. sellowiana* Kunth.
Malmanche (1919) *M. michauxii* Schott. & Endl., *M. sellowiana* Kunth, *M. wendellii* Schott. & Endl.; floral axis only.
Poulsen (1886) *M. lagoensis* Wing, *M. wendellii* Schott. & Endl.
Solereder and Meyer (1929) *M. aubletii* Schott., *M. sellowiana* Kunth.
Van Tieghem (1887) *M. sellowiana* Kunth; root.
Uphof (1924) *M. fluviatilis* Aubl.; all parts.

Material Examined by the Author

Mayaca aubletii Michx.; P. B. T. s.n.; Florida. All parts.
M. fluviatilis Aubl.; P. B. T. 10.v.63M; Florida. All parts.
M. sellowiana Kunth; cultivated at Kew. All parts.

Bibliography for Mayacaceae

Boubier, A. M. (1895) Remarques sur l'anatomie systematique des Rapateacées et des familles voisines. *Bull. Herb. Boissier* 3, 115–20.
Cheadle, V. I. (1953) Independent origins of vessels in the Monocotyledons and Dicotyledons. *Phytomorphology* 3, 23–44.
Horn af Rantzien, H. (1946) Notes on the Mayacaceae of the Regnellian Herbarium in the Riksmuseum Stockholm. *Svensk bot. Tidskr.* 40, 405–24.
Hutchinson, J. (1959) *The families of flowering plants*, Vol. II, *Monocotyledons*, 2nd edn. Oxford.
Malmanche, L. -A. (1919) *Contribution à l'étude anatomique des Eriocaulonacées et des familles voisines: Restiacées, Centrolépidacées, Xyridacées, Philydracées, Mayacacées.* Thesis, St. Cloud. pp. 165.
Poulsen, V. A. (1886) Anatomiske studier over *Mayaca* Aubl. *Oversigt Kon. Vid. Dansk. Selbs. Forhand,* 85–100.

SOLEREDER, H., and MEYER, F. J. (1929) Mayacaceae. In *Systematische Anatomie der Monokotyledonen*, Heft IV, 34–36.

TIEGHEM, P. VAN (1887) Structure de la racine et disposition des radicelles dans les Centrolépidées, Eriocaulées, Joncées, Mayacées et Xyridées. *J. Bot., Paris* 1, 305–15.

UPHOF, J. C. T. (1924) The physiological anatomy of *Mayaca fluviatilis. Ann. Bot.* 38, 389–93.

XYRIDACEAE
(Figs. 18–26)

SUMMARY

A FAMILY of 4 genera; *Abolboda, Achlyphila, Orectanthe* restricted to South America; *Xyris*, the largest genus, widely distributed throughout the tropics and subtropics, but most abundant in South America. Usually small, perennial herbs with a corm-like, or shortly creeping, rhizome, the leaves spirally or distichously arranged in a basal rosette below a long, usually naked flowering scape. Axis in *Xyris* typically sympodial, rarely monopodial; branch system often complex but quite regular (Nilsson 1892). Rhizome in *Achlyphila* long, creeping, scaly; producing erect stems with distichously arranged foliage leaves. Leaves equitant only in *Achlyphila* and many *Xyris* spp.

Anatomical features common to the whole family include vessels with simple perforation plates in all parts; amphivasal vb's in the rhizome. Other features often present include irregular plates of short, stellate cells in the cortex of the root; a uniform distribution of phloem cells throughout the root stele especially in wider roots. Anatomical features common to *Achlyphila* and *Xyris* include an isolateral leaf structure without colourless hypodermal layers. Leaf vb's in *Xyris* frequently compound, each with two or more separate vascular strands. Anatomical features common to *Abolboda* and *Orectanthe* include a dorsiventral leaf structure with a hypodermis of colourless cells common beneath each surface, but rarely with compound vb's.

LEAF

The morphology and anatomy of the leaves of genera within the Xyridaceae is sufficiently distinct to merit separate description. The greatest differences exist between *Achlyphila* and *Xyris*, on the one hand, and *Abolboda* and *Orectanthe*, on the other. Hairs recorded only in *Xyris*.

XYRIS (Figs. 18–22)

Leaves distichously arranged, leaf equitant, with a keeled sheathing base passing gradually into the blade. Ligule often present but always inconspicuous. Blade narrow, either lanceolate or commonly terete or sub-terete, sometimes spirally twisted. Blade said to be flattened dorsiventrally in *X. reitzii* (Smith and Downs 1960), not laterally as in other spp. Outline of blade in T.S. fairly constant for each sp.

(i) *Hairs*

(*a*) Uniseriate glandular hairs (Fig. 20. G–H) with a variable number of stalk cells (1–6), always ending in a delicate clavate cell. Length of distal cell more or less constant for each sp. Hairs restricted to the inner surface of the sheath, most abundant at leaf insertion; possibly present in all spp. of *Xyris*, but observed only in a limited number. Mucilage apparently secreted by hairs; accumulating in leaf axils of Florida spp. examined by the author (p. 125) in the field; possibly a universal feature not persisting in dried specimens.

(*b*) Short unicellular unbranched hairs (Fig. 20. F, I) restricted to margins of blade and keel and margins of leaf sheath in some spp.; surface seldom uniformly pilose but this character recorded in *X. vestita* by Malme (1913*a*). Complete transition from minute marginal epidermal papillae to distinct cilia within *Xyris* as a whole (Fig. 20. D–F, I), but size of protuberances and their distribution quite constant for each sp. (e.g. Kral 1966). Margin of more conspicuously ciliate spp. bearing several series of hairs, as in *X. involucrata* (Fig. 20. F) and *tomentosa*.

Longer hairs on leaf sheath of *X. tenella* sometimes branched and septate.

(ii) *Lamina*

Always isolateral, except in bifacially asymmetrical leaves with each epidermis different as in *X. fallax* (Fig. 18. J–K), *imitatrix*, *vanderystii*; rarely radially symmetrical as in *X. foliolata*. **Epidermis** uniform (Fig. 18. A, B), usually without distinct costal and intercostal bands, except, e.g., in *X. elliottii*, *rubrolimbata* (Fig. 18. H), *lomatophylla*. Costal and intercostal cells of *X. stenocephala* differing in wall thickness according to Malme (1896). Cells always longitudinally extended, rectangular in surface view. Amount of wall thickening in surface view emphasized as a feature of specific diagnostic value by Malme (1909, 1913*a*).

The lists below summarize existing information from the following papers: Arber 1922 (A); Duvigneaud and Homes 1955 (DH); Heimerl 1906 and later papers (H plus date); Malme 1896 and later papers (M plus date); Nilsson 1892 and later papers (N plus date); Poulsen 1892 (P); Smith and Downs 1960 (SD); Solereder and Meyer 1929 (SM); and includes original observations (T).

(*a*) Epidermis with more or less uniformly thickened walls (e.g. Fig. 19. B, K, L) (wall thickening slight or considerable):

anceps (A)
asperata (P)
brownei (N, 1892)
calocephala (P)
complanata (N, 1892)
densa (DH)
eriophylla (N, 1892)
filifolia (N, 1892; M, 1901, 1909)
foliolata (DH)
gracilescens (M, 1898)
gracilis (T)

kwangolana (DH)
lacera (SM)
lanata (N, 1892; SM; T)
mima (SD)
neocaledonica (T)
operculata (N, 1892; T)
platystachya (M, 1913*a*)
quinquenervis (M, 1901, 1909)
ramboi (SD)
regnellii (M, 1909)
setigera (M, 1913*a*)

simulans (N, 1892)
sphaerocephala (DH)
subulata var. *macrotona* (H, 1906*b*)
teres (M, 1909)
teres var. *obscuriceps* (M, 1901, 1909)
teretifolia (P)
trachyphylla (N, 1892)
uninervis (M, 1908, 1909)
wallichii (A)
witsenioides (N, 1892)

Inner and outer epidermal walls in *X. witsenioides* equally thickened and cell lumen broad but shallow, according to Malme (1913*a*).

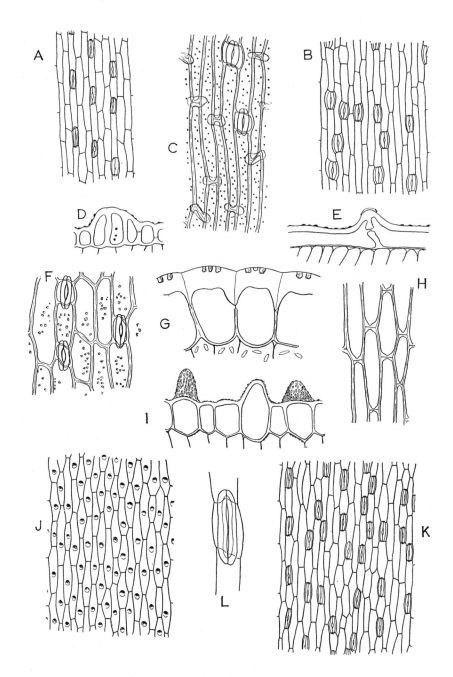

F<small>IG</small>. 18. XYRIDACEAE. Epidermal structures in *Xyris*.

A–E. Lamina epidermis.

A. *X. tenella.* Surface view (×50). B. *X. involucrata.* Surface view (×50). C. *X. lacera.* Surface view (×50). D. *X. lacera.* T.S. including protuberant end wall (×80). E. *X. lacera.* L.S. including protuberant end wall (×80).

F. *X. minarum.* Epidermis of outer surface of sheath, surface view (×50).

G–L. Lamina epidermis.

G. *X. minarum.* T.S. with crystals included in outer wall (×120). H. *X. rubrolimbata.* Surface view, costal region (×80). I. *X. fallax.* Papillose epidermis in T.S. (×80). J. *X. fallax.* Non-stomatal (papillose) epidermis, surface view (×20). K. *X. fallax.* Stomatal (non-papillose) epidermis, surface view (×20). L. *X. fallax.* Stoma, surface view (×80).

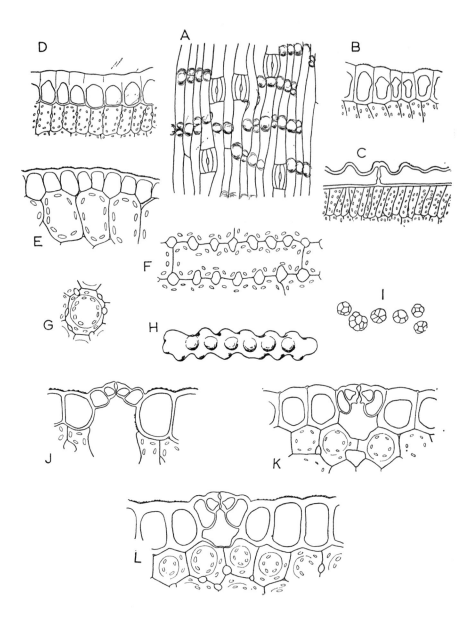

Fig. 19. XYRIDACEAE. Leaf anatomy in *Xyris*.

A–E. Lamina epidermis.

  A. *X. operculata*. Surface view (× 50). B. *X. operculata*. T.S. (× 80).
C. *X. operculata*. L.S. (× 50). D. *X. melanopoda*. T.S. (× 80).
E. *X. caroliniana*. T.S. (× 80).

F–H. Lamina mesophyll (× 80).

  F. *X. lanata*. L.S. G. *X. lanata*. Mesophyll cell in T.S.
H. *X. gracilis*. Isolated mesophyll cell.

I. *X. fimbriata*. tarch sgrains from leaf base (× 120).

J–L. T.S. stomata from lamina (× 120).

  J. *X. fallax*. K. *X. lanata*. L. *X. gracilis*.

H

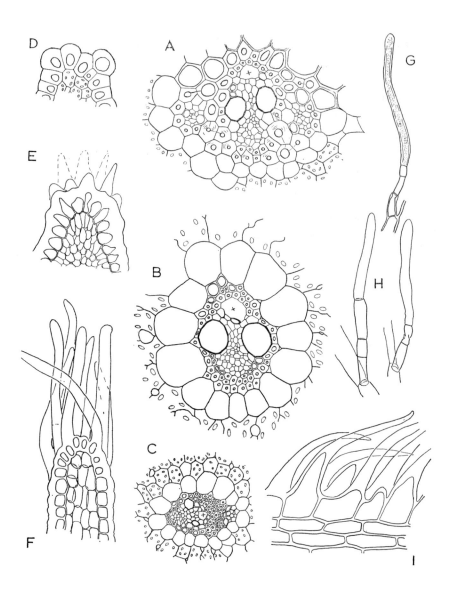

98

F‌IG. 20. XYRIDACEAE. Leaf anatomy in *Xyris*.

A–C. Vascular bundles of lamina in T.S. (×80).

    A. *X. lanata*. Tripolar compound vb. ×—protoxylem lacuna.
B. *X. flexuosa*. Simple vb. **C.** *X. flabelliformis*. Bipolar marginal vb.

D–F. Margin of lamina in T.S. (×50).

    D. *X. lanata*. E. *X. melanopoda*. F. *X. involucrata*.

G–H. Hairs from inner surface of leaf sheath; surface view (×50).

    G. *X. fimbriata*. H. *X. capensis*.

I. *X. schizachne*. Hairs on margin of lamina, surface view (×80).

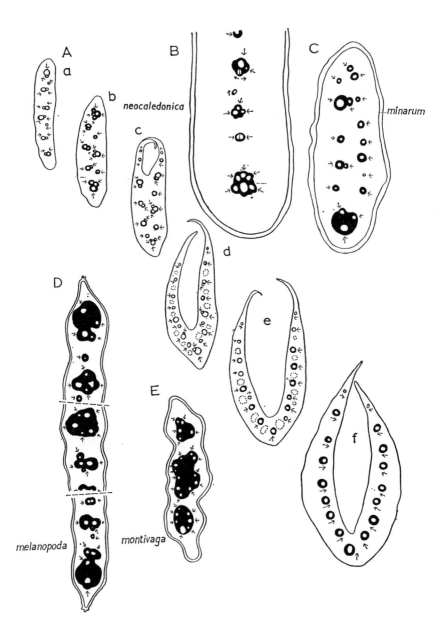

A
a
b
neocaledonica
c
B
C
minarum
d
D
e
E
melanopoda
montivaga
f

100

FIG. 21. XYRIDACEAE. Leaves of *Xyris* in T.S. (all ×8).

A. *X. elliottii.* Series of sections from a single leaf 11·2 cm long at the following heights above the insertion; *a.* 8·2 cm, *b.* 4·2 cm, *c.* 3·2 cm, *d.* 2·2 cm, *e.* 1·1 cm, *f.* 0·4 cm.

B–E. T.S. Lamina.

B. *X. neocaledonica.* C. *X. minarum.* D. *X. melanopoda.* E. *X. montivaga.*

The small arrows indicate the orientation of the vascular tissues in each vascular bundle, the head of the arrow indicating the xylem.

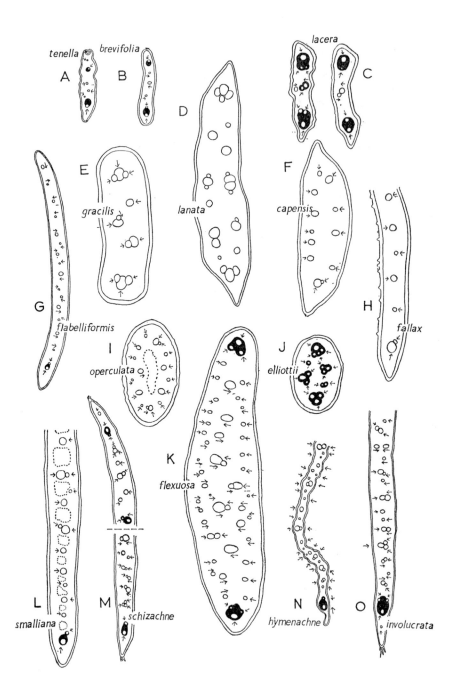

tenella brevifolia lacera

A B C

D

E gracilis lanata F capensis

G flabelliformis H fallax

I operculata J elliottii

K flexuosa

L smalliana M schizachne N hymenachne O involucrata

102

Fig. 22. XYRIDACEAE. Lamina of *Xyris* in T.S. (all ×8).

A. *X. tenella.* B. *X. brevifolia.* C. *X. lacera.* D. *X. lanata.* E. *X. gracilis.* F. *X. capensis.* G. *X. flabelliformis.* H. *X. fallax.* I. *X. operculata.* J. *X. elliottii.* K. *X. flexuosa.* L. *X. smalliana.* M. *X. schizachne.* N. *X. hymenachne.* O. *X. involucrata.*

The small arrows indicate the orientation of the vascular tissues as in Fig. 21. B–E.

(*b*) Epidermis with outer thicker than remaining walls.

(1) Walls relatively thick, especially outer (e.g. Figs. 18. G; 19. D):

baldwiniana (M, 1913*b*)
bicarinata (M, 1913*b*)
brevifolia (T)
calcarata (H, 1906*b*; M, 1913*a*)
calostachys (M, 1909, 1913*a*)
ciliata (M, 1913*a*)
complanata (N, 1892)
connectens (M, 1925*a*)
dusenii (M, 1925*a*)
flexuosa (T)
glaucescens (M, 1908)
globosa (M, 1913*a*)
goyazensis (M, 1898, 1909, 1913*a*)
graminosa (M, 1913*a*)
guianensis (H, 1906*b*)
hatsbachii (SD)
hildebrandtii (N, 1892; DH)

hymenachne (T)
insignis (N, 1892; M, 1909, 1913*a*)
involucrata (M, 1913*a*; T)
lacera (T)
laevigata (M, 1913*a*)
lanuginosa (M, 1909)
lomatophylla (T)
longifolia (M, 1913*a*)
macrocephala (N, 1892)
melanopoda (T)
minarum (T)
montivaga (M, 1913*a*; T)
moraesii (SD)
neglecta (M, 1913*a*; N, 1892)
nigricans (N, 1892)
paulensis M, 1925*a*)
piresiana (SD)
quinquenervis (M, 1909)
rehmanni (N, 1892)

reitzii (SD)
riedeliana (M, 1908)
rigida (M, 1909; N, 1892)
rigidaeformis (M, 1909)
rubrolimbata (T)
savanensis (N, 1892)
seubertii (M, 1913*a*)
spruceana (M, 1901, 1913*a*)
stenophylla (M, 1913*a*)
subulata var. *acutifolia* (H, 1906*b*)
tenella (T)
teres (M, 1909)
tortula (M, 1913*a*)
vacillans (M, 1898)
veruina (M, 1898, 1909, 1913*a*)
vestita (M, 1898, 1909)
zahlbruckneri (H, 1906*b*)

(2) Walls relatively thin (e.g. Fig. 19. E, J):

alata (P)
archeri (SD)
bahiana (M, 1901)
capensis (T)
caroliniana (SM; T)
egleri (SD)
ekmanii (M, 1925*b*)
elliottii (T)
fallax (T)
filiformis (DH)

fimbriata (T)
flabelliformis (T)
flexuosa (M, 1913*a*)
gardneri (M, 1901)
imitatrix (DH)
indica (SM; T)
intermedia (M, 1925*b*)
jupicai (T)
mexicana (M, 1913*b*)
montana (T)

navicularis (M, 1913*b*)
nilssonii (M, 1896)
pauciflora (SM)
plantaginea (P)
schizachne (P, T)
smalliana (T)
subtenella (M, 1898)
tomentosa (SD)
vanderystii (DH)

Thick-walled epidermis distinguished as a 'mechanical' epidermis from thin-walled 'transpiring' epidermis by Nilsson (1893). Outer wall of epidermis sometimes conspicuously and **minutely papillose**, the thickening either of cuticular, or of wall, material. Papillae recorded or observed in:

capensis (T)
fallax (T)
gracilis (T)
indica (T)
insignis (M, 1909)

lacera (T)
macrocephala (T)
operculata (T)
pauciflora (SM)
seubertii (M, 1913*b*)

simulans (M, 1913*b*)
subulata var. *acutifolia* (M, 1913*b*)
zahlbruckneri (H, 1906*b*)

Heimerl (1960*b*) recorded one variety of *X. subulata* with papillae, and another without. End walls sometimes thickened in a distinctive manner, as in *X. rubrolimbata* (Fig. 18. H); sometimes with copious deposits of wax or wall material, e.g. *X. caroliniana* var. *major*. Epidermis in many spp. distinctly rugose, due to transverse series of epidermal protuberances (Fig. 19. A, C)

(Kral 1966), these papillae commonly at the ends of the cells and sometimes restricted to this position (Fig. 18. D–E). *Xyris fallax* with 1 leaf surface free of stomata, and each epidermal cell with a conspicuous central papilla (Fig. 18. I–J); the other, stomata-bearing epidermis, not papillose (Fig. 18. K).

Stomata equally abundant on both surfaces, except in *X. fallax*. Stomata irregularly but uniformly scattered, rarely in distinct longitudinal files, as in *X. lomatophylla* and *rubrolimbata*. Each stoma with 2 thin-walled, shallow lateral subsidiary cells (Fig. 18. L). Terminal subsidiary cells never developed. Guard cells (Fig. 19. J–L) never sunken, each with a single prominent outer ledge above conspicuous wall thickening; inner ledge sometimes reduced or absent. Stomatal apparatus always shallower than remaining epidermal cells, sometimes described as slightly raised, e.g. in *X. platylepis* according to Kral (1966); outer part of substomatal chamber enclosed by epidermal cells.

Mesophyll without distinct colourless hypodermal layers; sometimes with a distinct palisade region of 1(–2) layers of anticlinally extended cells adjacent to epidermis, continuous except for conspicuous substomatal chambers, e.g. in *X. indica, involucrata, lacera, lomatophylla, melanopoda, minarum*. Palisade in *X. fallax* adjacent only to stomata-free surface. Cells adjacent to substomatal chambers often distinctly L-shaped in T.S. Mesophyll otherwise v. uniform, cells either isodiametric and compact, or often longitudinally extended and lobed. Distinctive mesophyll in, e.g. *X. gracilis, lacera, lanata* of elongated, regularly lobed cells, the lobes of adjacent cells regularly conjugating, such mesophyll cells in T.S. appearing to have 2 concentric walls (Fig. 19. F–H). Central mesophyll of thicker or more terete leaves composed of large colourless cells, sometimes collapsing to produce 1 or more irregular, longitudinal air-canals as in *X. capensis, operculata, teretifolia*. Mesophyll in *X. foliolata, kwangolana, sphaerocephala* described as having a central 'pith' by Duvigneaud and Homes (1955). Distinct longitudinal air-canals, pectinating with veins in wide leaves of *X. caroliniana* and *smalliana*; the veins then situated in distinct mesophyll buttresses. Veins in *X. indica* supported by compact mesophyll in relation to loose mesophyll elsewhere. Thick-walled, almost isodiametric idioblasts recorded in the assimilating tissue of *X. eriophylla*. Mesophyll cells quite thick-walled in *X. neocaledonica*.

Veins (Figs. 21; 22) varying considerably in number and distribution, but fairly constant in their arrangement for each sp., always independent of surface layers. (The series Fig. 21. A a–f, from a single leaf, indicates the difficulties involved in trying to categorize *Xyris* spp. according to leaf structure. This is also reflected when the same sp. is listed in different categories.) Veins either in 1 series with alternate vb's orientated in opposite directions (e.g. Fig. 22. H), or in 2 (rarely more) series, the bundles in each series all orientated alike (e.g. Fig. 22. F). Many intermediate conditions also noted. Total number of veins often constant within narrow limits; *X. uninervis* with 1 vein, *X. connectens* with 3, many spp. with fewer than 10, many with 10–20 veins; broader leaves with more than 20 veins. Veins of two main types: (i) In form of **compound vb's** with 2 or more vascular strands enclosed by common sheathing tissues. Such bipolar, tripolar . . ., etc. veins (i.e. with 2, 3 . . ., etc. constituent strands) usually with 1 large vb and 1 or more smaller bundles (e.g. Fig. 20.

A). Larger, multipolar bundles with several equivalent vascular strands occasional as in *X. montivaga*. (ii) In form of **simple vb's** each consisting of a single vascular strand (e.g. Fig. 20. B). Some spp. with veins almost all simple, other spp. with veins almost all compound; other intermediate spp. with approximately equal numbers of simple and compound bundles.

The following tables summarize the number, distribution, and type of veins. Information from same sources as indicated on p. 93:

(i) *Distribution of vascular bundles*

(a) Bundles more or less in one series (**uniseriate**)

anceps (A)
angustifolia (P)
asperata (P)
bahiana (M, 1901)
calcarata (H, 1906b)
caroliniana var. *caroliniana* (T)
complanata (N, 1892)
connectens (M, 1925a)
densa (DH)
ekmanii (M, 1925b)
eriophylla (N, 1892)
fallax (M, 1896 ; T) (Fig. 22. H)
filiformis (DH)
fimbriata (T)
flabelliformis (T) (Fig. 22. G)
glaucescens (M, 1908)

*gracilis (T) (Fig. 22. E)
guianensis (H, 1906b)
hildebrandtii (N, 1892; DH)
imitatrix (DH)
intermedia (M, 1925b)
jupicai (T)
lacera (M, 1913a) (Fig. 22. C)
lanata (N, 1892)
lomatophylla (T)
melanopoda (T) (Fig. 21. D)
montivaga (T) (Fig. 21. E)
neocaledonica (T) (Fig. 21. B)
nigricans (N, 1892)
nilssonii (M, 1896; 1913a)
operculata (N, 1892)

paulensis (M, 1925a)
radula (M, 1898)
rehmanni (N, 1892)
rupicola (N, 1892)
savanensis (N, 1892)
*schizachne (T) (Fig. 22. M)
setigera (M, 1913a)
simulans (N, 1892)
*smalliana (T) (Fig. 22. L)
stenocephala (M, 1896)
tenella (T) (Fig. 22. A)
trachyphylla (N, 1892)
vacillans (M, 1898)
vanderystii (DH)
*wallichii (N, 1892)
zahlbruckneri (H. 1906b)

* Species marked with an asterisk might be interpreted as biseriate.

(b) Bundles more or less in two series (**biseriate**)

asperula (N, 1892)
baldwiniana (N, 1892)
*brevifolia (T) (Fig. 22. B)
brownei (N, 1892)
brunnea (N, 1902)
capensis (T) (Fig. 22. F)
caroliniana (T)
dusenii (M, 1925a)
elliottii (T) (Fig. 22. J)
extensula (M, 1898)
filifolia (N, 1892)
flexuosa (T)
foliolata (DH)
gardneri (M, 1901)
glabrata (N, 1892)
goyazensis (M, 1898, 1909)

gracilescens (M, 1898)
*hymenachne (T) (Fig. 22. N)
indica (T)
insignis (N, 1892)
involucrata (T) (Fig. 22. O)
kwangolana (DH)
lacera (SM)
*lacera (T)
*lanata (T) (Fig. 22. D)
macrocephala (T)
minarum (T) (Fig. 21. C)
montana (T)
montivaga (P)
neglecta (N, 1892)
operculata (T) (Fig. 22. I)

regnellii (N, 1892)
riedeliana (M, 1908)
rigida (N, 1892)
rigidaeformis (M, 1896; 1913a)
rubrolimbata (T)
seubertii (N, 1892)
sphaerocephala (DH)
spruceana (M, 1901)
subtenella (M, 1898)
teres (M, 1909; N, 1892)
teres var. *obscuriceps* (M, 1901)
teretifolia (P)
ustulata (N, 1892)
veruina (M, 1898, 1909)
vestita (M, 1898, 1909)
wawrae (H, 1906b)

* Species marked with an asterisk might be interpreted as uniseriate.

Veins **multiseriate** in *X. flexuosa* (Fig. 22. K) and to some extent in *X. involucrata*. Veins fused laterally in *X. foliolata* and *kwangolana* to form central more or less **continuous cylinder** enclosing a central 'pith'; blade then closely resembling inflorescence axis, according to Duvigneaud and Homes (1955), and in *X. uninervis* according to Malme (1909).

(ii) *Proportion of compound and simple vascular bundles*

(*a*) Almost all bundles **compound**

brownei (N, 1892)
brunnea (N, 1902)
calcarata (H, 1906*b*)
calostachys (M, 1909)
densa (DH)
dusenii (M, 1925*a*)
elliottii (T) (Fig. 22. J)
eriophylla (N, 1892)
fallax (M, 1896)
filifolia (M, 1909)
filiformis (DH)
foliolata (DH)
gardneri (M, 1901)
goyazensis (M, 1898, 1909)
gracilescens (M, 1898)
gracilis (T) (Fig. 22. E)

hildebrandtii (N, 1892; DH)
insignis (N, 1892)
kwangolana (DH)
lacera (SM; T) (Fig. 22. C)
lanata (N, 1892) (Fig. 22. D)
lanuginosa (M, 1909)
melanopoda (T) (Fig. 21. D)
montivaga (T) (Fig. 21. E)
neglecta (N, 1892)
neocaledonica (T)
nigricans (N, 1892)
paulensis (M, 1925*a*)
quinquenervis (M, 1909)

regnellii (M, 1909; N, 1892)
rehmanni (N, 1892)
rigida (M, 1909; N, 1892)
sphaerocephala (M, 1896)
stenocephala (DH)
stenophylla (M, 1913*a*)
teres (M, 1909; N, 1892)
teretifolia (P)
tortula (M, 1913*a*)
trachyphylla (N, 1892)
uninervis (M, 1909)
ustulata (N, 1892)
vacillans (M, 1898)
veruina (M, 1898)
witsenioides (M, 1913*a*; N, 1892)

Veins of *X. foliolata, kwangolana, uninervis* interpreted as one large compound bundle.

(*b*) Almost all bundles **simple** (marginal bundles commonly compound)

acutifolia (M, 1913*a*)
asperula (N, 1892)
bahiana (M, 1901)
baldwiniana (SM)
brevifolia (A; T) (Fig. 22. B)
**brunnea* (N, 1902)
capensis (T) (Fig. 22. F)
caroliniana (T; SM)
complanata (N, 1892)
connectens (M, 1925*a*)
ekmanii (M, 1925*b*)
extensula (M, 1898)
fallax (T) (Fig. 22. H)
**filifolia* (SM)
flabelliformis (T) (Fig. 22. G)

flexuosa (T) (Fig. 22. K)
glabrata (SM)
glaucescens (M, 1908)
guianensis (H, 1906*b*)
imitatrix (DH)
indica (SM; T)
intermedia (M, 1925*b*)
**involucrata* (T) (Fig. 22. O)
**lanata* (SM; T)
macrocephala (T)
operculata (T; N, 1892) (Fig. 22. I)
pauciflora (SM)
plantaginea (N, 1892)
riedeliana (M, 1908)
rigidaeformis (M, 1909)

rubrolimbata (H, 1906*b*)
rupicola (N, 1892)
savanensis (N, 1892)
setigera (M, 1913*a*)
**seubertii* (SM)
simulans (N, 1892)
smalliana (T) (Fig. 22. L)
spruceana (M, 1901)
subtenella (M, 1898)
subulata (H, 1906*b*; M, 1913*a*)
tenella (T) (Fig. 22. A)
vanderystii (DH)
veruina (M, 1909)
wallichii (A)

* Species marked with an asterisk might well be included in the next category.

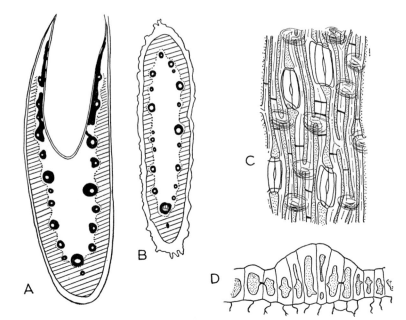

F IG. 23. XYRIDACEAE. Leaf anatomy in *Achlyphila disticha*.

A. T.S. leaf sheath (×8). B. T.S. blade (×8). C. Lamina epidermis, surface view (×50). D. Lamina epidermis, in T.S. (×80).

(c) Approximately equal numbers of compound and simple bundles

bahiana (M, 1901)
fimbriata (T)
glaucescens (M, 1908)
hymenachne (T) (Fig. 22.
  N)

jupicai (T)
lomatophylla (T)
minarum (T) (Fig. 21. C)
montana (T)
rubrolimbata (T)

schizachne (T) (Fig. 22.
  M)
spruceana (M, 1901)
vestita (M, 1898, 1909)
zahlbruckneri (H, 1906b)

(iii) *Total number of veins (including marginal veins)*

(a) Leaves with fewer than 10 veins (e.g. Fig. 22. A–C)

acutifolia (M, 1913a)
anceps (A)
bahiana (M, 1901)
brevifolia (T)
brunnea (N, 1902)
calostachys (M, 1909)
connectens (M, 1925a)
densa (DH)
elliottii (T)
extensula (M, 1898)
filifolia (M, 1909)
filiformis (DH)

foliolata (DH)
gardneri (M, 1901)
*gracilescens (M, 1898)
gracilis (T)
guianensis (H, 1906b)
kwangolana (DH)
lacera (SM; T)
lanuginosa (M, 1909)
montivaga (T)
quinquenervis (M, 1909)
regnellii (M, 1909)

riedeliana (M, 1908)
*rigida (M, 1909)
sphaerocephala (DH)
stenophylla (M, 1913a)
subtenella (M, 1898)
subulata (H, 1906b; M,
  1913a)
tenella (T)
uninervis (M, 1908, 1909)
vacillans (M, 1892)
wallichii (A)

* Species marked with an asterisk sometimes have more than 10 veins.

(b) Leaves with 10–20 veins (e.g. Figs. 21. C; 22. I)

brevifolia (A)
*capensis (T) (Fig. 22. F)
dusenii (M, 1925a)
fallax (T) (Fig. 22. H)
flabelliformis (T) (Fig. 22.
  G)
goyazensis (M, 1898, 1909)

*lanata (T)
lomatophylla (T)
melanopoda (T)
minarum (T)
montana (T)
*operculata (T) (Fig. 22.
  I)

paulensis (M, 1925a)
rigidaeformis (M, 1896,
  1909)
*spruceana (M, 1901)
teres var. obscuriceps (M,
  1901, 1909)
*vestita (M, 1898, 1909)

* Species marked with an asterisk sometimes have fewer than 10 veins.

(c) Broad leaves with more than 20 veins (e.g. Fig. 22. K, O)

caroliniana (T)
fimbriata (T)
flexuosa (T) (Fig. 22. K)
glaucescens (M, 1908)
hymenachne (T) (Fig. 22.
  N)

indica (T)
involucrata (T) (Fig. 22.
  O)
jupicai (T)
macrocephala (T)
neocaledonica (T)

rubrolimbata (T)
schizachne (T) (Fig. 22.
  M)
smalliana (T) (Fig. 22. L)
teres (M, 1909)
veruina (M, 1898, 1909)

Individual simple **vascular bundles** with vascular tissues somewhat like those of certain grasses (Fig. 20. B). Outer parenchymatous sheath of thin-walled, often chlorenchymatous cells sometimes indistinctly differentiated from mesophyll (e.g. *X. gracilis* and *lanata*); inner sclerotic sheath always well developed and complete around larger veins, of thick-walled cells but varying from massive (*X. melanopoda*) to poorly developed (*X. caroliniana*). Vascular tissues of larger vb's including a well-developed protoxylem lacuna, 2 wide metaxylem vessels, a strand of phloem cells (often regularly arranged). Large vascular strands in compound veins resembling those of simple veins (Fig. 20. A). Outer sheath of compound veins often incomplete or indistinct; inner sheath usually massive and well developed.

Transverse veins rarely present. Leaf **margin** commonly different from rest of blade, except in more terete-leaved spp. Epidermis of margin usually without stomata, with thickened walls, often slightly to markedly papillose with a transition to prominent hairs in some spp. (Fig. 20. D–F). Marginal cells in *X. anceps* overlapping and resembling a multiseriate epidermis. Margin including a purely fibrous strand in a few spp., e.g. *X. gardneri, guianensis, lomatophylla, rubrolimbata, stenocephala*, the arrangement of sclerotic cells, as seen in T.S., of diagnostic value. Marginal or sub-marginal vein (Fig. 20. C) commonly enlarged as a prominent rib, bi- or tri-polar, and its largest vb orientated perpendicular to remaining, often wholly simple, bundles throughout the leaf as a whole.

(iii) *Leaf sheath*

Outer epidermis as in blade, but walls thicker, stomata fewer. Inner epidermis usually thin-walled and without stomata. Mesophyll becoming colourless and starch-filled towards base. Air-canals frequent, pectinating with vb's but not usually continuous into blade. Simple or compound vb's arranged in a single series within each wing of the sheath, their continuation into the blade and complete or incomplete pectination producing 1 or 2 series; 1 series with apparent 'abnormal' orientation (e.g. Fig. 21. A). Dorsal keel often including a conspicuous vb, or a purely fibrous strand as in the margin of the blade, e.g. *X. lomatophylla.*

ACHLYPHILA (Fig. 23)

Differs from *Xyris* in the following anatomical features:

(i) *Lamina*

Hairs absent. **Epidermis**; cells with bluntly pointed, sometimes overlapping ends so as to appear biseriate in T.S. Walls massively and more or less uniformly thickened, anticlinal walls conspicuously pitted; distinct transverse protuberance of ends of cells producing a v. irregular epidermal outline (Fig. 23. C–D). **Margin**; cells most conspicuously protuberant, even shortly ciliate. **Mesophyll** with a peripheral chlorenchymatous layer including a superficial palisade, interrupted by substomatal chambers; chlorenchyma surrounding a central colourless region of slightly thick-walled cells (Fig. 23. B). **Vascular bundles** restricted to periphery of central parenchyma (Fig. 23. B), outer sheath continuous with colourless parenchyma. Inner bundle sheath well developed, complete around all vb's. Vascular tissues without protoxylem lacunae; metaxylem including irregular series of elements, without two obvious wide vessels and so unlike *Xyris.*

(ii) *Leaf sheath*

Ligule absent. Sheath (Fig. 23. A) including an adaxial band of thick-walled colourless parenchyma continuous with that of the blade. Sclerotic sheaths of

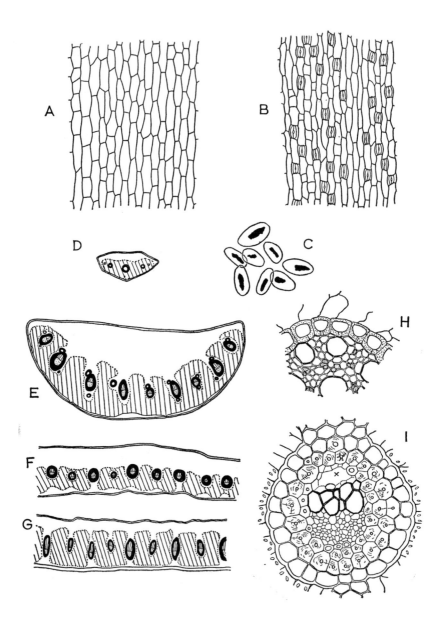

112

Fɪɢ. 24. XYRIDACEAE. *Abolboda* and *Orectanthe*.

A–B. *Abolboda grandis.* Epidermis of lamina, surface view (×20).
  A. Adaxial. B. Abaxial.

C. *Abolboda linearifolia.* Starch grains from rhizome (×120).

D–G. T.S. lamina (×8).

  D. *Abolboda acicularis.* E. *Abolboda linearifolia.* F. *Abolboda macrostachya* var. *macrostachya.* G. *Orectanthe ptaritepuiana.*

H. *Abolboda acicularis* var. *acicularis.* T.S. peripheral part of stele of root (×73).

I. *Abolboda macrostachya.* T.S. vb. from lamina (×80).
  ×—protoxylem lacuna.

marginal bundles irregular, continuous with each other and with sclerotic cells of inner epidermis, sclerotic layer continuous with all vb's in leaf base.

ABOLBODA (Fig. 24. A–F, H, I)

Leaves spirally arranged. Leaf lanceolate, eligulate, with a broad, sheathing base, the sheath not keeled or flattened as in *Xyris*. Leaf apex commonly with a blunt terminal appendage.

(i) *Lamina*

Always dorsiventral. **Hairs** absent. **Epidermis** without conspicuous papillae or rugae. Adaxial epidermis uniform (Fig. 24. A), cells longitudinally extended, more or less rectangular. Walls thin, outer wall never much thicker than remaining walls, walls more or less uniformly thickened in *A. acicularis*. Epidermal cells sometimes of irregular sizes and in T.S. resembling a multiseriate epidermis, as in *A. macrostachya*. Abaxial epidermis (Fig. 24. B) sometimes differentiated into distinct, narrow costal and wide intercostal bands; costal cells narrower and more longitudinally extended than short, wide, irregular intercostal cells.

Stomata always restricted to abaxial surface, either irregularly distributed or restricted to intercostal bands, never arranged in regular longitudinal files. Lateral subsidiary cells, as in *Xyris*, narrow and with thin walls but, unlike *Xyris*, as deep as the normal epidermal cells. Terminal subsidiary cells usually absent, except for frequent short polar cells in *A. linearifolia* and *macrostachya*. Guard cells asymmetrical, each with a conspicuous outer ledge; inner ledge usually absent. Guard cells in *A. acicularis, grandis, macrostachya* usually appreciably shallower than lateral subsidiary cells, but otherwise scarcely shallower than rest of epidermis.

Hypodermis (Fig. 24. D–F) of colourless, thick-walled cells conspicuous and well developed in the larger-leaved spp., except towards the leaf apex; inconspicuous except in the leaf apex in the smaller-leaved spp. Adaxial hypodermis multiseriate and conspicuous in *A. ciliata, grandis, linearifolia, macrostachya, sprucei* becoming less well developed marginally and towards the leaf apex. Adaxial hypodermis absent, or represented distally by only 1 (rarely more) layer of indistinct colourless cells in *A. acaulis*. Abaxial hypodermis always less well developed than adaxial; mostly 1–2-layered, sometimes restricted to a narrow median strand, as in *A. acicularis*; wholly absent in *A. sprucei*. Otherwise a continuous abaxial hypodermis of 1–2 layers in larger-leaved spp., interrupted by substomatal chambers and becoming discontinuous marginally and distally. Hypodermal cells often somewhat collenchymatous, described as gelatinous-walled by Carlquist (1960). Hypodermal cells commonly continuous with bundle sheath cells in larger-leaved spp., forming complete or incomplete buttresses.

Mesophyll not usually with distinct adaxial palisade layers, except in *A. ciliata, grandis*, and varieties of *A. macrostachya*; mesophyll cells fairly compact, not lobed, sometimes transversely extended. Centre of mesophyll in *A. acaulis* and *acicularis* including 2 or more irregular air-lacunae, incompletely filled with large, inflated colourless cells; air-lacunae occurring only proximally in *A. ciliata*. Similar lacunae in *A. linearifolia* pectinating with vb's. **Vascular bundles** equidistant from each surface and in one series, always orientated with xylem towards adaxial surface; almost invariably simple. Principal vb's in some of the larger-leaved spp. buttressed to adaxial hypodermis, rarely to each hypodermis as in *A. linearifolia*; in smaller-leaved spp. vb's mostly independent of surface layers. Outer sheath of conspicuous colourless cells complete around vb's, often continuous adaxially with hypodermis, less commonly in contact with abaxial hypodermis. Outer sheath cells in *A. macrostachya* with outermost walls conspicuously thickened (Fig. 24. I). Inner sclerotic sheath well developed and continuous around large veins, often 2-layered, sometimes 4-layered in varieties of *A. macrostachya*; inner sheath incomplete or absent around small veins. Vascular tissues in large bundles usually including a protoxylem lacuna, but with several wide metaxylem elements, rather than 2 as in *Xyris* (Fig. 24. I). Veins commonly in *A. linearifolia*, rarely in other spp., compound with 1 or 2 small vascular strands associated with large vb. Transverse veins not recorded.

(ii) *Leaf sheath*

Not distinctly articulate with the blade. Chlorenchyma absent from uniform ground tissue. Parenchymatous bundle extensions common, pectinating with air-lacunae. Hypodermal tissues well developed. Margin in *A. ciliata* becoming ciliate by irregular breakdown of scarious margin.

ORECTANTHE (Fig. 24. G)

Resembles closely broader-leaved spp. of *Abolboda* from which it differs as follows. **Epidermis** with inner walls thicker than outer, especially in *O. sceptrum*. Lateral subsidiary cells of **stomata** somewhat shallower than other epidermal cells. **Hypodermis** well developed on both surfaces, 2–3-layered adaxially, 1-layered abaxially. Most large vb's buttressed to each hypodermis. **Mesophyll** of lobed, elongated cells, appearing palisade-like in T.S.; air-lacunae absent.

INFLORESCENCE AXIS (SCAPE) (Fig. 25)

Naked in all genera except *Abolboda*, with 2 paired bracts. Peduncle ribbed or winged, wings often ciliate.

XYRIS (Fig. 25. C)

Surface sometimes ribbed (e.g. *X. caroliniana*) or winged (e.g. *X. complanata*, the wings markedly sclerotic). **Epidermis** usually resembling that of blade; epidermal cells of ribs or wings often specialized like those of leaf margin (cf. Duvigneaud and Homes). **Cortex** narrow, chlorenchymatous, usually 2–4 cells wide. Cortical cells said to resemble mesophyll of lamina in some diagnostic features, e.g. lobed chlorenchyma cells of Australian spp., as in *X. gracilis, lanata, operculata, ustulata*; stellate cells in *X. complanata, lacera, subulata*; spongy cells in *X. brevifolia, capensis*, etc. (Malmanche). Cortical cells somewhat palisade-like in several spp. Air-lacunae occasionally present,

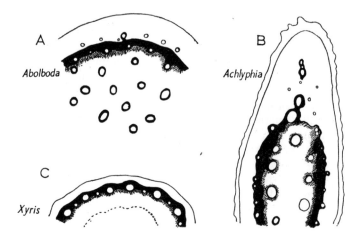

FIG. 25. XYRIDACEAE. T.S. inflorescence axes (×8).

A. *Abolboda macrostachya* var. *angustior*. B. *Achlyphila disticha*. C. *Xyris smalliana*.

as in *X. caroliniana,* beneath shallow ribs. Cortex normally without vb's, but vb's in wings in *X. laxifolia* and *schizachne* according to Poulsen. Innermost cortical layer compact, colourless, resembling an endodermis in T.S. but without Casparian strips. **Central cylinder** delimited by a conspicuous fluted sclerotic cylinder of thick-walled cells sometimes abruptly transitional to central ground parenchyma cells. Sclerotic cylinder including a regular system of more or less alternate large and small vb's. Large vb's with 'grass-type' of construction as in leaf, small vb's with reduced vascular tissue. Centre of axis always hollow due to breakdown of central ground parenchyma cells. *X. capensis* anomalous according to Malmanche, with no distinction between cortex and central cylinder. This sp. characterized by 5 large vb's buttressed to surface alternating with 5 small bundles independent of surface layers; chlorenchyma restricted to 5 shallow bands each opposite a small vb. This construction recalling base of scape in more orthodox spp. (e.g. Duvigneaud and Homes, *X. filiformis*).

ABOLBODA AND ORECTANTHE (Fig. 25. A)

Following important differences from *Xyris* noted. **Hypodermis** of 1–2 layers of thick-walled, colourless cells commonly developed, especially in larger spp. **Cortex** wholly colourless distally, sometimes including isolated vb's, especially in *Orectanthe.* Inner ring of cortical vb's in contact with outer side of sclerotic cylinder, rarely embedded within cylinder. **Central cylinder**; centre of axis solid, including scattered vb's, outermost bundles in contact with inner face of or embedded within sclerotic cylinder. Individual vb's with several equivalent metaxylem vessels, sometimes amphivasal or even biconcentric in *A. poarchon* according to Malmanche, but often with 2 wide metaxylem vessels as in the 'grass-type'.

ACHLYPHILA (Fig. 25. B)

Inflorescence axis flattened, somewhat intermediate between *Abolboda* and *Orectanthe,* on the one hand, and *Xyris,* on the other. Cortical vb's in the prominent wings. Small vb's adjacent to outer limit of sclerotic cylinder, as in *Abolboda,* but absent from the central region, as in *Xyris.*

RHIZOME

Rhizomes usually with congested internodes; in *Orectanthe* and larger spp. of *Abolboda* forming a stout, almost woody, axis. Rhizome in *Achlyphila* with distinct long internodes. Anatomical features indicate two groups:

(i) *Xyris* and *Achlyphila*

The following notes refer to *Xyris,* the differences between *Achlyphila* and this being recorded subsequently.

Peripheral cortical cells sometimes suberized. **Cortex** irregular, often quite wide as in *X. operculata;* narrow in *X. lanata.* Cortex including numerous obvious leaf and root traces, but without an independent cortical vascular system. Leaf traces in cortex always with a complete sclerotic sheath. Ground parenchyma cells sometimes loose and lobed. Inner limit of cortex without an obvious endodermis, but usually delimited from central cylinder by a continuous **sclerotic layer** of short, thick-walled, and conspicuously pitted elements. Sclerotic cylinder sometimes massive as in *X. lanata* and especially in *X. gracilis*; sometimes indistinct, 1-layered and incomplete, as in *X. operculata*. Sclerotic sheathing tissues of leaf traces and thick-walled endodermis of roots continuous with sclerotic cylinder of rhizome. **Central cylinder** including an indistinct peripheral vascular plexus immediately within sclerotic cylinder. Central tissues including scattered vb's, each irregular in outline and commonly with an amphivasal construction. Each vb in *X. lanata* and *gracilis* sheathed conspicuously by thick-walled cells, the sheaths of adjacent bundles contiguous and producing an irregular network of sclerotic cells separated by indistinct, thin-walled parenchyma. Centre of central cylinder almost always occupied by an unvasculated medulla of thin-walled ground parenchyma cells. Peripheral ground parenchyma cells of central cylinder sometimes thick-walled.

Achlyphila is closely similar to *Xyris*, but conspicuous differences, possibly related to the presence of long internodes, include the following: **Epidermis** persistent, thin-walled. **Cortex** narrow, without independent vb's; leaf traces with sclerotic sheath cells adjacent to xylem only. Inner limit of cortex differentiated as an **endodermis** with irregular wall thickenings, the cells appearing U-shaped in T.S. **Sclerotic cylinder,** immediately within endodermis, of thick-walled cells abruptly delimited from remaining ground parenchyma of central cylinder. **Central cylinder** including scattered vb's, those at the periphery embedded in the sclerotic cylinder. Each vb with sclerotic sheathing tissues completely enclosing amphivasal vascular tissues.

(ii) *Abolboda* and *Orectanthe*

The following notes refer to *Abolboda* alone, *Orectanthe* differing in ways indicated subsequently.

Surface layers often suberized. **Small-stemmed spp.,** e.g. *A. acaulis, acicularis, americana, ciliata* most resembling *Xyris*, according to Carlquist, with wide **cortex** including vb's of two kinds: (*a*) with a massive sheath of short sclereids, mostly adjacent to xylem only; (*b*) small vb's without sclerotic sheaths, interpreted as possible independent cortical strands. **Endodermis** absent. **Central cylinder** abruptly delimited from cortex by a wide band of sclerotic tissue including all central vb's. Central parenchymatous ground tissue without vb's, but sometimes including a strand of sclerotic tissue as in *A. acaulis* and *acicularis*.

Large-stemmed spp. without distinction between cortex and central cylinder except for peripheral starch-free layers of ground parenchyma. Central region including uniformly scattered vb's, or bundles sometimes more congested towards periphery of starch-bearing zone. Sclerenchyma restricted to bundle sheaths of central vb's, usually adjacent to the xylem only. Remaining bundles without sclerotic sheathing tissues and interpreted as the proximal part of leaf traces remote from their insertion into the leaf. Vb's in *A. macrostachya* var. *angustior* almost always with sclerotic sheath, the sheath often complete. All vb's in *A. sprucei* with sclerotic sheaths, the sheaths of adjacent bundles often being confluent.

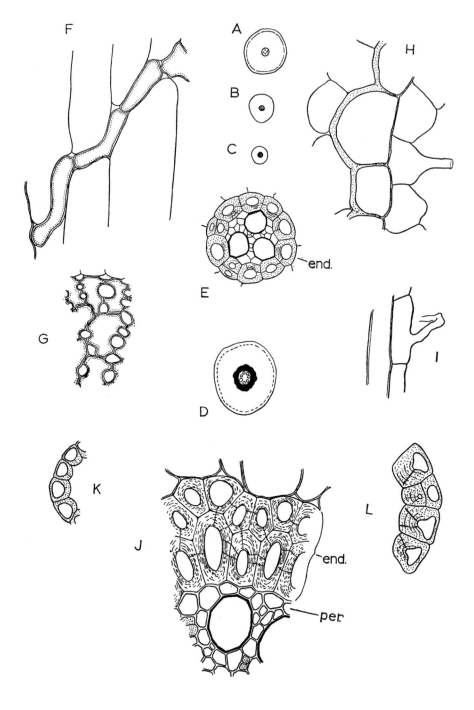

120

Fig. 26. XYRIDACEAE. Root structure in *Xyris*.

A–D. T.S. root (×7).

A. *X. caroliniana.* B. *X. flexuosa.* C. *X. brevifolia.* D. *X. lanata.*

E. *X. brevifolia.* T.S. Stele (×290).

F–I. *X. smalliana.* Cortical features (×290).

F. L.S. middle cortex, short-cells forming incipient transverse dia-phragms. G. Diaphragm cells as seen in T.S. H. T.S. surface layers including piliferous layer and exodermis. I. L.S. piliferous layer with root-hair cell.

J. *X. lanata.* T.S. periphery of stele with biseriate endodermis (×290).

K–L. Endodermal cells in T.S. (×290).

K. *X. flexuosa.* L. *X. operculata.*

end.—endodermis; per.—pericycle.

Orectanthe most like *A. sprucei,* with the vb's at the periphery of the central cylinder to form a continuous sclerotic cylinder; central vb's independent of this mechanical cylinder. Central ground parenchyma in *O. ptaritepuiana* wholly sclerotic.

ROOT (Figs. 24. H; 26)

Usually filiform, rarely somewhat fleshy as in *Xyris gracilis.* Mechanical roots said by Nilsson to be distinguished from remaining roots, in *Xyris baldwiniana, hymenachne, montivaga,* and *Abolboda vaginata,* because of well-developed sclerotic tissues, especially in pericyclic region and peripheral cortical layers. Root development in 2 spp. of *Xyris* described by Pillai and Pillai (1961). **Root-hairs** (Fig. 26. I) usually arising towards one end of an epidermal cell; root-hair cells not usually shorter than unmodified cells, sometimes in irregular vertical series. **Exodermis** (Fig. 26. H) of one or more compact, somewhat ligno-suberized layers usually differentiated beneath large-celled piliferous layer; absent from *Xyris brevifolia.* Exodermal cells often larger and thicker-walled than remaining cortical cells, or with slightly uneven wall thickenings, the cells U-shaped in T.S. (e.g. *X. lanata*). Middle cortex often narrow, sometimes consisting of a single layer of large cells as in *Abolboda sprucei* and *Xyris brevifolia.* Middle cortical cells in section *Euxyris* of *Xyris* said by Nilsson to consist of radial plates of cells separated by wide intercellular spaces, in contrast to more uniform cortex of section *Nematopus.* Horizontal but irregular plates of short-lobed or stellate cortical cells (Fig. 26. F, G) cut off from ends of long-cells forming either irregular **transverse diaphragms,** or an irregular reticulum in many spp. (e.g. *Xyris caroliniana*); short-cells sometimes absent. Innermost cortical cells, up to 6 layers deep, frequently uniformly thickened and resembling endodermal cells, as in *Xyris gracilis,* the endodermis then often mistakenly described as multiseriate (as probably by Malme and Nilsson in numerous *Xyris* spp.). **Endodermis** always conspicuous, of large, uniformly thickened cells, but variation in amount and distribution of wall thickening said to be of diagnostic value in *Abolboda* by Malme (1925*a*) and Carlquist (1960). Thus cells in T.S. uniformly thickened in *A. pulchella* and *vaginata*; with distinct U-shaped thickening, outer wall thin in *A. poeppiggii, grandis, macrostachya*; more or less intermediate in *A. poarchon* and *abbreviata.* Multiseriate endodermis, truly developed by occasional tangential division of endodermal mother cells into two narrower daughter cells, observed in *Xyris lanata* (Fig. 26. J). **Stele** usually narrow in relation to cortex (cf. Fig. 26. A–D). Pericycle of small, thin-walled indistinct cells only conspicuous in wide steles (e.g. *X. lanata*), occasionally or frequently interrupted by vessels lying adjacent to endodermis (e.g. *X. brevifolia,* Fig. 26. E, and in *X. nilagirensis, platycaulis, subulata* according to van Tieghem). Stele diarch to polyarch, with 2 or more peripheral vessels; without radial series of protoxylem elements forming distinct xylem poles. Protoxylem either absent or represented by isolated narrow elements. Number of peripheral vessels accorded systematic significance by earlier authors, but varying quite widely in different individuals of one sp. Presence or absence of 1 or more central vessels also accorded systematic significance. *Xyris* rarely with 1 central vessel, as in *X. capensis, caroliniana, gymnoptera, lacera, sellowiana* according to van Tieghem; vessels usually restricted to periphery of stele. Vessels scattered uniformly throughout stele in large roots of most *Abolboda* spp., e.g. *A. acicularis* (Fig. 24. H), *longifolia, macrostachya* but, not in wide roots of *Achlyphila*. Phloem elements not usually grouped in peripheral phloem strands, but scattered irregularly throughout the central ground tissue (Fig. 24. H).

SECRETORY, STORAGE, AND CONDUCTING ELEMENTS

Crystals. Calcium oxalate as small crystals recorded in mesophyll of leaf in several spp. of *Xyris* by Solereder and Meyer. Crystal sand observed in rhizome of *Abolboda*. Small crystals sometimes included within thick outer epidermal wall in leaf sheath of *Xyris*, less commonly also in the leaf blade as in *X. minarum* (Fig. 18. F–G).

Tannin usually restricted to epidermal cells, its distribution accorded taxonomic significance; sometimes absent; otherwise either present in all cells or scattered irregularly in certain cells, a condition readily recognizable in surface view.

Starch restricted either to rhizome, as in large-stemmed spp. of *Abolboda*, or commonly to ground parenchyma cells of leaf base, as in *Xyris*. Grains in *Xyris* probably always compound (Fig. 19. I); grains in *Abolboda* large, simple, ellipsoidal, or irregularly rounded (Fig. 24. C).

Xylem. Vessels with simple perforation plates recorded in all parts of all examined spp. of Xyridaceae. Perforations often in oblique or v. oblique end walls. Vessel elements in peripheral vascular plexus of rhizome in some *Xyris* spp., e.g. *X. lanata*, with more or less circular bordered pits; otherwise vessel pitting scalariform.

Tracheids in leaf tip of some *Abolboda* spp. with exceptionally broad annular or helical thickenings, extending up to half-way into the cell lumen, according to Carlquist.

TAXONOMIC NOTES

The Xyridaceae is a very heterogeneous family, but it is accepted as a natural unit, e.g. by Hamann (1961). The relationships of the genera have been discussed by Carlquist (1960), who finds that anatomical evidence fully substantiates that they are distinct. The genera are not equally closely related. The family falls into 2 groups, *Achlyphila* and *Xyris*, on the one hand, *Abolboda* and *Orectanthe*, on the other. *Abolboda* and *Orectanthe* are very closely related, but the affinities between *Achlyphila* and *Xyris* are not close and in some respects *Achlyphila* resembles *Abolboda* more than it does *Xyris*. This recent discovery of *Achlyphila* as a link between *Abolboda* and *Xyris* makes it difficult to accept Takhtajan's (1959) decision to distribute the genera among two families, Abolbodaceae and Xyridaceae *sensu stricto*.

The long-held contention that anatomical characters in *Xyris* are of specific diagnostic value may be true in a limited sense, especially when spp. within a restricted area are compared (e.g. Duvigneaud and Homes). Many anatomical features seem to be ecological adaptations and their taxonomic significance is restricted. This is probably why it is impossible to define groups of spp. within *Xyris* on an anatomical basis. Features of suggested specific or even sub-specific diagnostic value are recorded by Carlquist for *Abolboda*, *Achlyphila*, and *Orectanthe*.

GENERA AND SPECIES REPORTED ON IN THE LITERATURE

Arber (1922) *Abolboda grandis* Gris. var. *minor*, *Xyris anceps* Lam., *X. asperata* Kunth, *X. brevifolia* Michx., *X. wallichii* Kunth; leaf.

Carlquist (1960) *Abolboda acaulis* Maguire, *A. acicularis* Idrobo and Sm. var. *acicularis*, *A. americana* (Aubl.) Lanj., *A. ciliata* Maguire and Wurdack, *A. linearifolia* Maguire, *A. macrostachya* Spruce ex Malme var. *angustior* Maguire, *A. macrostachya* Spruce ex Malme var. *macrostachya*, *A. macrostachya* Spruce ex Malme var. *robustior* Steyermark, *A. sprucei* Malme, *Achlyphila disticha* Maguire and Wurdack, *Orectanthe ptaritepuiana* (Steyermark) Maguire, *O. sceptrum* (Oliver) Maguire, *O. sceptrum* (Oliver) Maguire ssp. *occidentalis* Maguire; all parts.

Duvigneaud and Homes (1955) *Xyris densa* Malme, *X. filiformis* Lam., *X. foliolata* Nilss., *X. hildebrandtii* Nilss., *X. imitatrix* Malme, *X. kwangolana* Duv. and Hom., *X. sphaerocephala* Malme, *X. vanderystii* Malme; leaf, scape.

Heimerl (1906*b*) *Xyris calcarata* Heim., *X. guianensis* Steud., *X. rubrolimbata* Heim., *X. subulata* Ruiz et Pav., *X. wawrae* Heim., *X. zahlbruckneri* Heim.; leaf.

Kral (1966) *Xyris ambigua* Beyr., *X. baldwiniana* Schult., *X. brevifolia* Michx., *X. caroliniana* Walt., *X. difformis* Chapm. var. *difformis*, & var. *curtissii* (Malme) Kral, *X. elliottii* Chapm., *X. fimbriata* Ell., *X. flabelliformis* Chapm., *X. iridifolia* Chapm., *X. isoetifolia* Kral, *X. jupicai* L. C. Rich., *X. platylepis* Chapm., *X. scabrifolia* Harper, *X. serotina* Chapm., *X. smalliana* Nash, *X. stricta* Chapm., *X. torta* J. E. Sm.; leaf epidermis.

Malmanche (1919) *Abolboda brasiliensis* Kunth, *A. poarchon* Seub., *Xyris brevifolia* Michx., *X. capensis* Thunb., *X. caroliniana* Walt., *X. complanata* R. Br., *X. fimbriata* Elliot, *X. gracilis* R. Br., *X. indica* L., *X. lacera* R. Br., *X. lanata* R. Br., *X. pauciflora* Willd., *X. robusta* Mart., *X. schoenoides* Nilss., *X. subulata* Ruiz et Pav.; scape.

Malme (1896) *Abolboda longifolia* Malme, *Xyris fallax* Malme, *X. nilssonii* Malme, *X. rigidaeformis* Malme, *X. stenocephala* Malme; leaf, root.

Malme (1898) *Xyris extensula* Malme; leaf, root. *X. goyazensis* Malme; leaf, root. *X. gracilescens* Malme; leaf. *X. platystachya* Nilss.; root. *X. radula* Malme; leaf, root. *X. subtenella* Malme; leaf, root. *X. vacillans* Malme; leaf, root. *X. veruina* Malme; leaf. *X. vestita* Malme; leaf.

Malme (1901) *Abolboda macrostachya* Spruce, *Xyris bahiana* Malme, *X. gardneri* Malme, *X. spruceana* Malme, *X. teres* Malme; leaf, root.

Malme (1908) *Xyris glaucescens* Malme, *X. riedeliana* Malme, *X. uninervis* Malme; leaf.

Malme (1909) *Xyris calostachys* Pouls., *X. filifolia* Nilss., *X. goyazensis* Malme, *X. insignis* Nilss., *X. lanuginosa* Seub., *X. quinquenervis* Malme, *X. regnellii* Nilss., *X. rigida* Kunth, *X. rigidaeformis* Malme, *X. teres* Nilss., *X. uninervis* Malme, *X. veruina* Malme, *X. vestita* Malme; leaf.

Malme (1913*a*) *Xyris laevigata* Nilss., *X. longifolia* Mart., *X. montivaga* Kunth, *X. neglecta* Nilss., *X. platystachya* Nilss., *X. spruceana* Malme, *X. stenophylla* Nilss.; leaf epidermis; together with frequent notes on other spp. scattered throughout the text.

Malme (1913*b*) *Xyris baldwiniana* Schult., *X. bicarinata* Gris., *X. fallax* Malme, *X. flexuosa* Muehl., *X. navicularis* Gris.; leaf epidermis; together with frequent notes on other spp. scattered throughout the text.

Malme (1925*a*) *Abolboda abbreviata* Malme, *A. grandis* Gris., *A. macrostachya* Spruce, *A. poarchon* Seub., *A. poeppiggii* Kunth, *A. pulchella* Humb. et Bonpl., *A. vaginata* Spreng.; root. *Xyris connectens* Malme, *X. dusenii* Malme, *X. paulensis* Malme; leaf, root.

Malme (1925*b*) *Xyris ekmanii* Malme, *X. intermedia* Malme; leaf.

Nilsson (1892) miscellaneous notes on numerous spp.

Nilsson (1902) *Xyris brunnea* Nilss.; leaf.

Pillai and Pillai (1961) *Xyris anceps* Lamk., *X. schoenoides* Mart.; root apex.

Poulsen (1892) *Xyris alata* Pouls.; leaf. *X. angustifolia* Pouls.; leaf, rhizome. *X. asperata* Kunth; leaf, scape. *X. calocephala* Pouls.; leaf. *X. montivaga* Kunth; leaf. *X. plantaginea* Kunth; leaf, scape, stem. *X. schizachne* Mart.; leaf. *X. teretifolia* Pouls.; leaf.

Smith and Downs (1960) *Abolboda egleri* Sm. and Downs, *Xyris archeri* Sm. and Downs, *X. egleri* Sm. and Downs, *X. hatsbachii* Sm. and Downs, *X. mima* Sm. and Downs, *X. moraesii* Sm. and Downs, *X. piresiana* Sm. and Downs, *X. ramboi* Sm. and Downs, *X. reitzii* Sm. and Downs, *X. tomentosa* Sm. and Downs; leaf.

Solereder and Meyer (1929) *Xyris caroliniana* Walt.; leaf, root, scape. *X. indica* L.; leaf, root. *X. lacera* R. Br.; leaf, scape. *X. lanata* R. Br.; leaf, scape, root. *X. pauciflora* Willd.; leaf.

Staudermann (1924) *Xyris brevifolia* Michx., *X. flabelliformis* Chapm., *X. platylepis* Chapm.; hairs.

Van Tieghem (1887) *Abolboda macrostachya, poeppiggii, Xyris capensis, caroliniana, gymnoptera, lacera, nilagirensis, platycaulis, sellowiana, subulata*; root.

MATERIAL EXAMINED BY THE AUTHOR

From dried material supplied by Dr. Lyman B. Smith from specimens in U.S. National Herbarium (US, with collector's name and number), from the pickled collection made by Dr. V. I. Cheadle (V. I. C., with collection number), from Dr. D.W. Bierhorst (CU,with collection number), in the pickled collection at the Jodrell Laboratory (Jodrell), or collected by myself (P. B. T., with collection number). Additional observations on material in collections of Dr. Sherwin Carlquist (see Carlquist, 1960 on p. 124).

Abolboda acicularis Idrobo and Sm.; (US) Schultes and Cabrera 19966. Leaf.
A. grandis Gris.; (US) Schultes 13179. Leaf.
A. macrostachya Spruce ex Malme; (US) Maguire 44178. Leaf.
Achlyphila disticha Maguire and Wurdack; (US) Maguire 42402. Leaf, scape.
Xyris anceps Lam.; (US) Drouet 2245. Leaf.
X. brevifolia Michx.; P. B. T. 24.I.63F; Florida. All parts.
X. capensis Thunb.; V. I. C. CA 764; Cape, S. Africa. All parts.
X. caroliniana Walt.; V. I. C. M 482; Rhode Island. All parts.
X. caroliniana Walt. var. *caroliniana*; (US) Pittier 14294. Leaf.
X. caroliniana Walt. var. *major* (Mart.) Idrobo and Smith; (US) Mello Barreto 4361. Leaf.
X. elliottii Chapm.; P. B. T. 31.III.63E; Florida. All parts.
X. fallax Malme; (US) Egler 1733. Leaf.

X. fimbriata Ell.; P. B. T. s.n.; Florida. All parts.

X. flabelliformis Chapm.; P. B. T. s.n.; Florida. All parts.

X. flexuosa Muhl.; P. B. T. s.n.; Florida. All parts.

X. gracilis R. Br.; V. I. C. CA 97; Australia. All parts.

X. hymenachne Mart.; (US) L. B. Smith 1982. Leaf.

X. indica L.; P. B. T. s.n.; Malaya. All parts.

X. involucrata Nees; (US) Tamayo 3050. Leaf.

X. jupicai Rich.; P. B. T. 2.VII.62E; Trinidad. All parts.

X. lacera Pohl.; (US) Malme 3194. Leaf.

X. lanata R. Br.; V. I. C. CA 468; Perth, Australia. Leaf.

X. lomatophylla Mart.; (US) Schultes and Cabrera 19978. Leaf.

X. macrocephala Vahl; Jodrell. All parts.

X. melanopoda Sm. and Downs; (US) Mello Barreto 3686. Leaf.

X. minarum Seub.; (US) Smith et al. 6768. Leaf.

X. montana H. Ries; Zimmermann s.n.; Massachusetts. All parts.

X. montivaga Kunth; (US) Segedad Vianna 3262. Leaf.

X. neocaledonica Rendle; (CU) Bierhorst NC 220. All parts.

X. operculata Labill.; V. I. C. CA 187; Brisbane. All parts.

X. rubrolimbata Heim.; (US) Williams 14280. Leaf.

X. schizachne Mart.; (US) Smith and Klein 8473. Leaf.

X. smalliana Nash.; V. I. C. M 484; Rhode Island. All parts.

X. tenella Kunth; (US) Hatschbach 5120. Leaf.

BIBLIOGRAPHY FOR XYRIDACEAE

Note. Taxonomic works have mostly been referred to only when they include anatomical information. This, however, is very extensive for *Xyris*.

ARBER, A. (1922) Leaves of the Farinosae. *Bot. Gaz.* **74**, 80–94.

CARLQUIST, S. (1960) Anatomy of Guayana Xyridaceae: *Abolboda, Orectanthe,* and *Achlyphila. Mem. N.Y. bot. Gdn* **10**, no. 2, 65–117.

CONERT, H. J. (1960) Beiträge zur Systematik und Anatomie der Xyridaceae. Cited by Hamann (1961). Manuscript in Bibliothek des Botan. Museums Berlin-Dahlem.

DUVIGNEAUD, P., and HOMES, P. (1955) Géographie de caractères et évolution de la Flora Soudano-Zambézienne. II. Les *Xyris* du Bas-Congo et du Kwango. Aperçu systématique et anatomique. *Bull. Soc. r. Bot. Belg.* **87**, 81–113.

HAMANN, U. (1961) Merkmalsbestand und Verwandtschaftsbeziehungen der Farinosae. *Willdenowia* **2** (5), 639–768.

HEIMERL, A. (1906a) Ergebnisse der Botanischen Expedition . . . Xyridaceae. *Denkschr. Akad. Wiss., Wien* Math.-nat. Kl., **74**, pp. 4.

—— (1906b) Über einige Arten der Gattung *Xyris* aus dem Herbare des Wiener Hofmuseums. *Annln naturh. Mus. Wien* **21**, 61–71.

KRAL, R. (1960) The genus *Xyris* in Florida. *Rhodora* **62**, 295–319.

—— (1966) *Xyris* (Xyridaceae) of continental United States and Canada. *Sida* **2**, 177–260.

MAGUIRE, B., WURDACK, J. J. et al. (1960) The botany of the Guayana Highland—Part IV. Xyridaceae. *Mem. N.Y. bot. Gdn* **10**, No. 2, 11–15.

MALMANCHE, L. A. (1919) *Contribution à l'étude anatomique des Eriocaulonacées et des familles voisines: Restiacées, Centrolépidacées, Xyridacées, Philydracées, Mayacacées.* Thesis, St. Cloud. pp. 165.

MALME, G. O. A. N. (1896) Die Xyridaceen der ersten Regnell'schen Expedition. *Bih. K. svenska VetenskAkad. Handl.* **22**, III, no. 2, 1–27.

—— (1898) Xyridaceae Brasilienses, praecipue Goyazenses a Glaziou lectae. Ibid. **24**, III, no. 3, 1–20.

—— (1901) Beiträge zur Xyridaceen—Flora Südamerikas. Ibid. **26**, III, no. 19, 1–18.

—— (1908) *Xyrides* austro-americanae novae II. *Reprium nov. Spec. Regni veg.* **5**, 101–3.

—— (1909) Beiträge zur Anatomie der Xyridaceen. *Svensk bot. Tidskr.* **3**, 196–209.

—— (1913*a*) *Xyris* L., Untergattung *Nematopus* (Seubert). Entwurf einer Gliederung. *Ark. Bot.* **13**, no. 3, 1–103.

—— (1913*b*) Die amerikanischen Spezies der Gattung *Xyris* L., Untergattung *Euxyris* (Endlicher). Ibid. no. 8, 1–32.

—— (1925*a*) Xyridologische Beiträge. Ibid. **19**, no. 13, 1–8.

—— (1925*b*) Die Xyridaceen der Insel Cuba. Ibid. no. 19, 1–6.

—— (1930) Xyridaceae, in Engler and Prantl: *Die natürlichen Pflanzenfamilien*, edn. 2, Bd. **15a**, 35–38.

Nilsson, A. (1892) Studien über die Xyrideen. *K. svenska VetenskAkad. Handl.* **24**, no. 14, 1–74.

—— (1893) Einige anatomische Eigenthümlichkeiten der Gattung *Xyris. Bot. Zbl.* **53** (1), 347–8.

—— (1902) Xyridaceae, in Engler, A. Beiträge zur Flora von Afrika. 22. Berichte über die botanischen Ergebnisse der Nyassa-See . . . etc. *Bot. Jb.* **30**, 271.

Pillai, S. K., and Pillai, A. (1961) Root apical organization in monocotyledons—Xyridaceae. *Proc. Indian Acad. Sci.* B **54**, 234–40.

Poulsen, V. A. (1892) Anatomiske studier over *Xyris*—slaegtens vegetative organer. *Vidensk. Meddr dansk naturh. Foren.* 133–52.

Smith, L. B., and Downs, R. J. (1960) Xyridaceae from Brazil. II. *Proc. biol. Soc. Wash.* **73**, 245–60.

Solereder, H., and Meyer, F. J. (1929) Xyridaceae. In *Systematische Anatomie der Monokotyledonen.* Heft IV; 36–50.

Staudermann, W. (1924) Die Haare der Monokotylen. *Bot. Arch.* **8**, 105–84.

Suessenguth, K., and Beyerle, R. (1936) Über die Xyridaceengattung *Abolboda* Humb. et Bonpl. *Bot. Jb.* **67** (2), 132–41.

Takhtajan, A. (1959) *Die Evolution der Angiospermen.* Jena. pp. 344.

Tieghem, P. van (1887) Structure de la racine et disposition des radicelles dans les Centrolépidées, Eriocaulées, Joncées, Mayacées et Xyridées. *J. Bot., Paris* **1**, 305–15.

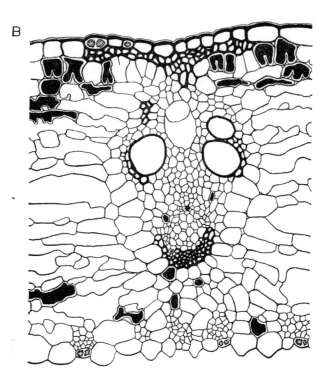

128

FIG. 27. RAPATEACEAE. *Rapatea paludosa* (Rapateeae) T.S. lamina.

A. Adaxial epidermis showing silica-bodies (×365). B. (×45).

RAPATEACEAE

(by SHERWIN CARLQUIST, Rancho Santa Ana Botanic Garden, Claremont, California)

(Figs. 27–29)

SUMMARY

A FAMILY of 16 genera, restricted to northern South America, with the exception of *Maschalocephalus* (Liberia) and *Epidryos* (*Epiphyton*) (northern South America to Panama). With these 2 exceptions, the family is particularly characteristic of the sandstone massifs of the Guayana Highlands. The plants are herbs with short, usually simple and erect subfleshy stems and linear or lanceolate leaves with blades rotated more or less 90°; the lower portion of the leaf is sheathing. Leaves of Rapateaceae are peculiar in the manner in which the lamina, which lies in the same plane as the 2 halves of the leaf base, is joined to the leaf sheath. As noted by Arber (1922), the midrib region is usually displaced to one side of the V-shaped sheath. Where the 2 halves of this sheath are connate below the lamina, the leaf axis is narrow and oval in outline, with bundles in many series. The 2 margins join this axis laterally, and fade into the transition region below the lamina.

Anatomical features of special interest in the family include: close association between silica-bearing epidermal cells and hypodermal fibres (Figs. 27. A; 28. A); **chlorenchyma cells** with infolded walls; large thin-walled non-photosynthetic cells in leaves, collapsing at maturity; large amounts of slime produced in axils of leaves and bracts by uniseriate trichomes. **Hairs** are represented exclusively by uniseriate non-glandular slime-producing trichomes. **Stomata** paracytic. Although members of the family often occupy wet ground or marshy habitats, **aerenchyma** is infrequent except in cortex of roots and ground tissue of inflorescence axes. **Fibrous sheaths** are exceptionally well developed around vb's in stem, leaf, and inflorescence axes. **Silica-cells** occur in the epidermis of leaves and inflorescence axes. Calcium oxalate crystals are absent.

LEAF

(i) *Lamina* (Figs. 27; 28).

Dorsiventral, with a tendency toward isolateral construction in some genera, either by virtue of a limited development of palisade on abaxial as well as adaxial surface or a more or less undifferentiated mesophyll. **Hairs** exclusively non-glandular, unbranched, uniseriate with 1–3 short stalk cells, 1–2 long terminal cells; apex blunt. Hairs producing large quantities of slime in axils of leaves and inflorescence bracts; absent from leaf blades, at least at maturity. Cutinized layer thick. **Epidermis** similar on both surfaces, or cells slightly larger on adaxial surface. Outer walls smooth or with fine papillate sinuate edges next to other cells. Silica-cells each with a suberized inner wall partly or wholly enveloping silica-bodies. **Stomata** on abaxial surface only, not in regular files; not sunken; each with 2 narrow lateral subsidiary cells. Guard cells with prominent thickenings, similar to those of Gramineae. **Hypodermis** either absent or of large, thin-walled, occasionally lignified, cells, 3–5-layered; continuous with fibrous sheaths of larger bundles. Large hypodermal cells sometimes replaced by one or more layers of **fibres** (Fig. 28. B). Fibres also present as strands beneath epidermis, on one or both faces of leaf (Fig. 27. A); otherwise scattered irregularly through the mesophyll, or absent. **Mesophyll** usually differentiated into palisade and spongy tissue. Palisade cells elongated, or, more frequently, more or less square, with predominantly anticlinal infolding of walls (Fig. 28. B), forming subdivisions resembling elongated palisade cells; described and figured by Solereder and Meyer. Spongy tissue largely composed of arm-parenchyma. Plates of compact cells in some genera subdividing spongy tissue transversely. Thin-walled non-photosynthetic sphaeroidal cells, mostly collapsed in mature leaves, present singly or in large groups in spongy tissue, the larger groups often excluding spongy cells. Idioblastic tannin-cells in hypodermis, mesophyll, and bundle sheath of some genera. **Vascular bundles** with a sheath of thin-walled large cells; thick-walled fibres present next to phloem, often also next to xylem or surrounding all conducting tissues and, of larger veins, forming bundle-sheath extensions to surface layers. One or two layers of irregularly shaped sclereids sometimes forming a hypodermis on abaxial surface. Vb's of basic graminean type in larger veins; simple, collateral in smaller. Margins of lamina mostly with one or more large strands of fibres. Most fibres in leaves, other than those adjacent to phloem of bundles, apparently gelatinous as revealed by staining and shrinkage reactions.

(ii) *Leaf sheath*

V-shaped in T.S., distally opposite halves joining each other in the transition region beneath lamina. Vb's in several series, usually with less well-developed fibrous sheaths than in lamina. Mesophyll without fibrous strands, at least in sheath base. Parenchyma composed of closely packed non-photosynthetic parenchyma cells.

STEM

Stem usually unbranched, wide with congested internodes; less commonly narrow with conspicuous internodes, as in *Rapatea angustifolia*, roots then restricted to nodes.

Following generalized account refers largely to *Monotrema xyridioides*, ways in which other spp. differ being indicated later. **Hairs** uniseriate, 1–3-celled, producing slime. **Cortex** wide, of thin-walled parenchyma with well-developed intercellular spaces, cortical cells including abundant starch and some silica sand. **Endodermoid layer** at inner limit of cortex represented by (2)–3–(5) layers of, often radially seriated, sclereids, continuous with endodermis of roots. **Central cylinder** with numerous crowded vb's including a peripheral plexus of congested, irregular, often horizontal bundles continuous with root but not leaf traces. Peripheral vascular plexus absent from long internodes of *Rapatea* spp. Central vb's, representing leaf traces close to their exsertion, mostly collateral; the remaining, mostly more peripheral bundles,

A

B

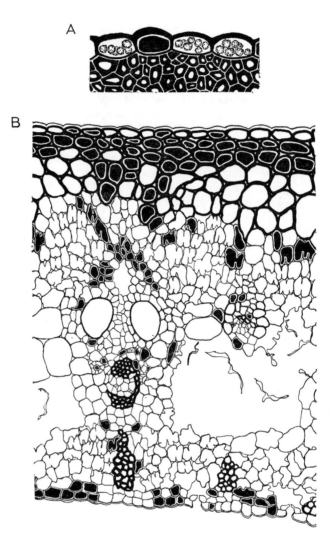

Fig. 28. RAPATEACEAE. *Schoenocephalium* and *Guacamaya* (Schoenocephalieae). T.S. lamina.

A. *Schoenocephalium coriaceum*. Adaxial epidermis showing silica-bodies (×365). B. *Guacamaya superba* (×45).

either amphivasal or intermediate between amphivasal and collateral. Stelar parenchyma sometimes including darkly staining compounds distributed idioblastically.

On the basis of his observations, Carlquist (1966) distinguishes according to stem anatomy the 4 tribes (in 2 sub-families) of Maguire (1958) as follows:

Tannin-filled parenchyma cells distributed
    idioblastically (not aggregated) in both
    cortex and central cylinder, or absent   .   subfamily **Rapateoideae**
    Epidermis without silica-cells; hypodermal fibrous strands absent
                                        .   .   .   tribe *Monotremeae*
    Epidermis with silica-cells; silica-cells in some genera
    associated with hypodermal fibrous strands   .   tribe *Rapateeae*
Tannin-filled parenchyma cells aggregated in both
    cortex and central cylinder   .   subfamily **Saxofridericioideae**
    Slime-canals and cavities present; parenchyma of
    central cylinder not lignified   .   .   tribe *Schoenocephalieae*
    Slime-canals and cavities absent; parenchyma of
    central cylinder slightly lignified   .   .   tribe *Saxofridericieae*

(The distribution of anatomical characters does not wholly correspond with this subdivision. *Spathanthus* (Rapateeae) has silica-bodies or silica sand in internal parenchyma, a feature otherwise present in *Monotrema* (Monotremeae) but not in other Rapateeae. *Spathanthus* also resembles Monotremeae in the absence of lignified ground parenchyma in the central cylinder, and differs from other Rapateeae in lacking hypodermal fibres.)

The following notes on individual spp. are from Carlquist (1966).

1. *Monotremeae.* Exemplified by *Monotrema xyridioides* described above

M. aemulans with tannin idioblasts in cortex as well as central cylinder. *M. affine* (older stem) outermost endodermal layer suberized; tannin-like deposits in intercellular spaces of outer cortex. *Maschalocephalus dinklagei* with many epidermal tannin idioblasts. *Potarophytum riparium* with endodermal sclereids relatively thick-walled.

2. *Rapateeae.* Represented by *Rapatea longipes*

Long, uniseriate slime-producing trichomes abundant. Epidermis either with tannin inclusions or with numerous small silica-bodies enclosed in cells with suberized inner walls, the epidermal silica-cells always immediately above 2–3 layers of hypodermal fibres. Thin-walled cortical parenchyma including a peripheral zone of relatively thin-walled sclereids. Parenchyma of central cylinder partly thick-walled and slightly lignified. Vb's close to their exsertion as leaf traces (collateral) sheathed by fibres; endodermal region markedly thick-walled. Starch abundant in ground parenchyma of cortex and central cylinder. Internal silica absent.

Other spp. of this tribe differing as follows. *Rapatea spruceana*: sclereids scattered in outer cortex (not a continuous band). *R. fanshawei*: cortical ground tissue without sclereids; ground tissue of central cylinder of thin-walled sclerenchyma transitional peripherally to sclereids of endodermal region. *R. angustifolia*: like *R. fanshawei* but stem narrow, with few vb's. Cortical fibrous strands v. narrow, each more or less associated with a single file of epidermal silica-cells. *R. yapacana*: cortical parenchyma wholly thin-walled, unlignified; endodermal region of thick-walled sclereids; central ground tissue of central cylinder of thick-walled sclereids, becoming thin-walled at periphery. *R. membranacea*: less lignified than *R. longipes*, a difference suggested by Carlquist to be related solely to age of stem; ground parenchyma of central cylinder with few lignified cells; fibres next to only a few leaf traces.

Cephalostemon affinis: resembles *Monotrema xyridioides*; hairs and epidermal silica-cells as in *Rapatea longipes*; cortex including unidentified droplets; endodermal cells sclerenchymatous.

Duckea flava and *squarrosa*: like *Monotrema xyridioides*; unidentified substances present in stelar parenchyma as well as cortex.

Spathanthus unilateralis differing from *Rapatea*, which it otherwise resembles, as follows: epidermal silica-cells present but hypodermal fibres absent; tannin idioblasts absent, tannin-like substances otherwise represented by occasional droplets; parenchyma relatively thin-walled and lignified; leaf traces sheathed by thick fibrous strands; endodermal region of thin-walled sclereids. Starch abundant. Silica as large solitary, roughened bodies. *S. bicolor* differing in features interpreted as earlier ontogenetic stages; less sclerenchyma associated with leaf traces; silica not in large bodies but as aggregates of silica sand; endodermal region of v. thick-walled sclereids.

3. *Schoenocephalieae*. Represented by *Guacamaya superba*

Hairs uniseriate, producing slime. Epidermal silica-cells absent. Cortical parenchyma uniformly thin-walled except for sclerified parenchyma band towards surface. Endodermal region well marked with 3 layers of thick-walled sclerenchyma enclosing several thin-walled, radially seriate layers resulting from periclinal divisions. Fibrous sheath associated with outgoing leaf traces only. Starch abundant in parenchyma of cortex and central cylinder. Tannin abundant as massive deposits in aggregated parenchyma cells of cortex and central cylinder. **Slime-cavities** abundant in, and often continuous from, cortex to central cylinder but never entering leaf. Each cavity lined with uniseriate slime-producing hairs, like those of epidermis except for shorter 3-celled stalk below globose head. Cavities interpreted as having an early, schizogenous origin. *Schoenocephalium* identical with *Guacamaya* except for more numerous tannin-filled cells in *S. coriaceum*; *S. teretifolium* with less sclerenchyma associated with leaf traces.

4. *Saxofridericieae*

Epidryos micrantherus as in *Guacamaya* but slime-cavities not observed. *Stegolepis celiae* like *Guacamaya* but without slime-cavities; ground parenchyma of central cylinder slightly lignified. *S. angustata*: endodermal region not sclerenchymatous, parenchyma of cortex and central cylinder thin-walled but lignified; tannin as intercellular deposits in various parts. *Phelpsiella ptericaulis* like *S. celiae* but tannin-cells abundant in outer cortex.

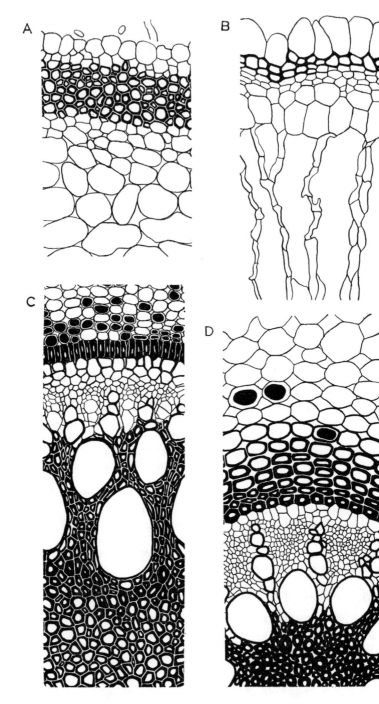

FIG. 29. RAPATEACEAE. T.S. root (×140).

A–B. Periphery of cortex.

  A. *Saxofridericia spongiosa.* B. *Duckea flava.*

C–D. Periphery of stele.

  C. *Guacamaya superba.* D. *Rapatea spruceana.*

Epidermis with or without silica-bodies. Hypodermal fibres present either as a continuous sheath (*Saxofridericia, Schoenocephalium, Stegolepis*) or as numerous (*Rapatea, Duckea*) or few (*Monotrema*) strands. Ground parenchyma composed of either compact sphaeroidal cells or arm-parenchyma, depending, at least in part, upon level sectioned. Tannin-cells present idioblastically. Peripheral vb's with normal orientation, each sheathed with fibres; fibrous sheaths sometimes continuous with hypodermal fibres. Vb's nearer centre in groups enclosed by a common fibrous sheath. Smaller bundles in these groups variously orientated and surrounding one or more larger, normally orientated bundles. Larger bundles of the basic graminean type, smaller ones simple, collateral.

ROOT (Fig. 29)

(a) General description

Epidermis either thin-walled and lost from mature roots (as in most Rapateoideae) or sometimes persistent and becoming suberized as root-hairs cease to function (as apparently in most Saxofridericioideae). **Exodermis** including 1–8 layers of hypodermal sclereids, either wholly thick- or thin-walled or with walls of varying thickness, thicker-walled cells either innermost or outermost.

Cortex including vertical files of tannin-cells, singly or in groups; tannin-cells otherwise absent. **Outer cortex,** immediately within exodermis, 1–4-layered, usually with starch grains to form a distinct starch sheath. **Middle cortex** including spongy or arm-parenchyma cells, in Saxofridericioideae compact, distributed idioblastically and sometimes with thickened, lignified walls, in Rapateoideae in horizontal tiers. **Inner cortex** of concentric rings of radially arranged spheroidal or tangentially elongated oval cells, often including starch grains to form a starch sheath, the cells separated by large intercellular spaces; some, or innermost, of these cells thick-walled and lignified and transitional to endodermal cells (as in *Rapatea*), others, especially innermost, modified as tannin-cells (as in *Saxofridericia* and *Schoenocephalium*).

Endodermis uniseriate (rarely locally 2-layered), cells either almost square in T.S. or radially or tangentially extended; walls lignified, moderately to extremely thickened. **Pericycle** thin-walled, uniseriate or sometimes multiseriate. **Stele** polyarch, xylem and phloem poles numerous (about 50) or few. **Medulla** usually of sclereids, sometimes with v. thick walls; thickest-walled cells either innermost or outermost. Metaxylem vessels extending towards centre of medulla in *Duckea*; more isolated medullary vessels occasional.

(b) Detailed description of root

The above generalized account refers to the family as a whole. The following account, from Carlquist (1966), provides more detailed information about individual taxa. Carlquist distinguishes the subfamilies and tribes as follows:

Middle cortex of 2 types of cells arranged in radial plates;
   sieve-tubes of metaphloem narrow . . subfamily **Rapateoideae**
Hypodermal sclereids of exodermis thick-walled   tribe *Monotremeae*
Hypodermal sclereids of exodermis thin-walled . tribe *Rapateeae*
Middle cortex of 3 types of cell, not arranged in
   distinct radial plates at maturity; sieve-tubes of
   metaphloem v. wide . . . subfamily **Saxofridericioideae**
Tanniniferous innermost cortical cells abundant,
   often in a majority . . . . tribe *Schoenocephalieae*
Innermost cortical cells mostly not tanniniferous; tannin-cells
   otherwise distributed idioblastically . . tribe *Saxofridericieae*

1. *Monotremeae.* Exemplified by *Monotrema xyridioides*

Epidermis remaining thin-walled in old roots. **Exodermis** including a single hypodermal layer of elongated, thick-walled sclereids, square in T.S. **Cortex.** Outer part, next to exodermis, consisting of 2 starch-containing layers of rigid, elongated cells, round in T.S. Middle cortex wide, cells radially seriated but of 2 distinct types. (*a*) **Short-cells,** thin-walled, unlignified but rigid and persistent, starch-containing and developing as arm-parenchyma cells, each cell typically with 4 arms, 2 radial and 2 tangential as seen in T.S. (*b*) **Long-cells,** large thin-walled, without starch, the cells collapsing at maturity to form radial plates 1(–2) cells wide. Long- and short-cells each in separate horizontal plates alternating to form superposed tiers. Inner cortex consisting of 4 layers of rigid, starch-containing cells like those of outer cortex. **Endodermis** uniseriate, thick-walled. **Pericycle** uniseriate, cells thin-walled next to proto-phloem but thick-walled with wide pits next to protoxylem. **Stele** without central vessels, conjunctive parenchyma somewhat thick-walled; xylem-free medulla of fibriform sclereids. Tanniniferous material as droplets in various parts but most common in cortex.

Other spp. differ in the following ways. *Monotrema aemulans* and *affine* resembling *M. xyridioides* but with massive tannin-like deposits accumulating idioblastically. *Potarophytum riparium*: exodermis including 2 layers of hypo-dermal, thin-walled sclereids and 2 layers of thick-walled sclereids; outer cortex 3-layered, inner cortex 5-layered; pericycle 1–2-layered, thick-walled; medulla v. thick-walled. *Windsorina guianensis*: exodermis including 5–6 layers of sclereids; cortex as in *Potarophytum*; pericycle 1–2-layered, thick-walled; ground tissue of stele wholly of thick-walled sclereids with tannini-ferous contents. *Maschalocephalus dinklagei*: exodermis up to 10-layered; cortex as in *Potarophytum*, endodermis as in *Monotrema*; pericycle thick-walled with broad pits; stele similar to *Windsorina* but less sclerotic.

2. *Rapateeae.* Exemplified by *Rapatea paludosa*

Exodermis with 4 hypodermal layers of thin-walled, possibly suberized sclereids; sometimes with tannin inclusions. **Cortex.** Outer part with 1–2 layers of thin-walled, ovoid, starch-containing cells. Middle cortex as in *Monotrema xyridioides*. Inner cortex of 9–10 layers of thin-walled, starch-containing cells in concentric series and radial rows, enclosing wide intercellular spaces;

tannin-bearing idioblasts common. **Endodermis** uniformly thickened.
Pericycle uniseriate, thin-walled next to phloem poles; thick-walled, with wide
conspicuous pits next to xylem. **Stele** including conjunctive parenchyma of
thin-walled sclereids similar to but smaller than those of medulla; isolated
medullary vessels occasional; phloem including scattered narrow sieve-tubes,
companion-cells and parenchyma.

Rapatea spruceana (Fig. 29. D). Exodermis 6-layered, thin-walled, cells often
tanniniferous; outer cortex 1–2-layered, thin-walled; inner cortex 10–12-
layered, succeeding layers towards stele successively longer, narrower, and
thicker-walled; innermost layers of sclereids resembling endodermal cells but
with wide pits; conjunctive parenchyma next to xylem arms not sclereid-like,
otherwise medulla thick-walled; medullary vessels absent.

Rapatea longipes. Exodermis 3-layered; inner cortex with 2 layers of sclereids next to endodermis; short-cells of middle cortex often with lignified
secondary walls; medullary vessels absent.

Rapatea yapacana. Exodermis 6-layered; short-cells of middle cortex with
rather thick, lignified walls; inner cortex of 7–8 layers of thin-walled cells and
a sclereidal layer next to endodermis; endodermis relatively thin-walled
but sclerenchymatous; pericycle uniseriate, uniformly thin-walled; medulla
including many narrow vessels, much narrower than peripheral metaxylem
vessels.

Rapatea angustifolia. Exodermis with outermost layer suberized; inner
cortical cells next to endodermis with thick, lignified secondary walls; medullary and conjunctive ground tissue v. thick-walled.

Rapatea fanshawei. Exodermis wide, with 6–7 layers of thin-walled sclereids, some including tannin; inner cortex of 10–12 layers of oval cells (in
T.S.), occasionally with tannin, cell walls becoming progressively thicker
towards centre; innermost 3–4 layers resembling sclereids. Endodermis thick-
walled, cells sclereidal with narrow lumina. Stele with 4 medullary vessels;
medullary and conjunctive tissue of stele thick-walled; phloem including
interpolated bands of xylem.

Rapatea membranacea. As in *R. angustifolia* but with bands of xylem interpolated within phloem as in *R. fanshawei.*

Duckea flava (Fig. 29. B). Epidermis of large, relatively persistent cells;
exodermis of 4 layers of thin-walled sclereids; outer cortex with large, starch-
containing cells; middle cortex as in other genera described above; inner
cortex 10–12-layered, innermost layer thick-walled and lignified; endodermis
of thick-walled, lignified cells, square in T.S.; pericycle uniseriate, thin-walled;
stele with thin-walled ground tissue; medulla including a few small cells like
those of *Rapatea yapacana.*

Duckea cyperaceoidea. Exodermis with 2 layers of thin-walled sclereids;
outer cortex of 1 layer of large, thin-walled cells; short-cells of middle cortex
sometimes with thick, lignified walls; inner cortex 7-layered, outermost layers
enclosing wide intercellular spaces and somewhat resembling short-cells of
middle cortex.

Duckea squarrosa. V. similar to *D. cyperaceoidea,* inner cortex 4–6-layered,
outer layers with large intercellular spaces and so resembling and transitional
to short-cells of middle cortex.

Cephalostemon affinis. Epidermis narrow, thin-walled. Exodermis narrow, of a single layer of thin-walled, hypodermal sclereids; middle cortex rather uniform because both long- and short-cells collapsed; inner cortex of 6 layers of ovoid cells sometimes tanniniferous, outermost cells of this region somewhat resembling short-cells as in *D. squarrosa.* Endodermis of lignified but thin-walled cells, square in T.S. Pericycle uniseriate, thin-walled; metaxylem vessels congested; centre of medulla of v. thick-walled sclereids.

Spathanthus unilateralis. Epidermis thin-walled, usually collapsed in old roots. Exodermis of 4 layers of thin-walled sclereids. Starch-containing cells of outer cortex absent; inner cortex 6–7-layered, only innermost layer with thickened, lignified walls. Endodermal cells relatively thin-walled; square in T.S. Pericycle thin-walled except for thick-walled cells with wide pits next to protoxylem. Stele with central thick-walled sclereids extending around xylem arms.

Spathanthus bicolor. As in previous sp. except for 2 layers of thin-walled cells in outer cortex next to exodermis.

3. *Schoenocephalieae.* Exemplified by *Guacamaya superba* (Fig. 29. C)

Epidermis persistent, thick-walled and somewhat suberized. **Exodermis** 5–7-layered, inner cells larger and thicker-walled than outer. **Cortex.** Outer part including 2–3 thin-walled, starch-containing layers. Middle cortex of 3 kinds of cells. (*a*) Thin-walled but lignified arm-parenchyma cells resembling short-cells of 2 previously described tribes, but irregular and not forming horizontal plates. (*b*) Collapsed (initially spheroidal) parenchyma cells, not arranged regularly. (*c*) Long, narrow tanniniferous cells, round in T.S., arranged in vertical series. Inner cortex with 10–12 layers of elongated cells, often including tanniniferous substances. **Endodermis**; cells v. thick-walled, lignified, radially extended with small lumina. **Pericycle** thin-walled, slightly lignified, pitted. **Stele** with many xylem and phloem arms, wide innermost metaxylem vessels each associated with 2 or more radiating xylem arms. Central medullary cells thinner-walled than those forming conjunctive parenchyma around metaxylem. Metaphloem sieve-tubes wide.

Schoenocephalium cucullatum. Epidermis persistent; exodermis with 3–4 layers of sclereids; outer cortex with 1–2 layers of thin-walled, starch-containing cells.

Schoenocephalium teretifolium. Exodermis narrower than in previous sp. with 1–2 layers of sclereids; outer cortex with starch-containing cells; pericycle uniseriate; central medulla of stele v. thin-walled.

Schoenocephalium coriaceum. Exodermis narrow; pericycle mostly 2-layered, probably as a result of late tangential divisions in a single mother-cell layer; stelar ground parenchyma of v. thick-walled sclereids; metaphloem sieve-tubes v. wide.

Epidryos micrantherus. Resembling *S. coriaceum.* Epidermis persistent. Exodermis with 3 layers of sclereids. Outer cortex with 4 starch-containing layers; inner cortex 5–6-layered, the innermost 2 layers sometimes with thicker, lignified walls. Endodermis of radially extended cells. Stele with central sclerenchyma, wall thickening most pronounced around large metaxylem vessels.

4. *Saxofridericieae.* Closely resembling roots of Schoenocephalieae

Saxofridericia spongiosa (Fig. 29. A). Epidermis persistent. Exodermis wide with 6–8 layers of hypodermal sclereids, outermost layers thinner-walled than inner. Outer cortex with 2–3 layers of starch-containing cells; middle cortex as in *Guacamaya*; inner cortex wide, 16–18-layered with idioblastic tannin cells. Endodermis as in *Guacamaya*. Pericycle uniseriate, cells with pitted lignified walls; wide metaxylem vessels usually opposite 2 or more protoxylem arms; metaphloem sieve-tubes v. wide; central medulla of thin-walled sclereids, becoming thicker-walled around metaxylem.

Saxofridericia inermis. Differing from previous sp. as follows. Exodermis with 5 layers of sclereids, outer 2 layers thick-walled; inner cortex 8–9-layered; pericycle 2-layered.

Stegolepis angustata. Exodermis relatively narrow with 1–2 layers of thin-walled sclereids. Outer cortex with 2 layers of parenchyma; middle cortex with 4 cell types (*a*) arm-parenchyma cells, (*b*) collapsed parenchyma cells, (*c*) solitary, narrow, thin-walled cells, circular in T.S., (*d*) aggregated narrow, thick-walled cells, circular in T.S.; inner cortex of 10 layers of non-lignified cells resembling type (*d*) above, together with 8 layers of thin-walled parenchyma and 1–2 layers of thin-walled sclereids. Endodermis of radially extended cells with U-shaped wall thickenings unlike those in any other member of Rapateaceae. Pericycle 2–3-layered. Stelar ground tissue thick-walled, cells surrounding xylem with only the wall next to tracheal elements thickened, unlike corresponding cells in any other Rapateaceae.

Stegolepis celiae. Exodermis as in *Saxofridericia spongiosa*, 5-layered with 3 inner thicker-walled than 2 outer layers. Outer cortex with 3 layers of starch-containing cells; middle cortex as in *Guacamaya*; inner cortex with 3 types of cells, as in *S. angustata*, outermost 2–3 layers thick-walled, unlignified, middle 3–4 layers thin-walled, inner 2–4 layers sclereidal but sclereids in T.S. angular-polygonal, compact and v. thick-walled, unlike corresponding cells in other Rapateaceae. Endodermis; cells relatively thin-walled. Pericycle 1–2-layered, thin-walled, slightly thick-walled next to protoxylem. Metaphloem sieve-tubes v. wide. Stelar ground tissue of moderately thick-walled sclereids, becoming thicker-walled towards centre.

Phelpsiella ptericaulis. Exodermis 5-layered, 3 outermost thinner than 2 innermost layers. Outer cortex 3-layered, inner cortex 8–10-layered; tannin-like substances present in idioblasts in both inner and outer cortex. Endodermis v. thick-walled, cells square in T.S. Stele with thick-walled sclerenchyma extending outward between large metaxylem vessels.

Secretory, Storage, and Conducting Elements

Silica present in leaf in epidermal cells only (Figs. 27. A; 28. A) as round, sphaeroidal bodies with rough or spiny surfaces, several to many per cell; silica-cells almost invariably in contact with hypodermal fibres. Diameter of silica-bodies sometimes more than half width of epidermal cell in some genera (e.g. *Rapatea*, Fig. 27. A) to smaller (Fig. 28. A), or even fine granular particles.

Tannin; cells with darkly staining contents, assumed to be tannin-like, in all parts of the plant. Tannin-cells especially abundant in inner cortex of some roots and in inflorescence bracts; tending to occur in files parallel to long axis of organs in which present, but distribution idioblastic.

Starch as oval grains; abundant in stems, rare in leaves, occasional in parenchyma of inflorescence axes and inner and outer cortex of roots. Compound starch grains occasional, sometimes constituting entire starch complement of a cell.

Xylem. Table B shows the distribution of vessels in the four tribes (after Carlquist 1966).

TABLE B

Perforation plates in tracheal elements of Rapateaceae

1. *Subfamily Rapateoideae*

	Monotremeae	Rapateeae
Root	Simple (wide vessels) or scalariform with 5–20 bars (narrow vessels)	Scalariform, 3–10 bars; (*Spathanthus* simple)
Stem	Simple	Scalariform-multiperforate, bars narrow (*Spathanthus* simple or with few vertical bars)
Leaf	Imperforate	Imperforate

2. *Subfamily Saxofridericioideae*

	Schoenocephalieae	Saxofridericieae
Root	Scalariform, in wide vessels perforations in several parallel series	Scalariform, up to 20 bars
Stem	Scalariform	Scalariform
Leaf	Imperforate	Imperforate

Phloem: for differences in diameter of metaphloem sieve-tubes of root which distinguish the 2 subfamilies, see Root, p. 139.

ECONOMIC USES

Schoenocephalium martianum is reported by Schultes (1954) to be sold as a cut flower in Bogotá, Columbia.

TAXONOMIC NOTES

As noted by Boubier, *Rapatea* and *Spathanthus* differ in leaf anatomy from the thick-leaved genus *Stegolepis*. Leaves of *Cephalostemon*, *Maschalocephalus*, and *Monotrema* resemble those of *Rapatea* (Fig. 27. B) and *Spathanthus*, whereas the thick leaves, possessing hypodermis, in *Guacamaya* (Fig. 28. B), *Kunhardtia*, *Saxofridericia*, and *Schoenocephalium* are similar to those of *Stegolepis* in complexity of structure. According to Boubier, species of *Rapatea* can be recognized by the appearance of the leaf in T.S.

The thicker-leaved genera of subfamily Saxofridericioideae have an outer root cortex consisting of fairly compact spongy tissue not arranged in radial plates (Fig. 29. A), whereas *Cephalostemon, Duckea* (Fig. 29. B), *Monotrema* and *Rapatea* of subfamily Rapateoideae have arm-parenchyma cells arranged in radial plates separated by prominent air spaces.

The contrast between the two groups of genera is visible also in size of silica-bodies: large in *Rapatea* (Fig. 27. A), small in *Schoenocephalium* (Fig. 28. A), a distinction mentioned by Solereder and Meyer (see also Carlquist 1961).

Contrasts among genera with respect to leaf anatomy and root structure have been illustrated by Carlquist (1961, 1966). The close agreement between anatomy and the taxonomy of the family, as recently revised by Maguire *et al.* (1958), is emphasized by Carlquist (1966).

Rapateaceae, although similar to Xyridaceae in a number of features, differ in the presence of silica-bodies and tannin-bearing cells, as well as in the peculiar chlorenchyma cells and the nature of the vascular core of the roots.

Genera and Species reported on in the Literature

Arber (1922) *Cephalostemon affinis* Koern., *Rapatea angustifolia* Spruce, *R. longipes* Spruce; leaf.

Boubier (1895) Notes on the genera *Rapatea, Schoenocephalium, Spathanthus, Stegolepis*; leaf, stem, root.

Carlquist (1961) *Duckea flava*; root. *Guacamaya superba*; leaf, root, silica-cells. *Rapatea paludosa*; leaf, silica-cells. *R. spruceana*; leaf, root, silica-cells. *Saxofridericia coriaceum*; root. *Schoenocephalium coriaceum*; leaf, silica-cells.

Carlquist (1966) see Material Examined.

Solereder and Meyer (1930) *Rapatea paludosa* Aubl., *Schoenocephalium arthrophyllum* Seub. (now *Monotrema arthrophyllum*), *S. martianum* Seub.; all parts.

Van Tieghem and Douliot (1888) *Rapatea* sp. (under Xyridaceae); root.

Material Examined by the Author

The following spp. were studied, including those cited in Carlquist (1966), either from liquid-preserved material collected by Bassett Maguire, or from herbarium specimens.

Cephalostemon affinis Koern.; Maguire *et al.* 41536 (NY).

Duckea cyperaceoidea (Ducke) Maguire; Maguire 35697, Maguire *et al.* 41682 (NY).

D. flava (Link) Maguire; Maguire and Wurdack 34492, Maguire *et al.* 41492 (NY).

D. squarrosa (Willd.) Maguire; Maguire and Wurdack 34536 (NY).

Epidryos micrantherus Maguire; O. Haught 5378 (US).

Guacamaya superba Maguire; Maguire *et al.* 41724 (NY).

Kunhardtia rhodantha Maguire; Maguire and Maguire 35400 (NY).

Maschalocephalus dinklagei Gilg and K. Schum.; J. T. Baldwin, Jr. 13054 (GH).

Monotrema aemulans Koern.; Maguire *et al.* 41654, 41659 (NY).

M. affine Maguire; Maguire *et al.* 41500 (NY).

M. bracteata Maguire; Maguire *et al.* 41547 (NY).

M. xyridioides Gleason; Maguire *et al.* 34644, 41539 (NY).

Phelpsiella ptericaulis Maguire; Cowan and Wurdack 31058 (NY).

Potarophytum riparium Sandw.; Maguire and Fanshawe 23396 (NY).

Rapatea angustifolia Spruce ex Koern.; Maguire *et al.* 41911 (NY).

R. fanshawei Maguire; Tillett and Boyan 44862 (NY).

R. longipes Spruce ex Koern.; Maguire *et al.* 41727 (NY).

R. membranacea Maguire; Tillett and Boyan 43972 (NY).

R. paludosa Aubl.; Maguire *et al.* 41544. (N.Y.)

R. spruceana Koern.; Maguire *et al.* 41728, 41848 (NY).

R. yapacana Maguire; Maguire *et al.* 41540 (NY).

Saxofridericia inermis Ducke; Maguire *et al.* 41624, 42624 (NY).

S. spongiosa Maguire; Maguire *et al.* 37485 (NY).

Schoenocephalium coriaceum Maguire; Maguire *et al.* 41455, 43852 (NY).

S. cucullatum Maguire; Maguire *et al.* 41901 (NY).

S. teretifolium Maguire; Maguire *et al.* 41812 (NY).

Spathanthus bicolor Ducke; Maguire *et al.* 29326 (NY).

S. unilateralis (Rudge) Desv.; Maguire 32140, Maguire *et al.* 43852 (NY).

Stegolepis angustata Gleason; Maguire *et al.* 45129 (NY).

S. celiae Maguire; Maguire *et al.* 42115, 42456 (NY).

Windsorina guianensis Gleason; Gleason 272, Maguire 34143 (NY).

BIBLIOGRAPHY FOR RAPATEACEAE

ARBER, A. (1922) Leaves of the Farinosae. *Bot. Gaz.* **74**, 80–94.

BOUBIER, A. -M. (1895) Remarques sur l'anatomie systématique des Rapateacées et des familles voisines. *Bull. Herb. Boissier* 3 (2), 115–20.

CARLQUIST, S. (1961) *Comparative plant anatomy.* New York. pp. 146.

—— (1966) Anatomy of Rapateaceae—roots and stems. *Phytomorphology* **16**, 17–38.

MAGUIRE, BASSETT, *et al.* (1958) Rapateaceae, pp. 19–49 in: The botany of the Guayana Highland—part III. *Mem. N.Y. bot. Gdn* **10**, no. 1, 1–156.

—— —— —— (1965) Rapateaceae, pp. 69–102 in: The botany of the Guayana Highland—part VI. Ibid. **12**, no. 3, 1–285.

SCHULTES, R. E. (1954) Plantae austro-americanae IX. Plantarum novarum vel notabilium notae diversae. *Leafl. bot. Mus. Harvard Univ.* **16**, 190–2.

SOLEREDER, H., and MEYER, F. J. (1930) Rapateaceae. In *Systematische Anatomie der Monokotyledonen.* Heft IV, 73–80.

TIEGHEM, P. VAN, and DOULIOT, H. (1888) Recherches comparatives sur l'origine des membres endogènes dans les plantes vasculaires. *Annls sci. nat. bot.* sér. 7, **8**, 1–660.

ERIOCAULACEAE[1]

(Figs. 30–39)

SUMMARY

A PREDOMINANTLY pan-tropical family of 12 genera (Moldenke 1957) and some 800 species, mostly belonging to the large genera *Eriocaulon*, *Paepalanthus*, *Syngonanthus*; few species in temperate regions. Most abundant in South America. Plants mostly small (less than 30 cm high, or diminutive, e.g. *Philodice*) but some species of *Paepalánthus* exceeding 1 m. Growth habit variable with a transition from large, unspecialized forms with erect leafy stems, to specialized forms reduced to a basal leafy rosette, or to submerged aquatics with only capitula emergent. Simple, but probably specialized form represented by temperate *Eriocaulon septangulare* (Hare 1950) with creeping, mostly sympodially branched rhizome, each segment with a terminal rosette of narrow, linear leaves, the axis extending into a terminal naked flowering scape. Scape in many other species of *Eriocaulon* terminal with renewal buds arising in axils of foliage leaves at base of scape (*E. decangulare*), but scapes often in complex terminal clusters, or axillary with monopodial branching (many *Paepalanthus* spp.), or in complex combinations which have not been analysed (*P. distichophyllus*), especially the apparent 'fasciated' scape of, e.g., *P. bromelioides*. Analysis of growth habit often made difficult because of (i) abundance of branching, (ii) variability within a single individual, (iii) absence of a distinctive bicarinate prophyll as first leaf of branch, (iv) spiral insertion of branch leaves from the start.

Paepalanthus including species with erect leafy stems (leafy stems sometimes procumbent), up to 1·5 m high in *P. formosus*, almost woody in *P. aculeatus*, the naked flowering scapes in terminal clusters. Branches sometimes restricted to base of erect stems, or branching occurring distally (*P. bahiensis*). Vegetative proliferation in scape producing successive leafy rosettes separated by elongated leafy axis (*P. argyrolinon*) a condition transitional to apparent 'vivipary' (*P. viviparus*). Successive leafy rosettes sometimes forming extensive cushions (*P. alsinoides*). Scape clusters sometimes fused to produce apparent fasciated shoots (*P. albo-vaginatus*). Long naked scapes of flowering shoots, whether solitary, clustered terminally, or axillary always subtended by a closed tubular sheathing leaf. Short scape in *Tonina fluviatilis* adnate to axis above a possible subtending leaf and occupying an extra-axillary position on anodic side of a more distal leaf (Poulsen 1893).

Anatomical features related in part to hydrophytic tendency of family, with frequent aquatic (e.g. *Eriocaulon capillaceus* and *natans*) or amphibious (e.g. *E. septangulare*) members, but many spp. subject to periodic drought and capable of enduring fluctuating conditions or even somewhat xerophytic (many *Paepalanthus* spp.).

---

[1] Includes a summary of Malmanche's detailed monograph, overlooked by Solereder and Meyer.

Hairs of two main types, but always with similar short, cutinized basal collar-cell. (i) Three-celled glandular hairs, the ephemeral distal cell either short (*Eriocaulon, Lachnocaulon*) or long and frequently elongated perpendicularly to the basal axis producing equal- or unequal-armed T-shaped hairs (*Paepalanthus, Syngonanthus*). (ii) Longer filamentous uniseriate hairs common at leaf margin but most typically forming dense axillary clusters especially in rhizomatous spp. **Epidermis** typically large-celled, the non-sinuous walls thin or often uniformly thickened. **Lamina** always dorsiventral, with a single series of vb's, each with a well-developed parenchymatous sheath, the sheath commonly extending to one or both surfaces in the form of conspicuous parenchymatous buttresses. **Hypodermis** of colourless cells occasionally developed by lateral extension of adaxial part of buttress. **Air-lacunae** not uncommon in more hydrophytic spp. of *Eriocaulon*, pectinating with vascular buttresses. **Stomata** always superficial, with 2 shallow thin-walled lateral subsidiary cells. Guard cells, with a prominent outer ledge, v. distinctive in T.S. **Vascular bundles** of leaf and scape usually with an outer parenchymatous and an inner, somewhat sclerotic, sheath; protoxylem lacunae well developed in larger bundles, between 2 wide lateral metaxylem vessels or clusters of metaxylem elements.

Inflorescence axis (scape) always leafless, often ribbed; epidermis resembling that of lamina. Cortical chlorenchyma usually radially segmented by vertical bands of parenchyma, less commonly of sclerenchyma, these bands usually corresponding externally to ribs and internally to large vb's situated in a single ring in the stele, less commonly ribs alternating with large vb's.

Leafy aerial vegetative **stems** of *Paepalanthus, Leiothrix* with a narrow, non-vascular, frequently assimilating cortex, delimited by a thin- or thick-walled parenchymatous sheath from the wide stele. Peripheral stelar ground tissues sclerotic and including several series of **amphivasal vb's. Rhizome**, both in spp. with or without leafy aerial stems, usually with a thin- or a thick-walled endodermis separating the wide cortex from the central cylinder; vb's of central cylinder amphivasal and resembling those of leafy aerial stems.

Roots commonly with paired or clustered **root-hairs. Cortex** in more specialized genera (*Eriocaulon, Lachnocaulon, Syngonanthus*) commonly differentiated into files of alternating long- and short-cells, the short-cells in many spp. of *Eriocaulon* elaborately lobed and aggregated into distinct transverse diaphragms responsible for 'vermiform' or articulate appearance of roots in this genus. **Endodermis** thin- or thick-walled, sometimes appearing biseriate owing to overlapping of oblique end walls of contiguous cells; rarely truly multiseriate. **Pericycle** usually uniseriate and commonly interrupted by protoxylem elements lying next to endodermis. **Stele** sometimes including uniformly scattered metaxylem and phloem strands when wide; when narrow typically with a solitary wide central metaxylem vessel.

Vessels in all parts; in root invariably with simple, more or less transverse perforation plates; elsewhere either simple or less specialized in the leaf. Calcium oxalate common as needle-like or prismatic **crystals**, sometimes forming druse-like clusters, in unspecialized cells in all parts of plant, but most typically associated with assimilating tissues.

Hairs on Vegetative Organs

Hairs basically of three main types: (i) filamentous hairs, in many spp.; (ii) 3-celled glandular hairs present in almost all spp.; (iii) multicellular capitate glandular hairs; infrequent. All hairs with 2 essentially similar basal cells; a **basal cell** (*Fusszelle* of German authors) either included within the epidermis (filamentous hairs) or superficial (glandular hairs) and a short usually cutinized **collar-cell** (*Halszelle* of German authors). Distal part of 3-celled glandular hair consisting of an ephemeral, usually thin-walled cell with densely staining contents (e.g. Fig. 32. K, L). Distal part of filamentous hair consisting of a long, uniseriate, usually pointed, multicellular filament (e.g. Fig. 33. E). Distal part of capitate glandular hair consisting of a short, usually 3-celled filament ending in an inflated cell. Hairs intermediate between glandular and filamentous not uncommon.

(i) *Filamentous hairs* (*Deckhaare*) (Fig. 33. E–G)

Most typically arising early in leaf axils, notably in rosette-leaves, forming dense beard-like protective tufts. Otherwise not uncommon on leaf margin as, e.g., *Paepalanthus alsinoides, brachypus, domingensis* (Fig. 31. L, M), *flaccidus*; *Lachnocaulon engleri*; *Tonina fluviatilis*; when more widely distributed forming a conspicuous silvery or woolly indumentum (*Paepalanthus argenteus* and *macrorrhizus*). Basal cell wedged into epidermis and usually much smaller than unmodified epidermal cells. Collar-cell almost invariably present (Fig. 33. G), usually cutinized and staining intensely with safranin. Distal filament usually persistent, long, pointed, septate, the smooth wall slightly thickened at the thin septa (Fig. 33. F). Distal filament rarely finely spinulose (*Paepalanthus distichophyllus*) in a manner recalling certain glandular hairs, or only the terminal cell spinulose (*Syngonanthus nitens*). Filamentous hairs short and producing a powdery indumentum on the upper surface in *Syngonanthus circinnatus* and *imbricatus*. Hairs in *Paepalanthus scytophyllus* v. short, with a single conical distal cell. Hairs transitional to glandular type include those with 1–2-celled filament, the terminal cell inflated (*Paepalanthus compactus*) or with a slightly inflated, irregularly lobed and somewhat T-shaped distal cell (*P. ciliolatus*). Filamentous hairs in leaf axils in *P. williamsii* commonly irregular and slightly inflated.

(ii) *Three-celled glandular hairs* (*Drüsenhaare*) (Figs. 30. E–F, I, L–M; 32. G–L; 33. D, H, I)

Occurring on surface of lamina and inflorescence axis of all spp. with possible exception of *Eriocaulon gracile* and *Paepalanthus weddellianus*. Best revealed in fresh material by staining with methylene blue. Sometimes uniformly distributed, but commonly less frequent on adaxial than abaxial surface (e.g. *Paepalanthus domingensis, tuerckheimii*; *Lachnocaulon engleri*), on abaxial surface typically restricted to costal regions. Differences in distribution of leaf hairs in various spp. of *Eriocaulon* stressed as a diagnostic feature by Malmanche. Hair initial in *E. helichrysoides*, according to Malmanche, arising by oblique division at one end of an elongated epidermal cell, subsequently dividing twice by transverse divisions and displaced into a super-ficial position above the end wall of 2 contiguous long cells. Hairs usually v. regularly distributed in cell files of abaxial costal regions (e.g. Figs. 30. B; 31. B), rarely on adaxial surface (e.g. Fig. 30. A) between each pair of long epidermal cells. Two most proximal cells usually persistent, densely staining distal cell usually ephemeral. Basal cell short, scarcely penetrating epidermis (Figs. 30. E, I; 33. H); collar-cell always present (Figs. 30. E, F, I; 33. H), often obliquely orientated.

Different types of glandular cell largely distinguished by shape of distal cell: (*a*) **Unbranched glandular hairs** (Fig. 32. G–L) with a smooth, elliptical, usually short distal cell, either continuous with the axis of the hair base or commonly adpressed against the leaf surface. Length of distal cell fairly con-stant and characteristic for a sp. although adaxial may be somewhat longer than abaxial hairs on the same leaf. Short distal cells (e.g. Fig. 32. G–K) (less than 10 μm long) characterize some *Eriocaulon* spp., e.g. *E. articulatum*, *decangulare, ravenelii, scariosum*; longer distal cells (Fig. 32. L) (10–20 μm long) characterize other spp., e.g. *E. compressum*; *Lachnocaulon engleri*, *minus*; *Tonina fluviatilis* (Fig. 33. D); much longer distal cells (over 20 μm long) present in *Paepalanthus* spp., e.g. *P. brachypus, claussenianus, hirsutus*, *oerstedianus, ramosus* and usually associated with branched glandular hairs.

(*b*) **Branched glandular hairs** (T-shaped or 'Malpighian' hairs) (Figs. 30. L, M; 31. I). Distal cell 2-armed, the arms extending parallel to the leaf surface along the longitudinal axis of the leaf. (Hairs of this type illustrated by Malmanche, conventionally represented in T.S. diagrams, are shown at right-angles to their natural position.) Hair as a whole then T-shaped, or the distal cell itself T-shaped with a v. short 'stem'. Arms of the T either almost equally long and producing symmetrical hairs (Fig. 30. M) (e.g. *Leiothrix turbinata*; *Paepalanthus alsinoides* (Fig. 31. I), *elongatus, flaccidus, freyreissii, minutulus*; *Syngonanthus caulescens, flavidulus* (Fig. 33. I), *nitens*), or v. unequal and pro-ducing asymmetrical hairs (Fig. 30. L) (e.g. *Paepalanthus elegans, plantagineus*, *tortilis*; *Syngonanthus appressus*). Symmetry of hair often constant for a given sp. but symmetrical and asymmetrical hairs sometimes present in same sp. (e.g. *Paepalanthus umbellatus* and *williamsii* (Fig. 30. L)). Distal cell of T-shaped hairs commonly smooth and scarcely thick-walled (e.g. *Leiothrix turbinata*; *Paepalanthus alsinoides, elongatus, williamsii*), but sometimes thicker-walled and finely spinulose (e.g. *Paepalanthus caulescens, umbellatus*; *Syngonanthus flavidulus* (Fig. 33. I), *niveus*), or with both smooth and occa-sional spinulose hairs together in *S. reflexus*. Both branched and unbranched hairs occur together in some spp. of *Paepalanthus*, according to illustrations by Malmanche (*P. nitens* and *ramosus*) (also Fig. 30. L). Early stages in development of T by lateral swelling of adpressed distal cell recorded for *P. warmingianus*. Transitional hair with adpressed and irregularly lobed distal cell recorded for *P. schenckii*.

(iii) *Capitate, multicellular glandular hairs*

Normally with 2 proximal cells extending into a usually 3-celled stalk and capped by an inflated distal cell recorded for *Paepalanthus curvifolius* and *flavescens*; resembling those on reproductive organs of some *Syngonanthus* spp.

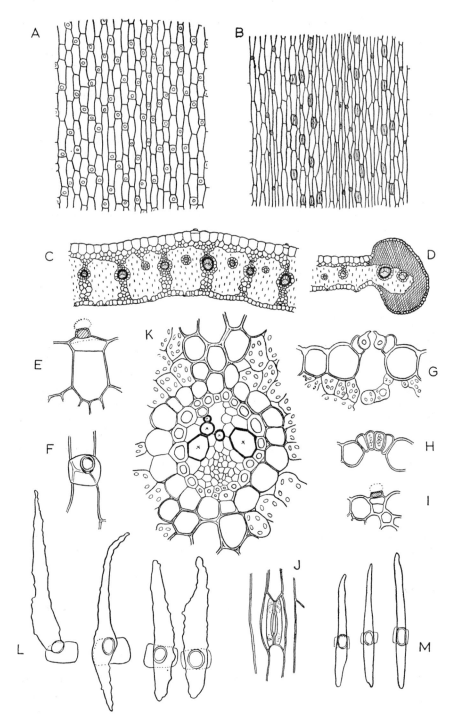

Fɪɢ. 30. ERIOCAULACEAE. Lamina.

A–M. *Paepalanthus williamsii.*

A. Adaxial epidermis, surface view (×50). B. Abaxial epidermis, surface view (×50). C. T.S. lamina (×50). D. T.S. lamina margin (×50). E. T.S. adaxial epidermis including hair base; distal cell detached (×230). F. Hair base, adaxial surface; distal cell detached (×230). G. Stoma, abaxial epidermis; T.S. equatorial level (×230). H. Stoma, abaxial epidermis; T.S. polar level (×230). I. T.S. base abaxial hair; distal cell detached (×230). J. Stoma, abaxial epidermis, surface view (×230). K. T.S. major vb in lamina (×460). L. Adaxial hairs, surface view; distal cell attached. Left, simple, unbranched; right, branched, unequally T-shaped (×230). M. Abaxial hairs, surface view; distal cell attached. Hairs branched, unequally T-shaped (×230).

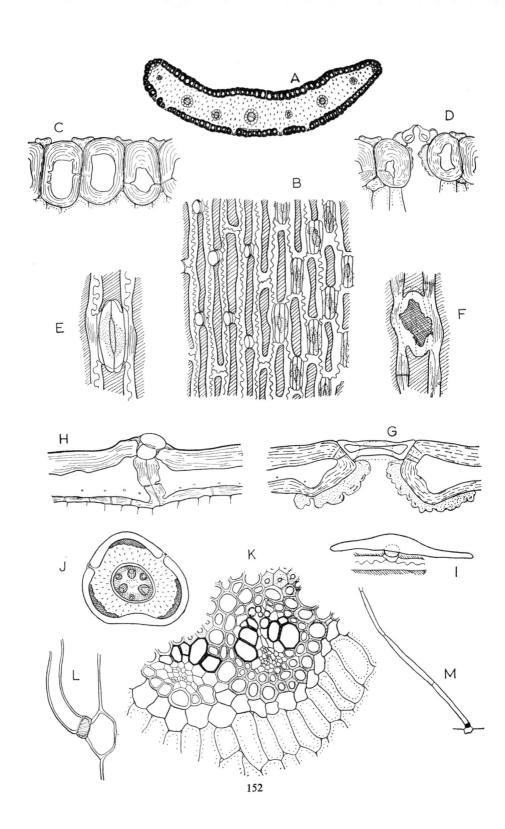

Fig. 31. ERIOCAULACEAE (after Tomlinson 1965).

A–K. *Paepalanthus alsinoides*. A–I. lamina.

A. Lamina T.S. (×60). B–C. Epidermis. B. Abaxial epidermis, surface view; costal band to left; intercostal (stomatal) band to right (×70). C. T.S. adaxial epidermis (×320). D–G. Stoma from abaxial surface (×320). D. T.S. E. Surface view, high focal level. F. Surface view, low focal level. G. L.S. H–I. Hairs. H. L.S. adaxial epidermis with persistent hair base (×320). I. Surface view of hair, with persistent distal cell from costal region of abaxial epidermis (×260). J–K. Peduncle. J. T.S. (×30). K. T.S. outer part of stele (×260).

L–M. *Paepalanthus domingensis*, uniseriate hairs.

L. Base of hair from leaf margin (×210). M. Hair from leaf margin, distal cells omitted (×65).

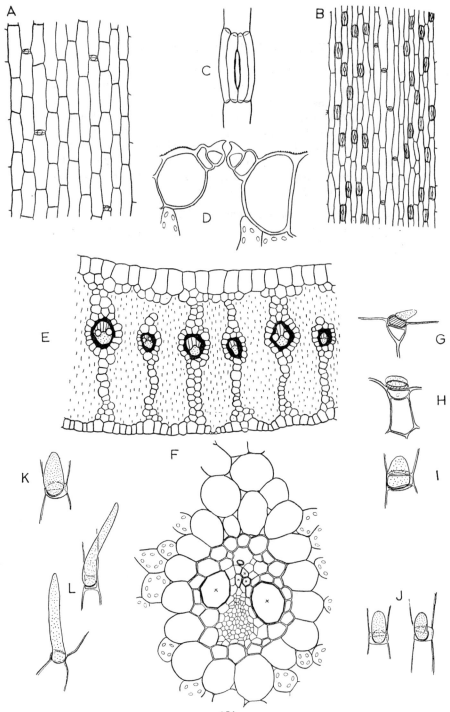

Fig. 32. ERIOCAULACEAE. Lamina.

A–F. *Eriocaulon decangulare.*

A. Adaxial epidermis, surface view ($\times$ 50). B. Abaxial epidermis, surface view ($\times$ 50). C. Abaxial stoma, surface view ($\times$ 230). D. T.S. abaxial stoma ($\times$ 370). E. T.S. lamina ($\times$ 50). F. T.S. main vb in lamina ($\times$ 230).

G–I. *Eriocaulon septangulare.* Adaxial glandular hairs ($\times$ 230).

G. L.S. H. T.S. I. Surface view.

J. *Eriocaulon scariosum.* Hairs from lamina, surface view ($\times$ 230).

K. *Eriocaulon articulatum.* Glandular hair from lamina, surface view ($\times$ 230).

L. *Lachnocaulon minus.* Glandular hairs from lamina, surface view ($\times$ 230).

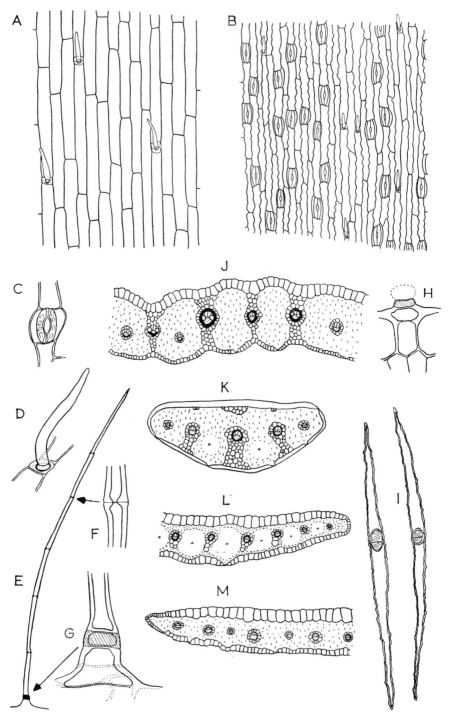

Fig. 33. ERIOCAULACEAE. Lamina.

A–G. *Tonina fluviatilis.*

A. Adaxial epidermis, surface view (×100). B. Abaxial epidermis, surface view (×100). C. Stoma, surface view (×230). D. Glandular hair, adaxial, surface view (×230). E–G. Filamentous hair, margin. E. Entire hair (×50). F. Details of distal septum (×230). G. Details of base (×230).

H–I. *Syngonanthus flavidulus.* Glandular hair, branched, equally T-shaped.

H. T.S., distal cell detached (×370). I. Surface view, distal cell attached (×230).

J. *Eriocaulon australe.* T.S. median part of lamina (×50).

K. *Syngonanthus flavidulus.* T.S. lamina (×50).

L. *Eriocaulon scariosum.* T.S. marginal part of lamina (×50).

M. *Lachnocaulon minus.* T.S. marginal part of lamina (×50).

Hairs on Reproductive Organs

(This subject is largely outside the scope of this account, which does not deal with reproductive organs, but the following notes taken from Solereder and Meyer are included because of the diagnostic value of such information.)

Hairs similar to those on foliage leaves typically present on ribs of scape, but hairs on bracts, receptacle, and other floral parts usually strikingly different from those on vegetative parts and often imparting characteristic colour to capitulum, e.g. brown in *Eriocaulon, Mesanthemum* spp.; chalky white in *Syngonanthus niveus*. Proximal 2 cells of all hairs, and 3 types of hairs based on characters of distal cells, similar to those on vegetative organs, but intermediate types more common. Basal cell abnormally elongated, bottle-shaped; collar-cell elongated in scape-hairs of *Philodice hoffmannseggii* according to Malmanche.

(i) *Filamentous hairs*

Pointed, uniseriate filament composed of shorter, thicker-walled cells than in hairs on vegetative organs (e.g. in spp. of *Leiothrix, Mesanthemum, Syngonanthus*); inner walls of filament cells in *Eriocaulon* spp. smooth or at most with slight irregularities; in spp. of *Paepalanthus* and *Blastocaulon* filament with one or more (the number of cells possibly of taxonomic significance) distal filament cells with minutely warty or otherwise irregularly thickened walls, responsible in many spp. for the chalky-white appearance of the capitulum. Irregularity of wall decreasing gradually from apex to base of filament, the lowest irregular cell frequently with fine helical striations (e.g. *P. ithyphyllus, sessiliflorus, speciosus*). Distal filament cell either shortly pointed (*P. lanato-albus* and *sessiliflorus*) but more commonly blunt, or distal and penultimate cell bluntly lobed (e.g. *P. speciosus* and other members of the section *Actinocephalus* of *Paepalanthus*). Other irregularities include globular swelling of distal (*P. argyrolinon*) or 2–3 distal (*P. gyrotrichus* and *polygonus*) cells; tuberculate hairs of *P. dendroides*; blunt hairs with irregular wall thickenings in *P. capillaceus* and some *Lachnocaulon* spp. Chalky white pubescence sometimes modified by coloured cell contents (yellow in *Paepalanthus flaviceps, P. ochrocephalus*; ochre-red in *P. capito*).

(ii) *Glandular hairs*

These occur in a few spp. and correspond to capitate glandular hairs of vegetative organs with 2 (*Syngonanthus helminthorrhizus*) or 3–4 (*S. appressus*) filament cells as recorded by Solereder and Meyer on inflorescence axis and subtending leaf, and by Koernicke for one group of *Paepalanthus* ('*capitulis glabriusculis*'). (It is significant that the latter section is ascribed to *Syngonanthus* by Ruhland.) Multicellular glandular hairs on involucral bracts in *Eriocaulon* and *Mesanthemum* stated by Solereder and Meyer to resemble 'stalkless blackberries'. Sugary content detected by Lecomte in such hairs of possible significance in pollination.

Glandular hairs of typical 3-celled type otherwise common on reproductive as well as floral parts. Size and shape of distal cell of hairs on scape emphasized as a diagnostic character by Malmanche.

(The taxonomic significance of hairs on reproductive organs, which seems to be considerable, is in need of more detailed exploration.)

LEAF (VEGETATIVE FOLIAGE) (Figs. 30; 31 except J, K; 32; 33)

Almost invariably spirally inserted (distichous in *Paepalanthus distichophyllus*) and commonly forming basal rosettes. Leaves linear, from broad to subulate, not differentiated into distinct regions; base slightly widened and incompletely encircling stem.

Dorsiventral. Rarely ribbed as in *Paepalanthus homomallus* and *macrorrhizus*. **Cuticle** thin, finely striated longitudinally in certain *Eriocaulon* spp., e.g. *E. articulatum, australe, compressum, decangulare, scariosum, sexangulare*. **Epidermis**; cells (Figs. 30. A, B; 32. A, B; 33. A, B) rectangular, longitudinally extended or shorter, wider and somewhat hexagonal. Anticlinal walls in surface view typically non-sinuous, but sometimes slightly sinuous in *Tonina fluviatilis* (Fig. 33. B); cutinized middle lamella of anticlinal walls distinctly sinuous in *Paepalanthus alsinoides* (Fig. 31. B) and *minutulus*. Adaxial epidermis usually uniform or rarely with indistinct costal bands of narrow cells above veins. Files of epidermal cells in surface view apparently regularly or more commonly irregularly divided into long- and short-cells. Short-cells produced by late division of long-cells (Figs. 30. A; 32. A), giving rise to hairs (Fig. 33. A) and usually displaced into a superficial position above common end wall of two contiguous long-cells. Abaxial epidermis sometimes uniform but mostly with distinct or indistinct stomata-free bands below veins pectinating with usually broader intercostal stomata-bearing bands (Figs. 30. B; 32. B). Hairs commonly restricted to costal bands (e.g. Fig. 32. B). Epidermal cells typically large, adaxial usually somewhat larger than abaxial cells (Figs. 30. C; 32. E; 33. J); costal abaxial often larger than intercostal abaxial cells (the reverse of the usual monocotyledonous construction) especially in many *Eriocaulon* spp. Inward enlargement of abaxial costal cells marked in *Paepalanthus elongatus* and *schraderi* and especially in *P. compactus* with v. deep epidermis (up to two-thirds total depth of lamina).

Epidermal walls remaining thin in more hydrophytic or shade-loving spp. (e.g. most *Eriocaulon* spp.; *Paepalanthus caulescens, flavescens, nitens*) but otherwise uniformly thickened to form a mechanical epidermis, the lumen often much occluded in more xerophytic or sun-loving forms, e.g. *Paepalanthus alsinoides* (Fig. 31. A–C), *brachypus, claussenianus, elongatus*; *Syngonanthus niveus, reflexus*; thickened walls often distinctly lamellate (Fig. 31. C–D). Epidermis sometimes not uniformly thickened, but outer thicker than remaining walls as in *Paepalanthus ramosus* and *weddellianus*. Abaxial epidermis in *Leiothrix turbinata* with walls not uniformly thickened, in contrast to uniformly thickened adaxial cells. Partially occluded cell lumen in *P. alsinoides* slightly enlarged at end of each cell (Fig. 31. H). Secondary wall substance in *P. alsinoides* deposited externally above and below anticlinal walls (Fig. 31. C) but most obvious around partially occluded substomatal chambers (Fig. 31. G). Adaxial epidermis sometimes appearing irregularly biseriate in T.S. owing to oblique overlapping end walls as in *Paepalanthus domingensis, falcifolius, polyanthus, senaeanus, tortilis, tuerckheimii*; similar epidermis in *Leiothrix turbinata* also occasionally genuinely biseriate. Epidermis of abaxial, or less commonly both, surfaces, as first recorded by Ebel, in many *Paepalanthus* spp. with large inwardly growing protuberances penetrating deeply into the mesophyll, either singly from the middle of relatively short cells, or in pairs one from each end of longer cells, the cells then appearing somewhat n-shaped in L.S. Alternatively with 3 or more lobes from longer cells as in *P. applanatus, claussenianus, domingensis, falcifolius, flaccidus, hilairei, macrocephalus* var. *pachyphylla, polyanthus, speciosus, tuerckheimii.* In *P. falcifolius* internal lobes, as seen in surface view, collectively form regular transverse files. Further towards interior of leaf, compact mesophyll cells conform to irregular contours produced by epidermal unevenness or protuberances, forming points of attachment to cells of loose mesophyll. Slight epidermal lobing of latter kind also noted in *Eriocaulon australe* and *Leiothrix turbinata.* In T.S. sometimes difficult to distinguish localized inward epidermal lobes of this kind from inward protrusion of entire cells (as in *Paepalanthus compactus* and *elongatus*).

Stomata usually restricted to abaxial surface but not uncommon adaxially in distal parts of lamina of some *Eriocaulon* spp. (*E. helichrysoides* and *septangulare*); otherwise restricted to abaxial intercostal regions and often with each epidermal file composed of regularly alternating stomata and long epidermal cells (e.g. Fig. 31. B). Stomatal apparatus always shallower than rest of epidermis, situated superficially or slightly elevated (Figs. 30. G; 32. D), even in xerophytic types (Fig. 31. D), the substomatal chamber thus largely enclosed by epidermal cells. Substomatal chamber in *Paepalanthus alsinoides* partially occluded by additional uneven wall deposits (Fig. 31. D, G). Terminal subsidiary cells not developed. Two shallow thin-walled lateral subsidiary cells parallel to and slightly longer than guard cells accompanying each stoma (Figs. 32. C; 33. C). Guard cells from 75 μm (*P. falcifolius*) to 36 μm (*P. niveus*) long, each with a single prominent outer ledge producing a characteristic beak-like structure in T.S. Possible slightly developed inner ledge for guard cells of *Eriocaulon* spp. suggested by Solereder and Meyer. Guard cells thin-walled in hydrophytic spp. (Fig. 32. D) becoming thicker-walled in more xerophytic spp. (Figs. 30. G; 31. D), the lumen constricted most in equatorial regions, more or less circular in T.S. (cf. Fig. 30. G and H). Abnormal double stomata recorded for *Paepalanthus bifidus* and *tortilis* by Poulsen.

Appearance of leaf in T.S. (Figs. 30. C; 32. E; 33 J–M) determined largely by extent to which chlorenchymatous mesophyll is interrupted by parenchymatous bundle sheath extensions (buttresses) (Fig. 32. E) and the lateral extension of buttresses to form colourless hypodermal layers (Fig. 30. C). Size of buttresses and their association with surface layer changing continuously from base to apex of leaf. Following description refers largely to a standard level half-way between base and apex of leaf.

Hypodermis of colourless cells sometimes developed, largely as lateral extensions of uppermost and lowermost parts of buttresses. Adaxial hypodermis forming a more or less continuous layer in *Eriocaulon humboldtii; Paepalanthus amoenus, claussenianus, consanguineus, elegans, elongatus, warmingianus, weddellianus, williamsii* (Fig. 30. C), *xeranthemoides; Syngonanthus* *niveus, reflexus*, the layer often multiseriate, especially in the median part of semi-terete leaves, e.g. up to 8 cells deep in *Paepalanthus elegans*. Adaxial hypodermis discontinuous in *Eriocaulon decangulare* (Fig. 32. E). Abaxial hypodermis less well developed, usually forming narrow costal bands as lateral extensions of buttresses, interrupted by intercostal chlorenchyma, rarely forming a more or less continuous abaxial layer as in *P. warmingianus* and *xeranthemoides* except for interruptions above stomata. Hypodermis in **P. claussenianus** differentiated into outer slightly thick-walled hypodermal cells and larger, inner thin-walled cells, the latter continuous with bundle sheath extensions. Isolated bands of hypodermal cells, above or below bundles, common in distal parts of leaves but becoming continuous with bundle sheaths in proximal parts (e.g. *P. alsinoides*; *Syngonanthus flavidulus* (Fig. 33. K)).

Veins (vb's) always arranged in a single series, somewhat alternately large and small, more or less equidistant from each surface, but closest to adaxial surface in some *Eriocaulon* spp. (e.g. *E. alatum, annamense, banani, buergerianum, crassiscapum, dregei, fenestratum, henryanum, kouroussense, modestum*). Bundles rarely forming a few irregular series at different levels (*Paepalanthus polyanthus*). Number of veins in a leaf often fairly constant in narrow-leaved spp., e.g. 1 in *Eriocaulon setaceum*; *Paepalanthus capillaceus*; 3 in *P. curvifolius, elegans*; 5 in *Syngonanthus flavidulus* (Fig. 33. K), *nitens*; 8 in *Eriocaulon alatum*; several to many and less constant in number in broader-leaved spp.

The following summarizes the general distribution of vb's as seen in T.S. at the standard level.

(i) Almost all veins buttressed to each surface (except for a few minor or marginal veins in some spp.): *Eriocaulon alatum* and other *Eriocaulon* spp. listed above under 'Veins'; also in *E. decangulare* (Fig. 32. E), *helichrysoides, humboldtii, ravenelii*; *Paepalanthus amoenus, caulescens, clausse-nianus, curvifolius, elegans, flaccidus, nitens*; *Syngonanthus reflexus*. In some spp. of *Eriocaulon*, e.g. *E. septangulare*, buttresses separated from each epidermis by only one compact chlorenchyma layer and therefore belonging to this category.

(ii) Only largest veins buttressed to each surface. Minor veins buttressed in one of the three following ways. (*a*) Wholly independent of surface layers, e.g. *Eriocaulon australe* (Fig. 33. J); *Leiothrix turbinata*; *Paepalanthus williamsii* (Fig. 30. C); *Tonina fluviatilis* (the buttresses in this sp. uniseriate and v. shallow). (*b*) Frequently or wholly attached to adaxial surface only, e.g. *Eriocaulon australe, sexangulare*; *Mesanthemum pubescens, radicans, rutenbergianum, tuberosum*; *Paepalanthus brachypus, compactus, elongatus, falcifolius, flavescens, ramosus, tuerckheimii, weddellianus, xeranthemoides*. (*c*) Most frequently attached to abaxial epidermis, e.g. *Syngonanthus flavidulus* (Fig. 33. K).

(iii) Veins buttressed only to abaxial surface, e.g. *Paepalanthus schenckii*; *Syngonanthus nitens*.

(iv) Veins wholly independent of surface layers (Fig. 33. L, M), e.g. *Eriocaulon articulatum, compressum, septangulare, scariosum* (Fig. 33. L) (the buttresses often completed above and below by a single layer of chlorenchyma); *Lachnocaulon anceps, engleri, minus* (Fig. 33. M); *Paepalanthus alsinoides* (Fig. 31. A), *bifidus*. Independent veins said by Ruhland to be supported by a compact chlorenchyma, at least in *Paepalanthus*.

Categories (i)–(iv) are only partly reliable for diagnostic purposes since all of them can sometimes be seen in transverse sections taken at different levels in a single leaf. Veins buttressed to each surface in the leaf base become isolated from one or both surfaces in the distal part of the leaf. 'Vestiges' of buttresses may be represented by narrow isolated hypodermal strands above and below veins (e.g. *P. alsinoides*).

Bundle-sheath extensions (buttresses) usually parenchymatous; commonly I-shaped in T.S., the horizontal part of adjacent girders tending to become united into a continuous hypodermis. Buttresses usually equally tall above and below each vein but in *Eriocaulon alatum* and related spp. listed above abaxial much taller than adaxial buttresses, the vb close to adaxial but remote from abaxial surface. Buttresses either uniseriate (least common and typical only in tall buttresses) or more usually bi- to multi-seriate especially in tereteleaved spp. (e.g. *Paepalanthus curvifolius, elegans*; *Syngonanthus flavidulus* (Fig. 33. K), *reflexus*). Buttress cells (and associated hypodermal cells) sometimes collenchymatous (e.g. *Eriocaulon australe, decangulare*; *Leiothrix beckii*; *Paepalanthus curvifolius, schenckii*) or even fibre-like (e.g. *Paepalanthus niveus*; abaxial but not adaxial buttress cells in *P. elegans*). In *Syngonanthus reflexus* outermost buttress cells sometimes thicker-walled than those elsewhere.

Mesophyll between veins consisting of an assimilatory tissue, either restricted to longitudinal bands in spp. with well-developed buttresses or continuous above and below vb's in spp. without complete buttresses. One–2 adaxial layers of palisade tissue sometimes distinct as in *Lachnocaulon minus*; *Leiothrix pedunculosa, turbinata*; *Paepalanthus alsinoides, domingensis, hilairei, tuerckheimii*; *Tonina fluviatilis*. Adaxial assimilatory layer otherwise compact, with cells scarcely anticlinally extended but distinct from looser abaxial mesophyll, or difference between 'palisade' and 'spongy mesophyll' expressed largely by differences in number of chloroplasts. Adaxial mesophyll layer of more hydrophytic spp. often represented by elongated and not anticlinally extended cells (e.g. *Eriocaulon septangulare*). Abaxial mesophyll between veins represented by isodiametric cells, scarcely lobed in xerophytic spp., becoming looser and more prominently lobed in more hydrophytic spp., sometimes radiately arranged around veins (e.g. *Eriocaulon australe*; *Lachnocaulon engleri, minus*; *Paepalanthus alsinoides*); in most extreme hydrophytes replaced by air-lacunae, but degree of development of lacunae within a single individual much influenced by wetness of habitat.

Air-lacunae recorded in *Eriocaulon articulatum, compressum, crassiscapum, decangulare, ravenelii, scariosum* (Fig. 33. L), *septangulare, sexangulare*, and group of spp. described by Malmanche with adaxially situated vb's, i.e. *E. alatum*, etc., listed under (i) on p. 161 above. Lacunae present in leaf base tending to be replaced distally by a continuous loose mesophyll (e.g. *E. decangulare*). Lacunae not usually developed in other genera, but observed in *Paepalanthus williamsii*. Air-lacunae lined by one or more assimilatory layers, the lining cells often elongated, especially towards leaf base. Transverse uniseriate **diaphragms** of chlorophyll-rich cells segmenting lacunae at regular intervals, producing regular fenestrate or articulated leaves of more hydrophytic spp. of *Eriocaulon* (e.g. *E. septangulare* described by Hare), the diaphragm cells usually regularly stellate.

Leaf structure in *Paepalanthus capillaceus* distinctive according to Ruhland, with a cylindrical leaf encased in a stomata-free, chlorophyll-bearing epidermis; mesophyll wholly colourless, of uniformly elongated cells, outermost layer somewhat specialized as a hypodermis, innermost layers forming distinct parenchyma sheath around solitary vein.

Vascular bundles (Figs. 30. K; 32. F) immediately surrounded by parenchymatous outer sheath (O.S.) extended above and below as buttresses. Sclerotic inner sheath (I.S.) immediately surrounding veins either distinct as a single layer of fibre-like cells (sometimes biseriate) as in larger-leaved spp. of *Mesanthemum* and in *Paepalanthus brachypus, curvifolius, elegans, xeranthemoides*; sometimes only distinct around phloem (e.g. *P. alsinoides* and *elongatus*). I.S. in hydrophytic spp. less distinct and cells scarcely thick-walled (e.g. most *Eriocaulon* spp.) (cf. Figs. 30. K; 32. F). Vascular tissues of larger vb's usually including a distinct protoxylem lacuna, remains of annular wall thickenings of disrupted elements persisting within the lacuna. Metaxylem in larger-leaved spp. of *Eriocaulon* including 2 wide vessels; metaxylem in *Paepalanthus* often represented by a Λ-shaped (in T.S.) strand of angular and narrower elements enclosing the phloem. Phloem always represented by a single, non-sclerotic strand. Smaller vb's or all vb's in smaller-leaved spp. with less regularly arranged and often reduced vascular tissue. **Transverse veins** few (but not absent as suggested by Poulsen), sheathed by colourless parenchyma; restricted to transverse diaphragms in fenestrate leaves of hydrophytes, otherwise often forming incipient diaphragms in spp. with loose mesophyll (e.g. *Eriocaulon australe*).

Leaf margin rounded or flattened, its variation of some diagnostic significance. Marginal cells commonly slightly thicker-walled and narrower than remaining epidermal cells, e.g. in *E. decangulare* and *humboldtii*; especially *Paepalanthus oerstedianus*; the thick-walled marginal cells in *Lachnocaulon minus* forming a distinct biseriate wing. Leaf margin in a few *Paepalanthus* spp. (e.g. *P. amoenus, williamsii* (Fig. 30. D)) including a massive subepidermal strand of fibres.

Leaf apex in some *Eriocaulon* spp. developing a hydathode-like organ (Arber) with the convergent veins terminating in a mass of tracheal tissue below a discontinuous epidermis (e.g. *E. septangulare*).

Leaf base differing from distal parts of lamina largely in greater development of colourless hypodermal and buttressing tissues, the buttresses frequently continuous with each surface although discontinuous distally. Mechanical tissues somewhat more pronounced.

INFLORESCENCE LEAF (SPATHE)

Closed, tubular sheathing organ at the base of the scape; enclosing the immature scape. Inflorescence leaf essentially equivalent to a wide rolled foliage leaf with opposite margins fused; outer epidermis anatomically

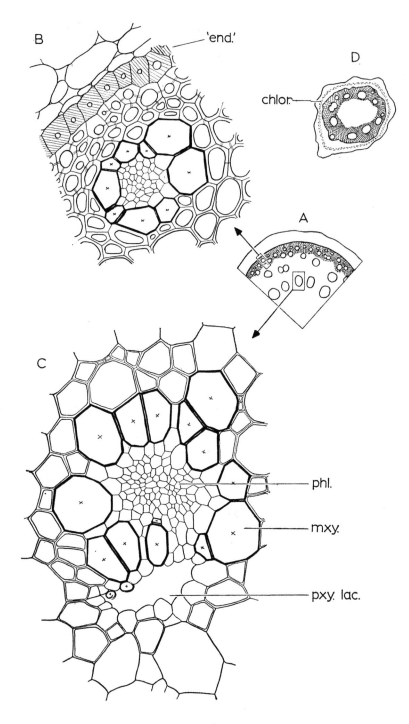

B   'end.'

D

chlor.

A

C

phl.

mxy.

pxy. lac.

Fig. 34. ERIOCAULACEAE. Leafy aerial stem.

A–C. *Paepalanthus williamsii.*

A. T.S. stem sector ($\times 20$). B. T.S. amphivasal vb from periphery of central cylinder ($\times 460$). C. T.S. amphivasal vb from centre of central cylinder ($\times 460$).

D. *Paepalanthus tuerckheimii.* T.S. stem ($\times 20$).
'end.'—endodermoid layer; chlor.—chorenchyma; phl.—phloem; mxy.—metaxylem; pxy. lac.—protoxylem lacuna.

resembling abaxial, inner epidermis resembling adaxial epidermis of foliage leaf. Internal anatomy corresponding to that of foliage leaf except for: (i) palisade like layers restricted to outer (abaxial) surface; (ii) all veins equivalent and buttressed to each surface. Continuous hypodermis commonly developed below outer surface.

STEM (VEGETATIVE)

General morphology

Leafy, vegetative, aerial stem developed only in more robust spp. e.g. of *Paepalanthus*, *Leiothrix*. Stem then erect, tall (e.g. *P. formosus*), sometimes sparingly branched (e.g. *P. amoenus*). Axis otherwise usually reduced to a congested rhizome with terminal leafy rosettes (most *Eriocaulon* spp.) and only rarely with an elongated but decumbent aerial stem (e.g. *Tonina fluviatilis*; some aquatic *Eriocaulon* spp. such as *E. capillus-najadis*, *melanocephalum*, *setaceum*).

(iA) *Aerial axis* (Fig. 34); in spp. with well-developed stems

The following account refers initially to well-developed aerial stems of *Paepalanthus* spp. Ways in which other spp. with relatively reduced stems differ are described later. Surface occasionally slightly ridged below leaf insertion. **Epidermis** uniform or with stomata, glandular and filamentous hairs as on lamina. **Cortex** always narrow, uniformly parenchymatous, rarely including a narrow chlorenchymatous zone as in *P. tuerckheimii* (Fig. 34. D). Specialized cortical vascular system not developed apart from transient leaf-traces. Leaf traces mostly collateral but amphicribal in *P. polyanthus* according to Poulsen, thus recalling amphicribal bundles observed by Malmanche in rhizome of *P. xeranthemoides*. Cortex described by Malmanche as becoming lacunose by breakdown of tangential walls of cortical cells in *Eriocaulon bifistulosum*, *Paepalanthus caulescens*, *Philodice hoffmannseggii*, and by Solereder and Meyer as lysigenously lacunose in *Syngonanthus caulescens*.

Central cylinder always wide in proportion to cortex (Fig. 34. A), delimited externally by a single endodermoid layer (Fig. 34. B; 'end') of usually thick-walled cells, the cells often with lumen almost occluded by wall thickening (e.g. *P. alsinoides*) but apparently never suberized or with Casparian strips although described as an endodermis by Solereder and Meyer and earlier authors. Endodermoid cells with uneven wall thickenings, U-shaped in T.S. in *Paepalanthus dasynema*, *freyreissii*, *minutulus*, *plumosus*, *schenckii*, *warmingianus*. Ground parenchyma at periphery of central cylinder thick-walled, sclerotic, forming distinct mechanical layer with gradual transition internally to thin-walled parenchymatous medulla; medulla hollow in *P. densiflorus*. **Vascular bundles** narrow, congested within peripheral mechanical zone; becoming wider, more diffuse centrally (Fig. 34. A); medulla often devoid of vascular tissue. Peripheral vb's (Fig. 34. B) often irregular because of frequent tangential anastomoses. Large central, or most, vb's **amphivasal** (Fig. 34. C), xylem an irregular series of angular elements more or less surrounding and enclosing central phloem strand; largest bundles each with a distinct proto-xylem lacuna towards stem centre, next to widest metaxylem elements.

Smaller and peripheral vb's without distinct protoxylem, irregularly collateral, xylem U- or V-shaped in T.S. and only partly enclosing phloem. **Bi-concentric vb's**[1] consisting of 2 series of xylem elements separated by a single cylinder of phloem recorded by Poulsen for *Paepalanthus polyanthus*, by Ruhland for *P. incanus*, by Solereder and Meyer for *P. falcifolius*, and by Malmanche (occasionally) for *P. densiflorus*. Vb's commonly sheathed completely or incompletely by fibrous tissue as in *P. elongatus* and *falcifolius* or sheathing tissues parenchymatous as in *P. polyanthus*. Fibrous sheathing tissues of individual vb's becoming continuous with peripheral mechanical ground tissue. Vascular tissues in *P. alsinoides* not arranged in discrete bundles but united to form irregular tracheal strands with or without associated protoxylem, the phloem being scattered without reference to the xylem. Irregular vascular masses, apparently formed by similar fusions, recorded for *P. bifidus, schenckii, tortilis.*

(iB) *Axis*; in spp. with reduced stems

(*a*) *Tonina fluviatilis*. **Cuticle** papillose. **Cortex** of 4–6 layers of colourless parenchyma without vascular tissues. **Central cylinder** delimited by single layer of thick-walled cells. Vascular bundles restricted to a single series immediately within the sclerotic layer, enclosed by narrow, slightly thick-walled cells. Individual vb's essentially amphivasal and each typically including several wide outer tracheal elements, smaller inner elements in an indistinct cylinder enclosing phloem, inner xylem of largest vb's represented by a distinct protoxylem lacuna.

(*b*) *Paepalanthus minutulus, scandens, tuerckheimii* (Fig. 34. D); *Philodice hoffmannseggii*, with a similar single peripheral series of vb's. Medullary parenchyma rarely disorganized to produce a central lacuna as in *P. scandens*.

(*c*) *Eriocaulon bifistulosum* (aquatic), endodermoid layer thin-walled, indistinct, stele narrow with single peripheral series of vb's.

(*d*) *Eriocaulon setaceum* (floating aquatic), epidermis cutinized only above largest vb's. Peripheral ground tissue chlorenchymatous. Cortex and central cylinder not distinctly delimited. Vascular bundles in a single series, alternately large and small; each large vb attached to epidermis by lignified buttress; small vb's independent of surface cells. Medulla including wide lacuna. Peripheral layers including large inflated cells, described by Malmanche as **internal hairs**, each originating by internal enlargement of an epidermal cell, becoming filled with yellowish material and apparently functioning as a flotation organ.

(ii) *Rhizome*

Epidermis usually thin-walled, large-celled, uniform except for indumentum of persistent filamentous hairs in leaf axils. **Cortex** wide with a narrow hypodermal region of compact, sometimes slightly ligno-suberized cells and wide middle region of loose, mostly starch-filled cells. Middle cortex wide in many

---

[1] The central lignified cells within the phloem may represent part of the phloem itself which has become sclerotic. If this is so, these cells are not tracheal elements, so the vb's may not be truly bi-concentric.

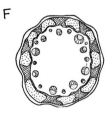

F

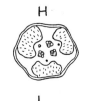

H

G

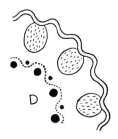

I

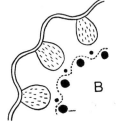

B

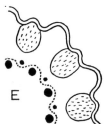

D

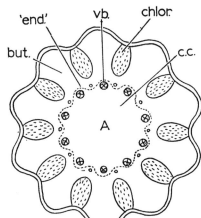

'end.'   vb.   chlor.

but.   c.c.

A

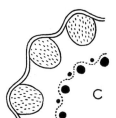

C

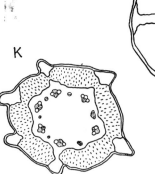

E

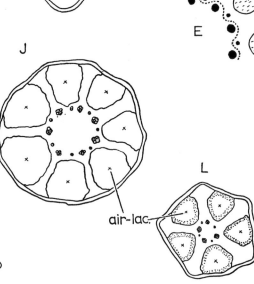

J

K

L

air-lac.

Fig. 35. ERIOCAULACEAE. Scape.

A–L. T.S. (×20).

A. *Eriocaulon decangulare* (somewhat diagrammatic showing basic construction of eriocaulaceous scape). B. Diagrammatic representation of periphery of Fig. A to show relation between ribs, buttresses, and vb's. C–E. Common variants. C. Large vb's and buttresses opposite furrows; ribs corresponding to chlorenchyma bands. D. Ribs fluted. E. Minor ribs opposite chlorenchyma bands. F. *Leiothrix turbinata.* G. *Paepalanthus tuerckheimii.* H. *Lachnocaulon engleri.* I. *Syngonanthus flavidulus.* J. *Eriocaulon articulatum.* K. *Eriocaulon scariosum.* L. *Eriocaulon austeral.*

but.—buttress; 'end.'—endodermoid layer; vb—vascular bundle; chlor.—chlorenchyma band; c.c.—central cylinder; air-lac.—air-lacunae.

Eriocaulon spp., e.g. *E. articulatum, compressum, decangulare, helichrysoides, septangulare*; *Leiothrix beckii*; *Syngonanthus nitens*, consisting of isodiametric or (e.g. *E. septangulare*) elongated cells with numerous interconnecting peg-like protrusions. Few inner cortical layers sometimes somewhat more compact than rest of cortex, rarely slightly thick-walled as in *Eriocaulon scariosum.* Cortical cells wholly smooth and not lobed in *Lachnocaulon* spp. Cortex without distinct vascular tissues except for numerous leaf-traces and intra-cauline portion of roots. Cortical part of leaf traces in *Paepalanthus xeranthemoides* amphicribal, according to Malmanche, each trace with a complete well-developed fibrous sheath, the sclerotic sheath cells continuous with peripheral sclerotic tissue of central cylinder. **Stele** relatively narrow, delimited from cortex either by a distinct 1-layered thin-walled **endodermis**, or the equivalent layer without Casparian strips as in *E. decangulare* according to Holm, or *E. septangulare* according to Hare, and replaced by slightly sclerotic biseriate endodermoid layer. Indistinct, mostly uniseriate **pericycle** commonly present within the endodermis. Peripheral vascular tissues represented either by a plexus of irregular xylem and phloem strands not arranged in distinct vb's (e.g. most *Eriocaulon* spp.) or by indistinctly amphivasal strands. Central region including discrete, diffusely distributed mostly irregular amphivasal vb's. Parenchymatous medulla free of vascular tissue in *Lachnocaulon* spp. Vb's in *E. septangulare* more or less collateral, xylem reduced to spirally thickened, feebly lignified vessels.

INFLORESCENCE AXIS (SCAPE) (Figs. 31. J, K; 35)

Single internode between inflorescence leaf and lowest bract of capitulum, rarely short as in *Tonina*, usually long; v. long in aquatic *Eriocaulon* spp., the length varying sufficiently to bring capitulum above water surface. Capitulum either solitary, terminal in some *Eriocaulon* spp. (*E. septangulare*) or capitula in complex terminal clusters (detailed morphology not understood) (many *Paepalanthus* spp.) or axillary. Terminal clusters of scapes sometimes fused to produce apparent fasciated shoots (e.g. *P. albo-vaginatus*). Extra-axillary scape in *Tonina* said by Poulsen to be truly lateral. Scape anatomy basically identical throughout family (Fig. 35. A) but varying in quantitative ways much emphasized as diagnostic features (notably by Lecomte, Malmanche).

Surface usually ribbed, the ribs related in a direct way to internal structures. Number of ribs constant for each sp. within quite narrow limits and emphasized as a diagnostic feature (reflected in specific names, e.g. *Eriocaulon decangulare, septangulare, sexangulare*).

The following description refers to the family generally; detailed features which distinguish genera and spp. are listed later. **Hairs** on scape essentially similar to those of lamina or more rarely resembling those of capitulum and unlike those on vegetative parts. **Epidermis** resembling that of lamina closely; differentiated into costal bands lying above ribs with frequent glandular or filamentous hairs and intercostal bands including abundant stomata within furrows, as in all *Eriocaulon* and *Lachnocaulon* spp. as well as in many *Paepalanthus* spp. Situation reversed in some *Leiothrix, Paepalanthus, Syngonanthus* spp. with stomatal bands occupying ribs and non-stomatal bands in furrows.

Cortex wide, 2–3 times diameter of stele in many *Eriocaulon* spp., divided into distinct chlorenchymatous bands (usually below furrows (Fig. 35. A; chlor.)) alternating with colourless, usually broad parenchymatous buttresses (Fig. 35. A; but.) extending from epidermis to stele. Buttresses usually corresponding to external ribs (Fig. 35. A), rarely extending only part-way across cortex (Fig. 35. K). Cortex of scape suggested by Lecomte to represent fused adpressed leaves. **Stele** not usually delimited clearly from cortex except by an indistinct **endodermoid layer** (Fig. 35. A; 'end.') (described as 'endodermis' by earlier authors in acceptance of Lecomte's analysis, but cells of layer without typical Casparian strips although showing other specialized staining properties according to Malmanche). Stele usually a parenchymatous cylinder continuous externally with cortical buttresses, including a single series of alternately large and small vb's. Large vb's always opposite buttresses, small vb's opposite chlorenchymatous bands; relative position of bundles changing slightly throughout scape, distally almost in two distinct series, larger bundles innermost. Medulla almost invariably of uniform parenchyma. Rigidity of scape often increased by mechanical specialization of outer layers of buttresses and stele (e.g. Fig. 35. F, G). Endodermoid layer, when distinct, a fluted cylinder running outside large but inside small vb's. **Vascular bundles** almost always related constantly to number of buttresses and hence of ribs according to formula: number of ribs = buttresses = large vb's = small vb's; or total number of vb's = 2 × number of buttresses or ribs (Fig. 35. A, B). (Most frequent variants recorded diagrammatically in Fig. 35. C–E; cf. Fig. 35. B.) Large vb's commonly resembling those of lamina, each with 2 wide metaxylem vessels flanking phloem, and well-developed protoxylem lacuna (cf. Fig. 32. F). Metaxylem less commonly irregular or represented by distinct strand of vessels, more or less V-shaped in T.S. and enclosing phloem. Smaller vb's with reduced vascular tissues; xylem not arranged regularly, rarely absent, each bundle then including only a small phloem strand (e.g. *E. septangulare*).

Following refers to details for each genus; structure of scape constant and often diagnostic for each sp. (For detailed illustrations see Malmanche.)

(*a*) *Eriocaulon.* Number of ribs in individual spp. (Since the number of ribs (or buttresses, or large vb's when the surface is smooth as in *E. crassiscapum*) can vary within a sp. the following figures may be accepted only as a rough guide to the numbers that are to be found in each sp. The figures do, however, indicate the range throughout the genus.)

4 ribs in *alpestre*.

5 ribs in *alatum*, *australe* (Fig. 35. L), *benthami*, *bifistulosum*, *brownianum*, *buchananii*, *echinulatum*, *gibbosum*, *henryanum*, *kouroussense*, *miquelianum*. Superficially 10 ribs in *E. bifistulosum* because of supplementary ribs opposite chlorenchyma bands (Fig. 35. E).

6 ribs in *cristatum*, *eberhardtii* (plus supplementary ribs), *gracile*, *modestum*, *sexangulare* (5–6).

7 ribs in *bromelioideum*, *buergerianum*, *crassiscapum* (6–7), *longipedunculatum*, *pancheri*, *septangulare*, *ubonense* (7–9).

8 ribs in *fluviatile*.

9 ribs in *helichrysoides*.

10 ribs in *banani, decangulare* (9–14), *dregei, fenestratum* (10–11), *neo-caledonicum.*

11 ribs in *humboldtii, kunthii.*

Scape somewhat flattened, with bilateral symmetry in *E. alpestre, benthami, dregei, eberhardtii, fluviatile, gibbosum, longipedunculatum, septangulare* according to Malmanche. (Possibly Malmanche's record for *septangulare* is based on an artefact, since the scape of this sp. is described as radially symmetrical by other authors, e.g. Hare.) Bilateral symmetry more genuine in *E. longipedunculatum* and *pancheri* with slightly winged scape and cortical lacunae enlarged below wings.

Hairs as on lamina typically restricted to costal regions, length of distal cell of glandular hair (*'poils'*) emphasized as diagnostic feature by Malmanche. **Epidermis** thin-walled, resembling closely that of lamina. **Stomata** restricted to furrows and thus directly above assimilating bands. Stomatal frequency in *E. septangulare* increasing from base to apex of scape, distal stomata 10 times more frequent per unit area on scape than lamina, a feature associated with assimilating function of the scape (Hare 1950). Stomata absent from scape base where enclosed by spathe. Epidermal costal bands situated above buttresses on slight to prominent ribs usually with slightly smaller, thicker-walled cells than intercostal bands, but larger-celled in *E. crassiscapum.*

Cortex usually much wider than stele. **Clorenchyma** corresponding generally to that of lamina, either represented by uniform tissue, or becoming loosely reticulated (e.g. *E. decangulare*), but replaced in more hydrophytic spp. by wide **lacunae** delimited by buttresses (Fig. 35. J, L; air-lac.). Each lacuna lined more or less completely by a single compact layer of chlorenchyma (discontinuous on inner surfaces) and segmented regularly by uniseriate **diaphragms** of stellate chlorophyll-rich cells producing a distinctly fenestrate scape (e.g. *E. banani, fenestratum, septangulare*). Chlorenchyma in *E. longifolium* reduced to narrow tangential bands by massive enlargement of buttresses. Parenchymatous **buttresses** continuous across cortex (occasionally discontinuous in *E. scariosum* (Fig. 35. K)), enlarged tangentially to become more or less T- or Y-shaped in T.S., hypodermal extensions sometimes almost continuous tangentially. Innermost part of buttress in hydrophytic spp. sometimes only bi- or even uniseriate (e.g. *E. banani* and *crassiscapum*). Inner part of buttress, continuous with central tissue, parenchymatous, large-celled, thin-walled, remaining large-celled externally or becoming small-celled in more hydrophytic spp. (e.g. *E. banani*). Outermost buttress cells slightly thick-walled (e.g. *E. australe, bromelioideum, brownianum, decangulare, gracile, humboldtii, longifolium*) or even slightly sclerotic in more rigid scapes (e.g. *E. buergerianum, cristatum, flavidulum, helichrysoides, henryanum, kunthii*), but in any one scape mechanical tissues always most pronounced distally. Collenchyma-like wall thickening sometimes observed (e.g. *E. compressum* and *decangulare*), but true collenchyma recorded by Malmanche only in *E. modestum*; otherwise collenchymatous appearance possibly a stage in development of thicker walls.

Stele represented by a parenchymatous cylinder not clearly demarcated from cortex. **Endodermoid layer** rarely distinct, its recognition by Malmanche (as an endodermis) in many spp. of *Eriocaulon* being rather arbitrary and determined by staining properties different from those of a true suberized endodermis. Endodermoid layer with slightly thickened cell walls recorded by Malmanche in *E. alatum, decangulare* (but not by other authors, e.g. Holm), *longipedunculatum, miquelianum, modestum, neocaledonicum.* Wall thickenings U-shaped in T.S. in *E. alatum, longipedunculatum, modestum.* Cells of endodermoid layer markedly sclerotic in *E. cristatum, helichrysoides, henryanum, kunthii* and correlated with narrow stele. Endodermoid layer described by Malmanche as passing both inside and outside small vb's in *E. decangulare.* Vascular bundles usually enclosed by uniform, small-celled parenchyma. Conjunctive parenchyma becoming somewhat sclerotic in spp. with pronounced mechanical development of buttress tissues, or with a thickened endodermoid layer (i.e. less hydrophytic spp.).

(*b*) *Lachnocaulon.* With 3 (Fig. 35. H), or rarely 4, ribs opposite buttresses in all spp. examined. Epidermis thick-walled in *L. glabrum.* Chlorenchyma often loose, spongy but never lacunose or septate. Endodermoid layer slightly thickened. Smaller vb's sometimes represented by irregular groups of vascular tissue rather than by typical single bundle.

(*c*) *Leiothrix.* More xeromorphic, approaching *Paepalanthus* more than *Eriocaulon.* Ribs 3–7 in *L. beckii,* up to 10 in *L. turbinata* (Fig. 35. F); corresponding to assimilating bands and not buttresses (cf. Fig. 35. C). Chlorenchyma neither lacunose nor septate. Buttresses distinctly sclerotic. Stele with distinctly sclerotic peripheral layers surrounding vb's in *L. urbinata.*

(*d*) *Mesanthemum.* Number of ribs, buttresses or large vb's in individual spp.

4 ribs in *albidum.*
6 ribs in *auratum.*
10 ribs in *pubescens, radicans, rutenbergianum, tuberosum.*

Ribs not corresponding to buttresses; opposite chlorenchyma in *M. albidum, auratum* (Fig. 35. C), in other spp. twice as many (20) ribs as buttresses, the ribs situated above radial junction between chlorenchyma and buttress (Fig. 35. D).

Buttresses typically sclerotic, especially in distal parts of old scapes. Chlorenchyma spongy, with somewhat stellately-lobed cells, especially in *M. rutenbergianum,* but never lacunose or septate. Stele wide, up to 6 times diameter of cortex; medulla hollow in *M. radicans.* Endodermoid layer thickened in all spp. studied. Vb's sclerotic in *M. rutenbergianum.*

(*e*) *Paepalanthus.* Scape structure always more xeromorphic than in *Eriocaulon.* Scape sometimes smooth as in *P. bifidus, brachypus, compactus, falcifolius, polyanthus;* otherwise ribs complementary to cortical buttresses, rarely with additional ribs, each major divided into 2 minor ribs as in *P. elegans, hirsutus, xeranthemoides.*

Number of ribs, buttresses or large vb's in individual spp.

2 ribs in *spixianus.*
3 ribs in *alsinoides* (Fig. 31. J), *bongardii, brachypus, caespititius, caulescens,*

claussenianus, elegans, freyreissii, hilairei, minutulus, neglectus, nitens, oerstedianus, plantagineus, polyanthus, ramosus, tortilis, xeranthemoides.

4 ribs in *bifidus* (4–5), *falcifolius, flaccidus, flagellaris, polyanthus* (4–5 or 6), *schenckii, viviparus.*

5 ribs in *compactus, hirsutus, spathulatus, warmingianus.*

6 ribs in *amoenus, ensifolius, langsdorffii, plumosus.*

7 ribs in *blepharocnemis, flavescens.*

8 ribs in *consanguineus* (8–10), *curvifolius, densiflorus, elongatus, weddellianus, williamsii.*

Bilaterally symmetrical scape, recorded by Malmanche for *P. ensifolius, langsdorffii, neglectus*, possibly artefacts; *P. spixianus* with 2 buttresses probably genuinely bilateral. Ribs typically above buttresses, as in *Eriocaulon*, but above chlorenchyma (Fig. 35. C) in many spp. as in *P. blepharocnemis, caespititius, consanguineus, curvifolius, ensifolius, flagellaris, flavescens, freyreissii, hirsutus, langsdorffii, neglectus, nitens, plantagineus, plumosus, warmingianus.*

Epidermis typically thicker-walled than in *Eriocaulon*, sometimes markedly so (e.g. *P. alsinoides*); epidermal cells enlarged anticlinally in *P. ramosus* and *polyanthus* in a manner recalling that to be seen in lamina, but epidermis not otherwise specialized to same degree as that of lamina. Cortex unique in *P. compactus*, because uniformly parenchymatous, without distinction between buttresses and assimilating bands. Chlorenchyma usually compact or at most slightly spongy, never lacunose or septate; sometimes restricted to narrow strands almost wholly enclosed by sclerenchyma of buttress, as in *P. elegans*. Scape emphasized as a major assimilating organ by Ruhland in *P. argyrolinon* and *dasynema*.

Buttresses wholly or almost wholly of sclerenchyma in *P. amoenus, bongardii, brachypus, claussenianus, curvifolius, densiflorus, elegans, elongatus, flaccidus, flagellaris, flavescens, hirsutus, nitens, polyanthus, viviparus, weddellianus, williamsii*. Other spp., with thin-walled buttress cells, probably shade-dwellers according to Malmanche. Buttresses incomplete in *P. alsinoides* (Fig. 31. J), represented by hypodermal strands of sclerenchyma opposite large vb's.

Endodermoid layer thin-walled in *P. bongardii, brachypus, claussenianus, falcifolius, hilairei, polyanthus, ramosus, spathulatus*, according to Malmanche and said to be sclerotic in remaining spp. studied, but this interpretation perhaps artificial owing to the difficulty of distinguishing the endodermoid layer from sclerotic ground tissue of stele. Peripheral stelar tissue around vb's often sclerotic, sometimes markedly so. Large vb's more usually with an irregular strand of tracheal elements than in *Eriocaulon*; V-shaped in T.S. (e.g. Fig. 31. K). *Paepalanthus consanguineus* unique in possessing medullary bundles in addition to normal peripheral stelar bundles.

(*f*) *Philodice*. Ribs 5 in *P. hoffmannseggii*. Hairs with basal cell often elongated, bottle-shaped; collar-cell elongated, unlike corresponding cell in other Eriocaulaceae. Chlorenchyma compact, scarcely spongy; endodermoid layer thickened. Ground tissue of stele thick-walled in contrast to thin-walled parenchymatous buttresses.

(g) *Syngonanthus*. Number of ribs, buttresses or large vb's in individual spp.

3 ribs in *caulescens, nitens, niveus*.
5 ribs in *flavidulus* (Fig. 35. I).
10 ribs in *reflexus*.

Ribs correspond to buttresses in *S. caulescens* and *nitens*, but more or less to assimilating bands in *S. niveus* and *reflexus*, major ribs themselves each somewhat divided into 2 minor ribs. Epidermis markedly thick-walled in *S. reflexus*. Buttresses sclerotic, massive in *S. reflexus*, chlorenchyma then reduced to narrow bands. Endodermoid layer not usually distinct. Stelar peripheral cells surrounding vb's somewhat thick-walled, especially in *S. reflexus*.

(h) *Tonina*. Surface irregularly ribbed, without regular correspondence between ribs, buttresses, or vb's. Buttresses 3, unequal. Chlorenchyma compact, scarcely spongy, not septate. Endodermoid layer and outermost cells of stele somewhat thick-walled. Vb's 5 large and 5 small.

Diagnostic characters of scape emphasized by Malmanche in Eriocaulaceae as a whole include the following: (i) Variations in size and shape of distal cell of glandular hairs and in thickness of cell walls of epidermis. (ii) Variations in the number of ribs and their corresponding buttresses and large vb's. (iii) Differences in position of ribs in relation to buttresses. (iv) Presence or absence of septate lacunae in cortical assimilating bands and degree of spongyness of chlorenchyma. (v) Amount of wall thickening in endodermoid layer (although it is doubtful if this layer is a consistent morphological entity). (vi) Degree of sclerification of buttresses and outer layers of stele. Further details will be found in Malmanche's monograph on which this account is based.

ROOT (Figs. 36–39)

Adventitious, of two fairly distinct types, either (i) vermiform or articulate, due to distinct cortical diaphragms as in almost all spp. of *Eriocaulon*, or (ii) uniform, non-vermiform, without cortical diaphragms as in most spp. of remaining genera. Former type usually spongy white in external appearance, latter compact and brown (Malmanche). Roots in *Eriocaulon decangulare* described by Holm as either (*a*) thick, white, mostly unbranched, with few root-hairs or (*b*) less white, thinner, longer with many lateral rootlets and root-hairs. (This difference refers only to external appearance and is possibly one of age since internal structure of roots of both types is identical.)

Piliferous layer usually differentiated into long-cells and short-cells, the latter producing hairs (Fig. 36. A–H). Root-hairs apparently absent from some samples of *E. australe*, and from *E. septangulare* according to Hare. Root-hairs in *Carptotepala jenmanii* arising from one end of a long-cell, not from a short-cell. Root-hairs commonly in irregular groups of 2 or more (e.g. Fig. 36. E, H) as e.g. in *Paepalanthus acuminatus, bahiensis, compactus, rigidus*; most typically in pairs (Figs. 36. C, D, F; 39. C), the paired cells side by side (e.g. in many spp. of *Eriocaulon* and *Lachnocaulon*) or sometimes one above the other (e.g. in *Leiothrix turbinata*). Paired and solitary root-hairs

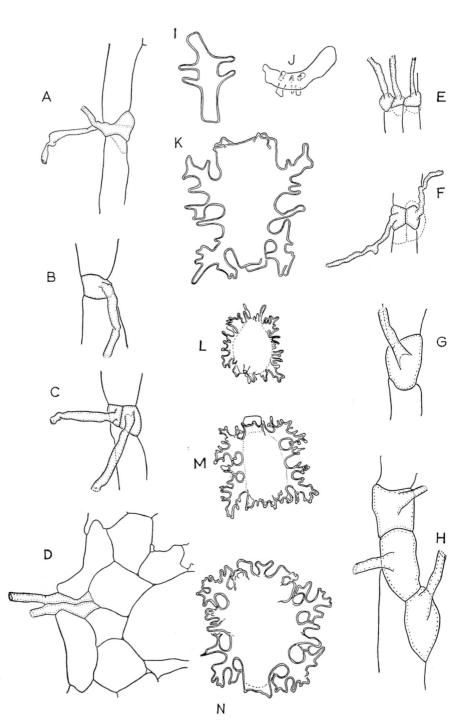

Fig. 36. ERIOCAULACEAE. Root (all ×290).

A–H. Root-hairs.

A. *Eriocaulon scariosum*, optical L.S. twin root-hairs. B–D. *Eriocaulon decangulare*. B. Solitary root-hair, surface view. C. Twin root-hair, surface view. D. T.S. periphery of root with twin root-hairs. E–F. *Lachnocaulon minus*. E. Triplet of root-hairs, surface view. F. Twin root-hairs, surface view. G–H. *Leiothrix turbinata*. G. Solitary root-hair, surface view. H. Triplet of root-hairs in vertical series.

I–N. Short-cells from middle cortex, all as seen in T.S. root except J.

I–J. *Paepalanthus williamsii*. Short-cells with relatively simple outline. I. From T.S. root. J. Obliquely horizontal view of isolated cell. K–N. *Eriocaulon* spp. K. *E. scariosum*. L. *E. articulatum*. M. *E. compressum*. N. *E. decangulare*. The series I–N illustrates increasing complexity of outline (cf. Fig. 39. E–H).

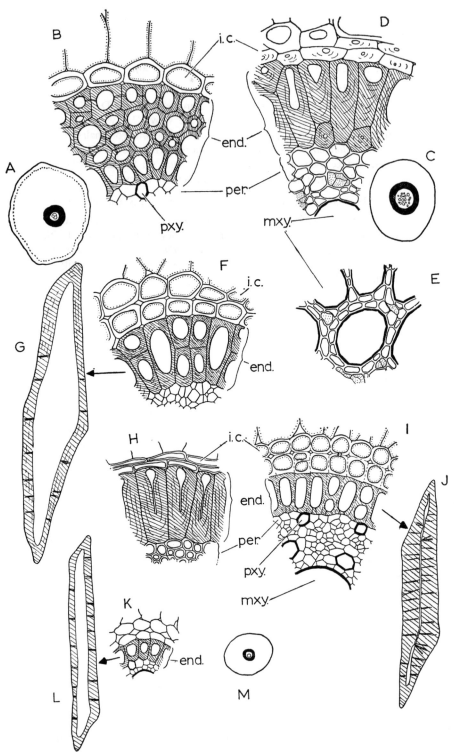

Fig. 37. ERIOCAULACEAE. Root.

A, B. *Carptotepala jenmanii.*

A. T.S. root ($\times$17). B. T.S. endodermal region ($\times$290).

C–E. *Paepalanthus albo-vaginatus.*

C. T.S. root ($\times$17). D. T.S. endodermal region ($\times$290). E. T.S. central part of stele ($\times$290).

F, G. *Mesanthemum radicans* ($\times$290).

F. T.S. endodermal region. G. Isolated endodermal cell.

H. *Leiothrix nubigena.* Endodermal region ($\times$290).

I, J. *Paepalanthus williamsii* ($\times$290).

I. Endodermal region. J. Isolated endodermal cell.

K, L. *Leiothrix arechavaletae* ($\times$290).

K. T.S. endodermal region. L. Isolated endodermal cell.

M. *Leiothrix pilulifera.* T.S. root ($\times$17).

i.c.—inner cortex; end.—endodermis; per.—pericycle; pxy.—protoxylem; mxy.—metaxylem.

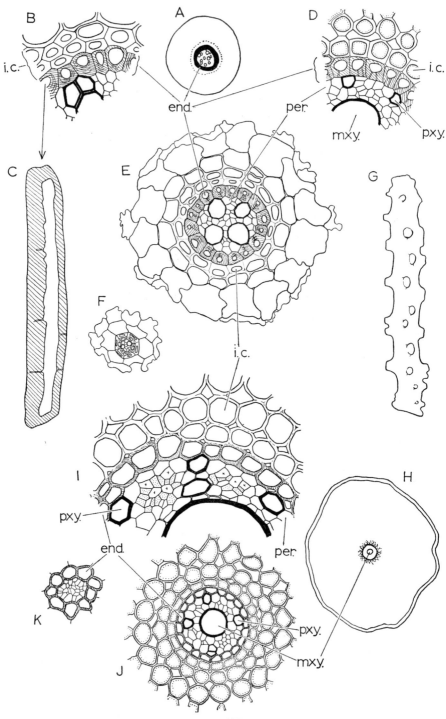

180

Fig. 38. ERIOCAULACEAE. Root.

A–C. *Eriocaulon caulinum.*

  A. T.S. root ($\times 40$).

B. T.S. endodermal region ($\times 290$). C. Isolated endodermal cell ($\times 290$).

D. *Eriocaulon australe.* T.S. endodermal region ($\times 290$).

E, F. *Lachnocaulon engleri.*

  E. T.S. entire root ($\times 290$). F. T.S. branch root ($\times 290$).

G. *Eriocaulon arechavaletae.* Isolated lobed inner cortical cell ($\times 290$).

H. I. *Eriocaulon decangulare.*

  H T.S. root ($\times 17$). I. T.S. endodermal region ($\times 290$).

J. *Eriocaulon compressum.* T.S. complete stele ($\times 290$).

K. *Eriocaulon melanocephalum.* T.S. complete stele ($\times 290$).

  i.c.—inner cortex; end.—endodermis; per.—pericycle; pxy.—proto-xylem; mxy—metaxylem.

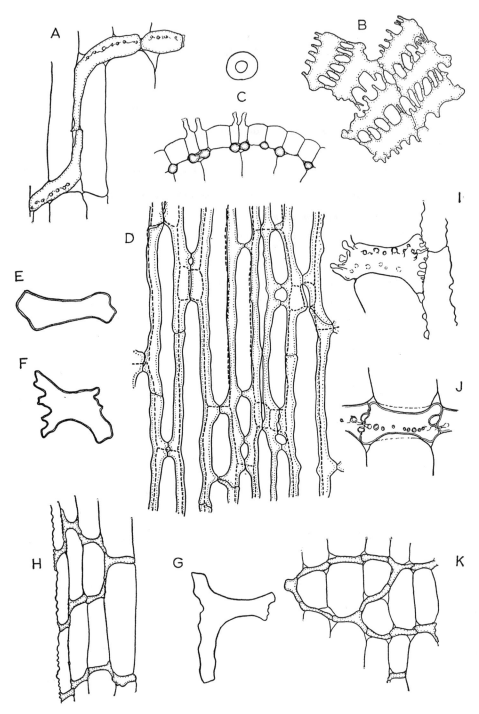

182

Fɪɢ. 39. ERIOCAULACEAE. Root cortex.

A–D. *Syngonanthus flavidulus.*

A. Vertical connexion between two adjacent diaphragms from L.S. root (×290). B. Portion of diaphragm from T.S. root (×290). C. Diagrammatic T.S. peripheral layers (not to scale). D. Surface layers, surface view, at focal plane of hypodermis, piliferous layer with dotted outline (×230).

E–H. *Eriocaulon australe.*

E. Short-cell, simple outline, optical L.S. (×290). F. Short-cell, somewhat lobed, optical L.S. (×290). G. Short-cell next to innermost cortical layers, optical L.S. (×290). H. L.S. middle cortex, short-cells arranged in incipient diaphragms (×100).

I, J. *Eriocaulon compressum.*

I. Short-cell next to innermost cortical layers, radial L.S. root (×290). J. Short-cell from radial L.S. root (×290).

K. *Leiothrix flavescens.* Radial L.S. middle cortex with reticulum of short-cells (×100).

sometimes in more or less equal numbers (e.g. in *Lachnocaulon engleri*), or root-hairs mostly single with occasional pairs (e.g. in *Syngonanthus reflexus*). Malmanche's illustration of continuous vertical series of root-hairs in *Paepalanthus brachypus* possibly incorrect. Individual root-hairs typically inflated below root surface, their bases overarched by adjacent long-cells (Fig. 36. A, E, F). Clustered root-hairs commonly thicker-walled and less ephemeral than solitary or paired root-hairs.

Cortex usually with regular radial seriation of cells, especially in innermost layers; divided into three fairly distinct zones: (i) outer, (ii) middle, (iii) inner cortex, especially in more specialized roots.

(i) **Outer cortex** usually of one compact layer of thin-walled or at most slightly thick-walled, slightly ligno-suberized cells; 2-layered and forming a fairly distinct exodermis in *Carptotepala jenmanii*. Outermost cortical layer in *Paepalanthus williamsii*, *Philodice hoffmannseggii*, and especially in *Syngonanthus*, e.g. *S. caulescens*, *flavidulus*, *nitens*, discontinuous, represented by a single series of narrow, slightly thick-walled cells below anticlinal walls of piliferous layer, the remaining space occupied by enlarged cortical cells abutting directly on piliferous layer (Fig. 39. C). Small cells of outer cortex connected by tangential protrusions usually meeting below pairs of root-hairs, the whole system forming an interconnected reticulum between middle cortex and piliferous layer (Fig. 39. D).

(ii) **Middle cortex** varying throughout the family as a whole, but quite constant for each sp.; either wholly unspecialized (e.g. many spp. of *Paepalanthus*) or highly specialized (most *Eriocaulon* spp.) with several intermediate types.

(*a*) Unspecialized cortex usually narrow in proportion to stele (e.g. Figs. 37. C; 38. A), as little as 2–4 cells wide in *Paepalanthus bifidus*, *minutulus*, consisting of uniformly long cells, thin-walled externally, usually with gradual or sharp transition to thicker-walled cells of inner cortex. Unspecialized cortex observed in, e.g., *Blastocaulon rupestre*; *Eriocaulon caulinum*, *nigrum*, *seemanii* and possibly *E. melanocephalum*; *Lachnocaulon engleri* (Fig. 38. E), *minus*; *Leiothrix nubigena*, *turbinata*; *Paepalanthus acuminatus*, *amoenus*, *bahiensis*, *balansae*, *brittonii*, *capillaceus*, *compactus*, *lamarckii*, *rigidus*, *seslerioides*, *tuerckheimii*; *Tonina fluviatilis*.

(*b*) Slightly specialized cortex showing features transitional to highly specialized condition. Early stage in *Paepalanthus duidae* with middle cortex differentiated into vertical files of more or less alternate long-cells and short-cells, with regular outline, independent of one another. Short-cells in this and subsequently more specialized types apparently derived by an equal transverse division of a cortical mother cell with subsequent elongation of only one daughter cell, not by unequal division of a mother cell. In somewhat more specialized roots, originally contiguous short-cells, despite elongation of long-cells, retain continuity in two directions. (1) Vertically, by extensions maintaining contact by growth at same rate as over-all root elongation (Fig. 39. A), the short-cells thus forming an irregular reticulum in the intercellular system between long-cells (e.g. Fig. 39. H, K), as in the following spp.: *Carptotepala jenmanii*; *Eriocaulon alpestre*, *australe*, *benthami*, *caesium*, *formosanum*, *heterodoxum*, *longifolium*; *Leiothrix curvifolia*, *dielsii*, *echinulata*, *flavescens*, *fulgida, pilulifera*; *Mesanthemum radicans, rutenbergianum*; *Paepalanthus williamsii*; *Syngonanthus caulescens*; with a slight tendency, especially in *Eriocaulon* spp., for cells to be arranged in regular horizontal series. (2) Horizontally, by irregular lateral protrusions developed between adjacent short-cells at same level (Fig. 39. B).

(*c*) Specialized cortex developed by restriction of short-cells to **transverse diaphragms,** separated by a single whorl of long-cells, as in all spp. of *Eriocaulon* except those mentioned above. Diaphragms sometimes somewhat irregular, as in *E. compressum*, but otherwise sufficiently regular to produce characteristic vermiform appearance. Diaphragms rare in other genera as in *Syngonanthus flavidulus* and *Philodice hoffmannseggii* and exceptional for the genera *Leiothrix* in *L. arechavaletae* and *Paepalanthus* in *P. nitens* and *xeranthemoides*. Less highly organized diaphragms include those recorded by Malmanche with relatively smooth short-cells, not in lateral contact, as in *Eriocaulon australe, brownianum, longifolium*; *Paepalanthus curvifolius, flavescens, hirsutus* (cf. Fig. 39. E–G). Short-cells otherwise lobed horizontally. Lobes relatively few and simple, e.g. in *Carptotepala jenmanii* and *Syngonanthus flavidulus*, but in most *Eriocaulon* spp., short-cells lobed in a complex but characteristic manner (Hare 1950) (cf. series of increasing complexity, Fig. 36. I–N). Each short-cell essentially cubical, but elaborately lobed to form numerous peg-like contacts with adjacent short-cells, the pegs maintaining local continuity despite over-all expansion; rarely some of finer protrusions losing contact and ending blindly. Each short-cell with several major lobes, themselves subdivided into minor lobes or the minor lobes arising directly from main cell body. Major lobes sometimes in vertical pairs on each tangential wall, accompanied by four on radial walls, more or less one at each corner and extending horizontally. Upper and lower surfaces of the short-cell smooth and somewhat concave due to pressure of long-cells above and below (Fig. 39. I, J). Major lobes alternatively subdivided into numerous fine protrusions making minor lobes. Other, numerous, minor lobes arising directly from main cell body between major lobes. Minor lobes making contact with similar lobes either from a different or commonly from the same cell (Fig. 36. K–N). Short-cells commonly slightly thicker-walled than long-cells and often slightly lignified (e.g. *E. decangulare*), the 'nodal' diaphragms then much more rigid than the intervening long-celled 'internodal' regions. For more details of diaphragms see Hare (1950). Lacunae described by Malmanche in some spp. (e.g. *E. buergerianum*) said to be formed by breakdown of tangential walls of cortical cells, but probably an artefact. (The 'remains' of the tangential walls illustrated by Malmanche are probably minute longitudinal plications which are common in vertical walls of inflated long-cells. Developmental studies and isolation of long-cells by maceration do not suggest development of lysigenous lacunae.)

(iii) **Inner cortex** of radially and concentrically seriated layers one or more cells thick, usually differing from middle cortex (e.g. Figs. 37. B, D, F, H; 38. B, D, E, I, J). Inner cortical layers often flattened tangentially (e.g. Fig. 37. D, H), commonly with slight to pronounced wall thickening, the thickening usually uniformly distributed, the number of modified inner cortical layers usually constant for each sp. Inner cortex of mechanical significance in more hydrophytic spp. (e.g. most *Eriocaulon* spp.) supplementing and often closely resembling endodermis (Fig. 38. I, J), but in more xerophytic spp. (e.g. most *Paepalanthus* spp.), although often thicker-walled and more pronounced than in *Eriocaulon*, mechanically less significant in view of massive endodermis (e.g. Fig. 37. D). Innermost cortical cells in many *Eriocaulon* spp. (e.g. *E. septangulare*) with numerous peg-like outgrowths (Fig. 38. G) making contact with each other and especially with the enlarged short-cells forming innermost limit of each diaphragm (Fig. 39. I). Surface in contact with endodermis usually smooth.

Endodermis usually uniseriate, arising from same mother cells as inner cortical layers; occasionally biseriate in *Paepalanthus albo-vaginatus*; multiseriate, up to 5-layered in *Carptotepala jenmanii* (Fig. 37. B). Falsely biseriate endodermis developed from radial overlapping of markedly oblique end walls of short endodermal cells (Fig. 37. F), the tapering end walls sometimes as long as non-overlapping walls (Fig. 37. G), e.g. in *Blastocaulon rupestre*; *Leiothrix arechavaletae, echinulata*; *Mesanthemum radicans*; *Paepalanthus albo-vaginatus, balansae, brachypus, compactus, williamsii*; frequency of this pseudo-biseriation depending on obliqueness of end walls in relation to length of endodermal cell (cf. Fig. 37. F–G, I–J, K–L). Endodermal cells in *Eriocaulon* typically long and with truncate ends. Degree and distribution of wall thickening in mature endodermal cells v. constant and of some diagnostic value for each sp.; more hydrophytic spp. (e.g. *Eriocaulon*) including a narrow, thin-walled endodermis not well differentiated from inner cortex except for suberin deposits (Fig. 38. J); more xeromorphic spp. (e.g. *Leiothrix, Paepalanthus*) including a wide, thick-walled and mechanically significant endodermis abruptly differentiated from inner cortex and pericycle (e.g. Fig. 37. B, D, F, H), the unspecialized cortex typically associated with this mechanical endodermis usually sloughing early.

Types of endodermis and their distribution

(i) Cells of endodermis uniformly thin-walled, or walls at most slightly thickened. *Eriocaulon arechavaletae, australe* (slight thickening), *benthami, buergerianum, caesium, capillus-najadis, compressum, crassiscapum, cristatum, formosanum, fuliginosum, helichrysoides, heterodoxum, longifolium, longipedunculatum, nigrum, nipponicum, ovoideum, tropicanum, truncatum*; *Philodice hoffmannseggii*; *Syngonanthus caulescens*. Somewhat thicker-walled endodermis, transitional to next class in *Eriocaulon decangulare, kurtzii, melanocephalum, panamaense*. In *E. benthami, melanocephalum* (Fig. 38. K) endodermis forms sole mechanical tissue of root.

(ii) Cells of endodermis uniformly thickened, but extent of wall thickening quite variable, although massive and often distinctly lamellate in spp. marked (*). *Eriocaulon brownianum, longifolium, seemanii*; *Leiothrix arechavaletae, curvifolia (*), dielsii, echinulata (*), flavescens, fulgida (*), pilulifera, turbinata (*)*; *Mesanthemum auratum, radicans, rutenbergianum*; *Paepalanthus amoenus, bahiensis, brachypus, brittonii, compactus (*), curvifolius, duidae, elegans (*), flavescens, hirsutus (*), nitens, rigidus, vaginatus, weddellianus (*), williamsii*; *Syngonanthus flavidulus (*)*.

(iii) Cells of endodermis unevenly thickened, the inner tangential thicker than remaining walls and appearing more or less U-shaped in T.S. Walls relatively slightly thickened, as in *Eriocaulon alpestre*, some samples of *E. australe* and *Paepalanthus lamarckii*, but walls more usually thick, often distinctly lamellate as in *Blastocaulon rupestre*; *Eriocaulon caulinum*; *Lachnocaulon engleri, glabrum, minus*; *Leiothrix nubigena*; *Paepalanthus acuminatus, albo-vaginatus, alsinoides, balansae, lamarckii, seslerioides, tuerckheimii*. In massive-walled endodermis, cell lumen often almost occluded, frequently conspicuously pitted. Mechanical significance of thick-walled endodermal cells frequently indicated by their radial extension (Fig. 37. D, F, H), thereby increasing thickness of endodermis as in *Blastocaulon rupestre*; *Leiothrix curvifolia, echinulata, nubigena, turbinata*; *Mesanthemum radicans*; *Paepalanthus albo-vaginatus, brachypus, brittonii, compactus, curvifolius, elegans, weddellianus.*

Pericycle usually uniseriate, thin-walled, inconspicuous, but locally or continuously bi- or tri-seriate in *Leiothrix curvifolia*; *Paepalanthus brittonii, compactus, xeranthemoides*; lignified and appreciably thick-walled in *Leiothrix nubigena* (Fig. 37. H); *Paepalanthus claussenianus, compactus, falcifolius, ramosus, weddellianus*. Pericycle typically interrupted by protoxylem elements lying next to endodermis (Figs. 37. I; 38. B, D, I, J), a feature characteristic of the family according to van Tieghem, but sometimes not seen in roots with wide steles as in, e.g., *Leiothrix curvifolia*; *Paepalanthus balansae, brittonii, claussenianus, compactus, falcifolius, rigidus*. Number of protoxylem poles emphasized as a diagnostic feature by van Tieghem, but shown by subsequent authors to be somewhat variable within a single sp.

Stele varying in complexity, from oligarch to polyarch largely in proportion to diameter. Wide steles including several to many wide metaxylem vessels scattered more or less uniformly throughout medullary parenchyma. Peripheral metaxylem elements somewhat narrower and not arranged in distinct radial series (Fig. 37. C) in *Blastocaulon rupestre*; *Carptotepala jenmanii*; *Eriocaulon arechavaletae, caulinum, fenestratum, helichrysoides, humboldtii, kunthii, kurtzii*; *Leiothrix curvifolia, nubigena, turbinata*; *Mesanthemum radicans*; *Paepalanthus albo-vaginatus, amoenus, balansae, brachypus, brittonii, claussenianus, compactus, curvifolius, elongatus, falcifolius, hilairei, ramosus, rigidus, tuerckheimii, vaginatus, weddellianus, williamsii*. Stele transitional to more simple type in *Lachnocaulon* (e.g. *L. engleri* (Fig. 38. E), *L. glabrum*); *Tonina fluviatilis* (with 3–5 wide central vessels themselves often in direct contact with endodermis, a condition approached by *Paepalanthus tuerckheimii*). Stele in more hydrophytic spp. narrow (Fig. 38. H) and relatively simple, the xylem consisting only of a solitary wide central vessel and a fairly constant number of narrow, pericyclic protoxylem elements (Fig. 38. I, J) as in all *Eriocaulon* spp. not listed above; in most *Leiothrix* spp. except those listed above; in *Mesanthemum auratum, rutenbergianum*; *Paepalanthus alsinoides, caulescens, duidae, elegans, flaccidus, flavescens, lamarckii, nitens, xeranthemoides*; *Philodice hoffmannseggii*. Narrow steles often including only one conjunctive layer between central vessel and pericycle as in *E. scariosum*. Stele in *E. melanocephalum* v. narrow, xylem elements mostly vestigial (Fig. 38. K).

Phloem in wider steles sometimes in strands uniformly distributed throughout central ground parenchyma, between scattered vessels (Fig. 37. E), as in

Blastocaulon rupestre; *Eriocaulon caulinum, kurtzii*; *Leiothrix curvifolia, nubigena*; *Paepalanthus albo-vaginatus, brittonii, claussenianus, compactus, falcifolius, ramosus*, the phloem strands often reduced to a single sieve-tube, but more typically restricted to a peripheral position, alternating with the protoxylem elements but never situated in the pericycle. Phloem strands small and often inconspicuous, more obvious in spp. with thick-walled conjunctive parenchyma, such as *Leiothrix fulgida*; *Paepalanthus falcifolius, weddellianus*.

SECRETORY, STORAGE, AND CONDUCTING ELEMENTS

Crystals. Calcium oxalate common as prismatic, rhombohedral, and often needle-like crystals associated with assimilating tissue; druse-like aggregates occasional.

Starch mostly restricted to cortex of rhizome and colourless tissues of leaf base; grains small, mostly simple, irregularly spherical.

Xylem. Vessels in metaxylem of all parts, with mostly simple, more or less transverse perforation plates, less commonly scalariform with few thickening bars in leaf and scape. Elements in stem of *Tonina fluviatilis* with long, scalariform perforation plates on v. oblique end walls. Elements in root usually long with pitted walls, thickening least developed in roots of hydrophytic spp., often represented by annular thickenings connected by frequent vertical bars. Elements in rhizome short, irregular; end wall often irregularly oblique.

TAXONOMIC NOTES

Diagnostic anatomical features in the Eriocaulaceae are most likely to be found in the structure of the hairs, especially those on the reproductive organs, which in some instances are critical for the separation of the genera. Otherwise, although the family is quite diverse in its anatomy the genera are not structurally sharply circumscribed one from the other. Rather there seems to be a trend throughout the family from genera such as *Paepalanthus* and *Leiothrix* with mesomorphic or even xeromorphic anatomy to others such as *Eriocaulon* and *Lachnocaulon* in which the structure is more hydromorphic. This trend is most pronounced in roots, which are unusually diverse in their structure compared with those of most monocotyledons. It should be noted that *Eriocaulon*, which is regarded by Ruhland as having the least specialized flowers, largely on the basis of number of parts, seems most specialized in its anatomy. *Paepalanthus* is generally least specialized in its anatomy. It is, however, difficult to interpret trends of increasing specialization in root anatomy except in the direction from *Paepalanthus* to *Eriocaulon*. On the other hand, the range of pollen morphology seems to support Ruhland's interpretation, since in *Eriocaulon* spiral apertures are several, narrow, and elongated whereas in the remaining genera the apertures are progressively reduced in number and become short and narrow (Thanikaimoni 1965). The recent discovery of *Wurdackia* with perfect flowers might throw light on this situation and its examination is much desired.

The association of Eriocaulaceae with *Aphyllanthes* (Liliaceae), suggested by Takhtajan (1959) largely on the basis of similarities in pollen morphology, seems unnatural in view of the marked anatomical dissimilarities between the two taxa, as pointed out by Tomlinson (1965).

GENERA AND SPECIES REPORTED ON IN THE LITERATURE

Arber (1922) *Eriocaulon cuspidatum* Dalz., *E. septangulare* With., *E. setaceum* L., *E. wallichianum* Mart. f. *submersa, Paepalanthus speciosus* Gardn.; leaf.

Hare (1950) *Eriocaulon septangulare* With.; all parts.

Holm (1901) *Eriocaulon decangulare* L.; all parts.

Lecomte (1908) *Eriocaulon ubonense* Lec.; scape.

Malmanche (1919) *Eriocaulon alatum* Lec.; leaf, scape, root. *E. alpestre* Hook. et Toms.; scape. *E. annamense* Lec.; leaf, root. *E. australe* R. Br.; leaf, scape, root. *E. banani* Lec.; scape, root. *E. benthami* Schldl.; scape. *E. bifistulosum* van Huerck et Muell.; stem, scape. *E. bromelioideum* Lec.; leaf, scape, root. *E. brownianum* Mart.; scape, root. *E. buchananii* Schldl.; scape. *E. buergerianum* Koern.; leaf, scape, root. *E. crassiscapum* Bong.; leaf, scape, root. *E. cristatum* Mart.; scape. *E. decangulare* L.; leaf, scape, root. *E. dregei* Hochst.; leaf, scape, root. *E. eberhardtii* Lec.; scape. *E. echinulatum* Mart.; scape. *E. fenestratum* Boj.; leaf, scape, root. *E. fluviatile* Trim.; scape, rhizome. *E. gibbosum* Koern.; scape. *E. gracile* Mart.; leaf, scape. *E. helichrysoides* Bong.; leaf, scape, root. *E. henryanum* Ruhl.; scape, root. *E. humboldtii* Kunth; leaf, scape, root. *E. kouroussense* Lec.; leaf, scape. *E. kunthii* Koern.; leaf, scape, root. *E. longifolium* Nees; leaf, scape, root. *E. longipedunculatum* Lec.; scape, root. *E. modestum* Kunth; scape, root. *E. neocaledonicum* Schl.; scape. *E. pancheri* Lec.; rhizome, scape. *E. septangulare* With.; scape. *E. setaceum* L.; stem. *Lachnocaulon anceps* Benth. et Hook.; scape, root. *L. beyrichianum* Sporled.; scape. *L. glabrum* Koern.; scape, root. *L. michauxii* Kunth; leaf, scape, root. *Mesanthemum albidum* Lec.; scape. *M. auratum* Lec.; leaf, scape, root. *M. pubescens* Koern.; leaf, scape. *M. radicans* Koern.; leaf, scape, root. *M. rutenbergianum* Koern.; leaf, scape, root. *M. tuberosum* Lec.; leaf, scape. *Paepalanthus amoenus* Koern.; leaf, scape. *P. blepharocnemis* Mart.; scape. *P. bongardii* Kunth; scape. *P. brachypus* Kunth; leaf, scape, root. *P. caespititius* Mart.; scape. *P. caulescens* Kunth; stem, scape, root. *P. claussenianus* Koern.; leaf, scape, root. *P. compactus* Gard.; leaf, scape, root. *P. curvifolius* Kunth; leaf, scape, root. *P. densiflorus* Koern.; stem, scape. *P. elegans* Kunth; leaf, scape, root. *P. elongatus* Koern.; leaf, scape, root. *P. ensifolius* Kunth; scape. *P. falcifolius* Koern.; leaf, scape, root. *P. flaccidus* Kunth; leaf, scape, root. *P. flagellaris* Kunth; scape. *P. flavescens* Koern.; leaf, scape, root. *P. hilairei* Koern.; root. *P. hirsutus* Kunth; leaf, scape, root. *P. langsdorffii* Koern.; scape. *P. neglectus* Koern.; scape. *P. nitens* Kunth; scape, root. *P. oerstedianus* Koern.; leaf, scape. *P. plantagineus* Koern.; scape. *P. plumosus* Koern.; scape. *P. polyanthus* Kunth; scape. *P. ramosus* Kunth; leaf, scape, root. *P. spathulatus* Koern.; scape. *P. spixianus* Mart.; scape. *P. tortilis* Mart.; scape. *P. viviparus* Mart.; scape. *P. weddellianus* Koern.; leaf, scape, root. *P. xeranthemoides* Mart.; leaf, rhizome, scape, root. *Philodice hoffmannseggii* Mart.; leaf, stem, scape, root. *Tonina fluviatilis* Aubl.; leaf, stem, scape, root.

Poulsen (1888) *Eriocaulon helichrysoides* Bong., *Paepalanthus (Carpocephalus) caulescens* Kunth, *P. (Platycaulon) consanguineus* Koern., *P. freyreissii* Koern., *P. (Lopophyllum) itatiaiae* Koern., *P. minutulus* Mart., *P. (Psilocephalus) nitens* Kunth, *P. plantagineus* Koern., *P. (Actinocephalus) polyanthus* Kunth, *P. schenckii* Pouls., *P. schraderi* Koern., *P. tortilis* Koern., *P. (Trichocalyx)* sp., *Tonina fluviatilis* Aubl.; all parts.

Ruhland (1903) claimed to have studied 'all spp. of *Paepalanthoideae*', his account only a preliminary study. No subsequent detailed account ever appeared. Following summarizes spp. mentioned in his account with reference to detailed

anatomical features: *Eriocaulon crassiscapum* Bong.; leaf. *Leiothrix crassifolia*
(Bong.) Ruhl.; scape. *L. luxurians* (Koern.) Ruhl.; root. *L. pedunculosa* Ruhl.;
leaf. *Paepalanthus acanthophyllus* Ruhl.; stem, hairs. *P. amoenus* (Bong.)
Koern.; leaf. *P. applanatus* Ruhl.; leaf. *P. argenteus* (Bong.) Koern.; leaf.
P. argyrolinon Koern.; scape. *P. blepharophorus* (Bong.) Koern.; leaf. *P. camp-
tophyllus* Ruhl.; stoma. *P. capillaceus* Klotsch.; leaf. *P. chloroblepharus* Ruhl.;
leaf; *P. ciliolatus* Ruhl.; hairs. *P. claussenianus* Koern.; leaf, scape. *P. compactus* Gardn.; hairs. *P. dasynema* Ruhl.; stem, scape. *P. dichotomus* Klotsch.;
leaf. *P. distichophyllus* Mart.; hairs. *P. elongatus* Koern.; leaf, stem, scape.
P. flaccidus (Bong.) Kunth; leaf. *P. geniculatus* (Bong.) Kunth; root. *P. guianensis* Klotsch.; leaf. *P. gyrotrichus* Ruhl.; hairs. *P. hilairei* Koern.; leaf, scape.
P. homomallus (Bong.) Mart.; leaf. *P. incanus* (Bong.) Koern.; stem. *P. loefgreni-
anus* Ruhl.; leaf. *P. macrorrhizus* (Bong.) Kunth; leaf. *P. pachyphyllus* Koern.;
leaf. *P. pilosus* (H. B. K.) Kunth; root. *P. plumosus* (Bong.) Koern.; stem. *P.
polyanthus* (Bong.) Kunth; root. *P. saxatilis* (Bong.) Koern.; root. *P. scandens*
Ruhl.; stem. *P. scytophyllus* Ruhl.; hairs. *P. sellowianus* Koern.; stem. *P.
senaeanus* Ruhl.; leaf. *P. suffruticans* Ruhl.; leaf.

Schwendener (1874) *Eriocaulon decangulare* L.; scape. *E. flavidulum* Michx.; scape.
Tonina fluviatilis Aubl.; stem.

Solereder and Meyer (1929) *Eriocaulon decangulare* L.; leaf, scape. *E. septangulare*
With.; all parts. *Paepalanthus falcifolius* Mart.; stem. *Syngonanthus niveus*
Ruhl.; leaf, scape. *Tonina fluviatilis* Aubl.; leaf, stem.

Solomon (1931) *Eriocaulon septangulare* With.; stem, root.

Van Tieghem (1887*a*) *Paepalanthus elongatus, P. polyanthus, P. ramosus*; root-
hairs.

Van Tieghem (1887*b*) *Eriocaulon septangulare, Lachnocaulon michauxii, Philodice
hoffmannseggii, Tonina fluviatilis*; root.

Tomlinson (1965) *Paepalanthus alsinoides* Wright; all parts.

MATERIAL EXAMINED BY THE AUTHOR

A. *Pickled material, all parts*

From collection of Dr. V. I. Cheadle (V. I. C. with collection number),
collected by myself (P. B. T. with collection number), collected by Mrs. A. M.
Moore, Ontario, Canada, or in pickled collection at Jodrell Laboratory
(Jodrell) or from Herbarium of Institute of Jamaica (IJ).

Eriocaulon articulatum Morong (= *E. septangulare* With.); V. I. C. M 166;
    Rhode Island.
E. australe R. Br.; V. I. C. CA 185; Brisbane.
E. compressum Lam.; P. B. T. 31.III.63C; Florida.
E. decangulare L.; P. B. T. 10.VI.63E; Florida.
E. ravenelii Chapm.; P. B. T. 27.XI.62B.
E. scariosum Smith (= *E. smithii* R. Br.); V. I. C. CA 184; Brisbane.
E. septangulare With.; A. M. Moore, s.n.; Canada.
E. sexangulare L.; P. B. T. s.n.; Singapore.
Lachnocaulon anceps (Walt.) Morong; P. B. T. 31.III.63A; Florida.
L. engleri Ruhl.; P. B. T. 10.VI.63L; Florida.
L. minus (Chapm.) Small; P. B. T. 10.VI.63K; Florida.
Leiothrix turbinata Gleas.; Jodrell.

Paepalanthus alsinoides Wright; Léon *et al.* 17797 (IJ).

P. domingensis Ruhl.; Ekman 13561 (IJ).

P. tuerckheimii Ruhl.; Jodrell.

P. williamsii Mold.; Jodrell.

Syngonanthus flavidulus (Michx.) Ruhl.; P. B. T. 31.III.63B; Florida.

S. reflexus Gleas.; Jodrell.

Tonina fluviatilis Aubl.; P. B. T. 8.VII.62A; Trinidad.

B. *Root material from herbarium specimens in U.S. National Herbarium* (US)

Supplied by Dr. Lyman B. Smith.

Blastocaulon rupestre (Gardn.) Ruhl.; Mexia 5779.

Carptotepala jenmanii (Gleason) Mold.; Maguire and Fanshawe 32312; Steyermark and Wurdack 364.

Eriocaulon alpestre Hook. f. and Thom. var. *robustius* Max.; Nakahara s.n. *E. arechavaletae* Herter; Pederson 812. *E. australe* R. Br.; Bot. Gard. Sydney 17733; Levine 833. *E. benthami* Hook.; Hinton 627. *E. caesium* Griseb ˹Trinidad 3292. *E. capillus-najadis* Hook. *vel aff.*; Belcher 722. *E. caulinum* ined.; Pennell 15756. *E. crassiscapum* Bong.; Regnell III 1259. *E. cristatum* var. *mackii* Hook.; Rock 24927. *E. formosanum* Hayata.; Tanaka and Shimada 13574. *E. fuliginosum* Wright; Combs 588. *E. heterodoxum* Mold.; Sandwith 1603. *E. koernickianum* van Huerck and Muell.; Cory 52778. *E. kunthii* Koern.; Smith and Klein 8242. *E. longifolium* Nees; Fraser 1850. *E. melanocephalum* var. *longipes* Griseb.; Killip 32380. *E. nigrum* var. *suishaense* Hals. and Koyuma; Hatusima 18099. *E. nipponicum* Max.; Iwashoro s.n. *E. ovoideum* Britt. and Small; Killip 44059. *E. panamaense* Mold.; Davidson 657. *E. seemanii* Mold.; Swallen 11173. *E. tepicanum* Mold.; Palmer 2029. *E. truncatum* Ham.; Faber s.n.

Leiothrix arechavaletae Ruhl.; Herter 95663. *L. curvifolia* var. *setacea* Ruhl.; Archer and Barreto 4945. *L. dielsii* Ruhl.; Vianna *et al.* 158. *L. echinulata* Mold.; Schultes and Cabrera 18355. *L. flavescens* (Bong.) Ruhl.; Steyermark and Wurdack s.n. *L. fulgida* Ruhl.; Mexia 5882. *L. nubigena* Kunth (Ruhl.); Chase 10358. *L. pilulifera* (Koern.) Ruhl.; Pickel 3165.

Mesanthemum radicans Koern.; Devred 1465. *M. radicans* (Benth.) Koern.; Baldwin 12056.

Paepalanthus acuminatus var. *longipilosus* Mold.; L. B. Smith 7040. *P. albovaginatus* Alv. Silv.; Smith and Klein 7400. *P. alsinoides* Wright; Léon *et al.* 17797; var. *minimus* Jennings; Killip 45388. *P. amoenus* (Bong.) Koern.; Chase 9221. *P. bahiensis* (Bong.) Kunth; Chase 8011. *P. balansae* var. *densiflorus* Mold.; Braga and Lange 92. *P. brittonii* Mold.; Léon *et al.* 20149. *P. caldensis* Malme; Smith *et al.* 7682. *P. capillaceus* var. *proliferus* Gleason; Maguire and Wurdack 34007. *P. compactus* Gardn.; Chase 10418. *P. duidae* Gleason; Maguire and Wurdack 42279. *P. hilairei* var. *maximiliani* Ruhl.; L. B. Smith 6401. *P. lamarckii* Kunth; Gentle 3780. *P. rigidus* (Bong.) Kunth; Archer 4111. *P. seslerioides* Griseb.; Ekman 17803. *P. tuerckheimii* Ruhl.; Ekman 1385; 13561. *P. vaginatus* Koern.; Regnell III 291.

Philodice hoffmannseggii Mart., R. and S.; Freund R 26 B.

Syngonanthus caulescens (Poir.) Ruhl.; Cabrera 11711.

BIBLIOGRAPHY FOR ERIOCAULACEAE

ARBER, A. (1922) Leaves of the Farinosae. *Bot. Gaz.* **74,** 80–94.

EBEL, G. (1885) *Bot. Zbl.* **24,** 287.

HARE, C. L. (1950) The structure and development of *Eriocaulon septangulare* With. *J. Linn. Soc.* (Bot.) **53,** 422–48.

HOLM, T. (1901) *Eriocaulon decangulare* L. An anatomical study. *Bot. Gaz.* **31,** 17–37.

KOERNICKE, F. (1863) Eriocaulaceae in Martius' *Flora Brasiliensis* **3** (1), 274–508.

LECOMTE, H. (1907) Espèces nouvelles d'*Eriocaulon* de l'Indochine. *J. Bot., Paris* ser. 2, **1,** 101–9.

MALMANCHE, L. -A. (1919) *Contribution à l'étude anatomique des Eriocaulonacées et des familles voisines: Restiacées, Centrolépidacées, Xyridacées, Philydracées, Mayacacées.* Thesis, St. Cloud. pp. 165.

MOLDENKE, H. (1957) Additional notes on the Eriocaulaceae XII. *Bull. Jard. bot. État Brux.* **27,** 115–41.

POULSEN, V. A. (1888) Anatomiske Studier over Eriocaulaceerne. *Vidensk. Meddr. dansk naturh. Foren.* ser. 4, **10,** 221–386.

—— (1893) Baemaerkninger om *Tonina fluviatilis* Aubl. *Bot. Tiddskr.* **18,** 279–92.

RUHLAND, W. (1903) Eriocaulaceae. In *Das Pflanzenreich* **4** (30). pp. 294.

SCHWENDENER, S. (1874) *Das mechanische Princip im anatomischen Bau der Monocotylen.* Leipzig. pp. 179.

SOLEREDER, H., and MEYER, F. J. (1929) Eriocaulaceae. In *Systematische Anatomie der Monokotyledonen,* Heft IV, 50–70.

SOLOMON, R. (1931) The anatomy of caudex and root of *Eriocaulon septangulare. J. Indian bot. Soc.* **10,** 139–44.

TAKHTAJAN, A. (1959) *Die Evolution der Angiospermen.* Jena. pp. 344.

THANIKAIMONI, G. (1965) Contribution to the pollen morphology of Eriocaulaceae. *Pollen Spores* **7,** 181–91.

TIEGHEM, P. VAN (1887a) Sur les poils radicaux géminées. *Annls Sci. nat. bot.* ser. 7, **6,** 127–8.

—— (1887b) Structure de la racine et disposition des radicelles dans les Centrolépidées, Eriocaulées, Joncées, Mayacées et Xyridées. *J. Bot., Paris* **1,** 305–15.

TOMLINSON, P. B. (1965) Notes on the anatomy of *Aphyllanthes* (Liliaceae) and comparison with Eriocaulaceae. *J. Linn. Soc.* (Bot.) **59,** 163–73.

BROMELIACEAE

(Figs. 40–66)

SUMMARY

A LARGE and predominantly tropical family of some 45 genera and 1900 species wholly restricted to the New World except for a species of *Pitcairnia* in West Africa. Most abundant in South and Central America. Plants either terrestrial or epiphytic, the former often spinous xerophytes retaining water in internal storage tissues of leaf, the latter either facultative or frequently obligate with an unusual water economy involving either collection of free water in overlapping leaf bases (tank- or cistern-epiphytes) or in most specialized forms with ability to absorb dew or free moisture over whole surface (extreme-atmospheric epiphytes) with a consequent elimination of roots as absorbing organs. Limit of specialization achieved by virtually rootless moss- or lichen-like epiphytes with Spanish-moss (*Tillandsia usneoides*) as most extreme and successful representative. Advance from terrestrial xerophytes to extreme epiphytes a presumed evolutionary one (see Ecological Anatomy, p. 275).

Growth habit typically a rosette of spirally arranged leaves on a short, erect congested axis, rarely woody as in *Deuterocohnia*, sometimes sub-arboreal as in *Puya* spp., especially the Andean *P. raimondii*. Rosettes otherwise close to soil. Axis often decumbent and branched to form cushion or sward-like colonies (spp. of *Dyckia*, *Hechtia*). Axis in tank-epiphytes markedly negatively geotropic but more or less ageotropic in extreme epiphytes e.g. *Tillandsia recurvata* and *usneoides*. Flowering rarely from lateral partial inflorescences without interruption of monopodial growth (*Greigia* spp., e.g. *G. sanctae-martae* according to Rohweder 1956; *Tillandsia incurva*). Axis normally ending in a terminal spike-like or paniculate inflorescence with transitional, often brightly coloured bracts. Terminal inflorescence sometimes not elongated, the flowers expanding within the cistern of the rosette, e.g. *Canistrum*, *Neoregelia*, *Nidularium*, *Wittrockia*. Axis sometimes unbranched and therefore monocarpic, e.g. *Puya raimondii* and *Tillandsia utriculata*. Inflorescences lateral in *Tillandsia complanata* and *multicaulis* but axis still monocarpic (Rohweder).

Axis normally branching sympodially from axillary suckers, the suckers usually originating from the base of the rosette; rarely developing distally close beneath inflorescence which is evicted in a sympodial manner, e.g. *Vriesea swartzii*. Additional suckers in *Ananas* produced distally beyond the fleshy inflorescence immediately below the terminal vegetative 'crown'. Suckers sometimes at first stoloniferous as in *Bromelia*, *Deinacanthon*, *Pseudananas*, the stolons covered with scale leaves. First leaves on offsets in some heterophyllous *Pitcairnia* spp. reduced to spinous protective scales. Axis in *Tillandsia usneoides* a much-branched, rootless sympodium; roots restricted to seedlings; each segment with a regular system of few (often only 3) foliage leaves, renewal bud of each unit usually arising in fourth leaf below terminal flower (itself a 1–flowered inflorescence) which becomes evicted into a pseudo-lateral position. Pendulous axis of sympodium thread-like, often persistent. Axis in other genera rarely elongated and leafy; then either decumbent, e.g. *Guzmania* (*Sodiroa*) *graminifolia*, or even scandent, e.g. *Pitcairnia* spp. (*P. scandens*), *Tillandsia* spp. (*T. duratii*). For further details see Leaf; Stem; Ecological Anatomy.

Anatomically a v. natural and distinctive family characterized by **peltate scales** each with a long uniseriate stalk, wholly immersed in the epidermis, and a distal shield-like expanse adpressed against epidermis. Less specialized types of scales, often restricted to epidermal furrows, and unorganized scales, often funnel-shaped. More specialized types of scales each with a flat and v. regularly constructed shield differentiated into central disk and marginal wing; wing sometimes elliptical or with appendages. **Stomata** often restricted to epidermal furrows, commonly elaborated either by proliferation of substomatal hypodermal cells or by various modifications of guard, subsidiary and neighbouring cells evidently making stomata non-functional. **Epidermis** frequently ribbed abaxially, especially in xerophytes. Epidermal cells in surface view with markedly sinuous walls; inner wall much thicker than outer, each cell usually including a large silica-body. **Hypodermis** commonly differentiated into outer and inner portions. (*a*) Outer sclerotic layer immediately beneath epidermis, this layer continued into marginal **spines** in Pitcairnioideae and Bromelioideae, (*b*) inner layers thin-walled, colourless, often forming a v. deep adaxial water-storage tissue. Mesophyll often with ill-defined longitudinal **air-lacunae.** Isolated fibrous strands sometimes developed. **Veins** of lamina arranged in a single series not clearly buttressed to surface layers; outer sclerotic bundle sheath not forming distinct vein buttresses. Vascular tissues in leaf reduced, immediately surrounded by a continuous suberized sheath.

Stem including a distinct meristematic layer associated with root-trace insertions between cortex and central cylinder. Cortex including numerous **intracauline roots.** Roots in both extra- and intra-cauline parts with a well-developed outer sclerotic layer and sclerotic stele. **Raphide-sacs** abundant in all parts. Resin-like deposits associated with veins in many spp. Gummosis of parenchyma in stem common. **Silica** almost invariably present as spherical bodies, one in each cell of epidermis in leaf and stem. Starch grains commonly compound. Chloroplasts of leaf mesophyll often diffuse and described as v. specialized. Conducting elements narrow, vessels occurring either in all parts or more restricted, usually v. unspecialized.

HAIRS (Peltate Scales) from leaf only (Figs. 40–49)

1. *Distribution*

Similar hairs sometimes present on inflorescence axis and reproductive organs, rarely on stem. Scales forming a continuous overlapping indumentum equally on both surfaces only in most extreme epiphytic spp. of *Tillandsia*. Scales sometimes uniformly distributed but not overlapping, as in spp. of *Catopsis, Guzmania, Vriesea*; distribution otherwise restricted. Adaxial scales rarely wholly absent as in spp. of *Pitcairnia*; v. infrequent in spp. of *Araeo-*

coccus, Fosterella, Orthophytum, Pitcairnia, Puya but otherwise sparsely distributed towards leaf base as in *Fosterella* or towards leaf margin as in *Orthophytum*. Adaxial scales in *Cryptanthus* restricted to conspicuous, irregular patches or bands. Scales otherwise uniformly scattered as in spp. of *Aechmea, Canistrum, Catopsis, Deinacanthon, Dyckia, Fascicularia, Glomeropitcairnia, Gravisia, Hohenbergia, Neoregelia, Nidularium, Portea, Tillandsia, Vriesea, Wittrockia*. Adaxial scales often restricted to regular longitudinal files as observed in *Abromeitiella, Ananas, Billbergia, Bromelia, Deuterocohnia, Encholirium, Hechtia, Neoglaziovia, Pseudananas, Quesnelia, Ronnbergia, Streptocalyx*. Marginal scales sometimes closely associated with spines.

Abaxial scales uniformly distributed in extreme epiphytic Tillandsias or other spp. without differentiation between costal and intercostal bands. Otherwise restricted to intercostal bands or furrows in association with stomata. Indumentum within the furrow often somewhat overlapping the rib on each side (e.g. *Ananas*). Close association between scales and stomata striking in *Brocchinia paniculata*, with scales restricted to intercostal patches associated with equally localized stomata.

Ratio of stomata to scales (Table C) showing decrease from least specialized (terrestrial) to most specialized (epiphytic) spp. Ratio of stomata to scales highest in *Cottendorfia* with many stomata and few scales. Scales in the same genus, and perhaps also in *Navia*, often in a single diffuse file within each stoma-rich costal band. Remaining Pitcairnioideae and Bromelioideae with a lower ratio of order 3–5 to 1; ratio in Tillandsioideae smaller and in extreme epiphytic Tillandsias stomata usually fewer than scales. Limit indicated by *T. bryoides* (*T. coarctata*) with few or no stomata. The relationship between stomata and scales needs much further investigation. This need is also indicated by similarity in early stages of development of both stomata and scales (Krauss). It is possible that in unspecialized Bromeliaceae the many stomata and few scales differentiate from a fixed number of common initial cells; whereas in specialized Bromeliaceae the same number of initials give rise to few stomata but many scales.

TABLE C

Preliminary indication of ratio of stomata to scales on abaxial epidermis of Bromeliaceae

Group	No. of spp. examined	Average ratio of stomata to scales
1. Pitcairnioideae (including *Cottendorfia*)	18	**13·6:1**
a. Cottendorfia alone	6	30·4:1
b. Pitcairnioideae (excluding *Cottendorfia*)	12	5·0:1
2. Bromelioideae	43	**3·2:1**
3. Tillandsioideae as a whole	29	**1·5:1**
a. Extreme epiphytic Tillandsias	14	0·5:1
b. Tillandsioideae (excluding extreme Tillandsias)	15	2·4:1

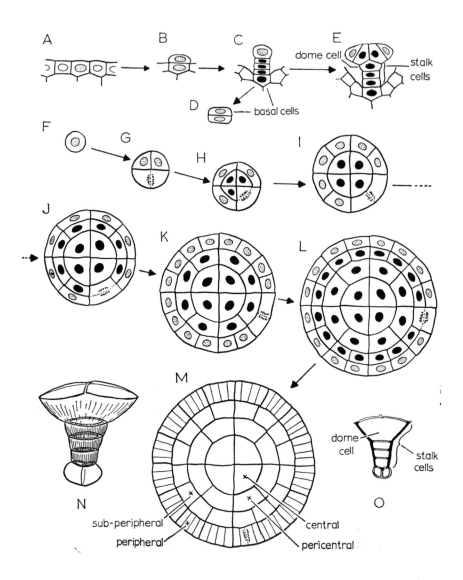

A

B

C

D — basal cells

E

dome cell

stalk cells

F

G

H

I

J

K

L

M

sub-peripheral

peripheral

central

pericentral

N

O

dome cell

stalk cells

Fig. 40. DEVELOPMENT OF THE TILLANDSIOID
SCALE, diagrammatic, not to scale (after Schacht, Billings).

A–E. T.S. (D, paradermal view of basal cell after vertical division).

F–M. Surface view, development of the shield.

N, O. The stalk.

   N. In perspective. O. T.S., cutinized walls solid black.

2. *Scales in Tillandsioideae* (for scales in Bromelioideae, Pitcairnioideae see p. 216)

Distinctive 'Tillandsioid' scale restricted to subfamily Tillandsioideae (*Catopsis, Glomeropitcairnia, Guzmania, Tillandsia, Vriesea, sens. lat.*).

(*a*) *Development and basic construction of 'Tillandsioid' scales*

The development of scales was studied by Schacht (cited by Bachmann 1886) in *Tillandsia* sp., by Billings (1904) in *T. usneoides*, and to some extent in *T. recurvata* by Birge (1911). Development is represented diagrammatically in Fig. 40. The scale is initiated by a periclinal division of a single epidermal cell (Fig. 40. A–B), the innermost daughter cell (basal cell) not contributing further to the scale. The remainder of the scale, i.e. the stalk and shield, are derived from the outer cell and are thus equivalent to an epidermal outgrowth. The basal cell remains continuous with the surrounding epidermis, but the whole of the stalk becomes deeply sunken within the leaf by invagination of the epidermis (Fig. 40. E). The basal cell normally divides only once by an anticlinal wall (Fig. 40. D), usually perpendicular to the long axis of the leaf and so visible only in L.S. It rarely divides twice by quadrant division, e.g. in *T. streptophylla*, or remains undivided as in *Vriesea psittacina* (Wetzel 1924). The distal cell divides 3 times by periclinal walls to produce 4 cells (Fig. 40. C). The lower 3 constitute stalk-cells and divide no further. The distal cell enlarges to become the shield mother cell, subsequently giving rise to the whole of the shield. The distal stalk-cell enlarges to become the dome-cell (Fig. 40. E, N, O).

The sinking of the scale within the epidermis begins with the development of the scale axis (Fig. 40. C). The shield mother cell undergoes a regular sequence of radial and tangential divisions (Fig. 40. F–M) producing 4 concentric rings of cells with a fixed number of cells in each ring. The divisions are as follows: (i) The quadrant division (4-celled stage, Fig. 40. G) where the plane of division is either parallel or at 45° to the long axis of the leaf. (ii) Four tangential divisions separate 4 central from 4 peripheral cells (8-celled stage, Fig. 40. H). No further divisions take place in the 4 central cells. (iii) Four radial divisions in the outer ring produce 8 peripheral cells (12-celled stage, Fig. 40. I). (iv) Eight tangential divisions in the peripheral ring give rise to a double ring of 8 marginal cells (20-celled stage, Fig. 40. J). No further divisions take place in the 8 pericentral cells. At this stage tangential sometimes precede instead of follow radial divisions. Billings's text and diagrams mutually contradict on this point and the sequence of events described above is according to Schacht's description. (v) Eight radial divisions in the outermost ring now produce 16 peripheral cells (28-celled stage, Fig. 40. K). (vi) Sixteen tangential divisions in the outermost series of cells next produce a double ring of 16 marginal cells (44-celled stage, Fig. 40. L). No further divisions take place in the sub-peripheral cells. (vii) Three radial divisions in each peripheral cell produce 64 peripheral cells (92-celled stage, Fig. 40. M). The sequence of divisions is now complete. The adult shield then consists of 4 central, 8 pericentral, 16 sub-peripheral, 64 peripheral cells. Various irregularities in the divisions sometimes upset this normal 4+8+16+64 formula (see p. 206). Peripheral cells usually elongate markedly in a radial direction to produce a conspicuous shallow wing which is distinct from the central disk of 3 inner rings (Fig. 41. A, B). The outline of the shield is commonly toothed owing to a slight separation of the peripheral margins of the wing cells (Figs. 41. A; 42. H).

(b) Structure of adult scale (Figs. 41–43)

Structure of adult scales intimately associated with their function and discussed in relation to water economy of leaves by Schimper (1884), Mez (1904), Steinbrinck (1905), Tietze (1906), Aso (1910), Haberlandt (1914), Barbaini (1921) but first interpreted correctly by Chodat and Vischer (1916) and in detail by Wetzel (1924), see Ecological Anatomy (p. 275).

Shield cells at maturity dead, losing cell contents; basal, stalk-, and dome-cells remaining densely cytoplasmic with conspicuous nuclei (e.g. Fig. 41. C, F). Distribution of cutin in living cells related to water-uptake mechanism (Wetzel 1924). Shield cells not or at the most very slightly cutinized. Stalk- and dome-cells with outer wall cutinized, cross walls uncutinized except for narrow peripheral cutinized annulus; basal cells with a narrow cutinized rib on common vertical wall; whole producing essentially a permeable funnel with non-permeable walls (Fig. 40. N, O). Cutinized annulus mistaken by early workers for completely cutinized cross-wall. Basal cells usually remaining thin-walled, when thick-walled always prominently pitted (Fig. 42. B, E). Shield cell normally developing massive wall thickenings before losing contents (see T.S. and L.S. in Figs. 41–43). Cells of central disk, especially outer wall of 4 central cells, with alternate pectin-rich and pectin-poor layers; vertical wall remaining thin and collapsing readily. Pericentral and sub-peripheral rings normally with uneven wall thickenings, usually with an unthickened hinge-like area in each cell generally in the outer wall, less commonly in inner wall. Wing cells usually slightly and more uniformly thickened, but distribution of wall material and localized thickenings varying considerably not only in different spp. but also in different scales from different parts of a single leaf (see illustration Figs. 41–43 and discussion under Ecological Anatomy, p. 275).

Fine structure of protoplasm of dome-cell in *Tillandsia usneoides* studied with electron microscope by Dolzmann (1964) revealing: (1) an 'intermediary substance' (not defined more closely) between protoplast of dome-cell and its outer wall; a water-storage function ascribed to this since it enlarges during water uptake, (ii) strong involution of outer surface of protoplast, evidently increasing its surface area, (iii) bladder-like invaginations of plasmalemma and similar vesicles surrounded by a 2-layered membrane throughout whole of cell, (iv) accumulation of mitochondria around central vacuole during water uptake, (v) small plastids with characteristic inclusions, each surrounded by a 1-layered membrane, the inclusions interpreted as polymerized sugars mobilized to increase osmotic potential of cell since they disappear during water uptake.

(c) Variation in scale structure

Variation in number of cells in both stalk and shield often of diagnostic significance.

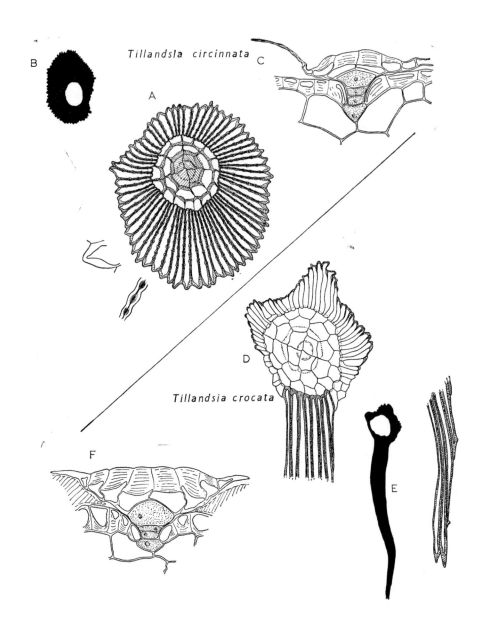

Tillandsla circinnata

B

C

A

Tillandsia crocata

D

F

E

200

Fig. 41. BROMELIACEAE–TILLANDSIOIDEAE SCALE STRUCTURE.

A–C. *Tillandsia circinnata*. Abaxial scale from distal part of lamina.

A. Surface view (×140). B. Outline (×40). C. T.S. (×275).

D–F. *Tillandsia crocata*. Abaxial scale from distal part of lamina.

D. Surface view (×140)—incomplete tip of 'tail' to right. E. Outline (×40). F. T.S. (×275).

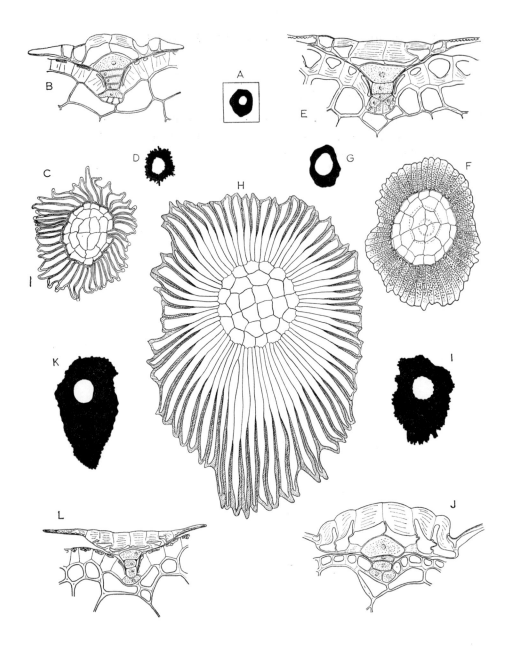

Fig. 42. BROMELIACEAE–TILLANDSIOIDEAE SCALE STRUCTURE.

A. *Glomeropitcairnia penduliflora*. Adaxial scale from leaf base, outline in surface view ($\times 40$), for comparative size of Figs. D, G, I, K, cf. Fig. 43 E.

B–G. *Tillandsia flexuosa*.

B–D. Adaxial scale from leaf base. B. T.S. ($\times 275$). C. Surface view ($\times 140$). D. Outline ($\times 40$) for comparative size. E–G. Abaxial scale from distal part of lamina. E. T.S. ($\times 275$). F. Surface view ($\times 140$). G. Outline ($\times 40$), for comparative size.

H–J. *Tillandsia recurvata*. Abaxial scale, distal part of lamina.

H. Surface view ($\times 140$). I. Outline ($\times 40$), for comparative size. J. T.S. ($\times 275$).

K. *Tillandsia usneoides*. Distal scale ($\times 40$), outline for comparative size.

L. *Tillandsia fasciculata*. T.S. distal scale ($\times 275$).

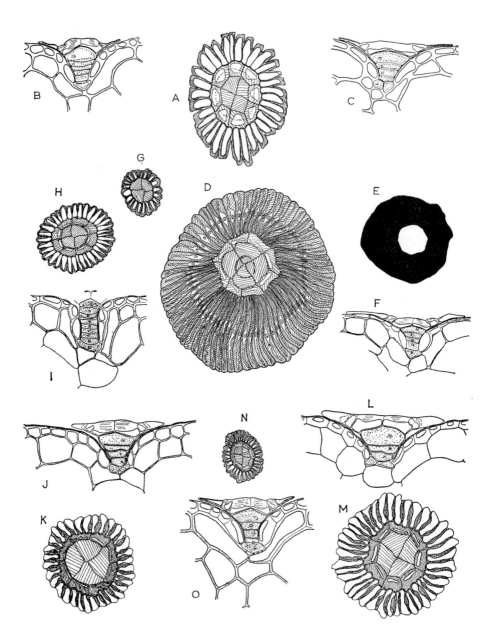

FIG. 43. BROMELIACEAE–TILLANDSIOIDEAE SCALE
STRUCTURE (×275, except Fig. E).

A–C. *Vriesea swartzii*. Abaxial scale from distal part of lamina.

A. Surface view. B. T.S. C. LS.

D–I. *Glomeropitcairnia penduliflora*.

D–F. Adaxial scale from leaf base. D. Surface view. E. Outline
(×140). Compare detailed drawings of *Tillandsia* scales (Fig. 42. C, F)
at same magnification. F. T.S. G–I. Scales from distal part of lamina.
G. Abaxial scale, surface view. H. Adaxial scale, surface view. I. T.S.
adaxial scale, stalk only.

J–M. *Catopsis floribunda*. Adaxial scales.

J, K. From distal part of leaf. L, M. From base of leaf. J. T.S. K.
surface view. L. T.S. M. Surface view.

N, O. *Tillandsia complanata*. Abaxial scale from distal part of lamina.

N. Surface view. O. T.S.

(i) *Number of basal cells.* Almost invariably 2 (Figs. 42. E, J; 43. C, J, L) (scale therefore not strictly radially symmetrical); 4 in *Tillandsia streptophylla.*

(ii) *Number of stalk-cells (including dome-cell, but excluding basal cells).* Normally 3–4 (Figs. 41. C, F; 42 B, E, J, L; 43. J, L), but 4–5 in *Tillandsia caput-medusae*; 4–6 in *T. complanata* (Fig. 43. O), *T. fendleri*; 4–6 in *Vriesea* spp. (Fig. 43. B, C); 4–5 in *Guzmania* spp.; typically more than 3 and up to 9 in *Glomeropitcairnia*, the stalk then long (Fig. 43. I).

(iii) *Number of shield cells.* Number sometimes varying by elimination of one (rarely more) ring of cells, by omission of one series of tangential divisions, or by variation in number of radial divisions in each series (see also p. 207). Standard sequence regarded by Tietze (1906) as $4+8+16+64$, other sequences described as derivatives of this. Following information largely after Tietze; information added by me indicated by (T):

Catopsis. $4+8+32$ (Fig. 43. K, M) in all spp. examined except for slight variation in number of peripheral cells as in *C. berteroniana* (T), *floribunda* (T); $4+8+32+64$ in *C. nitida* and *oerstediana*; $4+8+16+32$ in *C. magnispatha, morreniana, mosenii, nutans.*

Glomeropitcairnia. $4+8+32$ (Fig. 43. H) in *G. penduliflora* (T); cf. basal scales from same leaf $4+8+64$ (Fig. 43. D).

Guzmania (Sect. *Guzmania*). $4+8+32$ in *G. gracilior, lingulata, mucronata, multiflora, sprucei, zahnii* (T) and frequently in *berteroniana*; $4+8+64$ in *G. calothyrsus, lindenii, minor, straminea, van-volxemii*; transitional types with vestige of the 64-celled ring in *G. magna, morreniana, plumieri, roezlii, zahnii*; $4+8+32$ and $4+8+64$ equally frequent in *G. harrisii*; mixed condition as in the previous sp. but including scales with $4+8+16+32$ in *G. berteroniana* and *monostachya*; $4+8+16$ with often 8 instead of 4 divisions in the 16-celled ring to produce a 32-celled ring, i.e. $4+8+32+32$ in *G. angustifolia*; $4+8+16+32+64$ in *G. osyana*. Reduced scales with incompletely developed wings in *G. devansayana*, or irregularly developed scales recalling those of other subfamilies in *G.* (now *Vriesea*) *capituligera*. Localized doubling of 8- or 16-celled ring producing scales with 5–7 concentric rings in *G. acorifolia, erythrolepis, fuerstenbergiana* with formulae like $4+8+16+32+64$, all cells outside first 3 rings then wing-like in structure.

Guzmania (Sect. *Sodiroa*). $4+8+32$ in all spp. examined.

Tillandsia. $4+8+16+64$ in most spp. examined (e.g. Figs. 41. A, D; 42. F, H); $4+8+16+32+64$, an additional sub-peripheral ring of 32 cells, usually complete, common in subgenus *Tillandsia* (section *Platystachys*) as in *T. pruinosa* (T) and *streptophylla*; ring incomplete in *T. myosura* and *vestita*; $4+8+32$ in *T. complanata* (T) (Fig. 43. N) and *fendleri* (T); $4+8+64$ in *T. triglochinoides.*

Vriesea (Sect. *Vriesea*). $4+8+16+64$ (sometimes with an additional incomplete 32-celled sub-peripheral ring) in *V. oligantha* and *platzmannii*, these 2 spp. being the only extreme-atmospheric epiphytes in the genus; $4+8+64$

in *V. macrostachya, morrenii, pardalina, recurvata, sanguinolenta, triligulata, tucumanensis*; 4+8+32 (Fig. 43. A) in *V. panniculata, paraibica, philippocoburgii, procera* var. *typica* (var. *procera*), *psittacina, rostrum-aquilae (incurvata), rubida, scalaris, sceptrum, splendens, swartzii, tessellata, unilateralis, ventricosa*; transitional types 4+8+(32–64) in *V. mosenii, muelleri, platynema, poenulata, rodigasiana, subsecunda, thyrsoidea, tweedieana, viminalis, wawranea*; scales in *V. modesta* and *pastuchoffiana* 4+8+32 and 4+8+64 but typically stellate and poorly organized, cf. *Guzmania*.

Vriesea (Sect. *Thecophyllum*). Closely resembling scales of *Guzmania*; 4+8+32 in *Th. dussii* and *sintenisii*; 4+8+64 in *Th. balanophorum* and *ororiense*; 4+8+(32 to 64) in *Th. urbanianum*; 4+8+16+64 occasional in *Th. palustre*; 4+8+(16 to 32) in *Th. mosquerae*, closely resembling those of *Guzmania angustifolia*; 4+8+32 with whole or partial absence of 8-celled ring in *Th. kraenzlinianum*, as in *Guzmania* (now *Vriesea*) *capituligera*.

(Tietze assumed that the 4+8+32 formula represents a primitive type, and that increasing elaboration of the wing took place in response to more specialized epiphytism. In general this seems to be true. The data recorded above show an increase in elaboration of the wing. Starting with genera such as *Catopsis, Guzmania, Vriesea* which have small scales with narrow wings and often an imprecise number of cells we pass on to *Tillandsia* in which the wide scales have well-developed wings and precise cell numbers. This trend is generally correlated with a decrease in number of stalk-cells (see Ecological Anatomy, p. 275). The relative size of the scales in *Tillandsia* and remaining tillandsioid genera is indicated when the outline in Fig. 42. A is compared with those in Figs. 42. D, G, I, K and 41. B, E which have been drawn to the same scale. Fig. 42. A is repeated at a larger scale in Fig. 43. E.)

(d) Additional variation between different spp.

Diameter of shield usually small in less specialized scales as in *Catopsis* (Fig. 43. J–M), *Glomeropitcairnia* (Fig. 43. D–I), *Guzmania, Vriesea* (Fig. 43. A–C), rarely in *Tillandsia* (e.g. Fig. 43. N–O), scales usually much wider in more specialized epiphytes (e.g. Fig. 42. B–L, cf. 42. A) especially in extremely specialized epiphytes (Fig. 42. H–J). Increase in shield size largely due to increased radial extension of peripheral cells and consequent increase in wing. Wing typically eccentric in larger scales, peripheral cells on 1 side either longer (Figs. 42. H; 41. A), or subdivided, e.g. *Tillandsia caput-medusae* and *pruinosa*, in extreme instances developing a long tail-like appendage as in *T. crocata* (Fig. 41. D–E), *myosura, schenckiana* (now *paleacea*), *streptocarpa*; outline of scale then either toothed or smooth. Walls of wing cells in several spp. of subgenus *Tillandsia* (Section *Platystachys*) developing minute warts as in *T. compressa, dasyliriifolia, fasciculata, flexuosa* (Fig. 42. F), *kegeliana, polystachia, utriculata*, and in *T. lineatispica* and *Vriesea oligantha* according to Mez (1904). (Warts enhance glaucous appearance of leaf in these spp. and said by Baumert (1907) to scatter light and reduce insolation.)

(e) Scale variation within a single leaf

Basal scales typically different from distal scales (cf. Figs. 42. C–D with F–G; 43. D with G–H; K with M). Basal scales usually with wider shields, more com-

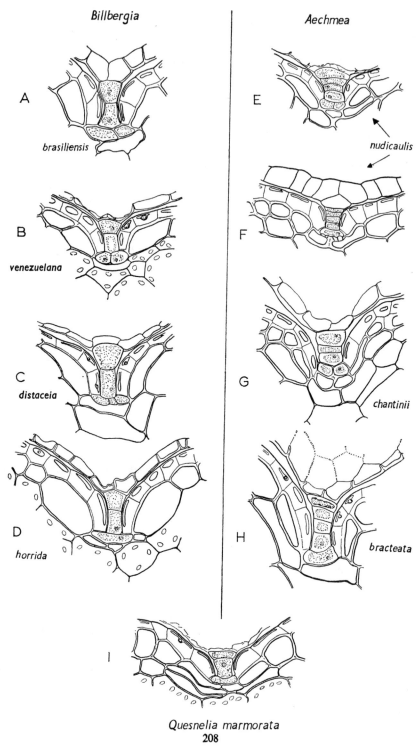

Billbergia

Aechmea

A *brasiliensis*

B *venezuelana*

C *distaceia*

D *horrida*

E

nudicaulis

F

G *chantinii*

H *bracteata*

I

Quesnelia marmorata

Fig. 44. BROMELIACEAE–BROMELIOIDEAE PEL-
TATE SCALES. All scales from abaxial surface in distal part of
lamina, except for Fig. F. which is an adaxial scale from leaf base.
T.S. (×370).

A–D. *Billbergia*, constantly with 2 stalk cells.

A. *B. brasiliensis*. B. *B. venezuelana*. C. *B. distaceia*. D. *B. horrida*.

E–H. *Aechmea*, constantly with 3 or more stalk cells.

E. *A. nudicaulis*. F. *A. nudicaulis* (adaxial scale from leaf base).
G. *A. chantinii*. H. *A. bracteata*.

I. *A. (Quesnelia) marmorata*, 2-celled stalk, suggesting this species to be
anomalous in *Aechmea*.[1]

[1] This sp. recently transferred to *Quesnelia*.

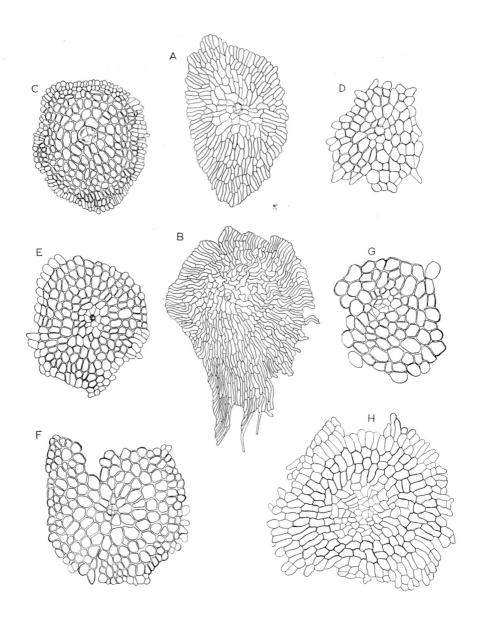

F<small>IG</small>. 45. BROMELIACEAE–BROMELIOIDEAE. *Aechmea* and *Billbergia* scale structure. All (×140), surface view.

A–D. *Aechmea*.

A. *A. penduliflora*. Abaxial scale from distal part of leaf. B. Same. Adaxial scale from leaf base. C. *A. chantinii*. Abaxial scale from distal part of leaf. D. *A. bracteata*. Abaxial scale from distal part of leaf.

E–H. *Billbergia*.

E. *B. minarum*. Abaxial scale from distal part of leaf. F. *B. brasiliensis*. Abaxial scale from distal part of leaf. G. *B. distaceia*. Abaxial scale from distal part of leaf. H. Same. Adaxial scale from clasping part of leaf base.

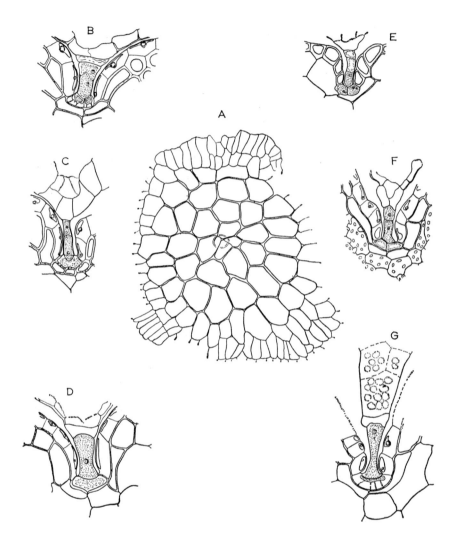

FIG. 46. BROMELIACEAE–PITCAIRNIOIDEAE SCALE STRUCTURE.

A. *Abromeitiella brevifolia*. Abaxial scale from distal part of lamina, surface view (×140).

B–G. Basal part of scale from abaxial surface, distal part of lamina. T.S. (×275).

B. *Dyckia fosteriana*. C. *Hechtia capituligera*. D. *Abromeitiella brevifolia*. E. *Pitcairnia xanthocalyx*. F. *Puya alpestris*. G. *Deinacanthon urbanianum*.

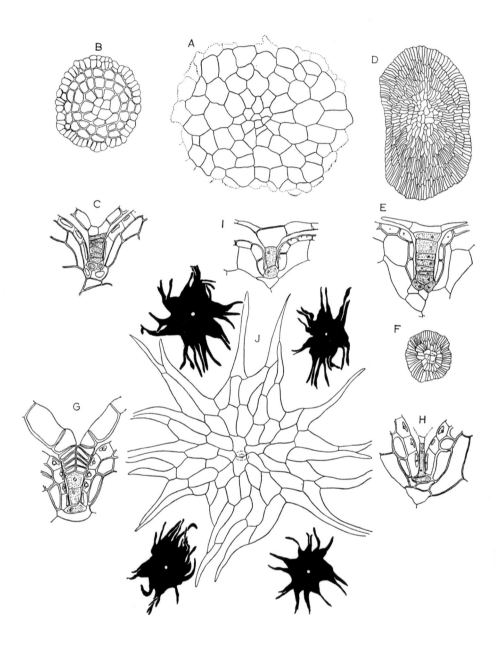

Fig. 47. BROMELIACEAE. Scale structure.

A–H. Bromelioideae.

A. *Cryptanthus fosterianus*. Abaxial scale, distal part of lamina, surface view (×140). B–C. *Canistrum fosterianum*. Abaxial scale, distal part of lamina. B. Surface view (×140). C. T.S. (×275). D–F. *Nidularium innocentii*. Abaxial scale. D. From leaf base, surface view (×140). E. From distal part of lamina T.S. (×275). F. Same, surface view (×140). G. *Bromelia pinguin*. T.S. abaxial scale from distal part of lamina (×275). H. *Fascicularia bicolor*. T.S. abaxial scale from distal part of lamina (×275).

I–J. Pitcairnioideae. *Fosterella penduliflora*. Abaxial scale, distal part of lamina.

I. T.S. (×275). J. Surface view (×140). Inset, outline of scales (×40).

monly overlapping but reverse situation observed, e.g. *Tillandsia polystachia*. Basal scales also commonly differing in number and arrangement of shield cells and often with more stalk-cells than distal scales, e.g. *Tillandsia flexuosa* typically with 4-celled stalk in basal (Fig. 42. B) and 3-celled stalk in distal scales (Fig. 42. E). Wall thickening usually much less pronounced in basal than distal scales. Wing cells in basal scale of *Glomeropitcairnia penduliflora* with persistent cell contents, thickened walls (Fig. 43. D). Wall papillae in shield cells of *Tillandsia flexuosa*, etc. absent from adaxial scales at base of leaf (cf. Fig. 42. C with F). Aborted or incompletely developed scales some-times present close to leaf insertion, perhaps accounting in part for stellate or irregular scales recorded by Tietze in a few spp.

3. *Scales in Bromelioideae, Pitcairnioideae* (Figs. 44–47) (for scales in or Tillandsioideae see p. 198)

(a) Development

The detailed study by Krauss (1949) shows that scales of *Ananas comosus* each originate from a single initial cell in the epidermis. In the earliest stages it is difficult to distinguish the initial cell of a scale from the mother cell from which the guard cells of a stoma are derived. The initial cell of the scale is surrounded by 4 cells which recall the 4 cells surrounding the mother cell of the guard cells of the stoma. In the stoma the 4 surrounding cells develop into subsidiary cells. The initial cell of the scale enlarges, but becomes sunken in a shallow depression by the upgrowth of the surrounding cells. The basal cell is cut off by a transverse wall and then undergoes no further division. The acroscopic daughter cell divides by 2 successive transverse walls to differentiate 3 cells. Of these the innermost 2 become stalk-cells. The outer-most cell of this pair enlarges to become the dome-cell, but this is never so large as the corresponding cell in the tillandsioid scale. The distal cell becomes the shield mother cell, sometimes initiating divisions before the dome-cell of the stalk is produced. The distal cell divides by vertical walls to produce the uniseriate shield. The first divisions usually produce a quadrant of cells. The subsequent divisions are irregularly orientated and never produce cells in distinct concentric series. The original central quadrant is usually obscured as the shield develops, although in other genera some attention is drawn to it as a diagnostic feature by Tietze. A similar developmental sequence has been noted for the scales of *Billbergia iridifolia* by Bulitsch (1892a) and for those of *Karatas plumieri* by Hedlund (1901). Stellate hairs in the leaf bases of *Ananas comosus* pass through a similar sequence of cell divisions during the early stages of their development. These stellate hairs are regarded by Krauss as a variant of the normal type of scale.

(b) Adult scale

Basal and stalk-cells retaining dense cell contents and conspicuous nuclei (Figs. 44, 46); becoming cutinized, apparently in same way as stalk-cells of tillandsioid scales although this point not examined in detail. Cuticle other-wise thinly developed above central cells and below all shield cells. Shield never organized into distinct disk and wing (e.g. Fig. 45). Shield cells developing slight wall thickenings on inner and vertical walls (e.g. Figs. 44; 47. C, G), appearing U-shaped in T.S. Cell contents disorganizing and lumen typically becoming air-filled, especially in scales within epidermal furrows; thin outer wall normally collapsed against thickened inner wall. Shield remaining inconspicuous if adpressed against epidermis, as on adaxial surface in *Ananas*, or remaining free from epidermis and conspicuous to naked eye as on abaxial surface in *Ananas*. Shield cells in *Ananas* more or less iso-diametric at maturity, peripheral cells somewhat smaller and somewhat radially extended, but shape of shield cells varying in scales from different parts of a single plant.

(c) *Variation between different spp. in structure of scale* (refers to scales half-way between base and apex of leaf)

Basal cell commonly divided by a vertical wall, as in tillandsioid scales and this probably the normal condition (e.g. Figs. 44. B, E, G; 46. B, E, F); some-times surrounded by a distinct sclerotic cylinder of thick-walled cells as in *Neoglaziovia*, *Quesnelia*, *Ronnbergia*. Basal cells themselves commonly with markedly thickened inner walls, the walls then prominently pitted (e.g. Fig. 46. B, G). Dome-cell often shorter than remaining stalk-cells, obconical but never markedly inflated as in tillandsioid scale. Number of stalk-cells (includ-ing distal dome-cell) varying from 2 to several, but apparently always con-stant and diagnostic for each genus.

TABLE D

Number of stalk-cells in genera of Bromeliaceae (*excluding Tillandsioideae*)

(Based on original observations unless otherwise stated)

(i) Stalk-cells 2

Abromeitiella (Fig. 46. D)	*Dyckia* (Fig. 46. B)	*Orthophytum*
Acanthostachys (–3)	*Encholirium*	*Pitcairnia* (–3) (Fig. 46. E)
Ananas	*Fascicularia* (Fig. 47. H)	*Pseudananas*
Billbergia (–3) (Fig. 44. A–D)	*Fosterella* (Fig. 47. I)	*Puya* (–3) (Figs. 46. F; 59. G)
Bromelia (Fig. 47. G)	*Hechtia* (Fig. 46. C)	*Quesnelia* (Figs. 44. I)
Cryptanthus	*Hohenbergia* (rarely e.g. *H. urbaniana*)	*Ronnbergia* (–3)
Deinacanthon (Fig. 46. G)	*Karatas* (Hedlund)	*Streptocalyx* (–3)
Deuterocohnia	*Neoglaziovia*	

(ii) Stalk-cells more than 2

Aechmea (3–4+) (Fig. 44. E–H)	*Cottendorfia* (4–8)	*Neoregelia* (5–8)
Araeococcus (4–5+)	*Gravisia* (4–6)	*Nidularium* (6–8) (Fig. 47. E)
Brocchinia (up to 12)	*Greigia* (3)	*Portea* (5+)
Canistrum (5–8) (Fig. 47. C)	*Hohenbergia* (3–5 commonly e.g. *H. salz-mannii*)	*Wittrockia* (7–10)

Length of stalk independent of number of stalk-cells. Long stalks mainly composed either of 1 long basiscopic cell (e.g. *Deinacanthon*, Fig. 46. G; *Fascicularia*, Fig. 47. H) or of many short stalk-cells (e.g. *Brocchinia*;

Canistrum, Fig. 47. C; *Nidularium*, Fig. 47. E). Shield normally uniseriate but central cells occasionally becoming biseriate by horizontal division, as in *Bromelia* (Fig. 47. G), *Neoregelia* spp., a situation probably most common in basal scales. (The multiseriate condition recorded by some earlier authors is probably due to misinterpreting thick or oblique sections.)

Shield of *Ananas*-type, i.e. uniseriate, flattened, well organized and with a regular outline also in *Aechmea* (Fig. 45. A, C, D), *Billbergia* (Fig. 45. E–G), *Bromelia, Canistrum* (Fig. 47. B), *Gravisia, Hohenbergia, Nidularium* (Fig. 47. D). Scales in other genera, especially those with pronounced epidermal furrows, often more or less funnel-shaped (e.g. Fig. 46. G), poorly organized and with an irregular outline. Cells in funnel-shaped scales typically thin-walled, inflated, and forming a loose indumental mass occluding grooves, e.g. in *Abromeitiella, Acanthostachys, Canistrum, Deinacanthon, Deuterocohnia, Fascicularia, Neoglaziovia, Orthophytum, Portea, Puya*. Limits of shield commonly indistinct or irregular because of ephemeral marginal cells (Figs. 46. A; 47. A). Shield in *Fosterella* (Fig. 47. J) and *Streptocalyx* with stellate outline, shield cells angular. Shield cells in *Quesnelia liboniana* with an irregular sinuous outline, a condition more usual in basal scales in other genera, e.g. *Aechmea* (Fig. 45. B), *Ananas*. Persistent cytoplasmic remains in *Acanthostachys, Deinacanthon* (Fig. 46. G), *Encholirium, Pseudananas* visible as foam-like material but perhaps confused with epiphytic micro-organisms commonly developed on old scales, notably unicellular green algae such as *Chlorococcus*. Shield in some genera with regular orientation of peripheral cells, remaining cells tending towards a concentric zonation as if produced by regular divisions and so recalling tillandsioid scale, e.g. in spp. of *Canistrum* (Fig. 47. B), *Neoregelia, Nidularium* (Fig. 47. F) and in *Gravisia* according to Tietze. Shield rarely eccentric (e.g. Fig. 45. B). (For further details of shield structure in non-tillandsioid scales see Tietze, although variation recorded seems of little diagnostic value.)

(d) Variation within a single leaf

Scale structure within a single leaf often quite variable; basal differing from distal scales in such features as number of stalk-cells, size of scales (cf. Fig. 47. D and F) and degree of overlapping of shield, as well as in shape and degree of wall thickening of shield cells (cf. Figs. 45. A and B; 44. E and F). Similar differences at the same leaf level between scales from opposite surfaces also noted. Variegation of leaf perhaps partly due to localized development of bands or patches of enlarged scales e.g. *Aechmea chantinii, Cryptanthus* spp.

4. *Hairs in* Brocchinia, Cottendorfia, Navia (Figs. 48; 49)

Sufficiently diverse compared with remaining genera to merit separate description; commonly with more than one type of hair on a single leaf. Following data obtained from herbarium material in which hair structure not well preserved. Four arbitrary types recognized but intermediates perhaps common. These hairs may be interpreted as equivalent to uniseriate stalk-like portion of peltate scale but with frequent modification of distal part into something other than a shield.

(*a*) **Peltate scales.** Closely resembling those of *Ananas*-type, but with a many-celled, often flattened stalk, elliptical in surface view. Shield consisting of thin-walled irregularly organized cells (Fig. 49. C), e.g. in *Cottendorfia guyanensis, navioides, serrulata, simplex; Navia fontoides, mima.* Stalk-cells thick-walled in material of *N. mima* examined. Scales in *Brocchinia paniculata* each with a v. long stalk of up to 12 cells; shield differentiated into a central thickened multiseriate disk, slightly conical in section, and a uniseriate wing of a single peripheral series of radially extended cells (Fig. 49. H). Cells of shield thickened, minutely warted in a manner recalling warted scales of spp. in *Tillandsia* subgenus *Tillandsia* (cf. Fig. 42. F).

(*b*) **Stellate scales** (Fig. 48. B). Resembling peltate scales but shield irregularly stellate in outline and cells often thick-walled; somewhat recalling those of *Fosterella* (cf. Fig. 47. J), e.g. in *Cottendorfia argentea, paludosa; Navia aloifolia, caulescens, crispa, mima.* In *Cottendorfia paludosa* cells somewhat sinuous and so transitional to peltate scales. Irregularly stellate hairs of this type most conspicuous and well developed in angle between marginal curved spines and leaf margin itself.

(*c*) **Uniseriate hairs.** Resembling peltate scales with shield replaced by a terminal appendage of long, thin- or even thick-walled cells, in *Cottendorfia wurdackii* (Fig. 48. C–H); *Navia aloifolia, caulescens.* Similar but with few-celled appendage in *N. crispa.* (Some of scales in spp. listed under (*a*) may be of this type. Similar hairs observed in juvenile foliage of an unnamed *Navia* sp. (Fig. 49. J–M).)

(*d*) **Uniseriate capitate hairs** (Fig. 49. D–F). Uniseriate, rarely branched (Fig. 49. F) hairs each ending in a slightly inflated clavate cell; with a v. localized distribution towards leaf base in *Navia fontoides.* Hairs of this kind strongly recalling those described by Krauss as common on the first few leaves of seedling *Ananas comosus* but not observed by Thomas and Holmes (1930). Early stages in development of these *Ananas* seedling hairs identical with early stages in development of normal *Ananas* peltate scales.

(Re-examination of hairs of these 3 genera in fresh material, so far only poorly observed in dried material, is much needed as it may throw interesting light on the evolution of the bromeliad scale (see Taxonomic Notes).)

STOMATA (Figs. 50–58)

Sufficiently variable throughout the family to merit detailed description. Structure constant for each sp. and often diagnostically useful at generic level. Stomatal specialization often accompanying specialization of other epidermal features associated with unusual water economy (cf. also Ziegenspeck 1939). Stomata almost invariably restricted to abaxial surface of leaf, infrequently present adaxially in *Catopsis berteroniana* and said to be present adaxially in *Tillandsia usneoides* where, however, because of invagination of blade, adaxial surface v. narrow (cf. Fig. 63. A–G). Stomata v. infrequent in *T. rupestris* (3–4 per mm^2) according to Chodat and Vischer (1916) and virtually absent from *T. bryoides* (*T. coarctata*) according to Mez. Stomata never in regular longitudinal files, normally restricted to longitudinal series in intercostal bands or to base and sides of furrows in spp. with prominent ribs. Stomata

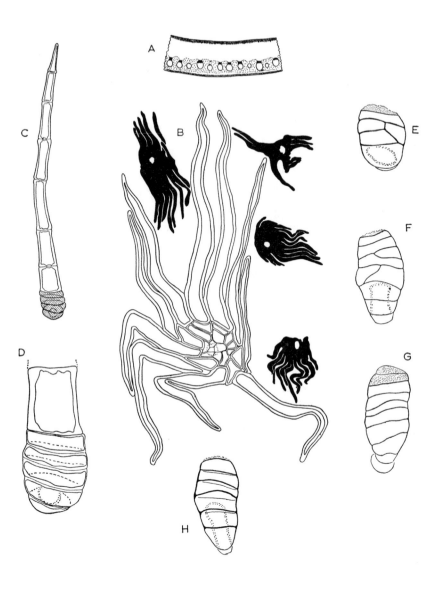

Fig. 48. BROMELIACEAE–PITCAIRNIOIDEAE.
Cottendorfia lamina.

A. *Cottendorfia serrulata*. T.S. median part of lamina (×20).

B. *Cottendorfia paludosa*. Adaxial scale, distal part of lamina, surface view (×140). Inset, outline of scales (×40).

C–H. *Cottendorfia wurdackii*. Filamentous hairs from abaxial epidermis, surface view (×140).

C. Complete. D. Base only. E–H. Base only, distal filament presumably lost.

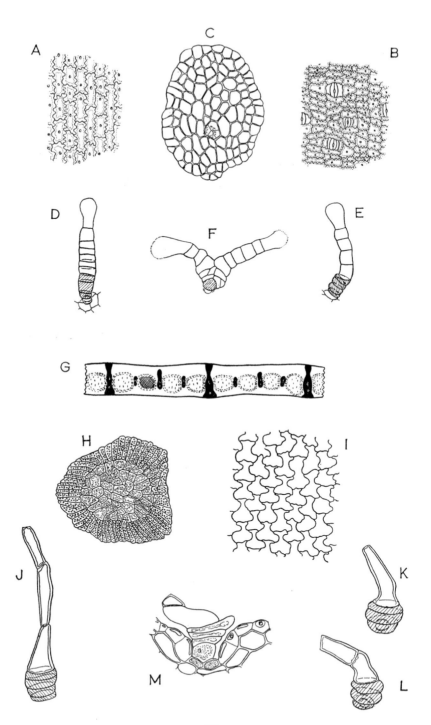

FIG. 49. BROMELIACEAE–PITCAIRNIOIDEAE LAMINA

A–F. *Navia fontoides.*

A. Adaxial epidermis, surface view ($\times 230$). B. Abaxial epidermis, surface view ($\times 230$). C. Abaxial scale, distal part of leaf, surface view ($\times 180$). D–F. Capitate hairs from abaxial epidermis from a narrow band towards leaf base ($\times 180$). D and E. Simple hairs. F. Branched hair.

G–I. *Brocchinia paniculata.*

G. T.S. lamina ($\times 10$). H. Adaxial scale from leaf base, surface view ($\times 180$). I. Abaxial epidermis (costal region), surface view ($\times 180$).

J–M. *Navia* sp. Uniseriate, filamentous hairs from juvenile foliage.

J–L. Surface view, distal part of filament absent ($\times 180$). M. T.S. base of filamentous hair from abaxial surface ($\times 460$).

less commonly each situated in an individual depression. Stomata of *Brocchinia paniculata* in clusters associated with scales in intercostal bands. Stomatal complex usually deeper than normal shallow epidermal cells, each consisting of 2 **guard cells,** the length ranging from 24 to 45 μm according to Solereder and Meyer; 2 narrow lateral and 2 short terminal **subsidiary cells.** These in turn surrounded by a number of **neighbouring cells,** the latter commonly differing from normal epidermal cells, and bearing a special developmental relation to guard cells. Terminal subsidiary and neighbouring cells often with large **silica-bodies,** lateral subsidiary cells never including silica. Guard cells giving no positive Millon's reaction unlike rest of epidermis according to Kenda and Weber (1951).

Stomatal development (based on Krauss's description for *Ananas comosus*). The **guard mother cell** (g.m.c) originates as an acroscopic daughter cell by unequal division of a protodermal cell. Two oblique divisions in cells lateral to the g.m.c., i.e. belonging to files on either side of that containing the g.m.c., produce 2 lateral **wedge-shaped cells.** The terminal subsidiary cells are produced by transverse divisions in each polar cell and the lateral subsidiary cells cut off by longitudinal divisions in each wedge-shaped cell. The guard cells arise from the g.m.c. by longitudinal division. Cell configuration in other Bromeliaceae suggests that a similar sequence is involved but this has not been verified by a study of development (see also p. 390).

The stomata in a few genera are unspecialized, but, apart from these, a majority shows specialization along 2 different lines. These involve elaboration either of substomatal cells, or of subsidiary and neighbouring cells themselves. The following 3 arbitrary classes are recognized largely for descriptive purposes but they may correspond to functional differences.

1. *Simple, unspecialized stomata* (Figs. 50. A–L; 51. E–H). Guard cells at same level as and not or scarcely deeper than (e.g. *Catopsis* (Fig. 51. F), *Cottendorfia* (Fig. 50. B)) remaining epidermal cells, each with a prominent outer cutinized ledge, inner ledge absent or represented by a narrow ridge opposite narrowest part of stomatal aperture (e.g. Fig. 51. F); walls occasionally thin (e.g. *Pitcairnia* spp. Fig. 50. J, L) but usually much thickened; cell lumen always distinctly dumb-bell shaped in L.S. (e.g. Fig. 51. H), equatorial part narrow and almost occluded in thick-walled guard cells (cf. Fig. 51. F and G). Lateral subsidiary cells narrow, thin-walled, sometimes including chloroplasts, usually underarching guard cells somewhat (e.g. *Cottendorfia* Fig. 50. B, *Fosterella* Fig. 50. F, *Pitcairnia* Fig. 50. J) but never occluding substomatal chamber as in more specialized stomata. Terminal subsidiary and neighbouring cells with slightly-or non-sinuous walls but otherwise scarcely different from remaining epidermal cells, except for thick-walled cells in *Brocchinia*. Substomatal chamber typically surrounded (Fig. 50. H, K) by 2 (3–4) thin-walled U-shaped unlobed hypodermal cells, often including chloroplasts in contrast to normal colourless hypodermis (e.g. *Catopsis* Fig. 51. F, H). Simple stomata observed in spp. of *Brocchinia, Catopsis, Cottendorfia, Fosterella, Glomeropitcairnia* (*G. erectiflora*), *Navia, Pitcairnia* (e.g. *P. bromeliifolia* and *xanthocalyx*). Stomata in other spp. of *Glomeropitcairnia* (*G. penduliflora*, Fig. 51. A- D) and *Navia* with a

pronounced tendency to develop lobed substomatal cells as in the following class. For other spp. of *Pitcairnia* see *Puya*, p. 245.

2. *Stomata with modified substomatal cells* (Figs. 50. M–O; 51–55). Guard cells usually deeper than normal epidermal cells, often sunken but depth of sinking varying considerably within a genus (cf. Fig. 52. A–H). Guard cells usually thick-walled, commonly underarched somewhat by lateral and terminal subsidiary cells making them appear elevated even when sunken (e.g. Fig. 52). Stomata commonly sunken in epidermal furrows or even within individual depressions as in spp. of *Araeococcus, Billbergia, Gravisia*. Substomatal chambers usually surrounded by 2 (Figs. 54. D, H, L; 55. D), less commonly 3–4 (Fig. 51. D; 55. E), but typically 4 in *Tillandsia* (Fig. 53. C), *Vriesea* (Fig. 51. L), thin-walled, U-shaped, and commonly chlorophyll-containing hypodermal cells forming a distinctive annulus. Substomatal cells characteristically with slight to pronounced lobes from their polar ends (e.g. Fig. 54. D), or from each end when more than 2 cells present (e.g. Fig. 51. L), the lobes extending into the substomatal chamber, often meeting below or even growing into stomatal pore (e.g. Fig. 53. D–E). Neighbouring cells and terminal subsidiary cells commonly deeper than normal epidermal cells, sometimes thick-walled. Substomatal hypodermal cells in *Gravisia rubens, Neoregelia caroliniae,* and in *Canistrum aurantiacum* according to Linsbauer, thick-walled and so further occluding chamber; corresponding cells in *Wittrockia* (Fig. 54. J–L) thick-walled, but lobes remaining thin-walled. Stomata of this type present in *Aechmea* (Fig. 52. E–G), *Araeococcus* (Fig. 55. A–E), *Billbergia* (Fig. 52. A–D), *Canistrum, Gravisia, Glomeropitcairnia penduliflora* (Fig. 51. A–D), *Guzmania, Hohenbergia, Navia, Neoregelia* (Fig. 54. E–H), *Nidularium, Portea, Quesnelia* (Figs. 52. H; 54. A–D), *Ronnbergia, Streptocalyx, Tillandsia* (Fig. 53. A–E), *Vriesea* (Fig. 51. I–L), *Wittrockia* (Fig. 54. I–L). Further details shown in illustrations.

3. *Stomata with modified subsidiary and neighbouring cells* (Figs. 56–58). Substomatal hypodermal cells never conspicuously modified, but substomatal chamber occluded to greater or lesser degree by inflated subsidiary cells underarching guard cells. Lateral subsidiary cells frequently meeting below guard cells (e.g. Figs. 56. J, N; 58. E, I, M), their back wall sometimes thickened (e.g. Fig. 58. E, I). Terminal subsidiary cells always thick-walled, protruding beneath guard cells, in the most specialized stomata the guard cell then appearing to be attached to distal part of each terminal cell (e.g. Figs. 56. K; 58. F, J). (This indicates how the situation must have developed as the stoma matured.) When pronounced, enlargement of subsidiary cells causing guard cells to be curved as seen in L.S. and elevated above surrounding epidermal cells (Figs. 56. K, O; 58. F, J) although still included within epidermal furrow or depression. Degree of occlusion of substomatal chamber indicated by paradermal views in Figs. 56. D, H, L; 58. C, G, K, O). Guard cells usually thick-walled; also in *Abromeitiella* (Fig. 58. M), *Deinacanthon* (Fig. 56. N), *Deuterocohnia* with an additional outer chamber enclosed by specially developed cutinized ledges. Stomata of the most specialized type situated within deep epidermal depressions; in *Bromelia balansae* depressions largely due to massive enlargement of neighbouring cells (Fig. 57. A–C). Stomata in *Bromelia magdalenae* most complicated in whole family, outer stomatal cavity

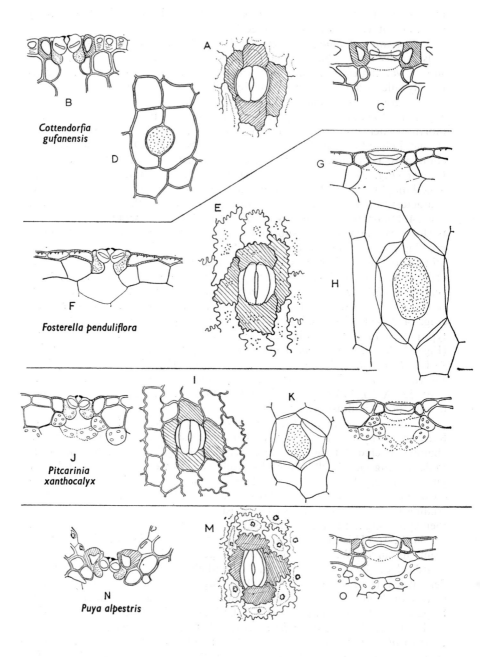

*Cottendorfia
gufanensis*

Fosterella penduliflora

*Pitcarinia
xanthocalyx*

Puya alpestris

226

A–D. *Cottendorfia gufanensis.*

A. Surface view. B. T.S. C. L.S. D. Hypodermal cells surrounding substomatal chamber, surface view.

E–H. *Fosterella penduliflora.*

E. Surface view. F. T.S. G. L.S. H. Hypodermal cells surrounding substomatal chamber, surface view.

I–L. *Pitcairnia xanthocalyx.*

I. Surface view. J. T.S. K. Hypodermal cells surrounding substomatal chamber, surface view. L. L.S.

M–O. *Puya alpestris*

M. Surface view. N. T.S. O. L.S.

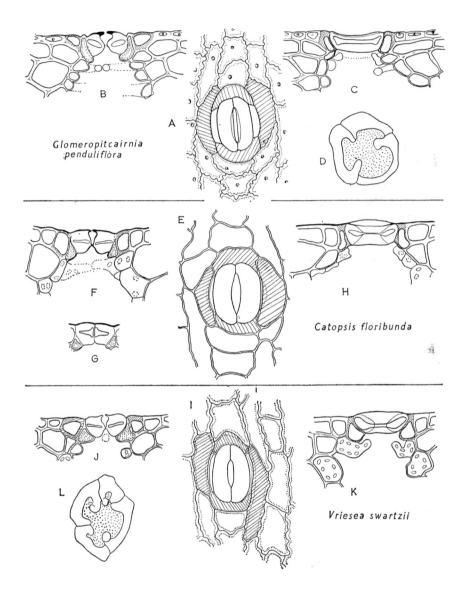

Glomeropitcairnia
penduliflòra

Catopsis floribunda

Vriesea swartzii

FIG 51. BROMELIACEAE–TILLANDSIOIDEAE STOMATA
(×345).

A–D. *Glomeropitcairnia penduliflora.*

A. Abaxial stoma, surface view. B. T.S. C. L.S. D. Hypodermal cells surrounding substomatal chamber, surface view.

E–H. *Catopsis floribunda.*

E. Abaxial stoma, surface view. F. T.S. G. T.S. guard cells close to poles. H. L.S.

I–L. *Vriesea swartzii.*

I. Abaxial stoma, surface view. J. T.S. K. L.S. L. Hypodermal cells surrounding substomatal chamber, surface view.

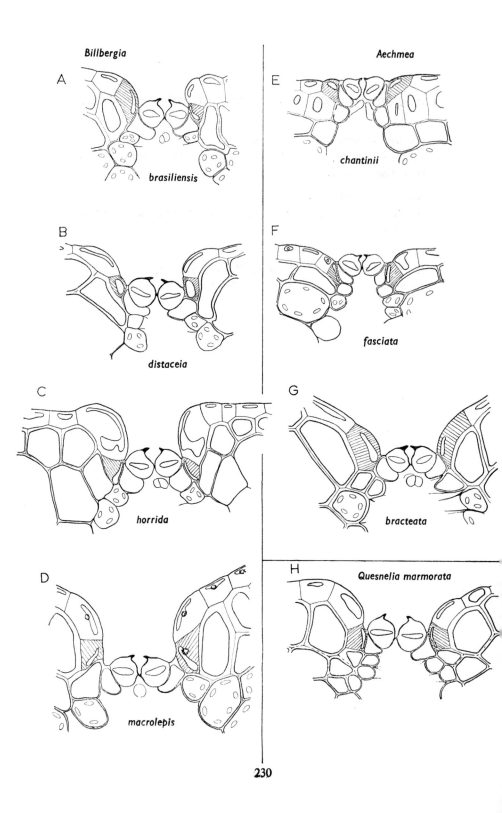

Billbergia

A *brasiliensis*

B *distaceia*

C *horrida*

D *macrolepis*

Aechmea

E *chantinii*

F *fasciata*

G *bracteata*

H *Quesnelia marmorata*

FIG. 52. BROMELIACEAE–BROMELIOIDEAE STOMA-
TA, T.S. (×460).

A–D. *Billbergia.*

  A. *B. brasiliensis.* B. *B. distaceia.* C. *B. horrida.* D. *B. macrolepis.*

E–G. *Aechmea.*

  E. *A. chantinii.* F. *A. fasciata.* G. *A. bracteata.*

H. *A. (Quesnelia) marmorata.*[1]

[1] See footnote p. 209

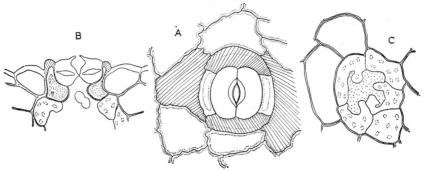

Tillandsia ionantha

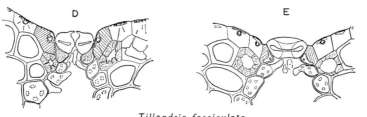

Tillandsia fasciculata

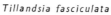

Tillandsia recurvata

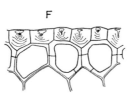

A–C. *Tillandsia ionantha*. Stoma ($\times$ 345).

A. Surface view. B. T.S. C. Hypodermal cells surrounding substomatal chamber; in surface view.

D, E. *Tillandsia fasciculata*. Stoma ($\times$ 345).

D. T.S. E. L.S.

F, G. *Tillandsia recurvata*. Abaxial epidermis, T.S. ($\times$ 275).

F. Leaf base. G. Distal part of leaf.

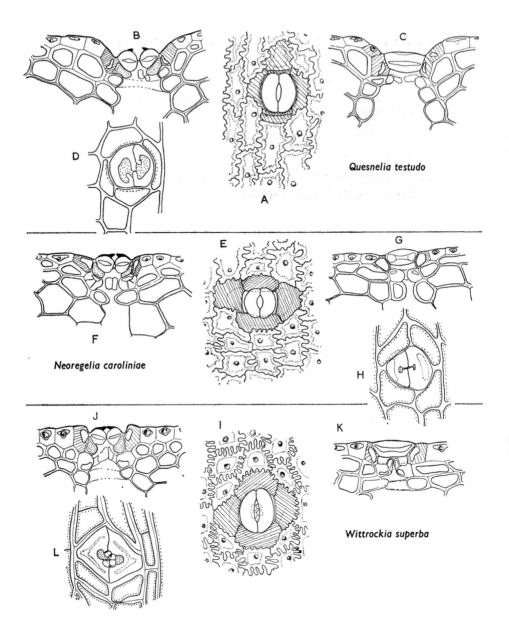

Quesnelia testudo

Neoregelia caroliniae

Wittrockia superba

234

Fig. 54. BROMELIACEAE–BROMELIOIDEAE STOMA-TA (×345).

A–D. *Quesnelia testudo*.

A. Surface view. B. T.S. C. L.S. D. Hypodermal cells surrounding substomatal chamber, surface view.

E–H. *Neoregelia caroliniae*.

E. Surface view. F. T.S. G. L.S. H. Hypodermal cells surrounding substomatal chamber, surface view.

I–L. *Wittrockia superba*.

I. Surface view. J. T.S. K. L.S. L. Hypodermal cells surrounding substomatal chamber, surface view.

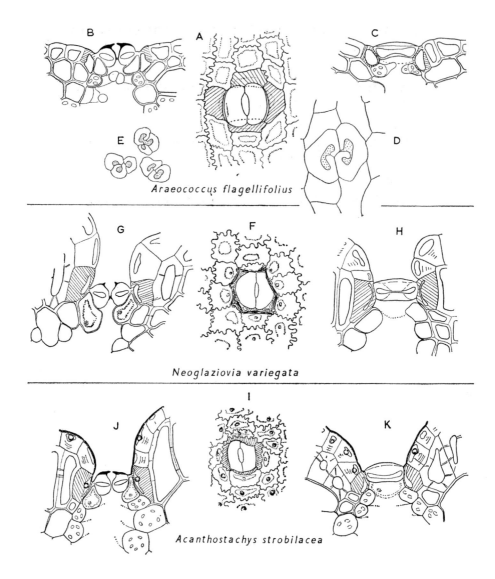

Araeococcus flagellifolius

Neoglaziovia variegata

Acanthostachys strobilacea

236

Fig. 55. BROMELIACEAE–BROMELIOIDEAE STOMATAL
STRUCTURE (×345, except E).

A–E. *Araeococcus flagellifolius*

A. Surface view. B. T.S. C. L.S. D. Hypodermal cells surrounding sub-stomatal chamber, surface view. E. Alternative arrangements of these cells (×140).

F–H. *Neoglaziovia variegata.*

F. Surface view. G. T.S. H. L.S.

I–K. *Acanthostachys strobilacea.*

I. Surface view. J. T.S. K. L.S.

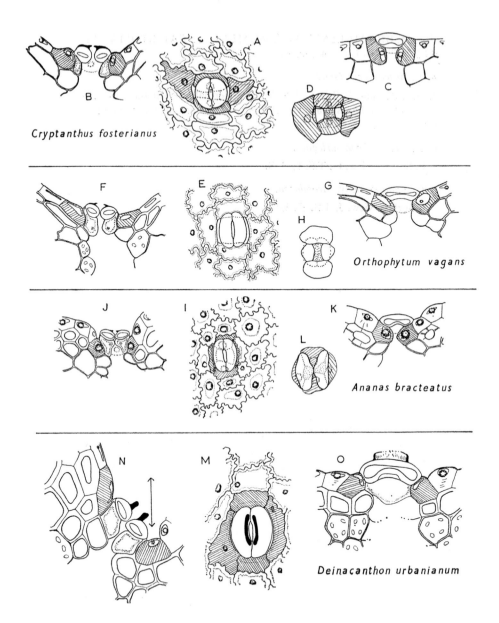

Cryptanthus fosterianus

Orthophytum vagans

Ananas bracteatus

Deinacanthon urbanianum

238

Fig. 56. BROMELIACEAE–BROMELIOIDEAE STOMATAL STRUCTURE (×345)

A–D. *Cryptanthus fosterianus.*

A. Surface view. B. T.S. C. L.S. D. Stomata seen from within the leaf, showing arrangement of subsidiary cells around substomatal chamber.

E–H. *Orthophytum vagans.*

E. Surface view. F. T.S. G. L.S. H. Subsidiary cells around substomatal chamber, surface view.

I–L. *Ananas bracteatus.*

I. Surface view. J. T.S. K. L.S. L. Subsidiary cells around substomatal chamber, surface view.

M–O. *Deinacanthon urbanianum.*

M. Surface view. N. T.S. (arrow indicates axis of groove in which stomata are situated). O. L.S.

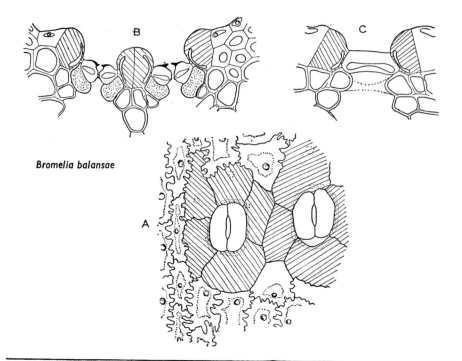

Bromelia balansae

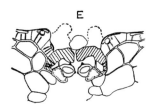
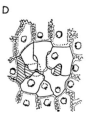
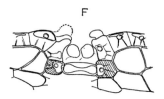

Bromelia magdalenae

Fɪɢ. 57. BROMELIACEAE–BROMELIOIDEAE STOMATAL STRUCTURE (×345).

A–C. *Bromelia balansae.*

A. Surface view. B. T.S. C. L.S.

D–F. *Bromelia magdalenae.*

D. Surface view. E. T.S. F. L.S.

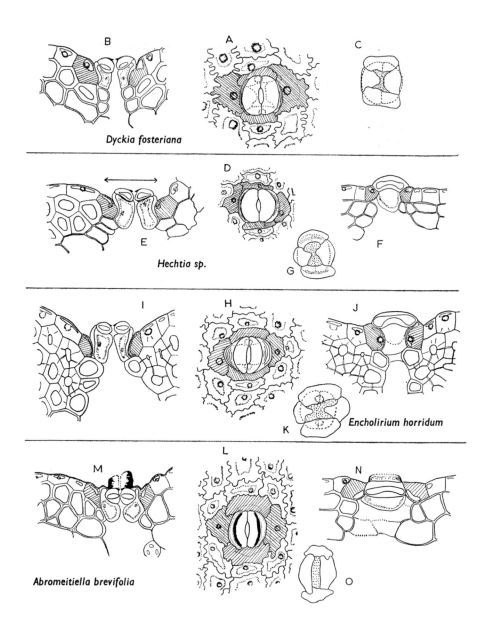

Dyckia fosteriana

Hechtia sp.

Encholirium horridum

Abromeitiella brevifolia

FIG. 58. BROMELIACEAE–PITCAIRNIOIDEAE STOMATAL STRUCTURE (×345).

A–C. *Dyckia fosteriana.*

A. Surface view. B. T.S. C. Arrangement of subsidiary cells around substomatal chamber, surface view.

D–G. *Hechtia* sp.

D. Surface view. E. T.S. (arrow indicates axis of groove in which stoma is situated). F. L.S. G. Arrrangement of subsidiary cells around substomatal chamber, surface view.

H–K. *Encholirium horridum.*

H. Surface view. I. T.S. J. L.S. K. Arrangement of subsidiary cells around substomatal chamber, surface view.

L–O. *Abromeitiella brevifolia.*

L. Surface view. M. T.S. N. L.S. O. Arrangement of subsidiary cells around substomatal chamber, surface view.

completely filled with overlapping protuberances from neighbouring cells, completely obscuring symmetry of stomatal apparatus (Fig. 57. D–F). Following notes indicate briefly the range of features found in stomata of this general category.

Abromeitiella (Fig. 58. L–O). Guard cells not elevated, underarched by lateral subsidiary cells, additional outer chamber formed by cuticular hood arising from junction between lateral subsidiary cell and back wall of guard cell; normal outer ledge v. narrow. Cuticular hood not recorded by Schulz in *A. pulvinata*.

Acanthostachys (Fig. 55. I–K). Guard cells, although appearing elevated and somewhat curved, nevertheless deeply sunken.

Ananas (Fig. 56. I–L). Guard cells elevated, curved; lateral and terminal subsidiary cells underarching guard cells and almost occluding substomatal chamber; neighbouring cells enlarged; cf. also Krauss.

Bromelia (Fig. 57. A–C). Terminal subsidiary and neighbouring cells enlarged in *B. balansae*, cf. also Schulz; *Pourretia achupalla* (now *Puya floccosa*) similar according to Linsbauer. Protuberances from neighbouring cells completely filling and obscuring stomatal depression in *B. magdalenae* (Fig. 57. D–F).

Cryptanthus (Fig. 56. A–D). Guard cells elevated and curved, underarched by terminal and lateral subsidiary cells. Stomata not in epidermal grooves. Lateral subsidiary cells, according to Linsbauer, Schulz, thick-walled.

Deinacanthon (Fig. 56. M–O). Guard cells elevated, additional outer chamber formed by erect and not horizontal outer ledge; terminal and lateral subsidiary cells underarching guard cells and somewhat occluding substomatal chamber; substomatal hypodermal cells occasionally protuberant (cf. *Abromeitiella, Deuterocohnia*).

Deuterocohnia. Similar to *Abromeitiella*. Substomatal chamber somewhat occluded by hypertrophy of hypodermal cells.

Dyckia (Fig. 58. A–C). Guard cells elevated and curved, lateral subsidiary cells with slightly thickened outer wall, thin-walled part underarching guard cells; neighbouring cells somewhat modified; cf. *D. floribunda* described by Chodat and Vischer.

Encholirium (Fig. 58. H–K). Guard cells elevated and curved, outer wall of lateral subsidiary cells thickened; substomatal chamber partly occluded by lateral and terminal subsidiary cells.

Fascicularia. Lateral and terminal subsidiary cells somewhat underarching guard cells.

Hechtia (Fig. 58. D–G). Guard cells curved and elevated; outer wall of lateral subsidiary cells slightly thickened; substomatal chamber partly occluded by lateral and terminal subsidiary cells.

Neoglaziovia (Fig. 55. F–H). Stomata sunken in individual depressions themselves within epidermal grooves; terminal subsidiary and neighbouring cells somewhat modified.

Orthophytum (Fig. 56. E–H). Guard cells slightly elevated and curved, under-arched by lateral and terminal subsidiary cells; neighbouring cells slightly modified.

Pseudananas. Resembles *Encholirium* closely.

Puya (Figs. 50. M–O; 59. H–I). Guard cells somewhat overarched by lateral subsidiary and neighbouring cells and also underarched by lateral subsidiary cells. Neighbouring and terminal subsidiary cells with similar uniform wall thickenings; some spp. of *Pitcairnia* (e.g. *P. ferruginea, mirabilis, nana*) resemble *Puya* closely. See also *Bromelia* (p. 244).

Additional details are illustrated by Linsbauer.

Specialized stomata, especially those with enlarged lateral subsidiary cells, probably not functioning like normal stomata, see Cedervall 1884; Haberlandt 1887; Krauss 1948; Mez 1904; Schulz 1930, and especially Linsbauer 1911; see also Ecological Anatomy.

(It will be noted that the above subdivision, the limits of which are not sharp, does not coincide with taxonomic grouping. However, all Tillandsioideae have stomata of either class 1 or 2 and never of class 3; those of Bromelioideae are predominantly of classes 2 or 3; those of Pitcairnioideae are mostly of classes 1 or 3. A correlation between stomatal structure and natural habitat is suggested, since terrestrial xerophytes tend to have elaborate stomata of class 3, whilst more specialized epiphytes have stomata of class 2.)

LEAF (Figs. 59–64)

General morphology

Entire, lanceolate, not usually differentiated into a distinct blade and sheath, although leaf base characteristically differing markedly from leaf apex in quantitative structural features, reflecting physiological differences (see p. 263). Leaf base usually completely sheathing; opposite margins of base often overwrapping, but not normally forming a closed tube except in more specialized spp. of *Tillandsia* (e.g. *T. recurvata*). Leaf blade rarely distinctly petiolate except in some *Pitcairnia* spp. (e.g. *P. multiflora* and *nigra*). Petiolate leaves also recorded in *Cryptanthus, Disteganthus, Ronnbergia* by Harms.

Heterophylly often pronounced (Lieske 1914), often reflecting changes from juvenile to adult form, correlated with change in water economy of plant with age (see Ecological Anatomy). Dimorphic leaves of some *Pitcairnia* spp., e.g. *P. heterophylla*, with basal **scale leaves,** the blade itself being reduced to a barbed spine contrasting with normal bladed leaves. Transitional forms also developed. Production of spinous scale leaves a seasonal phenomenon associated with annual drought (Rohweder). Leaf base in epiphytic spp. commonly inflated, successive bases overwrapping to form watertight pouches either individually, 1 for each leaf (**tank-epiphytes** of Chodat and Vischer) or collectively forming a central cavity (**cistern-epiphytes** of Chodat and Vischer). Intermediate types also common. Inflated proximal ends of leaves in many *Tillandsia* spp. collectively forming a distinct bulbous base (e.g. *T. bulbosa*) but not retaining water (see Rohweder 1956). Distal part of blade commonly abruptly narrowed above enlarged base. Channelled blades assuming the

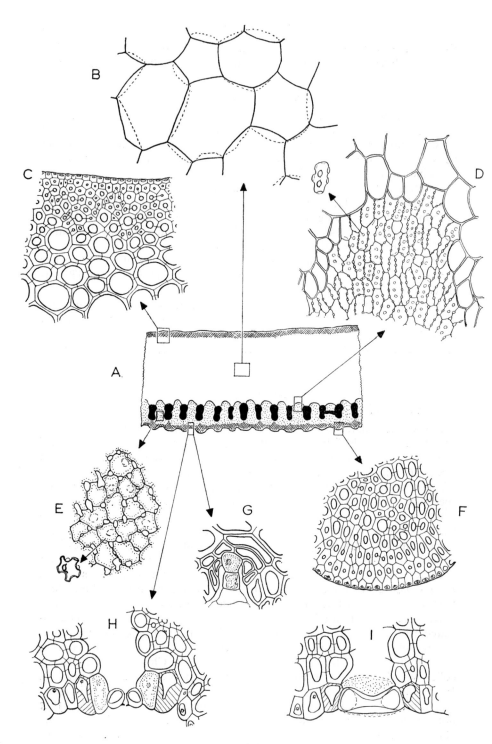

Fɪɢ. 59. BROMELIACEAE–PITCAIRNIOIDEAE LEAF

A–I. *Puya raimondii*. Anatomy of leaf at a level half-way between base and apex, equidistant from each margin.

A. T.S. (×10). B–F. (×230). B. Adaxial, colourless 'water tissue'. C. Adaxial surface layers. D. Adaxial mesophyll at junction with colourless tissue (inset, single palisade cell). E. Abaxial mesophyll (inset, single cell). F. Abaxial surface layers of rib. G–I. Details of abaxial epidermis within groove (×460). G. T.S. base of hair at base of furrow; distal shield cells missing. H. T.S. stoma. I. L.S. stoma.

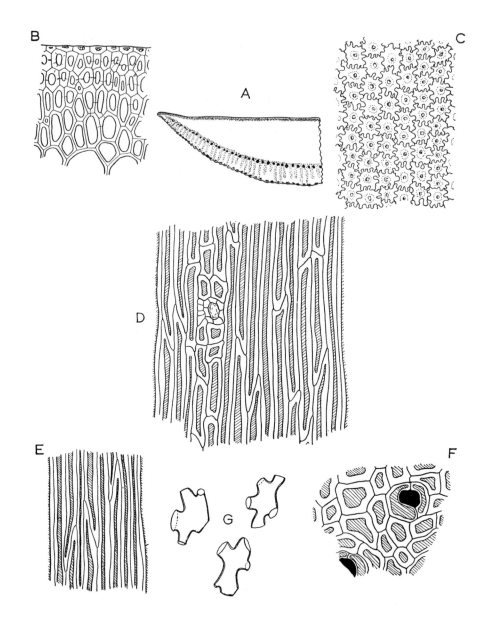

248

FIG. 60. BROMELIACEAE–PITCAIRNIOIDEAE LEAF

A–G. *Encholirium horridum*, lamina.

A. T.S. 1 half-lamina (× 3). B. T.S. adaxial surface layers (× 230). C. Adaxial epidermis, surface view (× 230). D. Adaxial hypodermis, outermost layer in surface view (× 230). E. Abaxial hypodermis in costal region, outermost layer in surface view (× 230). F. Abaxial hypodermis in intercostal region, outermost layer in surface view, substomatal chamber solid black (× 230). G. Isolated cells from incipient air-lacunae of abaxial mesophyll (× 370).

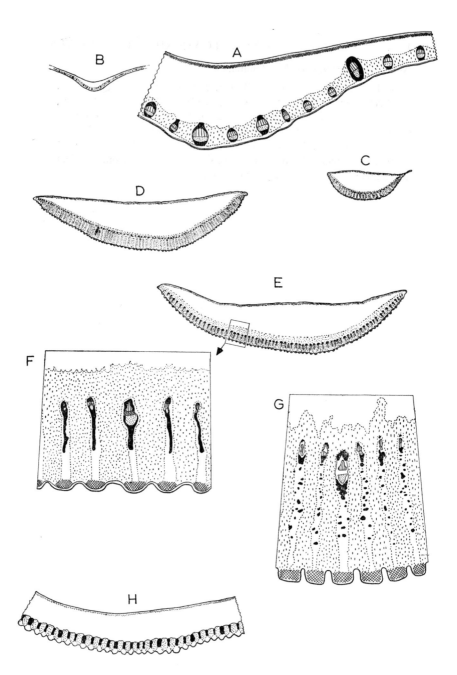

250

Fig. 61. BROMELIACEAE–PITCAIRNIOIDEAE. T.S. lamina.

A, B. *Pitcairnia xanthocalyx*. Midrib region.

   A. (×25). B. (×3).

C. *Dyckia fosteriana* (×3).

D. *Deuterocohnia schreiteri* (×3).

E, F. *Hechtia capituligera*.

   E. (×3). F. Enlargement of abaxial portion of E (×25).

G. *Hechtia* sp. Abaxial portion of lamina (×25).

H. *Puya alpestris*. Median part of lamina (×25).

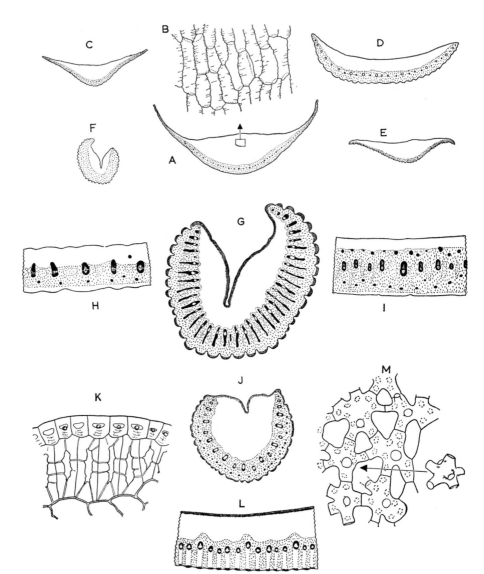

Fɪɢ. 62. BROMELIACEAE–BROMELIOIDEAE LAMINA.

A, B. *Cryptanthus fosterianus.* T.S.

   A. ($\times 2\frac{1}{2}$). B. Enlargement of part of adaxial water tissue ($\times 38$).

C. *Fascicularia bicolor.* T.S. ($\times 2\frac{1}{2}$).

D. *Streptocalyx longifolius.* T.S. ($\times 2\frac{1}{2}$).

E. *Greigia sphacelata.* T.S. ($\times 2\frac{1}{2}$).

F, G. *Deinacanthon urbanianum.* T.S.

   F. ($\times 2\frac{1}{2}$). G. ($\times 8$).

H. *Canistrum fosterianum.* T.S. median part of lamina ($\times 19$).

I. *Portea petropolitana.* T.S. median part of lamina ($\times 19$).

J, K. *Acanthostachys strobilacea.* T.S.

   J. ($\times 8$). K. Adaxial surface layers ($\times 345$).

L, M. *Bromelia balansae.* T.S.

   L. Part of lamina, half-way between midrib region and margin ($\times 8$).
M. Part of abaxial mesophyl ($\times 275$). Inset, single mesophyll cell.

253

shape and function of a gutter in tank-epiphytes; in more extreme terrestrial xerophytes blade thick, narrow, sub-terete and with a deep adaxial groove as in *Acanthostachys* (Fig. 62. J), *Deinacanthon* (Fig. 62. G).

Prominently thickened midrib region not developed except in some *Pitcairnia* spp. (Fig. 61. A, B). Leaf apex acute, often distinctly mucronate; leaf apex recurved or even tendril-like in some *Tillandsia* spp., e.g. *T. decomposita* and *duratii*. Margin of leaves in Bromelioideae and Pitcairnioideae mostly armed with straight or curved spines; leaf margin always smooth in Tillandsioideae.

General anatomy

Dorsiventral. **Cuticle** thin, rarely distinctly ribbed as in *Fosterella* and *Nidularium* spp.; slightly granular in *Tillandsia ionantha*; loose waxy covering developed adaxially in *Catopsis berteroniana* and *pendula*. **Epidermis** smooth, apart from longitudinal ribs, cells rarely irregularly papillose except in *Tillandsia bryoides, capillaris* f. *virescens* (as *T. pusilla* and *virescens*) or with marked papillae associated with ribs as in *T. loliacea* according to Mez. Epidermis usually v. shallow, deepest in spp. with thin cell walls. Mechanical function of epidermis largely replaced by thick-walled epidermal-hypodermal complex, according to Linsbauer.

Adaxial epidermis usually v. uniform (Figs. 49. A; 60. C), without stomata, never differentiated into distinct costal and intercostal bands but sometimes including distinct longitudinal files of scales; smooth, never papillose or ribbed although each adaxial scale commonly situated in a slight depression. Cells in regular longitudinal files, each cell square or rectangular in surface view but outline indefinite because of markedly sinuous cutinized middle lamella. Wall thickening not parallel to this outline except in thinner-walled cells. Sinuous outline of cells so exaggerated as to isolate small islands of lumen resembling 'ox-bows' in *Billbergia pyramidalis* (as *B. thyrsoidea*) and *Cryptanthus beuckeri* according to Linsbauer. Outer wall thin, wholly cutinized; inner wall usually markedly thickened (Figs. 59. C; 60. B), pitted. Cell lumen often almost occluded, more or less U-shaped in T.S., including a solitary, spherical-spinulose silica-body (Fig. 60. C). Walls of epidermal cells less commonly thin or more uniformly thickened, with less pronounced undulations, as in spp. of *Araeococcus, Canistrum, Catopsis, Fosterella, Gravisia, Guzmania, Pitcairnia, Portea, Tillandsia*. Thin-walled epidermis in distal part of blade sometimes continuous with thick-walled epidermis in leaf base (cf. Fig. 53. F, G). Shallow epidermis with inner thickened wall characteristic for family but variation within family not emphasized as diagnostic features because of cellular variation throughout a single leaf. Otherwise variation in wall thickness possibly only of ecological significance. Epidermal cells in *Brocchinia paniculata* distinctive (Fig. 49. I). Cells in this sp. more or less 'anchor-shaped' in surface view, but with sinuous walls; cells dove-tailing regularly; larger end of each cell inflated, the whole epidermis thus resembling a shingle-tiled roof.

Abaxial epidermis with shallow cells similar to those of adaxial surface but falling into 2 categories.

(i) Abaxial epidermis not ribbed, uniform, without marked differentiation of costal bands, e.g. in spp. of *Aechmea* (e.g. *Ae. chantinii*), *Araeococcus,* *Canistrum, Cryptanthus, Gravisia, Portea, Tillandsia*. Epidermis in distal part of leaf otherwise slightly differentiated into uniform bands of cells below veins and less uniform bands including scales and stomata pectinating with veins as in spp. of *Aechmea* (e.g. *Ae. bracteata*), *Catopsis, Fosterella, Hohenbergia, Pitcairnia*. Costal and intercostal bands most distinct in *Billbergia* (e.g. *B. distaceia*), *Canistrum, Glomeropitcairnia, Guzmania, Neoregelia, Nidularium, Quesnelia, Ronnbergia, Vriesea, Wittrockia*.

(ii) Abaxial epidermis ribbed, with prominent costal bands, separated from one another by shallow to v. deep intercostal furrows enclosing scales and stomata, e.g. in spp. of *Abromeitiella, Acanthostachys* (Fig. 62. J), *Ananas, Billbergia* (*B. macrolepis*), *Deinacanthon* (Fig. 62. G), *Encholirium, Fascicularia, Hechtia* (Fig. 61. E–G), *Neoglaziovia, Pseudananas, Streptocalyx*, and to a lesser extent in *Orthophytum* and *Puya* (Fig. 59. A). Correspondence between ribs and veins least regular in thick leaf of *Acanthostachys* (Fig. 62. J). Epidermal cells at base of deep furrows commonly deeper and thinner-walled than thick-walled cells above ribs as in *Deinacanthon* and *Puya* (cf. Fig. 59. F, H). An inverse mechanical correlation between hypodermal and epidermal cells in ribs and furrows noted by Linsbauer for *Bromelia fastuosa*. Depth of ribbing of abaxial surface often variable in large genera, e.g. *Aechmea, Billbergia, Tillandsia*, this feature being of more ecological than taxonomic significance.

Hypodermis, originating from mesophyll (Pfitzer 1872), usually differentiated adaxially into a peripheral mechanical tissue of one to several layers of sclerenchyma and an inner water-tissue of colourless thin-walled cells (Figs. 59–63). Hypodermal layers scarcely differentiated from assimilating mesophyll in small leaves of more extreme epiphytic Tillandsias, e.g. *T. recurvata* and *usneoides*. In more mesophytic spp. outer hypodermal cell layers thin-walled, occasionally slightly lignified but otherwise not well differentiated from colourless water-tissue, as in spp. of *Canistrum, Catopsis, Fosterella, Guzmania, Pitcairnia, Tillandsia, Vriesea*. Sclerotic hypodermis most commonly well developed (e.g. Figs. 59. C; 60. B); outermost layer of cells frequently elongated (Fig. 60. D, E), septate either with truncate end walls or more prosenchymatous or even fibre-like; most pronounced in following genera with presence of fibrous layer indicated: *Abromeitiella, Acanthostachys, Ananas* (fibrous), *Bromelia* (fibrous), *Deinacanthon* (fibrous), *Deuterocohnia* (fibrous), *Dyckia* (fibrous), *Encholirium* (fibrous), *Fascicularia, Hechtia, Neoglaziovia, Neoregelia, Pseudananas, Puya* (fibrous), *Quesnelia* (fibrous), *Streptocalyx* (fibrous), *Wittrockia* (fibrous).

Transition between sclerotic and inner layers often abrupt. Sclerotic layer in *Acanthostachys* of anticlinally extended cells (Fig. 62. K). Anticlinal walls of outermost hypodermal layer in *Neoglaziovia* appearing sinuous in surface view and somewhat resembling epidermis. Thickening of walls never truly collenchymatous as claimed by Richter. Adaxial sclerotic layer continuous, uniform or sometimes with files of short cells below files of epidermal scales. as in *Aechmea, Dyckia, Encholirium* (Fig. 60. D), *Neoglaziovia, Quesnelia*, Base of scale commonly enclosed by a distinct uniseriate ring of sclerotic, isodiametric hypodermal cells (Fig. 60. D).

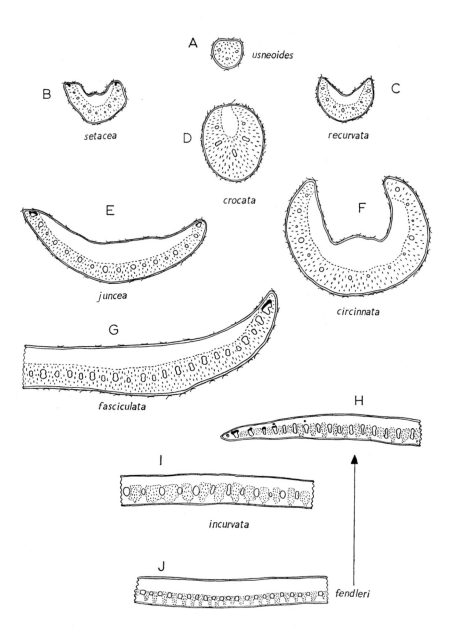

A *usneoides*

B *setacea*

C *recurvata*

D *crocata*

E *juncea*

F *circinnata*

G *fasciculata*

H

I *incurvata*

J *fendleri*

Fig. 63. BROMELIACEAE–TILLANDSIOIDEAES. LAMINA

A–J. *Tillandsia* lamina, diagrammatic T.S. half-way between base and apex (× 10).

A. *T. usneoides.* B. *T. setacea.* C. *T. recurvata.* D. *T. crocata.* E. *T. juncea.* F. *T. circinnata.* G. Half-lamina of *T. fasciculata.* H. Margin of lamina of *T. fendleri.* I. Median part of lamina of *T. incurvata.* J. Median part of lamina of *T. fendleri.*

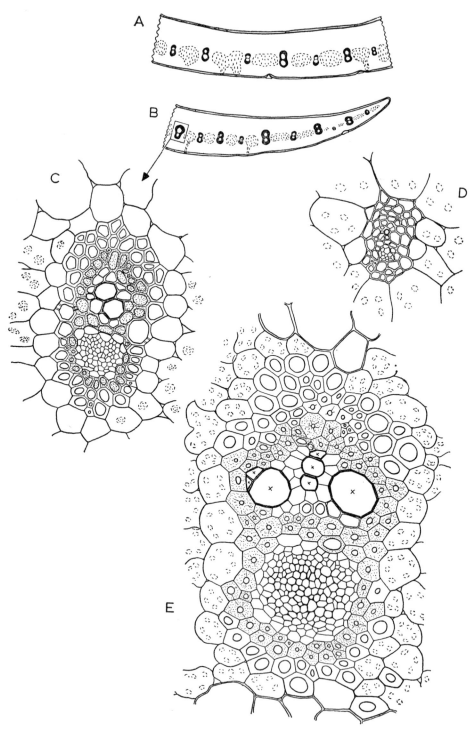

Fig. 64. BROMELIACEAE–TILLANDSIOIDEAE LAMINA STRUCTURE.

A–C. *Catopsis floribunda.*

A, B. Diagrammatic T.S. of lamina (×43). A. Median part. B. Margin. C. T.S. major vb of leaf (×370).

D. *Tillandsia usneoides.* T.S. median vb of lamina (×370).

E. *Tillandsia fendleri.* T.S. major vb of lamina (×370).

Endodermoid layer stippled in C and E.

Abaxial sclerotic layer less well developed, discontinuous, interrupted by substomatal chambers (Fig. 60. F). Commonly and especially in ribbed leaves intercostal markedly different from costal regions (cf. Fig. 60. E, F). Intercostal cells of abaxial hypodermis thin-walled, isodiametric or irregular; costal cells thick-walled, elongated and generally like those of adaxial surface. Intercostal cells somewhat anticlinally extended in *Neoglaziovia*. Sclerenchymatous tissues pronounced at leaf margins and continuous into marginal spines.

Inner hypodermal layers of adaxial surface usually sharply differentiated from external sclerenchyma and internal assimilating tissue, appearing as a water-storage tissue (**water-tissue**, Figs. 59–63) and so called on account of its presumed function as an internal water reservoir (Leclerc du Sablon 1914; Linsbauer 1911; Metzler 1926; Westermeier 1884). Development of cells continuing uniformly from their primordial stage until time of leaf expansion and therefore not serving as expansion cells according to Löv (1926). Tissue most well developed in extreme xerophytes, consisting of up to 10 layers of cells and up to or more than half total leaf tissue (e.g. Figs. 59. A; 60. A; 61. A, C–E; 62. A–D, G, J). Cells large, thin-walled (Fig. 59. B), often anticlinally extended (Fig. 62. B), the anticlinal walls appearing corrugated or resembling a concertina in T.S. as a result of reversible cell shrinkage.

Cell contents apparently often mucilaginous, e.g. in *Aechmea* and *Billbergia*. Water-tissue usually well developed towards leaf base and in midrib region, becoming less pronounced distally and marginally. Water-tissue most pronounced in thick, semi-terete, grooved leaves of *Abromeitiella*, *Acanthostachys* (Fig. 62. J), *Cryptanthus* (Fig. 62. A), *Deinacanthon* (Fig. 62. F–G), *Deuterocohnia* (Fig. 61. D), *Dyckia* (Fig. 61. C), *Encholirium* (Fig. 60. A), *Fascicularia* (Fig. 62. C), *Hechtia* (Fig. 61. E), *Neoglaziovia*, *Orthophytum*, *Pseudananas*, *Puya* (Figs. 59. A; 61. H). Water-tissue in *Streptocalyx* (Fig. 62. D) distinctly chlorenchymatous. Water-tissue less pronounced, usually forming a uniform shallow adaxial layer in *Ananas*, *Araeococcus*, *Billbergia*, *Bromelia* (Fig. 62. L), *Canistrum* (Fig. 62. H), *Dyckia* spp., *Hohenbergia*, *Portea* (Fig. 62. I), *Vriesea*, *Wittrockia*; scarcely developed in mesophytic leaves as in *Glomeropitcairnia*, *Gravisia*, *Guzmania*, *Neoregelia*, *Nidularium*, *Quesnelia*; only pronounced in midrib region in *Pitcairnia* spp. (Fig. 61. A, B) and *Ronnbergia*. Extent of water-tissue variable in *Tillandsia* (Fig. 63), usually less conspicuous than in other genera.

Abaxial hypodermal layers consisting of colourless thin-walled cells, but neither pronounced nor forming distinct water-tissues; commonly only 1–2-layered or even absent. Usually most well developed in costal regions and sometimes continuous with colourless, but rather indistinct vein buttresses as in *Abromeitiella*, *Bromelia* (Fig. 62. L), *Deinacanthon*, *Deuterocohnia*, *Dyckia*, *Encholirium* (Fig. 60. A), *Fascicularia*, *Hechtia* (Fig. 61. F–G), *Glomeropitcairnia*; buttresses not continuous with veins in *Puya* and *Vriesea* spp. Intercostal hypodermal cells often replaced by loose chlorenchyma associated with aerating system above stomata. For specific details of distribution of mechanical and thin-walled hypodermal layers see Solereder and Meyer.

Chlorenchyma usually abruptly delimited from colourless hypodermal layers above and below; distinct palisade-like layers of compact, anticlinally extended cells not usually well developed, except to a limited extent in *Acanthostachys, Pitcairnia, Puya* (Fig. 59. D) spp. Adaxial chlorenchyma layers often somewhat more compact than those elsewhere. Chlorenchyma usually showing marked contrast between compact layers associated with veins and looser regions between veins. Compact layers typically forming chlorenchymatous buttresses supporting veins, the loose tissue forming longitudinal bands of aerenchyma.

Intercostal chlorenchyma typically surrounding indistinct **air-lacunae** (aerating canals of Krauss) pectinating with veins. Lacunae filled with a reticulum (Fig. 62. M) of loose, stellately lobed cells (Figs. 59. E; 60. G); and sometimes traversed by indistinct transverse partitions usually associated with transverse veins, e.g. *Ananas, Catopsis, Glomeropitcairnia, Nidularium, Quesnelia*. Stellate cells of canals sometimes with long narrow arms and contrasting with remaining isodiametric mesophyll cells (e.g. Fig. 62. M). Air-lacunae in thinner, more mesophytic leaves continuous below with substomatal chambers via loose chlorenchyma. In thicker leaves longitudinal air-lacunae provided with distinct vertical branches (secondary aerating canals of Linsbauer) communicating with substomatal chambers and forming a continuous series above bands of stomata. Air-lacunae not or scarcely developed in extreme epiphytic spp. of *Tillandsia*. Air-lacunae usually most pronounced in leaf base no matter whether developed distally or not. Lack of air-lacunae in distal end of leaves of cistern-epiphytes said by Chodat and Vischer to be a result of poor contact between external atmosphere and this part of leaf. *Neoglaziovia* developing two series of air-canals one above the other in leaf base. Distinctive **chloroplasts** of Bromeliaceae described on p. 274.

Extra-fascicular **fibrous strands** sometimes developed in the mesophyll. Irregular, non-lignified, septate fibres, most commonly forming distinct adaxial and abaxial series in chlorenchyma above and below but never regularly associated with veins (Fig. 62. I). Although fibrous strands confined to a few genera, their diagnostic value restricted because not necessarily to be found in all spp. Fibrous strands present in *Aechmea* spp., *Ananas, Araeococcus, Billbergia* spp., *Canistrum* (few, Fig. 62. H), *Gravisia, Hohenbergia, Portea, Streptocalyx*; less commonly restricted to abaxial chlorenchyma as in *Acanthostachys, Aechmea* spp., *Billbergia* spp., *Bromelia* spp., *Neoglaziovia, Quesnelia* spp. Abaxial fibrous strands well developed in spp. of *Hechtia* and *Neoglaziovia*, consisting of many independent strands within each vascular buttress (Fig. 61. G). Extra-fascicular fibres absent from most Tillandsioideae, but flattened strands observed in spp. of *Guzmania* and *Vriesea* close to epidermis above but independent of largest veins. Occasional fibrous strands pectinating with veins probably representing free vein-endings. Fibres always most abundant in, or sometimes restricted to, leaf base. Fibrous strands sometimes surrounded by a distinct parenchymatous or even chlorenchymatous sheath, e.g. in *Ananas* according to Krauss; sheathing cells in *Aechmea* and *Billbergia* often elongated, resin-filled, and recalling O.S. of vb's.

Veins (vb's) always in a single series (e.g. Figs. 61–63), larger pectinating with smaller; mostly equidistant from each surface in thinner leaves but closer to abaxial surface in thicker leaves with well-developed colourless adaxial hypodermal layers (e.g. Fig. 61. C–E). Veins characteristically independent of surface layers but situated either within compact bands of chlorenchyma or less commonly within distinct colourless mesophyll buttresses (Figs. 61. F, G; 62. L), usually separated from colourless adaxial hypodermal tissues by 1 or more layers of chlorenchyma, the chlorenchyma sometimes penetrating irregularly into the water-tissue (Fig. 61. G). *Brocchinia paniculata* distinctive because larger veins buttressed to each hypodermis by well-developed fibrous sheath extensions (Fig. 49. G) (see also transverse commissures below); in *Navia* sometimes buttressed to abaxial surface. Uniseriate O.S. of longitudinally extended, usually chlorenchymatous, cells not always readily distinguishable from surrounding mesophyll in T.S. (Fig. 64. E) but commonly distinct because of resinous contents. Sclerotic I.S. well developed, usually complete, most pronounced above and below veins with an intervening lateral isthmus of 1–3 layers of thinner-walled cells with larger lumina. I.S. cells commonly lignified except for wider fibres above and below, remote from vascular tissues, these often forming massive unlignified sheath extensions. Smaller vb's commonly with taller extensions than larger (e.g. Fig. 61. F), a feature emphasized by Solereder and Meyer. Bundle-sheath extensions often narrow and girder-like, e.g. in *Hechtia* (Fig. 61. F), *Neoglaziovia*, *Quesnelia*, and especially in *Deinacanthon* (Fig. 62. G). Shape of outline of vb in T.S. stated by Solereder and Meyer to be of some diagnostic value. Marginal veins in *Fosterella* attached to adaxial hypodermis; in *Tillandsia* sometimes with well-developed adaxial fibrous sheaths and fused to form a marginal commissure (Fig. 63. G, H). Fibres in bundle sheath of *Ananas comosus* from 2·5 to 5·5 mm long according to Krauss.

Inner limit of bundle sheath represented by a distinct **ligno-suberized layer**, independently surrounding and so separating xylem from phloem. Layer described as endodermis by Richter (1891), although his report of Casparian thickenings not confirmed, and as endodermis-like sheath by Krauss. This endodermoid layer commonly thick-walled (e.g. in *Catopsis* (Fig. 64. C), *Guzmania*, *Tillandsia* (Fig. 64. E) and possibly distinctive of Tillandsioideae) and fairly conspicuous in unstained sections; otherwise thin-walled (e.g. in *Ananas*) and not easily recognizable without stains. Function of sheath discussed by Schwendener (1882), Richter (1891), Krauss (1949); function as endodermis supported by presence of unsuberized 'passage cells'.

Vascular tissues uniform throughout family, elements always v. narrow. Protoxylem developed, without forming lacunae, in larger vb's above two wider metaxylem elements (Fig. 64. E); less commonly wide veins with several wide metaxylem tracheal elements as in *Deinacanthon*, *Dyckia*, *Encholirium*, *Fascicularia*. Smaller veins with reduced tracheal elements (Fig. 64. C), especially in the reduced vascular system of extreme epiphytic Tillandsias such as *T. usneoides* (Fig. 64. D). Phloem elements v. narrow; sieve-tubes not readily distinguishable from remaining phloem cells in T.S. Sclerotic phloem parenchyma possibly diagnostic for certain *Pitcairnia* spp.

Transverse commissures frequent, narrow, often situated in distinct transverse septa of compact cells crossing air-lacunae, otherwise running above or below lacunae. Each with a continuous sheath of somewhat sclerotic parenchyma, single series of short, narrow tracheal elements and a narrow phloem strand; uniting with longitudinal veins at level of median thin-walled isthmus but xylem of transverse and longitudinal veins often apparently not in continuity. Endodermis-like sheath of longitudinal veins in *Ananas* continuous with a similar layer in transverse veins according to Krauss. *Brocchinia paniculata* distinctive with well-developed **transverse sclerotic girders** formed by anticlinal extension to limits of well-developed air-lacunae of sclerotic bundle sheath; girders not continuous but perforated by strands of thick-walled stellate parenchyma maintaining longitudinal continuity of aerating system; limiting layers of girder made up of similar thick-walled stellate parenchyma.

Leaf base

Typically differentiated from distal part of blade. Stomata absent; ribs reduced or absent; distribution and structure of scales, especially of shield, commonly different from that at distal end of leaf. Air-canals commonly well-developed, associated with the need for a more efficient aerating system in the leaf base according to Chodat and Vischer. Mechanical hypodermal tissues usually well developed and with a corresponding increase in thickness of epidermal walls. Fibrous extra-fascicular strands sometimes restricted to leaf base. Chlorenchyma reduced or absent, mesophyll generally of uniform, thin-walled colourless parenchyma without obvious differentiation of water-storage tissues. Starch commonly abundant, especially in bundle-sheath parenchyma.

Spines (Delbrouck 1875, Krauss 1949, Uhlworm 1873)

Developed distally on margins of leaf of almost all members of Bromelioideae and Pitcairnioideae, rarely obscure or absent as in spineless varieties of pineapples; absent from Tillandsioideae. Spines arising as lateral outgrowths without vascular tissue and differentiating sclerotic hypodermal layers continuous with hypodermal sclerotic layers in rest of lamina. Spines commonly bifurcated or in irregular aggregates, commonly recurved; often including a pronounced tuft of scales in acroscopic angle between spine and leaf margin. Spines on reduced scale-leaves of renewal buds of heterophyllous Pitcairnias v. pronounced but otherwise v. inconspicuous on foliage leaves of adult shoots. According to genetic studies of Collins (quoted by Krauss), spines in the normally spineless 'Cayenne' pineapple variety controlled by a gene complex, normally inhibited but expressed under drought conditions. Leaves with localized marginal bands of spines indicating growth under water-deficient conditions (see also Collins 1960). **Leaf margin** in all subfamilies smooth at leaf base, biseriate in tank-epiphytes, thin and forming a watertight joint between overlapping leaves.

Leaf abscission in some *Pitcairnia* spp., e.g. *P. heterophylla*, caused by drying of a succulent tissue outside sclerotic hypodermis situated a few mm above leaf sheath; persistent leaf sheath becoming rolled up.

Variegated leaves

Found in many Bromeliaceae of horticultural value resulting from 1 or more anatomical features occurring singly or in combination. (*a*) Variegation due to **anthocyanin** pigments, typically in vacuole of hypodermal cells immediately below epidermis, either of one or both leaf surfaces; often localized. (*b*) Variegation due to yellowish patches in regions of **chlorophyll deficiency**

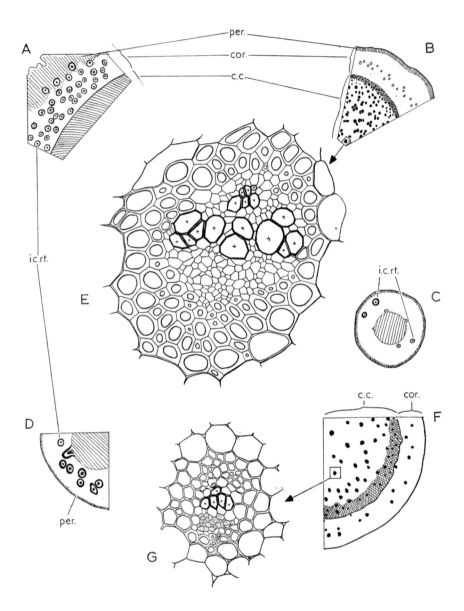

per.
cor.
c.c.

A

i.c.rt.

E

i.c.rt.

C

D

.per.

c.c.   cor.

F

G

Fig. 65. BROMELIACEAE AXIS.

A–E. Vegetative axis.

A. *Tillandsia fasciculata*. T.S. portion of rhizome to show position of intracauline roots in relation to stele (×3). B. *Bromelia pinguin*. T.S. stolon, without intracauline roots (×3). C. *Pitcairnia punicea*. T.S. vegetative axis (×3). D. *Tillandsia flexuosa*. T.S. rhizome (×3). E. *Bromelia pinguin*. T.S. collateral vb from axis. (×180).

F, G. Inflorescence axis, *Tillandsia flexuosa*.

F. T.S. (×10). G. T.S. vb, centre of central cylinder (×180).

per.—periderm; cor.—cortex; c.c.—central cylinder; i.c.rt.—intracauline root.

or high xanthophyll content. (*c*) Variegation due to white striations owing to localized **enlargement of epidermal scales** (e.g. *Aechmea chantinii*), or restriction of scales to transverse bands or patches (e.g. *Cryptanthus* spp.).

STEM (Fig. 65)

General morphology

Normally erect or creeping, with congested nodes; not or little-branched but with dormant bud in axil of each leaf (at least in pineapple). Renewal buds in *Bromelia balansae* at first stoloniferous, either above ground and covered with spinous scales or underground and covered with non-spinous scales according to Fiebrig (1922) (see also spines in relation to drought on p. 263). Stolons in *Bromelia* only rooting distally in association with terminal rosette, stolons in *Pseudananas* rooting throughout their entire length (Collins 1960). Lateral axes in *Cryptanthus* readily detached and acting as propagules according to Harms, otherwise branched axis system often producing cushion-like colonies, especially in saxicolous xerophytes, e.g. *Dyckia* and especially *Abromeitiella*. Stems less commonly elongated, sometimes semi-scandent as in *Tillandsia duratii* (Chodat and Vischer), *Pitcairnia sceptriformis* and *scandens*, *Nidularium bracteatum* (now *N. billbergioides*) (Harms 1930) and climbing by roots, tendril-like leaves or branches; otherwise pendent or decumbent. Elongated pendulous axis of *Tillandsia usneoides* a sympodium formed of successive short branches each with a fixed number of leaves terminating in a 1-flowered inflorescence. Corm-like rhizome recorded for *Puya tuberosa* by Harms.

General anatomy

(*a*) *Vegetative stem*

Quite uniform in the few spp. which have been studied. The following account is based on the description of stem anatomy in *Ananas* by Krauss; this is quite representative for the family as a whole.

Hairs resembling peltate scales of leaf base, but with irregularly stellate shields, more or less restricted to one or two horizontal series immediately above leaf insertion. **Stomata** absent. **Cuticle** thin. **Epidermis** uniform, cells in internodal regions square or longitudinally extended in distinct vertical files, anticlinal walls sinuous; inner and radial walls thickened, cells U-shaped in T.S. as in lamina and also each including a spherical silica-body. Nodal cells less regular, walls non-sinuous; cells containing smaller silica-bodies. **Cortex** narrow; outermost hypodermal layers of narrow elongated cells becoming thick-walled, lignified, and eventually suberized in old stems, continuous with abaxial hypodermis of leaf; inner hypodermal layers transitional to thinner-walled, more isodiametric cells of inner cortex. Outer sclerotic zone reduced to a single layer at base of internode.

Periderm (termed cork by Krauss) developed from secondary meristematic layers, in older parts of stems and over leaf-scars and wounds (e.g. Fig. 65. A–D) (see also Falkenberg 1876, Giovannozzi 1911, Matteucci 1897, Philipp 1923). Meristematic periderm layers often localized or discontinuous but generally of etagen-type originating by cell division beneath or even within sclerotic hypodermis, usually at varying depths from surface. Short radial series of daughter cells in *Ananas* either remaining thin-walled and becoming suberized, or becoming thick-walled, lignified, and resembling stone-cells in T.S. Periderm layers often delimited internally by a layer of stone-cells or including several layers of stone-cells alternating with thin-walled cells, especially in deep-seated cork tissue. Stone-cells otherwise in isolated groups. **Cortex.** Inner part consisting of thin-walled parenchyma including abundant starch. Cortex including the following kinds of vascular tissue: (i) Intracauline roots (cf. Fig. 65. A, C, D) (see p. 271). (ii) Girdling traces, representing the tangentially extended vascular system of each undeveloped axillary bud. (iii) Large leaf traces passing to central cylinder. (iv) Cortical vascular bundles, apparently originating in various ways as branches from leaf traces. Innermost cortical bundles narrow, resembling those of outer part of central cylinder; xylem surrounded by a suberized sheath as in leaf bundles.

Central cylinder delimited from cortex by narrow zone 2–4 layers wide of elongated cells, the zone becoming sclerotic and conspicuously pitted in older parts of stem. (This zone, described as 'endodermis' by earliest workers, lacks the suberized wall thickenings of a true endodermis. It is, however, more or less continuous with the endodermis of the root. It is more correctly referred to as endodermal-like peripheral sclerenchyma by Krauss.) Peripheral sclerenchyma separated from vascular tissue by a narrow thin-walled layer, termed 'pericycle' by some authors. Outermost vascular tissues of central cylinder consisting of a narrow **vascular plexus** of tangentially extended root traces; plexus largely a reticulum of tracheids with little phloem.

(This zone corresponds to the *réseau radicifère* of Mangin (1882) and originates from a **meristematic layer** (termed the meristematic or dictyogenous zone by Krauss), which is continuous with the apical meristematic tissues (cf. Fig. 66. D). Close to the shoot apex, root initials originate from it. The meristematic layer is incorrectly regarded as a secondary cambium by Boresch (1908), Petersen (1893), Ross (1895). For a detailed discussion of the nomenclature of this zone see Krauss.)

Vascular bundles diffuse in centre, but more congested at periphery of central cylinder, with frequent anastomoses according to Krauss's obscure and incomplete description of the course of the vb's. Individual vb's each collateral, with a poorly delimited sheath; narrow septate cells next to phloem becoming thick-walled and forming a distinct fibrous sheath. Ground parenchyma becoming starch-filled.

Rhizome of other Bromeliaceae showing little more than quantitative differences from above. Periderm often formed by suberization of outer cortex without cell division. Inner cortical layers and, less commonly, the central ground tissue as well, loose, with a well-developed system of intercellular air-spaces. Meristematic layer between cortex and central cylinder often remaining active for a long time. Vb's in *Tillandsia* commonly with a continuous sclerotic sheath (e.g. *T. balbisiana*) cf. also stolon of *Bromelia* (Fig. 65. B, E). Stem structure in more extreme epiphytic Tillandsias often v. reduced. Stem of *T. polytrichioides*, according to Chodat and Vischer, more or less erect but supported by intracauline roots. Central cylinder narrow and surrounded by a sclerotic 'pericycle' and large-celled, thin-walled 'endodermis'. Phloem little developed and largely obliterated. Extreme reduction

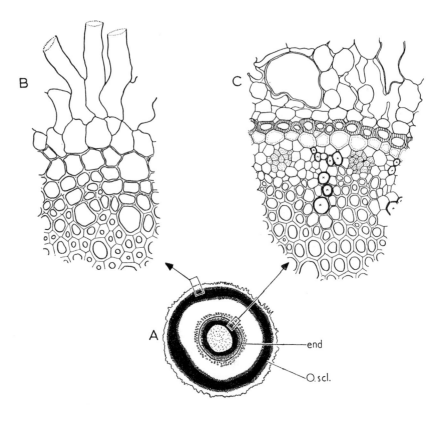

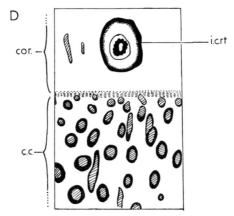

Fig. 66. BROMELIACEAE.

A–C. *Vriesea swartzii.* Extra-cauline root.

A. T.S. (×10). B. T.S. peripheral layers (×290). C. T.S. periphery of stele (×290).

D. *Vriesea capituligera.* Axis, diagrammatic T.S. of boundary between cortex and central cylinder (×10).

end.—endodermis; O.scl.—outer sclerotic cylinder; cor.—cortex; i.c.rt.—intracauline root; c.c.—central cylinder.

of *T. usneoides* approached by other spp. belonging to the Section *Diaphoran-thema* (see Billings 1904, Mez 1904, Solereder and Meyer 1929).Central cylinder in these spp. reduced to an almost solid sclerotic core except for a narrow thin-walled medulla, the whole enclosed in a ring of sclerotic parenchyma and includ-ing scattered phloem strands usually associated with a few v. narrow tracheids.

(*b*) *Inflorescence axis* (Fig. 65. F, G)

With distinct cortex and central cylinder, each region with discrete vascular system. Differing from vegetative axis in having more regularly distributed vb's and no intracauline roots. Divisible into 2 main types, according to Mez (see Solereder and Meyer): (1) Vb's isolated, scattered; peripheral narrower but with more massive fibrous sheaths than central vb's, e.g. in spp. of *Deuterocohnia, Dyckia, Guzmania, Prionophyllum, Puya.* (2) Vb's at periphery of central cylinder embedded in a sclerotic cylinder (Fig. 65. F) delimiting the cortex; central vb's with complete fibrous sheaths in spp. of *Aechmea, Bakeria, Billbergia, Catopsis, Dyckia, Hechtia, Pitcairnia, Lindmania, Tillandsia* (Fig. 65. G), *Vriesea.* Central vb's without sclerenchyma sheaths in spp. of *Aechmea, Araeococcus, Canistrum, Pitcairnia, Hohenbergia, Vriesea.* Following modi-fications also recorded: (*a*) Ring of vb's embedded in well-developed sclerotic cylinder in *Tillandsia* subgenus *Diaphoranthema.* (*b*) Congested peripheral vb's internal to but independent of sclerotic cylinder in spp. of *Aechmea, Canistrum, Gravisia, Portea, Streptocalyx, Tillandsia.* (*c*) Sclerotic cylinder poorly de-veloped, central vb's virtually without fibrous sheaths in spp. of *Guzmania.* (*d*) With fibrous strands in cortex, and sclerotic cylinder formed by outer vb's, in *Deuterocohnia meziana.* (*e*) Sclerotic cylinder absent and central scattered vb's with poorly developed conducting tissue, in subgenera *Anoplophytum* and *Pityrophyllum* of *Tillandsia.* This construction not constant for spp. in these subgenera as indicated by Solereder and Meyer, e.g. in *T. pulchella* (now *T. tenuifolia*) vb's in 2 rings, each vb with a well-developed sclerotic sheath, sheath of different bundles, especially those of outer ring occasionally confluent, together with 2 cortical series of vb's each with a sclerotic sheath. (*f*)Vb's numerous but v. congested in spp. of *Aechmea, Andrea, Billbergia, Bromelia, Hohenbergia, Puya, Rhodostachys* (now *Ochagavia*), *Streptocalyx, Tillandsia, Wittrockia.* Axis in *Acanthostachys strobilacea,* according to Solereder and Meyer, without sclerotic cylinder, cortex including 1–2 series of vb's; outer limit of central cylinder indicated by a ring of well-developed, isolated vb's, central vb's with well-developed fibrous sheaths.

'Secondary vascular cambium' recorded by Foster (1945) in perennial inflorescence axis of *Deuterocohnia schreiteri* actually a well-developed 'etagen'-type periderm in outer cortex.

(Although these notes indicate the range of structures recorded in in-florescence axes in Bromeliaceae, there is no information on the variation throughout a single axis.)

ROOT (Fig. 66)

General morphology

Roots often much modified, in more extreme epiphytes not absorbing but serving entirely as anchoring organs or even absent from all but seedling stages. Roots originating in meristematic layer (dictyogenous zone) between cortex and central cylinder of stem, close beneath shoot apex (Krauss, Chodat and Vischer, Weber), usually remaining within cortex of stem for greater or lesser distance as **intracauline roots** (cortical roots) before penetrating stem surface and conspicuous in T.S. of all bromeliaceous axes (e.g. Figs. 65. A, C, D; 66. D); rarely developed in inflorescences. Similar inclusion of branch within parent roots and even 'twin' roots with 2 steles recorded by Meyer (1940). Intracauline roots running more or less parallel to long axis, but with a somewhat sinuous course, towards base of stem, rarely branching, sometimes extending from cortex of lateral to that of parent axis (Borchert 1966). Intracauline roots sometimes more or less completely replacing cortical tissue, e.g. in *Navia schultesiana* according to Weber (1953, 1954) and especially in *Tillandsia benthamiana, plumosa, polytrichioides* according to Chodat and Vischer, there forming a cable-like structure with considerable mechanical strength. In *Tillandsia incarnata* intracauline roots originating in association with development of lateral branches, these in turn associated with appearance of terminal inflorescences, according to Borchert (1966). Root system in more specialized epiphytic Tillandsias often v. reduced as in *T. arhiza, rupestris*, according to Chodat and Vischer; roots often restricted to seedling, notably in *T. usneoides* but, according to Harms, 'rootless' condition not uncommon in several subgenera such as *Aerobia* (e.g. *T. tectorum*), *Anoplophytum* (e.g. *T. dianthoidea* = *T. aeranthus*), *Phytarrhiza* (e.g. *T. duratii*).

External roots in *Ananas* commonly remaining flattened within leaf axils as **girdling axillary roots** (Krauss, Pittendrigh 1948) but without absorptive function. Axillary roots rare in other bromeliads and not in any way characteristic for the family but recorded by Pittendrigh for *Bromelia humilis* as sole absorbing system and in *B. chrysantha* and *B. karatas* as present but not replacing soil roots. Root system showing progressively less vascular tissue and of less significance in absorption as spp. become more specialized as epiphytes (Schulz, see Ecological Anatomy on p. 275). This reflected in whether re-establishment of offsets begins with growth of either leaf and shoot (epiphytes) or root (terrestrial xerophytes) (Schimper).

General anatomy

Structure varying somewhat according to function and position of root but otherwise v. constant throughout family. **Piliferous layer** with well-developed root-hairs in soil roots of terrestrial spp. (e.g. *Ananas*, Bowers 1929). Reports of root-hairs modified as haustorial multiseptate papillae in intracauline roots by Jörgensen (1878) refuted by Krauss and not in any way typical for the family. **Cortex**; outer part in external roots differentiated as a narrow or often wide multiseriate **exodermis** of suberized cells. Outermost cortical layers immediately within exodermis always differentiated as a wide sclerotic cylinder (Fig. 66. A, B) forming a conspicuous mechanical layer. Wide raphide-sacs often conspicuous in this layer (e.g. Fig. 66. B), usually becoming thick-walled; in *Ananas* according to Krauss forming thick-walled tubes owing to breakdown of cross walls in continuous series of raphide-sacs. Middle cortex of thin-walled parenchyma, sometimes including starch. Inner cortex typically lacunose owing to collapse of cells producing an irregular reticulum of radially extended air-lacunae'separated by collapsed cells or cell-wall remains. Lacunae sometimes secondarily filled with enlarged, slightly thick-walled cells (Fig. 66. C). Lacunae said by Meyer (1940) to serve in transport of capillary water.

Endodermis uniseriate, narrow, thick-walled; walls either uniformly thickened as recorded for spp. of *Billbergia, Pitcairnia, Puya, Tillandsia, Vriesea* (Fig. 66. C), otherwise with unequal wall thickenings, appearing U-shaped in T.S. **Pericycle** 1–(2)-layered, thin-walled. Peripheral layers of **stele** typically with v. reduced polyarch vascular tissues enclosed by well-developed sclerotic conjunctive parenchyma, the whole forming a strong mechanical layer distinct from the lignified medulla with much wider cells (Fig. 66. A, C). Medullary vessels isolated from peripheral vascular elements rare, but recorded for spp. of *Hohenbergia* and *Pitcairnia*.

Intracauline roots differing somewhat from external roots. For example, in *Ananas*, according to Krauss, differing in (*a*) absence of root-hairs; (*b*) absence of exodermis; (*c*) absence of air-lacunae in inner cortex. **Mycorrhiza** recorded by Chodat and Vischer for *Tillandsia polytrichioides* and by Pittendrigh (1948) for *Bromelia humilis*; said to be of significance in functioning of axillary roots in the last sp.

For structure of root apex and root development see Krauss, Meyer (1940).

SECRETORY, STORAGE, AND CONDUCTING ELEMENTS

Crystals. Raphide-sacs common throughout ground tissues of all spp. studied; differentiated early in axis and sacs usually larger than cells of surrounding parenchyma. Abundant in mesophyll of leaf, often restricted to assimilating tissue and commonly suspended within air-lacunae. Slime surrounding raphide-crystals giving a glycogen reaction according to Politis (1914). Raphide-sacs in outer cortex of root of *Ananas comosus* arranged in longitudinal series, according to Krauss, becoming thick-walled in mature root and after collapse of end walls functioning as an air-canal. Calcium oxalate (and possibly other crystalline substances) also frequent in assimilating tissue as small rhombohedral bodies, solitary, in coarse clusters, or forming distinct sphaerocrystals as observed in spp. of *Canistrum, Neoregelia, Nidularium, Orthophytum, Quesnelia, Wittrockia*. 'Inulin' crystals recorded by Jörgensen in *Pitcairnia punicea*, but not confirmed by Solereder and Meyer, perhaps identical with sphaerocrystals; see also Boresch. **Calcium carbonate** recorded by Cedervall but not confirmed by Solereder and Meyer.

Silica (Baumert 1907, Bulitsch 1892*b*, Linsbauer 1911) present in all thick-walled epidermal cells of leaf and stem, never in guard and lateral subsidiary cells, as single rugose, more or less spherical bodies enveloped by inner wall thickenings (e.g. Fig. 60. B, C, p. 248). Silica-bodies up to 10 μm in diameter but usually much smaller; largest usually in cells around stomata (e.g. Fig. 56. J, K, p. 238). Size of body apparently correlated closely with degree of thickening of surface layers, e.g. bodies large and conspicuous in shallow thick-walled epidermal cells above sclerotic hypodermal layers. Size also correlated with supply of dissolved silica available to roots, as incidentally recorded by Krauss in *Ananas*.

Silica absent from thin-walled epidermis of leaf in spp. of *Canistrum, Guzmania, Pitcairnia, Tillandsia* (e.g. Fig. 53. G, p. 232), *Vriesea* and from stem of *Dyckia remotiflora, Tillandsia usneoides* according to Solereder and Meyer. Silica absent from a thin-walled epidermis when overlying a thin-walled hypodermis as observed by the writer in distal part of blade in spp. of *Araeococcus* (Fig. 55. A–C, p. 236), *Canistrum, Cryptanthus* (adaxial epidermis), *Fosterella, Pitcairnia, Portea, Tillandsia* but usually becoming conspicuous in basal part of the same leaves with thicker-walled surface layers, especially in *Tillandsia*. Silica in thinner-walled epidermal cells less commonly represented by **silica sand** (*Tillandsia* spp.) or by aggregates of several small bodies (*Cryptanthus*). Silica sometimes observed internally as fine sand in O.S. of vb's in spp. of *Billbergia, Bromelia, Fosterella, Hechtia, Neoregelia, Nidularium, Pitcairnia, Ronnbergia*. Silica sand more generally distributed in mesophyll of *Ronnbergia*. Hypodermal silica-bodies recorded by Baumert in *Tillandsia andicola* but not by other investigators.

Tannin not distinctly developed except for yellowish, resin- or oil-like droplets, commonly observed, especially in fresh material, typically in sheathing parenchyma of leaf veins or even around extra-vascular fibrous strands; less commonly in isolated mesophyll cells (Boresch) or even in stomata. Secreted material, when studied in detail by Wallin (1898), found to give chemical reactions of tannin, and since one fraction soluble in water, said to be osmotically active. Probably characteristic of all members of family but most widely distributed in Pitcairnioideae, there often in all chlorenchyma cells but often as v. small droplets.

Gum or **mucilage** not uncommon as intercellular secretion according to studies by Boresch (1908). Gum often restricted within distinct gum cavities, as noted by the author in the inflorescence axis of *Tillandsia fasciculata* and recorded by others in the cortical parenchyma of the vegetative stem or in the central cylinder. Gum rarely exuding into leaf base as observed by Boresch in *Pitcairnia roezlii* and by the author in *Tillandsia incurvata*; alternatively, vb's occluded by gum. Gum excreted into leaf base said to include protein-digesting enzymes by Picado (1913). Gum cavities said to originate schizolysigenously according to Boresch, the gum either secreted through cell walls or resulting from cell breakdown. Limiting cells often extending into cavities in a tylose-like manner. Raphide-sacs and cells surrounding intracauline roots also disposed to secrete gum. Mucilage formation perhaps induced artificially by wounding. (Whether this is a wholly natural phenomenon, as suggested by Boresch, is questioned by Solereder and Meyer.) Chagualgummi (Hartwich 1896) said to be derived from an ill-defined sp. of *Puya*. (In view of the peculiar water economy of the Bromeliaceae this marked tendency to gummosis may be very significant and is, together with other biochemical peculiarities of the family, in need of much closer investigation.)

Starch commonly abundant in ground tissues of stem. Starch grains more or less spherical, single or commonly aggregated into compound angular grains (cf. Krauss in *Ananas*); often abundant in leaf base, starch-rich cells then replacing assimilating mesophyll.

Chloroplasts in leaves of *Tillandsia usneoides* noted by Billings (cf. Barbaini 1921) to be compound with 'microchloroplasts' embedded within larger 'megachloroplasts'. Microchloroplasts subsequently shown by Krauss to be starch grains formed within chloroplasts (presumably during day) and released into cytoplasm (presumably during night). Chloroplasts in Bromeliaceae generally rather diffuse, heterogeneous, with little apparent chlorophyll. (Their fine structure would probably repay investigation.)

Xylem. Vessels, according to Cheadle (1955), present in all parts in some spp. (e.g. of *Acanthostachys*?, *Cryptanthus*, *Hechtia*, *Hohenbergia*?, *Orthophytum*?, *Pitcairnia*, *Vriesea*). Vessels restricted to root and stem in spp. of *Aechmea*, *Dyckia*, *Guzmania*; or restricted to root alone in spp. of *Aechmea*, *Ananas*, *Billbergia*?, *Dyckia*, *Neoglaziovia*, *Nidularium*?, *Ochagavia*, *Quesnelia*. Vessel elements normally with scalariform perforation plates but with simple perforations in roots of *Pitcairnia* (Cheadle) and in *Vriesea carinata* (Solereder and Meyer). Scalariform septa recorded by Waterston (1912).

Phloem. Sieve-tubes v. narrow; with reticulately compound sieve-plates in *Puya alpestris* according to Solereder and Meyer.

ECONOMIC USES

Pineapples are the fleshy infructescences of *Ananas comosus* (L.) Merr. (Okimoto 1948). A number of spp. with more sclerotic leaves, notably *Neoglaziovia variegata* Mez (see Denniston 1925, Fernandes 1942), have been used as a source of fibres. The fibres in many bromeliaceous leaves are probably equally long (Cedervall, Krauss) and potentially useful (Halama 1921). Many spp. of Bromeliaceae have long been cultivated in glasshouses in Europe and are becoming increasingly popular in the United States. Apart from their multi-coloured leaves and bracts together with their often striking inflorescences and fruits, their undemanding cultural requirements make them ideal house plants. Although not a family of major economic importance, the Bromeliaceae have had a very pronounced and insidious influence on human welfare, albeit indirectly. Bromeliaceous tank-epiphytes in the humid tropics are commonly the hosts of malarial mosquitoes; some of these vectors are specific to certain bromeliads (see Picado 1913, Downs and Pittendrigh 1946, Pittendrigh 1948).

TAXONOMIC CONCLUSIONS

The Tillandsioideae can be recognized instantly by their distinctive peltate scales, which are much more highly organized than those in the other two subfamilies. The Pitcairnioideae and Bromelioideae, on the other hand, show no clearly circumscribed anatomical differences apart from those which reflect an increasing tendency towards epiphytism in the latter group. Within each subfamily certain genera, or less commonly groups of genera, tend to have common diagnostic anatomical features. This tendency needs closer investigation by examination of more spp. within large genera. Stomatal structure is often quite uniform in certain genera, or closely related genera (e.g. *Aechmea*, *Billbergia*, *Quesnelia* (Fig. 52, p. 230), but the number of stalk-cells in the scales may more precisely delimit taxa (e.g. distinguishing *Aechmea*, on the one hand, from *Billbergia* and *Quesnelia*, on the other (Fig. 44)). Anatomical features, however, seem more closely correlated with the habitat of a sp. than with its taxonomic position (see Ecological Anatomy). The groupings proposed by Cedervall (1884) and Keilene (1915) reflect this, although they are themselves rather artificial.

The chief result of a reinvestigation of the anatomy of the Bromeliaceae has been to establish the isolation of *Cottendorfia* and *Navia*, a number of spp. of which show peculiarities of hair structure not otherwise found in the family. It is therefore of interest to note that Harms considered *Navia* the most primitive genus (cf., however, Smith 1934) and also that Krauss has described capitate hairs on the seedling leaves of *Ananas* (not found on adult foliage) which recall the hairs of adult and seedling foliage of some *Navia* spp. It must be emphasized finally that investigation of *Navia* and *Cottendorfia* has been carried out on minute fragmentary samples and a detailed reinvestigation is urgently needed. This should shed more light on the phylogeny of Bromeliaceae. Unfortunately this will be a difficult task because so many spp. in these genera are very inaccessible.

ECOLOGICAL ANATOMY

Early observers, notably Schimper, had indicated a peculiar water economy in the Bromeliaceae largely associated with epiphytism. This stimulated numerous detailed anatomical studies of members of the family. Understandably these were carried out less from a systematic point of view than with the object of examining microscopic features which might account for physiological peculiarities. These studies were facilitated to some extent by a relative abundance of bromeliads in cultivation in Europe where they had long been valued horticulturally. Some of the earliest observations and experiments were probably made by horticulturists. Duchartre (1868), for example, noted that *Tillandsia dianthoidea* (now *T. aeranthus*) required free water and could not survive simply in a humid atmosphere.

Much of the early investigation of the water economy of Bromeliaceae was experimental, but unfortunately the anatomical investigation which accompanied this was often inaccurate. For example, the structure of the tillandsioid scale was not described correctly until 1924. Until then it had seemed that the structure of the scale was unsuited for its presumed function. The careful investigation by Wetzel eventually showed there was no conflict. The following notes briefly survey the field of structure in relation to function in the Bromeliaceae as a whole. Additional comments based on original observation are indicated by italicized paragraphs.

1. *Origin of the epiphytic habit*

Schimper (1884) distinguished epiphytes with rosettes of leaves which held water (rosette-epiphytes, rain forms) and which were typically shade-dwellers, from more exposed forms which did not retain free water but were able to absorb through the whole leaf surface (extreme-atmospheric epiphytes, dew forms). This distinction is based partly on experiment. Schimper noted that many bromeliaceous leaves are unusual amongst flowering plants because they are readily wetted, added water spreading rapidly. He showed that leaves of extreme epiphytes increase in weight when wetted and that epidermal scales are responsible for water absorption. This can be observed directly, there being a change in colour from white (air-filled) to green (water-filled) as the scales are wetted. Schimper saw that the shield cells of the scale are not cutinized and that water-soluble dyes colour the stalk-cells. Apart from a water-absorbing function which these simple experiments demonstrated, Schimper also suggested that scales reduced transpiration when dry. Many species of Bromeliaceae were shown to survive either if the roots were cut off and only leaves wetted, or if water was applied only to the leaf base. A difference between root and leaf absorbers was also demonstrated in the way in which transplants re-establish themselves. Early growth of the former is marked by production of new roots but of the latter by new shoots. Schimper concluded that evolution of the epiphytic habit had occurred within the rain forest itself, a transition from the forest floor to the lower branches being facilitated by a prevailing high humidity; thence into the canopy as Bromeliaceae became independent of roots as water absorbers.

These observations stimulated much investigation and the following modified picture of evolution in the Bromeliaceae was built up, largely by Mez and Tietze. Tietze, after investigating herbarium specimens, recognized four groups based on differences in scale structure and general habit. The groups were presumed to show increasing evolutionary specialization, the criterion for their evolutionary status being the degree of xerophytism which the different forms exhibited.

(a) On this basis the primitive Bromeliaceae were pictured as terrestrial xerophytes absorbing water through roots, their unspecialized scales being largely associated with stomata in abaxial grooves and serving simply to reduce transpiration. Such leaves are generally unwettable. Anatomical features associated with this primitive type of xerophytism include marginal leaf spines, well-developed internal water-storage tissues, stomatal occlusion, sclerotic surface layers, and reduced vascular tissues. This biological group is represented by most genera in the Pitcairnioideae, e.g. *Cottendorfia, Deuterocohnia, Dyckia, Hechtia, Navia, Pitcairnia, Puya.*

(b) More specialized forms remain terrestrial but have channelled leaves which tend to drain towards and retain water in the expanding leaf bases. Scales are well developed on the leaf base but remain structurally unspecialized. Abaxial scales were considered capable of absorbing water. Xeromorphic features are largely retained but water-storage tissues are reduced. Modern representatives are mostly members of the Bromelioideae, and include species of *Acanthostachys, Ananas, Andrea, Bromelia, Cryptanthus, Deinacanthon, Disteganthus, Fascicularia, Greigia, Orthophytum, Pitcairnia.* Familiarity with these genera in the field shows that this is a very heterogeneous assemblage.

(c) Unspecialized facultative epiphytes are often to be found on rocks where they live a truly epiphytic existence. Their scales may or may not be highly organized, but, however this may be, they are all pictured as serving both for the absorption of water and reduction of transpiration. Water funnels (see p. 245) at the leaf base are well developed, roots are feebly developed and largely serve as hold-fasts. Water-storage tissues within the leaf are not pronounced. This group is also taxonomically diverse and includes species from genera of both Bromelioideae and Tillandsioideae such as *Aechmea, Androlepis, Billbergia, Canistrum, Catopsis, Gravisia, Guzmania, Hohenbergia, Neoregelia, Nidularium, Portea, Quesnelia, Streptocalyx, Tillandsia, Vriesea, Wittrockia.*

(*d*) Highly specialized extreme epiphytes are largely restricted to *Tillandsia* but include some species of *Vriesea* and possibly *Aechmea tillandsioides*. Water absorption is restricted to the leaves, which are completely covered with highly organized scales. The continuous scale cover serves for protection between short periods during which water is absorbed whilst the leaf is wet. The main water-supply may be dew, and, when this is so, the appendages of the scales in several species of *Tillandsia* (Fig. 41. D, E, p. 200) are thought to be points at which condensation takes place. Roots are reduced to hold-fasts, or even entirely eliminated from all but seedling stages. Water-storage tissues are little developed. Because water is absorbed through the surface of the plants, this limits their size, and epiphytes of this kind are invariably small, often resembling bryophytes (e.g. 'Ball-moss'—*Tillandsia recurvata*) or even lichens (e.g. *T. usneoides*). In these most highly specialized forms, the xeromorphic features found in their presumed ancestors tend not merely to be eliminated, so that sclerotic tissues are absent, surface layers tend to be thin-walled and stomata unobstructed, but they are even replaced by hydromorphic features. An extreme example is *Tillandsia bryoides* with few or no stomata, gas exchange according to Linsbauer being made possible by localized patches free from cuticle.

In the above scheme, the increasing degree of specialization of existing Bromeliaceae was itself regarded as indicating their general course of evolution. The Pitcairnioideae were considered to be the most primitive group. The Bromelioideae and Tillandsioideae were thought of as more specialized and divergent, but not in a linear sequence because Bromelioideae have evidently evolved a greater degree of specialization in reproductive features, e.g. the inferior ovary. The Tillandsioideae, on the other hand, have become more specialized vegetatively.

This picture is probably generally true, but tends to oversimplify a much more complex situation. It is very difficult to consider evolution of one organ independently of others so that a holistic approach must be adopted. For instance, inferior ovaries in Bromeliaceae are associated with fleshy fruits, the unappendaged seeds being presumably dispersed by animals. On the other hand, superior or rarely semi-superior ovaries in the Pitcairnioideae and Tillandsioideae are correlated with capsular fruits, winged or plumous seeds, widely disseminated by wind to exposed localities. It is not sufficient to emphasize one feature, the position of the ovary, as the criterion of advancement (e.g. Smith 1934).

A greater complexity for bromeliad ecology and evolution is suggested by the detailed investigations of Pittendrigh (1948). Even within a relatively small area (Trinidad) there were more biological types than Tietze recognized. The following categories were described.

(i) *Soil-root types* (terrestrial); Pitcairnioideae. This corresponds to Tietze's first group.

(ii) *Tank-root types* (terrestrial); represented by *Ananas comosus* and **3** species of *Bromelia*. These have axillary roots as described by Krauss. Two subgroups were recognized by Pittendrigh who found that the axillary roots function only in *Bromelia humilis*, doing so with the aid of mycorrhiza in the debris accumulated within the leaf axils. Soil roots in this species are poorly developed. The second subgroup is represented by 3 members in which soil roots are well developed and axillary roots probably do not function. This is true at least in *Ananas* where the roots are described as non-absorbing (Krauss).

(iii) *Tank-absorbing trichome types* (terrestrial or epiphytic). This group includes most Trinidadian bromeliads. Roots serve essentially as hold-fasts. Mineral nutrition is dependent on material collected within the tanks. These commonly hold a rich and varied fauna (cf. Picado 1913; Laessle 1961). Four subgroups are recognized within this category. In the first, tanks are not supplemented in any way; the rosettes tend to be unbranched. In the second subgroup, plants branch vigorously producing dense clusters so that humus collects between individual rosettes as well as within the rosettes. This additional humus is exploited by secondary mycotrophic 'nest-roots'. In the third subgroup, the plants retain little water and are described as 'ephemeral' tank types. Plants in subgroup four draw attention to the special relationship between epiphytic bromeliads and ants and are classed as myrmecophilous tank types. An association between bromeliads, ants, and other epiphytes to form 'ant-gardens' has already been described in tropical America by Ule (1901).

(iv) *Atmospheric-absorbing trichome types* (extreme atmospheric epiphytes of earlier authors). This corresponds to Tietze's last group which Pittendrigh subdivides. Subgroup (1) includes plants which are essentially intermediate between this and the previous general type because they can retain some free water in the leaf base but also have a continuous covering of scales. Subgroup (2) includes the familiar extreme epiphytes which, however, may be 'rain' or 'dew' forms depending on the source from which they obtain free water. Subgroup (3) includes plants habitually associated with ants.

These groupings often seem arbitrary, but are valuable because they draw attention to the diversity of ecological types in the family. Pittendrigh himself recognized that quite different groups might be constructed if their classification was based on some factor other than the degree of dependence of plants directly on the substrate. This was done and a number of new categories, which often cut across the above scheme, was created according to the degree of tolerance of Bromeliaceae in Trinidad, first of shade, and second of humidity.

Three classes were recognized with increasing tolerance of shade: an exposure group, a sun group (subdivided into 3 minor classes), and a shade-tolerant group. The differences between these classes are reflected in the zonation of epiphytic Bromeliaceae in forest areas of uniform humidity. Members of the first group occupy the most exposed (i.e. highest) situations in the forest canopy, those of the last group the least exposed (i.e. lowest), with the second group somewhat intermediate. There is some correlation between the habit of a plant and its tolerance of light. Members of the exposure group are exclusively tank species; members of the shade-tolerant group belong largely to the ephemeral tank category, retaining little water for only short periods.

Finally Pittendrigh examines the geographical distribution of bromeliads in Trinidad in relation to the variation in the rainfall in order to determine their tolerance of drought. He finds that distribution may or may not be influenced by rainfall. Some species such as *Gravisia aquilega, Guzmania monostachya, Vriesea procera* are relatively unaffected by the abundance of rain; others may be restricted in various ways either to wetter or drier areas.

From his analysis Pittendrigh concludes that there is great variation in the factors which determine the distribution of epiphytic Bromeliaceae. Some, especially the tank-epiphytes of the exposure and sun groups, are light demanding and relatively indifferent to change in humidity. Others, notably the shade-tolerant forms thrive in a wide variety of light intensities so long as a prime requirement for a high humidity is met. They are normally absent from well-lighted situations in the forest because these are driest, not because sunlight is inimical to their growth. Extreme-atmospheric epiphytes appear to be not only light demanding, but also to require low humidities. Pittendrigh follows Mez in assuming that this last peculiar requirement is because regular desiccation of the capillary system is needed to enable gaseous exchange to proceed. It has already been noted (p. 195) that these forms have the lowest ratio of stomata to scales and it is presumed that with few stomata gaseous exchange is sluggish. This might also account for the absence of epiphytes such as *Tillandsia usneoides* and *T. recurvata* from moist habitats. Continued anatomical investigation of epiphytic Bromeliaceae with Pittendrigh's ecological classification in mind is much to be desired.

On the basis of this ecological evidence and a re-examination of existing information Pittendrigh reinterprets bromeliad evolution. He concludes that it is incorrect to infer, as does Tietze, that the Pitcairnioideae are ancestors of the two divergent stocks, Bromelioideae and Tillandsioideae, but prefers to consider each of the three subfamilies as originating from an unknown common ancestor. *Good evidence for this is in the diversity and often marked specialization within the Pitcairnioideae themselves.* Therefore each subfamily must have diverged independently and for this reason the epiphytic habit must have evolved separately in the Bromelioideae and Tillandsioideae. These taxa differ markedly in ovary structure, and it seems unlikely that there could be a simple linear transition from one to the other. Presumably the baccate-fruited Bromelioideae split off from the ancestral stock whilst this was still capsular-fruited. Pittendrigh then states that evolutionary trends must be sought within each subfamily separately. With this approach he argues that the Tillandsioideae have entered the rain forest primarily as light-demanding xerophytes in the uppermost levels of its canopy, subsequently moving into the lower levels of the forest as indicated by the 'residual' tolerance for light that these species show. Apart from the ecological evidence, Pittendrigh supports his argument by a consideration of floral structure, which he regards as most primitive in *Tillandsia*, to which genus all the more xerophytic epiphytes belong, whereas the shade-tolerant species have more specialized floral parts, notably *Glomeropitcairnia* with a half-inferior ovary. However, Harms regards *Glomeropitcairnia* as the most *primitive* member; at one time this genus was even included within Pitcairnioideae. *Pittendrigh assumes that specialization in one part (the flowers) must accompany specialization in unrelated organs.*

Within the Bromelioideae, since the terrestrial habit is common, Pittendrigh suggests that stages in the evolution of epiphytism may be more evident and he implies that a migration into the lower forest canopy must have occurred much as Schimper envisaged. *Bromelia humilis*, independent of the substratum because of its axillary, mycotrophic roots is pictured as representing an important possible stage in this process. Continued investigation along the lines pioneered by Pittendrigh may throw light on these evolutionary problems. In view of facultative epiphytism of many Bromeliaceae it is very likely that the obligate condition has originated independently many times.

Before leaving this subject, it must be pointed out that anatomical evidence may conflict with Pittendrigh's interpretation of evolution within the Tillandsioideae. If his views are accepted there is the problem that the most highly specialized tillandsioid scale, with its dual function, and elaborately developed shield wing (Figs. 41; 42. C, pp. 200-3) *is primitive; the simpler scales in* Catopsis, Glomeropitcairnia, Guzmania, Vriesea (Fig. 43. A–M, p. 204) *without elaborate wings and functioning solely as water-pumps would be unspecialized by reduction, which is rather the reverse of the sequence as normally understood. Anatomy could be crucial in answering this question of the direction (or directions) in which these sequences should be read. It seems significant that the less-specialized scales in the above genera tend to have most stalk-cells, notably in* Glomeropitcairnia (Fig. 43. I). *This supports Harms's interpretation closely, that* Glomeropitcairnia *is primitive. Scales in* Tillandsia *have few stalk-cells* (Figs. 41; 42). *There is some evidence from the study of the anatomy of* Cottendorfia *and* Navia (Figs. 48; 49, pp. 220-3) *(which on other grounds might be regarded as coming closest to the original bromeliaceous stock, see Harms 1930) that primitive hairs in the Bromeliaceae before the elaboration of a distinct shield, had uniseriate, many-celled axes. Variation in number of stalk-cells in the Bromelioideae is also appreciable* (Fig. 47, p. 214), *and perhaps a similar reduction has occurred in this subfamily.*

Rohweder (1956) more recently has discussed the distribution of Bromeliaceae in El Salvador with Pittendrigh's classification in mind. He finds variation according to vegetation type. In general, epiphytes of cloud forest are almost exclusively tank-epiphytes of class (iii), those of savannas atmospheric epiphytes of class (iv). Intermediate habitats are predominantly occupied with either a mixture or the intermediate types in Pittendrigh's classification. Rohweder also lists morphological features which characterize epiphytes in contrasted environments. For example, epiphytes in cloud forest have well-developed tanks, a negatively geotropic response, glabrous lamina, ligulate turgid leaves, as opposed to those in savannas which have no tanks, no negatively geotropic response, a scaly lamina, and tubular or linear mechanically rigid leaves. Restriction of deciduous species of *Pitcairnia* to dry habitats is an obvious example of this adaptive distribution.

2. *Neoteny*

Before leaving the subject of evolution in the Bromeliaceae, emphasis should be laid on seedling stages. In ecological studies, little attention has been given to this phase of the life cycle and yet this must largely determine the establishment of epiphytes. Juvenile may be more significant ecologically than adult stages. Lieske was one of the first to note that in collecting Bromeliaceae in their native habitats, it is often impossible to distinguish species in the juvenile stage which are otherwise quite distinct as adults. In general, as Schulz points out, seedlings are more xeromorphic than adults. Notable differences between juvenile and adult phases of tank-epiphytes, described by Lieske, are the narrow leaves and ageotropic response of the former, compared with the broad leaves and negative geotropism of the latter. There is marked heterophylly between the juvenile and adult phases, usually with a sudden transition from the seedling which is essentially a 'dew-form' with narrow leaves to the adult 'rain-form' with broader, gutter-shaped leaves with inflated water-retaining bases. The contrast between the two phases is often pronounced in tufted species in which the parental, erect, adult tank rosette is surrounded by juvenile, irregularly orientated (ageotropic) offshoots. Lieske concluded that there could be no direct evolutionary sequence from the terrestrial to the epiphytic condition, because the seedling stages of epiphytes are not adapted to a terrestrial existence.

However, if we do not admit an intrusion of the theory of recapitulation, we can still reinterpret the evolutionary relation between tank-epiphytes and extreme epiphytes by regarding the latter as persistent juvenile stages (neotenous forms) of the former. The ageotropic response of extreme epiphytes is often very obvious (e.g. Tillandsia circinnata). *This idea can only be substantiated, however, by detailed studies of the anatomy and physiology of all stages in the life history of selected bromeliads.*

3. *Functions of bromeliad scales*

Most investigation of the functional mechanism of scales in Bromeliaceae has centred on the tillandsioid type. Some investigators seem not to have appreciated that this is only one of many kinds of peltate scale formed in the family. This type will be considered first although it is the most specialized. These scales have a dual function; (*a*) rapid uptake of water and dissolved mineral salts when wet, (*b*) a reduction of transpiration and insolation when dry. The water-absorbing function can be verified easily by repeating Schimper's experiments. The pathway from the shield via the stalk-cells through the sclerotic hypodermis, which is interrupted or pitted below the scale, and so to the water-storage tissues can be followed with water-soluble dyes. The mechanism of the scales is less clear, but Mez's interpretation fits the general facts. Each scale operates as if it were a minute 'pump' (*trichompompe*) with a one-way valve. When dry the shield is contracted, and the lumina of cells in the disk are occluded by thickened walls above and below because of collapse of thin vertical walls. On wetting, the thick walls expand because of their rich pectin content and so water is drawn into the expanded lumen. The question of whether or not a vacuum is created in the lumina of the disk cells is discussed in the literature (Mez 1904, Steinbrinck 1905). The over-all result of the pumping action is that water comes into contact with the protoplast of the dome-cell which behaves like an osmometer. In this way water is drawn osmotically through the stalk-cells to the mesophyll. According to Mez the stalk-cells are rich in sugars which he observed crystallizing out in herbarium specimens. The cytoplasm of the dome-cell seems specialized for rapid water uptake (Dolzmann 1964) (see p. 199). Attention should also be drawn to the osmotic potential of dissolved tannins which Wallin (1898) has mentioned. Schimper regarded the stalk-cells as non-cutinized and permeable; Mez more accurately noted the cutinization of stalk-cells but misinterpreted the distribution of cutin, describing the cells as wholly cutinized which would suggest they were impermeable. This gave a paradoxical picture of cells, which could be shown to transport water, being structurally impermeable.

However, it was not necessary to consider these apparently cutinized walls permeable because of special chemical properties of the cuticle, or because they were perforated by ultramicroscopic pores, as Haberlandt suggests, but merely to examine them more carefully. Wetzel (1924) and also Chodat and Vischer (1916) did this and saw that only the lateral walls of the stalk are cutinized, the transverse walls being non-cutinized except for a narrow peripheral annulus which, however, is readily mistaken for a continuous layer. The stalk as a whole thus forms a cutinized funnel, sealed laterally, but with permeable walls at each end and traversed by a number of permeable septa (Fig. 40. N–O, p. 196). When all free water has been absorbed, the shield dries out and collapses, the scale contracts into its epidermal cavity which is sealed, the thickened disk effectively corking the outer end of the funnel. This explanation of the mechanism of the pump accords well with its construction and depends on the distribution and chemical nature of wall thickenings and the semi-permeable properties of the stalk-cell protoplasts. *Unexplained, however, is the observation that dead leaves (e.g. killed by immersing in boiling water) absorb free water just as rapidly as living ones.*

Scales also absorb dissolved mineral salts, as indicated by Aso (1910). Wherry and Buchanan (1926) on the basis of an analysis of the ash of *Tillandsia usneoides* suggest that this absorption is selective. In the extreme-atmospheric epiphytes such as *T. recurvata* and *usneoides* the source of minerals is presumably wind-blown dust. Pittendrigh has suggested that the tendril-like leaves of *T. gardneri* by curling around nearby twigs may rub off additional salts.

The enlarged shields of the scales in the more exposed Tillandsias are said to have a protective function. They probably reduce transpiration because of the still air between overlapping scales, this air-cushion being augmented in some *Tillandsia* species by papillate or ribbed surfaces (Mez). This function seems not to have been tested experimentally. A reduction of insolation is indicated by the experiments of Baumert (1907) who measured changes in leaf temperature thermo-electrically. The highest reduction value of 23·8 per cent was measured in *Tillandsia flexuosa*. It may be significant that this is one of the species in which the distal scales are warted (Fig. 42. F, p. 202). That this reduction is necessary was suggested by Billings (1904) who considered the dispersion of 'microchloroplasts' in *T. usneoides* an adaption necessitated by constant high light intensities. Krauss, however, interprets Billings's observations differently (see chloroplasts, p. 274).

Overlapping of scale shields in Tillandsioideae also causes a capillary spread of free water. This is easily observed. Mez considered this a mechanism whereby free water is rapidly dispersed so that the task of 'pumping' it into the leaf is carried out by the maximum number of scales. The rapid elimination of free drops added to these leaves supports this. Finally the shields may serve as points for water condensation and Schimper regarded the unilateral extension of the shield into a long appendage in some species (e.g. Fig. 41. D, p. 200) as facilitating this in some way.

Hitherto no one has commented upon the unequal wall thickening in pericentral and subperipheral cells in tillandsioid scales (Figs. 41–43). Thin-walled areas may simply represent major entrances to the scale, either of free water from above the shield (thin areas in the outer wall) or of capillary water held between scale and epidermis (thin areas in the inner wall). Distal scales may have both kinds of thickening (e.g. Fig. 42. E, J). Central cells always have thick outer walls in distal scales because of their 'plug' function. It is possible that thin areas in outer walls also serve as hinges. When dry, the wing of the shield is then held somewhat erect, improving its insulating and light scattering abilities. The first effect of wetting the semi-erect wings of the scales is that they flatten, being drawn down by surface tension between wing and epidermis and pushed down by swelling of the disk cells. Conversely the last movement on drying as the scale collapses into the epidermal depression is the erection of the wing. Scales on distal and proximal parts of the same leaf may operate differently since their construction is not usually the same (e.g. Fig. 42. C, F). This may, however, also reflect a difference of age since basal scales are always younger.

Scales in tillandsioid tank-epiphytes seem well constructed to serve as 'pumps', but their wings are scarcely developed (Fig. 43) and do not form a continuous cover. Their value as insulators must be negligible. Scales are not restricted to the leaf base, where free water is held, as suggested by some earlier authors. Presumably in the submersed basal scales a turgor equilibrium with free water is established. A peculiar adaptation is shown by Catopsis berteroniana *which has waxy, non-wettable leaves so that free water runs straight into the basal tank.*

4. Functions of unspecialized scales

Little is known about the behaviour of less-organized scales in terrestrial, saxicolous, and epiphytic members of the Pitcairnioideae and Bromelioideae. In tank-epiphytes of this kind their absorbing function is presumed rather than proved. Aso (1910) says that in *Ananas* they do not absorb salts. Stalk construction seems basically identical with that of the tillandsioid scale, but it is difficult to see how the pathway could be plugged by the unthickened shield when dry. Limited observations suggest that leaves with these scales are not wetted readily. On the other hand, the collective indumentum may reduce transpiration and it commonly fills the furrows in xeromorphic leaves of the Pitcairnioideae. The close association between scales and stomata also supports this functional interpretation. Linsbauer has recorded a close moulding of the shield cells around the outer aperture of stomata. In tank-epiphytes distal and basal scales may function differently. *It is also possible that distal scales may have only a brief absorptive life, operating as pumps only when they are on that part of the developing leaf growing through the water held in the central 'cistern'. These unexplained problems are largely physiological.*

5. *Stomatal mechanisms*

In reviewing the complexity and variety of bromeliaceous stomata (p. 219) it was pointed out that many differ so much from normal stomata that it is doubtful if they operate in the usual way, that is by movement of the guard cells. This has been emphasized by a number of previous investigators. Stomata of the simplest class (1, see p. 224) probably do operate in the normal way. Those of classes 2 and 3 represent divergent trends with alternative mechanisms which are not necessarily mutually exclusive. In stomata of class 2 outgrowths below the guard cell may reduce transpiration by occluding the substomatal chamber or even the inner aperture of the pore itself. Linsbauer, however, also suggested that they may act as props and actually keep the pore *open* when the leaf is flaccid. Consequently they may perhaps promote transpiration. Evidence in support of this is that the protrusions are always thin-walled, even when the cell out of which they grow is thick-walled (e.g. Fig. 54. K, p. 234). In this connexion, a tendency towards hydromorphism in extremely epiphytic Tillandsias, which typically have class-2 stomata, should again be emphasized. *It may be that this promotion of water loss is related to mineral nutrition rather than water-economy itself. An adequate supply of salts may become available only if a continual uptake of large volumes of water is promoted. A high resistance to water loss might be disadvantageous.*

Billings mentions the probable non-functional guard cells of *Tillandsia usneoides*. This is further discussed by Linsbauer and Krauss. Thick-walled guard cells, typical of class-3 stomata, are characteristic of xeromorphic bromeliads. It has been suggested that it is by changes in the turgor of thin-walled lateral subsidiary cells that the aperture between otherwise non-functional guard cells is closed. *It may be that the only controllable aperture in these stomata is that below otherwise rigid guard cells and that this aperture is closed by movement of the pair of lateral subsidiary cells which seem to be able to meet* (e.g. Fig. 56. J, p. 238). No experiments have been done to test the validity of these speculations.

6. *Epidermal functions*

Linsbauer (1911) recognized a division of labour in the surface layers of bromeliaceous leaves. There are 3 functions which, in normal mesophytic leaves, are performed by a 1-layered epidermis alone. These functions are to provide mechanical protection, to store water, and to reduce transpiration (Westermeier 1884). In bromeliaceous leaves each of these purposes is exclusively performed by a different cell layer, this being most noticeable in extreme xeromorphic leaves. Reduction of transpiration is still the function of the shallow cutinized epidermis. Its sinuous cell walls and the manner in which they dove-tail with the outer hypodermal layer are both mechanical adaptations holding the surface layers together during reversible leaf expansion and contraction as the water content changes. Mechanical support is provided by the outermost sclerotic hypodermis and water storage occurs in the inner colourless cells with their 'accordion-pleated' walls.

Baumert (1907) in addition regarded the bromeliad epidermis as an effective light reflector, reflection being promoted both by the minute concavities represented by each unevenly thickened cell and by the silica-bodies. Baumert and Linsbauer comment upon the correlation between wall thickness of epidermal cells and the size of silica-bodies. It should be noted that this correlation seems general whenever monocotyledonous cells contain silica.

7. *Root functions*

Reduction of the root system and its effectiveness as an absorbing system are discussed by Schulz (1930). The amount of conducting tissue in roots progressively decreases from Pitcairnioideae through Bromelioideae to Tillandsioideae. Roots of Pitcairnioideae are adapted to periodic uptake of water. Intracauline roots in some instances may be mechanically advantageous (see Chodat and Vischer 1916, Weber 1953). Jörgensen (1878) suggests that initially they are adaptive towards fire resistance, apart from being a xeromorphic feature.

8. *Structures associated with water-economy*

Apart from internal and external water-storage features, water movement along the tracheal system of extreme epiphytes is negligible as can be demonstrated with cut leaves stood in aqueous dye solutions. The reduced conducting system in Bromeliaceae generally, with narrow tracheal elements and particularly the suberized sheath which envelops the vascular tissues suggests that water conduction is sluggish and interchange between vascular and ground tissues is limited. Occlusion of vascular tissues by gummosis has been recorded (Boresch, Chodat and Vischer).

9. *Gummosis*

The tendency for Bromeliaceae to develop mucilaginous substances requires investigation. Picado (1913) has suggested that gums excreted into the leaf base of tank-epiphytes may contain protein-digesting enzymes. Excretion of gums does not seem a general property, but should be investigated (cf. also Xyridaceae). The key to epiphytism in the family may be biochemical.

GENERA AND SPECIES REPORTED ON IN THE LITERATURE

Aso (1910) *Ananas sativus, Nidularium purpureum, Pitcairnia imbricata, Tillandsia usneoides*; epidermal scales.

Bachmann (1886) *Tillandsia bartrami* Ell., *T. bracteata* Chapm., *T. bryoides* Gris., *T. bulbosa* Hook., *T. caespitosa* LeConte, *T. dianthoidea* Ten., *T. ixioides* Gris., *T. juncea* LeConte, *T. myosura* Gris., *T. propinqua* Gay., *T. recurvata* Pursh., *T. retorta* Gris., *T. usneoides* L., *T. utriculata* LeConte; epidermal scales.

Barbaini (1921) *T. dianthoidea* Ros., *T. ixioides* Gris.; epidermal scales.

Baumert (1907) *Acanthostachys strobilacea* Klotsch, *Tillandsia aloifolia, T. andicola* Gill., *T. duratii* Vis., *T. gardneri, T. ixioides* Gris., *T. karwinskyana* Schult., *T. streptophylla* Scheid., *T. vernicosa* Bak., *T. vestita* Ch. et Schdl.; epidermis.

Billings (1904) *Tillandsia usneoides* L.; all parts.

Birge (1911) *T. recurvata* L.; all parts.

Borchert (1966) *Tillandsia incarnata* H. B. K.; stem, root.

Boresch (1908) *Aechmea pineliana, Pitcairnia roezlii, Quesnelia roseo-marginata*; ergastic substances, stem.

Bulitsch (1892a) *Billbergia iridifolia* Lindl.; epidermal scales.

Bulitsch (1892*b*) *Ananas sativus, Billbergia iridifolia, Bromelia karatas, Dyckia remotiflora, Hechtia dasylirioidea, Puya* sp.; silica inclusions.

Cedervall (1884) spp. of *Aechmea, Ananas, Billbergia, Bromelia, Cryptanthus, Dyckia, Hohenbergia, Nidularium, Pitcairnia, Puya, Tillandsia*; leaf.

Chodat and Vischer (1916) *Aechmea polystachya, Ae. pulchra, Bromelia serra, Dyckia floribunda, Nidularium morrenianum, Tillandsia arhiza*; leaf. *T. duratii*; stomata. *T. polytrichioides* (now *T.tricholepis*); stem. *T. pseudo-stricta*; epidermal scales, stem.

Delbrouck (1875) *Hohenbergia* sp.; leaf, spines.

Denniston (1925) *Neoglaziovia variegata* Mez; leaf.

Dolzmann (1964) *Tillandsia usneoides* L.; epidermal scales.

Duchartre (1868) *T. dianthoidea*; leaf.

Falkenberg (1876) *Aechmea fulgens*, '*Nidularium rigidum*'; stem.

Fiebrig (1922) *Bromelia balansae, Dyckia hassleri*; leaf.

Haberlandt (1887) *Billbergia nutans, Hohenbergia strobilacea, Pitcairnia xantho-carpa, Tillandsia zonata*; stomata.

Haberlandt (1914) *Vriesea psittacina*; epidermal scale.

Halama (1921) *Ananas* spp.; leaf.

Hassack (1886) *Vriesea splendens*; leaf.

Hedlund (1901) *Karatas plumieri* (now *Bromelia karatas* or *B. pinguin*); epidermal scales.

Holm (1915) *Ananassa sativa* Lindl.; all parts.

Jörgensen (1878) *Aechmea fulgens* Brongn., *Billbergia liboniana* de Jong., *B. nutans* Braun., *B. zebrina* Lindl., *Bromelia immersa* Braun., '*Boptophytum rosea-purpurea*' Decais., *Caraguata lingulata* Lindl., *Dyckia rariflora* Schult., *Lampro-coccus fulgens* Beer, *Nidularium agavaefolium* Braun., *Pitcairnia punicea* Hort., *P. xanthocalyx* Mart., *Pourretia* sp., *Puya longifolia* Morr., *P. polyanthos* Braun., *Tillandsia usneoides* L., *T. utriculata* L., *Vriesea psittacina* Lindl.; root.

Keilene (1915) *Aechmea fasciata, Ae. fulgens, Ananas sativus, Billbergia zebrina, Caraguata musaica, Catopsis nitida, Cryptanthus beuckeri, C. zonatus, Dyckia frigida, Karatas purpurea, Ortgiesia tillandsioides, Pitcairnia corallina, P. inaeci-folia, Quesnelia cayennensis, Rhodostachys pitcairniifolia, Tillandsia recurvata, T. strobilantha, T. vigeri*; leaf.

Kenda and Weber (1951) *Aechmea bracteata, Vriesea carinata*; stomata.

Krauss (1948–9) *Ananas comosus* (L.) Merr.; all parts.

Linsbauer (1911) spp. of *Aechmea, Ananas, Aregelia, Billbergia, Bromelia, Cani-strum, Caraguata, Catopsis, Chevalieria, Cryptanthus, Disteganthus, Dyckia, Echinostachys, Encholirium, Greigia, Guzmania, Hechtia, Hohenbergia, Karatas, Lamprococcus, Macrochordium, Massangea, Nidularium, Ochagavia, Ortgiesia, Pitcairnia, Portea, Pothuava, Puya* (incl. *Pourretia*), *Quesnelia, Schlumbergeria, Tillandsia, Vriesea*; leaf.

Matteucci (1897) *Billbergia iridifolia* Lindl., *B. quesneliana* Brongn., *B. vittata* Brongn.; leaf.

Metzler (1926) *Dyckia remotiflora, D. sulphurea, Hechtia ghiesbreghtii*; leaf.

Meyer (1940) *Aechmea fasciata* (Lindl.) Bak., *Ae. miniata* (Beer) van Houtte var. *discolor* Beer, *Ae. weilbachii* Didr., *Ananas sativus* (Lindl.) Schult., *Billbergia rosea* Beer, and miscellaneous notes on other spp.; root.

Mez (1896) studied a larger number of spp. than any other investigator; his account is a general summary of his observations.

Mez (1904) illustrates following spp. of *Tillandsia: coarctata, ionantha, loliacea, myosura, schenckiana, straminea, variegata, xiphioides*; leaf.

Petersen (1893) *Bromelia* sp., *Lamprococcus fulgens, Pitcairnia recurvata*; stem.

Pfitzer (1872) *Acanthostachys strobilacea*; leaf.

Philipp (1923) *Billbergia zebrina, Nidularium meyendorffii*; stem periderm.

Politis (1914) *Billbergia nutans* Wendl., *Cryptanthus zonatus* Beer, *Pitcairnia xanthocalyx* Mart.; raphide-sacs.

Richter (1891) numerous spp. investigated.

Ross (1895) *Bromelia fastuosa* Lindl., *Quesnelia cayennensis* Bak.; stem.

Sablon (1914) *Billbergia speciosa*; leaf.

Schimper (1884) *Tillandsia flexuosa*; root. *T. usneoides*; epidermal scales.

Schulz (1930) leaf, root of following spp., with other parts as indicated: *Abromeitiella* sp., *Acanthostachys strobilacea, Aechmea glaziovii, Ananas sativus, Aregelia princeps, Billbergia vittata, Bromelia humilis, Cryptanthus acaulis*, leaf, root, rhizome; *Dyckia altissima, D. brevifolia*, rhizome; *Guzmania cardinalis, Nidularium paxianum, Pitcairnia undulata, Puya spathacea, Tillandsia juncea, T. leiboldiana, T. usneoides*, leaf, stem; *Vriesea major*.

Solereder and Meyer (1929) *Acanthostachys strobilacea* Klotzsch, *Aechmea bromeliifolia* Bak., *Ae. coelestis* Morr., *Ananas sativus* Schult. f., *Aregelia spectabilis* Mez, *Billbergia pyramidalis* Lindl., *Cryptanthus undulatus* Otto et Dietr., *Dyckia remotiflora* Otto et Dietr., *Guzmania monostachya* Rusby, *G. zahnii* Mez, *Hepetis (Pitcairnia) punicea* Mez, *Nidularium fulgens* Lem., *Puya alpestris* Poepp., *Tillandsia ixioides* Gris., *T. karwinskyana* Schult., *T. usneoides* L. var. *major* André.

Staudermann (1924) *Tillandsia aloifolia* Hook., *T. bryoides* Gris., *T. dianthoidea* Rossi, *T. ixioides* Gris., *T. propinqua* Gay., *T. recurvata* L., *T. retorta* Gris., *T. setacea* Sw., *T. usneoides* L., *T. vestita* Cham. et Schdl.; epidermal scales.

Tassi (1899) *Tillandsia dianthoidea* Rossi; epidermal scales.

Thomas and Holmes (1930) *Ananas sativus*; seedling.

Tietze (1906) studied epidermal scales in a great number of Bromeliaceae from herbarium material, following indicates spp. mentioned: *Acanthostachys strobilacea* Klotsch, *Aechmea aureo-rosea* Bak., *Ae. calyculata* Bak., *Ae. candida* Morr., *Ae. coelestis* Morr., *Ae. distichantha* Lem., *Ae. fasciata* Bak., *Ae. fernandae* Bak., *Ae. friedrichsthalii* Mez et Donn.-Smith, *Ae. fulgens* Brongn., *Ae. galeottii* Bak., *Ae. gamosepala* Wittm., *Ae. glomerata* Mez, *Ae. hystrix* Bak., *Ae. kienastii* Morr., *Ae. kuntzeana* Mez, *Ae. legrelleana* Bak., *Ae. nudicaulis* Gris., *Ae. panniculigera* Gris., *Ae. pitcairnioides* Mez, *Ae. pittieri* Mez, *Ae. pulchra* Bak., *Ananas sativus* Schult., *Andrea* spp., *Androlepis skinneri* Brongn., *Araeococcus micranthus* Brongn., *A. parviflorus* Lindm., *Aregelia ampullacea* Mez, *A. carcharodon* Mez, *A. chlorosticta* Mez, *A. compacta* Mez, *A. concentrica* Mez, *A. cruenta* Mez, *A. cyanea* Mez, *A. leucophaea* Mez, *A. morreniana* Mez, *A. princeps* Mez, *A. sarmentosa* Mez, *A. spectabilis* Mez, *A. tristis* Mez, *Billbergia elegans* Mart., *B. euphemiae* Morr., *B. morelii* Brongn., *B. reichardtii* Wawra, *B. rosea* Beer, *B. tweediana* Bak., *B. vittata* Brongn., *Bromelia agavifolia* Brongn., *B. balansae* Mez, *B. binotii* Morr., *B. exigua* Mez, *B. fastuosa* Lindl., *B. glaziovii* Mez, *B. scarlatina* Morr., *Canistrum amazonicum* Mez, *C. aurantiacum* Morr., *C. cyathiforme* Mez, *C. lindenii* Mez, *C. roseum* Morr., *C. schwackeanum* Mez, *C. superbum* Mez, *C. viride* Morr., *Catopsis magnispatha* Mez, *C. morreniana* Mez, *C. mosenii* Mez (= *C. berteroniana*), *C. nitida* Gris., *C. nutans* Gris., *C. oerstediana* Mez, *Chevalieria sphaerocephala* Gaud., *Cottendorfia florida* Schult., *Cryptanthus praetextus* Morr., *C. schwackeanus* Mez, *Deuterocohnia chrysantha* Mez, *D. longipetala* Mez, *D. meziana* O. Ktze., *Disteganthus* spp., *Dyckia affinis* Bak., *D. brevifolia* Bak., *Gravisia aquilega* Mez, *G. chrysocoma* Mez, *G. exsudans* Mez, *Greigia albo-rosea* Mez, *G. sphacelata* Regel, *Guzmania acorifolia* Mez, *G. angustifolia* Mez, *G. berteroniana* Mez, *G. calothyrsus* Mez, *G. (= Vriesea) capituligera* Mez, *G. devansayana* Morr., *G. erythrolepis* Mez, *G. fuerstenbergiana* Wittm., *G. gracilior* Mez, *G. harrisii* Mez, *G.*

lindenii Mez, *G. lingulata* Mez, *G. magna* Mez (= *G. megastachia*), *G. minor* Mez, *G. monostachya* Rusby, *G. morreniana* Mez, *G. mucronata* Mez, *G. multiflora* André, *G. osyana* Mez, *G. plumieri* Mez, *G. roezlii* Mez, *G. straminea* Mez, *G. van-volxemii* André, *G. zahnii* Mez, *Hechtia argentea* Bak., *H. morreniana* Mez, *H. myriantha* Mez, *H. pedicellata* Wats., *H. rosea* Morr., *H. stenopetala* Klotzsch, *H. suaveolens* Morr., *H. texensis* Wats., *Hohenbergia antillana* Mez, *H. augusta* Mez, *H. ferruginea* Carr., *Lindmania guyanensis* Mez, *L. neogranatensis* Bak., *L. weddelliana* Mez, *Navia acaulis* Mart., *N. caulescens* Mart., *Nidularium antoineanum* Wawra, *N. bracteatum* Mez, *N. ferdinando-coburgi* Wawra, *N. fulgens* Lem., *N. innocentii* Lem., *N. longiflorum* Ule, *N. neglectum* Morr., *N. paxianum* Mez, *N. procerum* Lindm., *N. purpureum* Beer, *N. rutilans* Morr., *N. scheremetiewii* Regel, *Orthophytum leprosum* Linden, *Pitcairnia albucifolia* Schrad., *P. andreana* Linden, *P. angustifolia* Bak., *P. bracteata* Dryand., *P. caricifolia* Mart., *P. carnea* Beer, *P. cinnabarina* Dietr., *P. consimilis* Bak., *P. corallina* Linden et André, *P. echinata* Hook., *P. latifolia* Lindl., *P. panniculata* R. et P., *P. pauciflora* Dryand., *P. petiolata* Bak., *P. ramosa* Jacq., *P. recurvata* C. Koch., *P. roezlii* Morr., *P. schiedeana* Bak., *P. sellowiana* Bak., *P. suaveolens* Lindl., *P. tenuis* Mez, *Portea kermesina* Brongn., *P. noettigii* Mez, *P. petropolitana* Mez, *Prionophyllum selloum* C. Koch, *Puya aequatorialis* André, *P. boliviensis* Bak., *P. chilensis* Mol., *P. clava-herculis* Mez et Sodiro, *P. coquimbensis* Mez, *P. dyckioides* Mez, *P. floccosa* Morr., *P. humilis* Mez, *Quesnelia arvensis* Mez, *Q. blanda* Mez, *Q. humilis* Mez, *Q. indecora* Mez, *Q. lateralis* Wawra, *Q. roseo-marginata* Carr., *Q. tillandsioides* Mez, *Rhodostachys carnea* Mez, *R. elegans* Mez, *R. leiboldiana* Mez, *Sodiroa* spp., *Streptocalyx fuerstenbergii* Morr., *S. longifolius* Bak., *S. vallerandi* Morr., *Thecophyllum* (now equivalent to *Vriesea* (*V.*) or *Guzmania* (*G.*) according to sp.) (*V.*) *balanophorum* Mez, *T.* (*G.*) *dussii* Mez, *T.* (*G.*) *kraenzlinianum* Mez, *T.* (*G.*) *mosquerae* Mez, *T.* (*V.*) *ororiense* Mez, *T.* (*G.*) *palustre* Mez, *T.* (*V.*) *sintenisii* Mez, *T. urbanianum* Mez (= *Vriesea antillana*), *Tillandsia aloifolia* L., *T. myosura* Gris., *T. pruinosa* Sw., *T. streptophylla* Scheid., *T. vestita* Ch. et Schldl., *Vriesea macrostachya* Mez, *V. modesta* Mez, *V. morrenii* Mez, *V. mosenii* Mez (= *V. gigantea*), *V. muelleri* Mez, *V. oligantha* Mez, *V. panniculata* Mez, *V. paraibica* Wawra, *V. pardalina* Mez, *V. pastuchoffiana* Gaz., *V. philippo-coburgii* Wawra, *V. platynema* Gaud., *V. platzmannii* Morr., *V. poenulata* Morr., *V. procera* var. *typica* Mez, *V. psittacina* Lindl., *V. recurvata* Gaud., *V. rodigasiana* Morr., *V. rostrum-aquilae* Mez, *V. rubida* Morr., *V. sanguinolenta* Cogn. et March., *V. scalaris* Morr., *V. sceptrum* Mez, *V. splendens* Lem., *V. subsecunda* Wittm., *V. tessellata* Morr. (= *V. gigantea*), *V. thyrsoidea* Mez, *V. triligulata* Mez, *V. tucumanensis* Mez, *V. tweedieana* Mez (= *V. rodigasiana*), *V. unilateralis* Mez, *V. ventricosa* Mez (= *V. corcovadensis*), *V. viminalis* Morr., *V. wawranea* Ant., *Wittmackia lingulata* Mez.

Weber (1954) *Navia schultesiana* L. B. Smith, *Pitcairnia pungens* H. B. K.; root.

Wetzel (1924) *Cryptanthus zonatus, Tillandsia araujei, T. lindenii, T. morreniana, T. pruinosa, T. pulchella, T. punctulata, T. streptophylla, T. tectorum, T. tenuifolia, T. usneoides, Vriesea psittacina, V. saundersii, V. splendens*; epidermal scales.

Wherry and Buchanan (1926) *Tillandsia usneoides* L.; composition of ash.

MATERIAL EXAMINED BY THE AUTHOR

A. Pickled material from M. B. Foster's living collection of Bromeliaceae at Orlando, Florida (M. B. F.);[1] otherwise cultivated at Fairchild Tropical Garden

---

[1] The naming of this material has been checked by Dr. Lyman Smith at the Smithsonian Institution, Washington.

(FTG), collected by myself (P. B. T. with collection number) or in pickled collection of Jodrell Laboratory (Jodrell). Leaf only unless otherwise stated.

Abromeitiella brevifolia Castell.; (M. B. F.).
Acanthostachys strobilacea Klotzsch; (M. B. F.).
Aechmea bracteata Gris.; (FTG).
Ae. chantinii Bak.; (M. B. F.).
Ae. distichantha Lem.; (M. B. F.).
Ae. fasciata Bak.; (FTG).
Ae. fulgens Brongn.; (FTG).
Ae. nudicaulis Gris.; (FTG).
Ae. penduliflora André; (FTG).
Ae. recurvata L. B. Smith; (M. B. F.).
Ananas bracteatus Roem. and Schult.; (M. B. F.).
Araeococcus flagellifolius Harms; (M. B. F.).
Billbergia brasiliensis L. B. Smith; (FTG).
B. distaceia Mez; (M. B. F.).
B. horrida Regel; (FTG).
B. minarum L. B. Smith; (FTG).
B. venezuelana Mez; (FTG).
B. windi Hort.; (FTG).
Bromelia balansae Mez; (M. B. F.).
B. magdalenae C. H. Wright; Jodrell. Leaf.
B. pinguin L.; P. B. T. 14.IX.63A; Jamaica. All parts.
Canistrum fosterianum L. B. Smith; (M. B. F.).
C. lindenii Mez; (M. B. F.).
Catopsis berteroniana Mez; P. B. T. 14.I.64B; Florida.
C. floribunda L. B. Smith; P. B. T. 29.V.63B; Florida.
C. nutans Gris.; P. B. T. 24.III.64A; Florida.
Cryptanthus fosterianus L. B. Smith; (M. B. F.).
Deinacanthon urbanianum Mez; (M. B. F.).
Deuterocohnia schreiteri Castell.; (M. B. F.).
Dyckia fosteriana L. B. Smith; (M. B. F.).
Encholirium horridum L. B. Smith; (M. B. F.).
Fascicularia bicolor Mez; (M. B. F.).
Fosterella penduliflora L. B. Smith; (M. B. F.).
Glomeropitcairnia penduliflora Mez; (M. B. F.).
Gravisia rubens L. B. Smith; (M. B. F.).
Greigia sphacelata Regel; (M. B. F.).
Guzmania monostachya Rusby; P. B. T. All parts.
G. zahnii Mez; (M. B. F.).
Hechtia sp.; (M. B. F.).
Hohenbergia proctori L. B. Smith; P. B. T. 10.IX.63A; Jamaica.
H. salzmannii Morr.; (M. B. F.).
H. urbaniana Mez; P. B. T. 10.IX.63B; Jamaica.
Navia sp.; (M. B. F.).
Neoglaziovia variegata Mez; (M. B. F.).
Neoregelia caroliniae (Beer) L. B. Smith; (M. B. F.).

N. spectabilis L. B. Smith; (M. B. F.).

Nidularium innocentii Lem.; (M. B. F.).

Orthophytum vagans M. B. Foster; (M. B. F.).

Pitcairnia bromeliifolia L'Hérit.; P. B. T. 15.IX.63M; Jamaica.

P. punicea Scheidw.; (FTG Read 942). Leaf, axis.

P. xanthocalyx Mart.; (M. B. F.).

Portea petropolitana Mez; (M. B. F.).

Pseudananas sagenarius Camargo; (M. B. F.).

Puya alpestris Gay; (M. B. F.).

P. raimondii Harms; Iltis s.n.; Peru. Dried leaf material.

Quesnelia arvensis Mez; (M. B. F.).

Q. liboniana Mez; (M. B. F.).

Q. marmorata R. W. Read; (FTG).

Q. testudo Lindm.; (M.B.F.).

Ronnbergia columbiana Morr.; (M.B.F.).

Streptocalyx longifolius Bak.; (M. B. F.).

Tillandsia balbisiana Schult.; P. B. T. 29.I.63I; Florida. All parts.

T. caput-medusae Morr.; (M. B. F.).

T. circinnata Schld.; P. B. T. 25.I.64B; Florida. All parts.

T. complanata Benth.; P. B. T. 17.IX.63J; Jamaica. All parts.

T. crocata (Morr.) Bak.; (FTG).

T. fasciculata Swartz; P. B. T. 25.I.64E; Florida. All parts.

T. fendleri Gris.; P. B. T. 17.IX.63L; Jamaica. All parts.

T. flexuosa Swartz; P. B. T. 24.I.63B; Florida. All parts.

T. incurvata Gris.; P. B. T. 17.IX.63I; Jamaica. All parts.

T. juncea Lec.; P. B. T. 24.I.63A; Florida. All parts.

T. polystachia L.; P. B. T. 6.XI.65C; Florida. All parts.

T. pruinosa Swartz; P. B. T. 11.IX.63A; Jamaica. All parts.

T. recurvata L.; P. B. T. s.n.; Florida. All parts.

T. setacea Swartz; P. B. T. 19.I.64A; Florida. All parts.

T. usneoides L.; P. B. T. 8.VI.63A; Florida. All parts.

T. utriculata L.; P. B. T. s.n.; Florida. All parts.

T. valenzuelana A. Rich.; P. B. T. 25.I.64F; Florida. All parts.

Vriesea capituligera (Gris.) L. B. Smith and Pittendr.; P. B. T. 17.IX.63H; Jamaica. All parts.

V. glutinosa Wawra; (M. B. F.).

V. swartzii Mez; P. B. T. 17.IX.63K; Jamaica. All parts.

Wittrockia superba Lindm.; (M. B. F.).

B. In addition leaf fragments supplied by Dr. Lyman B. Smith from following specimens in the U.S. National Herbarium (US) were studied.

Brocchinia paniculata Schult. f.; Maguire *et al.* 36903.

Cottendorfia argentea L. B. Smith; Steyermark 74936.

C. guyanensis (Beer) Mez; Maguire and Fanshawe 23158.

C. minor L. B. Smith; Steyermark and Wurdack 394.

C. navioides L. B. Smith; Steyermark 75892.

C. paludosa L. B. Smith; Steyermark and Nilsson 556.

C. serrulata L. B. Smith; Steyermark and Wurdack 396.

C. simplex L. B. Smith; Steyermark and Wurdack 873.

C. wurdackii L. B. Smith; Wurdack 34244.

Glomeropitcairnia erectiflora Mez; Foster 2792.

G. penduliflora Mez; Cowan 1601.

Guzmania monostachya Rusby; Jiminez 2942.

G. pearcei L. B. Smith; Barclay 9432.

G. sprucei L. B. Smith; Killip 35246.

Navia aloifolia L. B. Smith; Maguire 42109.

N. caulescens Mart. var. *caulescens*; Garcia-Barriga 14536.

N. crispa L. B. Smith; Maguire 35158.

N. fontoides L. B. Smith; Schultes 15557.

N. lopezii L. B. Smith; Wurdack 43564.

N. mima L. B. Smith; Maguire 28680.

Pitcairnia ferruginea R. and P.; Herrera 2180.

P. mirabilis Mez; Cardenas 3588.

P. nana L. B. Smith; Cardenas 5533.

Tillandsia anceps Lodd.; Downs 34.

T. mallemontii Glaz.; Gevieski 101.

T. recurvata L.; Maguire 27208.

T. stricta Sol.; Smith s.n.

BIBLIOGRAPHY FOR BROMELIACEAE

Aso, K. (1910) Können Bromeliaceen durch die Schuppen der Blätter Salze aufnehmen? *Flora, Jena* **100**, 447–50; see *Just's bot. Jber.* **38** (2), sec. 21, no. 164 (1910).

BACHMANN, O. (1886) Untersuchungen über die systematische Bedeutung der Schildhaare. Diss. Erlangen; see *Flora, Jena* **69**, 387–400 (1886).

BARBAINI, MARIA (1921) Ricerche anatomo-fisiologiche sulle foglie delle '*Tillandsia*'. *Atti Ist. bot. Univ. Lab. crittogam. Pavia*, ser. 2, **18**, 95–107; see *Just's bot. Jber.* **49** (2), sec. 9, no. 473 (1921).

BAUMERT, K. (1907) Experimentelle Untersuchungen über Lichtschutzeinrichtungen an grünen Blättern. Diss. Erlangen; see *Beitr. biol. Pfl.* **9**, 83–162 (1904–9).

BILLINGS, F. H. (1904) A Study of *Tillandsia usneoides*. *Bot. Gaz.* **38**, 99–121.

BIRGE, W. J. (1911) The anatomy and some biological aspects of the 'ballmoss' *Tillandsia recurvata* L. *Bull. Univ. Texas* **194**, pp. 24; see *Just's bot. Jber.* **39** (2), sec. 21, no. 88 (1911).

BORCHERT, R. (1966) Innere Wurzeln als Festigungselement der epiphytischen Bromeliacee *Tillandsia incarnata* H.B.K. *Ber. dt. bot. Ges.* **79**, 253–8.

BORESCH, K. (1908) Über Gummiflus bei Bromeliaceen nebst Beiträgen zu ihrer Anatomie. *Sber. Akad. Wiss. Wien* **117**, 1033–80; see *Just's bot. Jber.* **36** (2); sec. 17, no. 174 (1911).

BOWERS, F. A. I. (1929) The root system of Pineapple plants. *Bull. Ass. Hawaiian Pineapple Cann. Exp. Stn* **12**, pp. 35.

BULITSCH, A. (1892a) Zur Anatomie der Bromeliaceen I. Der schilferige Ueberzug der *Billbergia iridifolia* Lindl. und seine Entwicklungsgeschichte. (In Russian.) *Uebers. Leist. Bot. Russland*; St. Petersburg (*Trudy kazan. Univ. Obshchestva Estestvoispytatelei* 35–36 **24** (1), 3–53); see *Just's bot. Jber.* **21** (1), sec. 14, 30 (1893).

—— (1892b) Zur Anatomie der Bromeliaceen. II. Ausscheidung von Kieselerde in den Blattepidermiszellen einiger Bromeliaceen. (In Russian.) *Uebers Leist. Bot. Russland*; St. Petersburg (*Trudy kazan. Univ. Obshchestva Estestvoispytatelei* **24** (4), 3–28); see *Just's bot. Jber.* **21** (1), sec. 14, 31 (1893).

CEDERVALL, E. V. (1884) Anatomisk-fysiologiska undersökningar öfver bladet hos Bromeliaceerna. (Anatomisch-physiologische Untersuchungen über das Blatt bei den Bromeliaceen.) *Göteborgs K. Vetensk.-o. VitterhSamh. Handl.* **19**, pp. 56; see *Just's bot. Jber.* **12** (1), IIB, 191 (1884).

CHEADLE, V. I. (1955) Conducting elements in the xylem of Bromeliaceae. *Bull. Bromel. Soc.* **5** (1), pp. 4.

CHODAT, R., and VISCHER, W. (1916) Résultats scientifiques d'une mission botanique suisse au Paraguay IV. Broméliacées. *Bull. Soc. bot. Genève*, ser. 2, **8**, 83–160, 186–264.

COLLINS, J. L. (1960) *The Pineapple*. Interscience, New York. pp. 294.

DELBROUCK, C. (1875) *Die Pflanzenstacheln*; see *Hanstein's Bot. Abh. Geb. Morph. Physiol.* II, Heft 4, pp. 119; see *Just's bot. Jber.* **3**, IIB, no. 22 (1875).

DENNISTON, R. H. (1925) The anatomy of the leaf of a new fibre plant. *Ann. appl. Biol.* **12**, 307–13.

DOLZMANN, P. (1964) Elektronenmikroskopische Untersuchungen an den Saughaaren von *Tillandsia usneoides* (Bromeliaceae). I. Feinstruktur der Kuppelzelle. *Planta* **60**, 461–72.

DOWNS, W. G., and PITTENDRIGH, C. S. (1946) Bromeliad malaria in Trinidad, British West Indies. *Am. J. trop. Med.* **26**, 47–66.

DUCHARTRE, P. (1868) Expériences sur la végétation d'une Broméliacée sans racines. *J. Soc. impér. centrale d'Hort. Fr.* ser. 2, **2**, 546–56.

FALKENBERG, P. (1876) *Vergleichende Untersuchungen über den Bau der Vegetationsorgane der Monocotyledonen*. Stuttgart. pp. 202.

FERNANDES, C. S. (1942) O caroá—a planta e a fibra. *Bot. Sec. Agric., Indust. Comercio (Pernambuco)* **9**, 209–13; see *Biol. Abstr.* **21**, no. 20661 (1947).

FIEBRIG, C. (1922) La flora del jardin botánico de la Trinidad-Asunción. Ensayo de un estudio ecológico sobre la flora Paraguaya. *Revta Jard. bot. Mus. Hist. nat. Parag.* **1**, 13–63; see *Just's bot. Jber.* **50**, sec. 6, no. 423 (1922).

FOSTER, M. B. (1945) Lateral inflorescences in Bromeliaceae. *Nat. hort. Mag.* Jan., 14–22.

GIOVANNOZZI, U. (1911) Intorno al sughero delle Monocotiledoni. *Nuovo G. bot. ital.* **18**, 5–79.

HABERLANDT, G. (1887) Zur Kenntniss des Spaltöffnungsapparates. *Flora, Jena* **70**, 97–110: see *Just's bot. Jber.* **15** (2), sec. 13, no. 94 (1887).

—— (1914) *Physiological plant anatomy*. Macmillan, London.

HALAMA, M. (1921) Untersuchungen über Manilhauf. *Faserforschung* **1**, 169–90; see *Just's bot. Jber.* **49** (2), sec. 9, no. 381 (1921).

HARMS, H. (1930) Bromeliaceae in Engler and Prantl *Die natürlichen Pflanzenfamilien* edn. 2, **15a**, 65–159.

HARTWICH, C. (1896) Chagualgummi. *Z. allg. öst. ApothVer.*, 565.

HASSACK, C. (1886) Untersuchungen über den anatomischen Bau bunter Laubblätter, nebst einigen Bermerkungen, betreffend die physiologische Bedeutung der Buntfärbung derselben. *Bot. Zbl.* **28**, 84–85 et seq.

HEDLUND, T. (1901) Om fjällens byggnad och deras förhållande till klyföppningarne hos en del Bromeliaceer. (Von den Schuppen und deren Verhältnisse zu den Spaltöffnungen bei einigen Bromeliaceen.) *Bot. Notiser*, 217–24; see *Just's bot. Jber.* **29** (2), sec. 15, no. 58 (1901).

HOLM, T. (1915) Medicinal plants of N. America. 92. *Ananassa sativa* Lindl. *Merck's a. Rep. rec. Adv. pharm. Chem. Ther.* **24**, 192–94; see *Just's bot. Jber.* **43** (1), sec. 9, no. 65 (1915).

JÖRGENSEN, A. (1878) Om Bromeliaceernes Rodder (Bidrag til Rodens Naturhistorie). *Bot. Tiddskr.*, ser. 3, **2**, 144–70; see *Just's bot. Jber.* **6** (1), IB, no. 48 (1878).

KEILENE, E. (1915) Recherches anatomiques sur les feuilles des Broméliacées. *Revue gén. Bot.* **27**, 77–95; see *Just's bot. Jber.* **43** (1), sec. 9, no. 69 (1915).

KENDA, G., and WEBER, F. (1951) Die Membran der Bromeliaceen-Schliesszellen. *Phyton, Horn* **3**, 227–30.

KRAUSS, B. H. (1948–9) Anatomy of the vegetative organs of the Pineapple, *Ananas comosus* (L.) Merr. *Bot. Gaz.* **110**, 159–217 (1948); 333–404 (1949); 555–87 (1949).

LAESSLE, A. M. (1961) A micro-limnological study of Jamaican bromeliads. *Ecology* **42**, 499–517.

LIESKE, R. (1914) Die Heterophyllie epiphytischer, rosettenbildender Bromeliaceen. *Jb. wiss. Bot.* **53**, 502–10.

LINSBAUER, K. (1911) Zur physiologischen Anatomie der Epidermis und des Durchlüftungsapparates der Bromeliaceen. *Sber. Akad. Wiss. Wien* **120**, 319–48; see *Just's bot. Jber.* **39** (2), sec. 21, no. 112 (1911).

LÖV, L. (1926) Zur Kenntnis der Entfaltungszellen monokotyler Blätter. *Flora, Jena* **120**, 283–343.

MANGIN, L. (1882) Origine et insertion des racines adventives et modifications corrélatives de la tige, chez les Monocotylédones. *Annls sci. nat.* bot. ser. 6, **14**, 216–353.

MATTEUCCI, E. (1897) Contributo allo studio delle placche sugherose nelle piante. *Nuovo G. bot. ital.* N.S. **4**, 224–44; see *Just's bot. Jber.* **25** (1), sec 14, no. 23 (1897).

METZLER, W. (1926) Beiträge zur vergleichenden Anatomie blattsukkulenter Pflanzen. *Bot. Arch.* **6**, 50–83.

MEYER, L. (1940) Zur Anatomie und Entwicklungsgeschichte der Bromeliaceenwurzeln. *Planta* **31**, 492–522.

MEZ, C. (1896) Broméliacées in De Candolle's *Monographiae phanerogamarum*, vol. 9.

—— (1904) Physiologische Bromeliaceen-Studien 1. Die Wasserökonomie der extrem atmosphärischen Tillandsien. *Jb. wiss. Bot.* **40**, 157–229.

MICHEELS, H. (1904) Sur les poils écailleux des Broméliacées (Notes de botanique appliquée). *Revue Hort. belge étrang.* **30**, 122–4; see *Just's bot. Jber.* **32** (2), sec. 11, no. 63 (1904).

OKIMOTO, M. C. (1948) Anatomy and histology of the Pineapple inflorescence and fruit. *Bot. Gaz.* **110**, 217–31.

PETERSEN, O. G. (1893) Bemaerkninger om den monokotyledone Staengels. Tyekklsevaext og anatomiske Regioner. *Bot. Tiddskr.* **18**, 112–26.

PFITZER, E. (1872) Beiträge zur Kenntniss der Hautgewebe der Pflanzen. *Jb. wiss. Bot.* **8**, 16–74.

PHILIPP, M. (1923) Ueber die verkorkten Abschlussgewebe der Monokotylen. *Bibl. bot.*, *Stuttgart* **92**, 1–28.

PICADO, C. (1913) *Sur les Broméliacées épiphytes considérées comme milieu biologique.* Thesis, Paris. pp. 145.

PITTENDRIGH, C. S. (1948) The Bromeliad-*Anopheles*-malaria complex in Trinidad. I. The Bromeliad Flora. *Evolution* **2**, 58–89.

POLITIS, I. (1914) Sulla presenza del glicogeno nelle fanerogame e sua relazione coll'ossalata di calci. *Atti Ist. bot. Univ. Lab. crittogam. Pavia*, ser. 2, **14**, 385–96.

RICHTER, P. (1891) *Die Bromeliaceen vergleichend anatomisch betrachtet. Beitrag zur Physiologie der Gewebe.* Diss. Berlin, pp. 23; see *Beih. bot. Zbl.* **2**, 506 (1892); *Just's bot. Jber.* **9** (1), sec. 16, no. 117 (1891)—original not seen.

ROHWEDER, O. (1956) Die Farinosae in der Vegetation von El Salvador. *Abh. Gebiet Auslandskunde* **61**. Reihe C. *Naturwissenschaften* **18**, pp. 197. Universität Hamburg.

ROSS, H. (1895) Conni preliminari sull'anatomia del fusto delle bromeliacee. *Bull. Soc. bot. Ital.* 195–6; see *Just's bot. Jber.* **23** (1), sec. 12, no. 126 (1895).

SABLON, LECLERC DU (1914) Sur le fonctionnement des réserves d'eau. *Revue gén. Bot.* **25** (2), 459–73.

SCHIMPER, A. F. W. (1884) Ueber Bau und Lebensweise der Epiphyten Westindiens. *Bot. Zbl.* **17**, 192–5 et seq.

SCHULZ, E. (1930) Beiträge zur physiologischen und phylogenetischen Anatomie der vegetativen Organe der Bromeliaceen. *Bot. Arch.* **29**, 122–209.

SCHWENDENER, S. (1882) Die Schutzscheiden und ihre Verstärkungen. *Abh. K. Akad. wiss. Berlin* iii, 1–75.

SMITH, L. B. (1934) Geographical evidence on the lines of evolution in the Bromeliaceae. *Bot. Jb.* **66**, 446–68.

SOLEREDER, H., and MEYER, F. J. (1929) Bromeliaceae. In *Systematische Anatomie der Monokotyledonen*, Heft IV, 80–129.

STAUDERMANN, W. (1924) Die Haare der Monokotylen. *Bot. Arch.* **8**, 105–84.

STEINBRINCK, C. (1905) Einführende Versuche zur Cohäsionsmechanik von Pflanzenzellen nebst Bemerkungen über den Saugmechanismus der wasserabsorbierenden Haare von Bromeliaceen. *Flora, Jena* **94**, 464–77.

TASSI, F. (1899) Struttura delle foglie della *Tillandsia dianthoidea* Rossi in rapporto col suo modo di vegetazione. *Bull. Lab. bot. Univ. Siena* **2**, 99–102; see *Just's bot. Jber.* **28** (2), sec. 11, no. 38 (1900).

THOMAS, E. N. M., and HOLMES, L. E. (1930) The development and structure of the seedling and young plant of the Pineapple (*Ananas sativus*). *New Phytol.* **29**, 199–226.

TIETZE, M. (1906) Physiologische Bromeliaceen-studien II. Die Entwickelung der wasseraufnehmenden Bromeliaceen-Trichome. *Z. Naturw.* **78**, 1–51; see *Just's bot. Jber.* **34** (2), sec. 9, no. 134 (1906).

UHLWORM, O. (1873) Beiträge zur Entwicklungsgeschichte der Trichome, mit besonderer Berücksichtungen der Stacheln. *Bot. Ztg.* **31**, 753–65 et seq.

ULE, E. (1901) Ameisengärten im Amazonasgebiet. *Bot. Jb.* **30**, Beibl. 68, 45–52.

WALLIN, G. S. (1898) Ueber gerbstoffähnliche Tröpfchen im Zellsafte der Bromeliaceen-Blätter. *Bot. Zbl.* **75**, 323–6.

WATERSTON, J. (1909) Note on the septa in root vessels of Bromeliaceae. *Trans. Proc. bot. Soc. Edinb.* **24**, 25–26; see *Just's bot. Jber.* **37** (1), sec. 13, no. 56 (1909).

WEBER, H. (1953) Las raices internes de *Navia* y *Vellozia*. *Mutisia* **13**, 1–4.

—— (1954) Wurzelstudien an tropischen Pflanzen I. *Abh. math.-naturw. Kl. Akad. Wiss. Mainz* **4**, 211–49.

WESTERMEIER, M. (1884) Ueber Bau und Funktion des pflanzlichen Hautgewebesystems. *Jb. wiss. Bot.* **14**, 43–51.

WETZEL, K. (1924) Beitrag zur Anatomie der Saughaare von Bromeliaceen. *Flora, Jena* **117**, 133–43.

WEVRE, A. DE (1887) Note préliminaire sur l'anatomie des Broméliacées. *Bull. Soc. r. Bot. Belg.* **26** (2), 103–6; see *Just's bot. Jber.* **15** (2), sec. 13, no. 153 (1887).

WHERRY, E. T. and BUCHANAN, R. (1926) Composition of the ash of Spanish-Moss. *Ecology* **7** (3), 303–6.

ZIEGENSPECK, H. (1939) Die Micellierung der Turgeszenzmechanismen. Teil I. Die Spaltöffnungen (mit phylogenetischen Ausblicken). *Bot. Arch.* **39**, 268–309, 332–72.

PART II

CLASSIFICATION OF THE ZINGIBERALES (SCITAMINEAE) WITH SPECIAL REFERENCE TO ANATOMICAL EVIDENCE

THE Zingiberales of Hutchinson are the Scitamineae of earlier authors. They formed 1 of the 8 families of monocotyledons in Bentham and Hooker's order Epigynae which included most monocotyledonous families with inferior ovaries. Taxonomists have subsequently continued to recognize the naturalness of the group but its relationship with other monocotyledonous groups is not clear. Since the inferior ovary is no longer regarded as a feature of value in recognizing major taxonomic subdivisions in the monocotyledons there is no reason to suppose a special relationship with other groups possessing this character. The modern tendency is to regard the Scitamineae as an isolated but closely knit assemblage and it is very likely that all members have had a common ancestor.

Authors subsequent to Bentham and Hooker gave the Scitamineae ordinal status and subdivided it (Table 3). This subdivision has been discussed in detail by the author (Tomlinson 1962), largely with the aid of anatomical information. The following notes are based on this earlier discussion since I have had no subsequent reason to change my opinions. Anatomical and morphological evidence does not conflict. The evidence shows that 8 groups of equal distinctiveness, all previously recognized by taxonomists, occur in the Scitamineae. The groups are all equally differentiated from each other by a combination of morphological and anatomical features. Some groups have long been recognized as families (the remainder being subfamilies). I suggest that the logical way to express their relationship is to elevate all groups to the same taxonomic rank, i.e. family.

The following indicates the combination of morphological and anatomical features which distinguishes the Zingiberales from other monocotyledonous orders. Subsequently the early taxonomic history of each of the 8 families that I recognize is outlined together with an indication of the anatomical features that distinguish each family.

Zingiberales (Scitamineae)

Rhizomatous herbs, usually sympodially branched, rarely arborescent. Leaves mostly with an open sheath, sometimes ligulate. Lamina with many lateral veins diverging from a common midrib to the entire margin. One-half of the leaf blade completely rolled around the other in bud. Inflorescence

TABLE 3

Systems of classification of Zingiberales (Scitamineae)

Bentham and Hooker (1883) *Genera plantarum* Family: Scitamineae	Engler and Prantl edn. 1 (1889) *Nat. Pflanzenfamilien* Reihe: Scitamineae	Engler (1900–1912) *Pflanzenreich* Reihe: Scitamineae	Engler and Prantl edn. 2 (1930) *Nat. Pflanzenfamilien* Reihe: Scitamineae	Hutchinson edn. 2 (1959) *Fam. Fl. Plants* Order: Zingiberales	According to anatomical evidence (supported by morphology)
Tribe Zingibereae	Family Zingiberaceae (Petersen)	Family Zingiberaceae (Schumann)	Family Zingiberaceae (Loesner)	Family Zingiberaceae	Family Zingiberaceae
	(*Costus* and *Tapeinochilus* in tribe Zingibereae)	Subfamily I. Zingiberoideae II. Costoideae	Subfamily Zingiberoideae Costoideae	Tribe 1. Costeae Tribe 2–4. Remainder	Family Costaceae
Tribe Marantae	Family Marantaceae	Family Marantaceae	Family Marantaceae	Family Marantaceae	Family Marantaceae
Tribe Canneae	Family Cannaceae	Family Cannaceae	Family Cannaceae	Family Cannaceae	Family Cannaceae
Tribe Museae	Family Musaceae (Petersen)	Family Musaceae (Schumann)	Family Musaceae (Winkler)	Family Musaceae (*Musa*)	Family Musaceae (*Musa, Ensete*)
	Tribe 1. Museae (*Musa, Ravenala, Strelitzia*) 2. Heliconieae (*Heliconia*)	Subfamily I. Musoideae II. Strelitzioideae Tribe 1. Heliconieae 2. Strelitzieae	Subfamily Musoideae Strelitzioideae Tribe Heliconieae Strelitzieae	Family Strelitziaceae (*Heliconia, Phenakospermum, Ravenala, Strelitzia*)	Family Heliconiaceae (*Heliconia*) Family Strelitziaceae (*Phenakospermum, Ravenala, Strelitzia*)
		III. Lowioideae	Lowioideae	Family Lowiaceae	Family Lowiaceae

mostly terminal (hapaxanthic), less commonly lateral (pleonanthic) with conspicuous bracts, basic unit probably a cincinnus. Flowers zygomorphic. Perianth consisting of separate calyx and corolla. Perfect stamens rarely 6, usually 5 or 1. Sterile 1–5 stamens often represented by staminodes of great diversity. Ovary inferior, 3-locular with 1–many ovules in each loculus. Seeds with abundant endosperm, often arillate.

Hairs, if present, commonly unicellular, rarely branched. Guard cells each with 2 narrow lateral subsidiary cells parallel to the stomatal pore. Hypodermis of colourless cells usually present below each surface of the lamina. Leaf axis including: air-canals, each canal segmented at intervals by transverse diaphragms consisting of stellate cells; a single main arc of large vascular bundles, each bundle with the same appearance in transverse section; additional subsidiary systems of smaller vascular bundles usually one or more above, one or more below the main arc, the abaxial system usually most conspicuous. Silica-cells, or stegmata with unequally thickened walls, associated with the vascular bundles in all parts except the root. Vessels rarely present in the leaves, often restricted to the root.

Musaceae

The Museae of Bentham and Hooker were later elevated to family rank. The Musaceae in this wide sense were retained by later authors but subdivided into a number of subfamilies (see Table 3). The Musaceae in the restricted sense are equivalent to one of these subfamilies and include only the genus *Musa* (together with *Ensete*, recently re-erected on good morphological evidence). The Musaceae as here treated correspond to the family as recognized by Hutchinson. Although *Musa* was given a relatively isolated position in earlier classifications there is some anatomical evidence that *Musa* may be closer to *Heliconia* than any other scitaminean group. Some species of *Heliconia* approach a few species of *Musa* very closely in leaf anatomy. A more extensive survey of leaf anatomy in the two groups may demonstrate that some features may be common to both of them. Nevertheless, if all other available evidence is taken into consideration there is no doubt that *Heliconia* should be retained separately from Musaceae (s.s.). Anatomical features characterizing the Musaceae are as follows.

Hairs absent. Anticlinal walls of epidermal cells in surface view never obviously sinuous. Guard cells with inner and outer ledges equal. Hypodermis usually 2- or more-layered adaxially, 1–2-layered abaxially. Mesophyll with transverse, vasculated or non-vasculated parenchymatous septa in air-canals. Longitudinal veins almost all buttressed to each surface. Transverse veins situated in transverse parenchymatous septa. Leaf axis including: one arc of large air-canals; main veins equidistant from each surface or towards adaxial surface; chlorenchyma restricted to abaxial ground tissue at all levels. Stem a massive corm. Root including more or less uniformly scattered medullary vessels and phloem strands, each phloem strand including several sieve-tubes. Raphide-sacs present. Articulated laticifers present. Silica-cells (stegmata) internal, mostly with unevenly thickened walls, each cell including a trough-shaped silica-body. Vessels more or less restricted to roots.

Heliconiaceae

Heliconia is included by Hutchinson in his Strelitziaceae. Previous authors had recognized its isolation by giving it tribal rank although both Schumann and Winkler associate it with *Strelitzia*, *Ravenala*, and *Phenakospermum* (Table 3). *Heliconia* is no closer to these than to other members of the Musaceae (s.l.) although a possible relationship with *Musa* has already been mentioned on p. 297. The only logical treatment is to assign *Heliconia* to a separate family and this course is adopted in this volume, thereby departing from Hutchinson's system. The following combination of anatomical features is diagnostic for the Heliconiaceae.

Hairs mostly absent. (Possibly occasional, uniseriate or branched?) Anticlinal walls of epidermis sinuous in surface view. Guard cells with inner and outer ledges equal. Hypodermis 1-layered below each surface. Mesophyll unspecialized. Longitudinal veins not markedly buttressed to each surface. Transverse veins independent of surface layers, sheathed by thin-walled cells. Leaf axis including: 2 separate systems of air-canals, one above and one below main veins, each with only one arc of lacunae; main veins equidistant from each surface; chlorenchyma often in adaxial ground tissue. Stem without clear differentiation into cortex and central cylinder, peripheral bundles somewhat congested. Root with normal polyarch stele or with occasional internal phloem strands. Raphide-sacs frequent in all parts. Silica-cells (stegmata) internal, next to veins, with unequally thickened walls, each including a trough-shaped silica-body. Vessels restricted to roots.

Strelitziaceae

The family as here treated differs from Hutchinson's Strelitziaceae in including only *Phenakospermum*, *Ravenala*, and *Strelitzia* and excluding *Heliconia*. The evidence, both morphological and anatomical, for doing this is considerable and has been presented in detail elsewhere (Tomlinson 1962). I have also pointed out that the Strelitziaceae (s.s.) probably come closest to the ancestral stock for the Scitamineae. The three genera are isolated from the remaining Zingiberales by a combination of anatomical and morphological characters which is of the same order of magnitude as combinations which circumscribe other families. The family may be diagnosed anatomically by the following combination of characters.

Hairs absent. Anticlinal epidermal walls in surface view either sinuous (*Phenakospermum*) or non-sinuous (*Ravenala*, *Strelitzia*). Guard cells with inner and outer ledges equal. Hypodermis always 2- or more-layered adaxially, 1–2-layered abaxially. Mesophyll with transverse, vasculated parenchymatous septa in air-canals. Leaf axis including: 2 distinct systems of air-canals often with several arcs of air-canals in each system; main veins equidistant from each surface; chlorenchyma in abaxial ground tissue. Stem commonly arborescent, including a peripheral mechanical layer of congested bundles. Root including medullary vessels and phloem strands with a single sieve-tube in each phloem strand. Raphide-sacs present. Silica-cells either (i) thick-walled superficial cells each with a spherical silica-body or (ii) thin-walled internal cells next to vascular bundles, each with a druse-like silica-body. Vessels in root and stem.

Lowiaceae

The isolated position of *Orchidantha* (*Lowia*) within the Musaceae (s.l.) has long been recognized. Its elevation to family rank by Hutchinson is fully supported by anatomical evidence. The following combination of anatomical features is diagnostic for Lowiaceae.

Hairs absent. Anticlinal walls of epidermal cells not sinuous in surface view. Guard cells with inner and outer ledges unequal. Hypodermis 1-layered below each surface. Mesophyll of irregularly arranged large and small cells. Longitudinal veins mostly independent of surface layers. Transverse veins mostly sheathed by thick-walled cells. Leaf axis including: 2 systems of air-canals, 1 above and 1 below the main veins, each system with 2 rather indistinct arcs of canals; main veins equidistant from each surface or towards adaxial surface. Chloroplasts diffusely distributed throughout the ground tissue. Stem reduced. Root with normal polyarch stele or with occasional internal strands of phloem. Raphide-sacs present. Silica-cells (stegmata) with unevenly thickened walls, internal, next to veins, each including a hat-shaped silica-body. Vessels restricted to roots.

Zingiberaceae

The composition of this family as here treated is more restricted than usual since it is pictured as consisting of the Zingiberoideae of earlier authors (e.g. Schumann, Loesner) but with the Costoideae excluded. In this way the Zingiberaceae (s.s.) become a much more natural unit and can be diagnosed anatomically in the following way.

Hairs common, unicellular, simple, base often swollen or sunken. Anticlinal walls of epidermal cells not sinuous in surface view. Guard cells with inner and outer ledges unequal. Hypodermis commonly 1-layered below each surface, sometimes multiseriate or absent. Mesophyll not specialized. Longitudinal veins sometimes attached to, but often independent of, surface layers. Transverse veins sheathed by thin-walled cells. Leaf axis (with an open, ligulate tubular sheath) including: a single abaxial arc of air-canals, always more or less pectinating with the main veins; chlorenchyma associated with tissue around main veins. Stem divided into a distinct cortex and central cylinder by a smooth fibrous cylinder. Root with normal polyarch structure, rarely with internal strands of phloem. Oil-cells present. Silica-cells frequent, mostly superficial and above veins, each including a spherical silica-body or silica sand. Vessels either restricted to roots or more widely distributed.

Costaceae

A departure from the orthodox treatment of the Zingiberaceae is to recognize *Costus* and its related genera as constituting a separate family, the Costaceae. This elevates a group, recognized by earlier authors (e.g. Schumann, Loesner) as a subfamily of Zingiberaceae, to family rank. Hutchinson, on the other hand, has minimized the isolation of the Costoideae since his Costeae are a tribe equivalent in rank only to the three remaining tribes of his Zingiberaceae. However, there is a considerable body of evidence from diverse disciplines to show that the Costoideae are isolated from the rest of the

Zingiberaceae and I have summarized this evidence elsewhere (Tomlinson 1956). Subsequently, on accumulating a like body of information about other scitaminean families it was evident to me that the Costoideae are isolated to a degree comparable with other families and it was a logical step to express this by following Nakai (1941), who raised the Costoideae to the rank of a family. The Costaceae can be recognized anatomically by the following combination of characters.

Hairs common, multicellular, uniseriate, unbranched; base never sunken. Anticlinal walls of epidermal cells in surface view not sinuous. Guard cells with unequal inner and outer ledges. Hypodermis always well developed, 1- or more-layered below each surface. Mesophyll consisting of palisade and spongy parenchyma but not otherwise specialized. Longitudinal veins independent of surface layers. Transverse veins often sheathed by thick-walled cells. Leaf axis (with a closed tubular sheath) including: 1 feebly developed system of air-canals pectinating with the main veins and often absent at certain levels; main veins situated adaxially and embedded in chlorenchyma. Stem divided into cortex and central cylinder by a fluted, fibrous cylinder. Root with normal polyarch stele. Silica-cells thin-walled, internal, next to veins, each with a druse-like silica-body. Vessels restricted to roots.

Cannaceae

The isolated position of this group has long been recognized since it was created as a tribe within the Scitamineae by Bentham and Hooker. Subsequent authors elevated this to family rank. Its closer association with the Marantaceae than with any other group, reflected in their being put together as 2 tribes of a single family by some earlier authors, is largely a consequence of their similar floral morphology. Anatomically they are quite distinct. Cannaceae are recognized by the following combination of anatomical features.

Hairs absent. Anticlinal epidermal cell walls not sinuous in surface view. Guard cells mostly with inner and outer ledges equal. Hypodermis 1-layered below each surface. Mesophyll consisting of palisade and spongy parenchyma. Longitudinal veins sometimes attached to surface layers. Transverse veins sheathed by thin-walled cells. Leaf axis including: a single arc of air-lacunae abaxial to main veins; main veins equidistant from each surface; chlorenchyma in abaxial ground parenchyma in sheath but adaxial in midrib. Stem without a clear differentiation between cortex and central cylinder, peripheral vascular bundles somewhat congested. Root with normal polyarch stele. Mucilage canals in stem and rhizome. Silica-cells internal, next to veins, each with a druse-like silica-body. Vessels restricted to roots.

Marantaceae

The isolated position of this group, apart from its association with the Cannaceae by some early authors, has long been recognized. This isolation is supported by the following unique combination of anatomical features.

Hairs simple, unicellular, usually embedded in a basal cushion of swollen epidermal cells. Anticlinal walls of epidermal cells sinuous in surface view. Guard cells with inner and outer ledges unequal. Hypodermis 1-layered below each surface. Mesophyll consisting of palisade and spongy parenchyma.

Longitudinal veins usually attached to surface layers. Transverse veins sheathed mostly by thick-walled cells. Leaf axis (pulvinate distally) including: 1 abaxial arc of air-canals; main veins equidistant from each surface; chlorenchyma in abaxial ground tissue in sheath but adaxial in midrib. Stem without clear demarcation between cortex and central cylinder; peripheral vascular bundles somewhat congested. Root with normal polyarch structure, internal phloem strands frequent. Silica-cells either (i) stegmata, internal, next to veins and with unevenly thickened walls; each including a hat-shaped silica-body, or (ii) thin-walled, spherical, scattered in mesophyll; each including a druse-like silica-body. Vessels either restricted to roots or more widely distributed.

Relationship of families within the Zingiberales

Although the 8 families described here are sufficiently isolated from each other for each to be readily characterized in the above way, it is evident that they are not equally related to each other. Elsewhere (Tomlinson 1962) I have discussed their mutual affinities in some detail and concluded that they have diverged from a common, proto-scitaminean ancestor. Some have probably diverged from this hypothetical ancestral stock less than others, as is indicated by the retention of a greater number of hypothetical ancestral features in the more 'primitive' families. Pairs of families in turn may have diverged from a common ancestor at a date subsequent to the initial diversification of the proto-Scitamineae.

Regarded in this way the Strelitziaceae approach closest to this common ancestor, the Musaceae have been somewhat further elaborated, the Heliconiaceae yet further. The Lowiaceae are much more highly specialized and probably have had a long period of independent evolution. Nevertheless these 4 families are relatively closely related. All have raphide-sacs, all have guard cells with outer and inner ledges equal except Lowiaceae. Musaceae and Strelitziaceae retain a massive leaf construction and 'anomalous' root structure of which vestiges appear in Heliconiaceae. The leaf in Lowiaceae is very reduced.

The remaining 4 families have guard cells with outer and inner ledges mostly unequal and no raphide-sacs. They have all diverged further from the ancestral stock than the 4 above-mentioned families. Two unrelated pairs of families can be recognized. Cannaceae and Marantaceae at some earlier date may have had a common ancestor since their floral morphology is basically similar. Cannaceae have oblique-cells in the leaf axis which recall cells that are an essential feature of the pulvinus in Marantaceae. Costaceae and Zingiberaceae likewise may have diverged from a common stock although again this is a conclusion largely based on presumed similarities in floral morphology. Anatomically the 2 families diverge widely.

Speculation about phylogeny is of limited value unless it is supported by evidence from fossils, and the reader is referred to the author's earlier article on this subject (Tomlinson 1962) for a full exposition.

LITERATURE CITED

BENTHAM, G., and HOOKER, J. D. (1883) *Genera plantarum*, Vol. 3. London.
HUTCHINSON, J. (1959) *Families of flowering plants*, Vol. II, *Monocotyledons*, edn 2. Oxford.

LOESNER, T. (1930) Zingiberaceae in Engler and Prantl. *Die natürlichen Pflanzenfamilien,* edn. 2. **15a,** 547–640.

NAKAI, T. (1941) Notulae ad plantas Asiae orientalis (XVI). *J. Jap. Bot.* **17,** 189–210.

PETERSEN, O. G. (1889) Musaceae and Zingiberaceae in Engler and Prantl. *Die natürlichen Pflanzenfamilien,* edn. 1. 1 (**6**), 1–10 and 10–30.

SCHUMANN, K. (1900, 1904) Musaceae and Zingiberaceae in Engler. *Das Pflanzenreich* **4,** 45. pp. 45 and 46. pp. 458.

TOMLINSON, P. B. (1956) Studies in the systematic anatomy of the Zingiberaceae. *J. Linn. Soc.* (Bot.) **55,** 547–92.

—— (1962) Phylogeny of the Scitamineae—morphological and anatomical considerations. *Evolution* **16,** 192–213.

WINKLER, H. (1930) Musaceae in Engler and Prantl. *Die natürlichen Pflanzenfamilien,* edn. 2. **15a,** 505–45.

FAMILY DESCRIPTIONS

MUSACEAE

(Figs. 67–69)

SUMMARY

A SMALL family including the 2 genera *Ensete* and *Musa* with a v. distinct habit; widely distributed in the tropics of the Old World. Massive herbs with v. tall aerial shoots arising from swollen, fleshy corms, the corms either suckering (*Musa*) or monocarpic (*Ensete*). Leaves arranged spirally in the aerial shoots, their long overlapping leaf bases forming a stout **pseudostem** with the terminal inflorescence growing up through its centre. Lamina rolled in bud, including a colourless **hypodermis** of 1 or more layers beneath each surface to which all veins are buttressed; abaxial mesophyll between veins largely replaced by longitudinal **air-canals.** Canals segmented by numerous **transverse septa** composed of colourless parenchyma and infrequently containing vascular tissues. Leaf axis including a single arc of wide air-canals, each canal segmented at intervals by multiseriate or uniseriate diaphragms. Cortex of **root** including radial air-lacunae; stele anomalous in possessing numerous scattered vessels and **phloem islands,** each phloem strand including several wide sieve-tubes. **Articulated laticifers** common next to vb's in all parts except root. Starch grains flattened and eccentric. **Silica** common in all parts except root; in lamina usually in **stegmata** with unevenly thickened walls, each stegma including a 'trough-like' silica-body. **Raphide-sacs** common.

LEAF

A. MUSA (for *Ensete* see p. 311)

(i) *Lamina*

  (a) *Structure in most spp.*

Dorsiventral. **Hairs** absent. **Cuticle** of rod-like particles arranged perpendicular to leaf surface, forming a bloom on abaxial side of young leaves. **Epidermis**; cells with outer walls slightly thicker than inner walls except in *M. textilis* with outer wall 3–4 times thicker than inner walls. Anticlinal walls not usually sinuous in surface view but distinctly sinuous in abaxial epidermis of *M. acuminata* subspp. *burmannica* and *siamea*, *M. beccarii, flaviflora, laterita.* Adaxial epidermis v. uniform except for files of short, wide cells above anticlinal hypodermal walls; cells rectangular, longitudinally extended (Fig. 67. A) except for isodiametric and not markedly elongated cells in *M. acuminata* subsp. *burmannica*, *M. maclayi, sanguinea, textilis.* Abaxial epidermis (Fig. 67. B) differentiated into narrow costal and wider intercostal bands; costal cells narrow and longitudinally extended; intercostal cells short, wide, and irregular. Cells in same files as stomata often appreciably shorter and wider than those elsewhere, as in *M. acuminata* subsp. *banksii, M. angustigemma,*

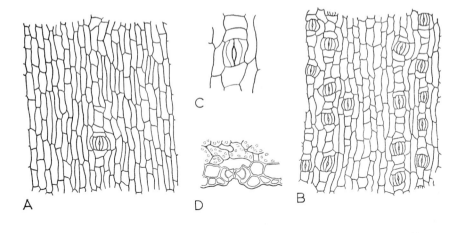

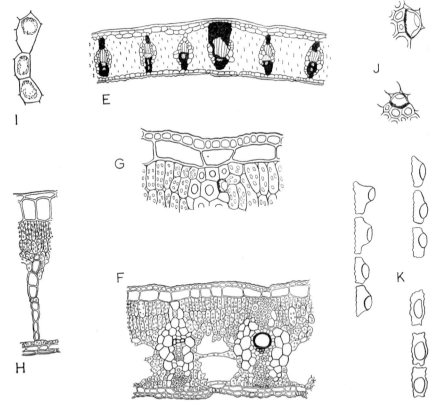

F<small>IG</small>. 67. MUSACEAE. *Musa.* Lamina (after Tomlinson 1959).

A–C. *M. 'sapientum'*, W. Africa. Epidermis, surface view.

   A. Adaxial ($\times$115). B. Abaxial ($\times$115). C. Stoma, abaxial epidermis ($\times$260).

D. *M. sumatrana.* T.S. stoma, abaxial epidermis ($\times$260).

E, F. T.S. lamina.

   E. *M. sumatrana* ($\times$52); assimilating tissue—short lines; mechanical tissue—solid black; xylem—hatched; phloem—stippled. F. *M. 'sapientum'*, Kew. Including a main vein ($\times$115).

G. *M. malaccensis.* Adaxial surface layers ($\times$260).

H. *M. sumatrana.* L.S. lamina, transverse septum in T.S. ($\times$115).

I–K. Silica-cells ($\times$400).

   I, J. *M. 'sapientum'*, Singapore. I. From transverse septum of lamina. J. T.S. part of fibre buttress of lamina with stegmata. K. *M. basjoo* and *M. 'sapientum'*, Singapore. Silica-bodies from lamina.

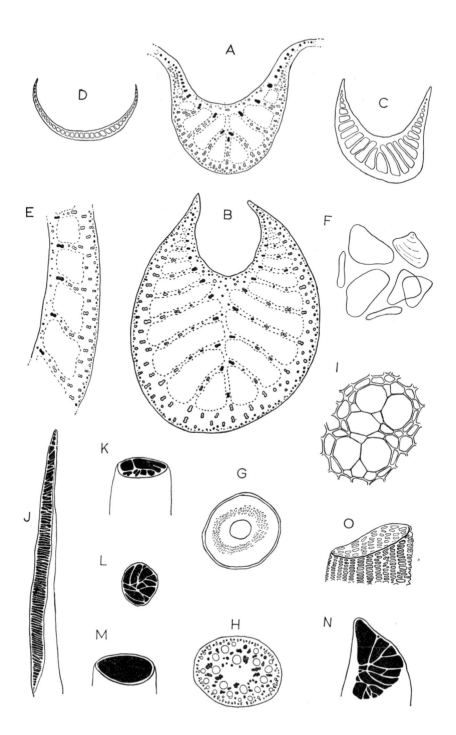

Fɪɢ. 68. MUSACEAE. *Musa* (after Tomlinson 1959).

A–E. *M. 'sapientum'*, W. Africa. T.S. Leaf axis at successively lower levels.

A. Midrib, half-way between base and apex of lamina ($\times 2\frac{1}{2}$). B. Petiole, just below insertion of lamina ($\times 2\frac{1}{2}$). C. Upper part of leaf sheath ($\times \frac{1}{2}$). D. Lower part of leaf sheath ($\times \frac{1}{2}$). E. Lateral part of leaf sheath ($\times 2\frac{1}{2}$). Main arc (I) bundles solid black in A, B, E.

F. *M. 'sapientum'*, W. Africa. Starch grains from corm ($\times 400$).

G–I. *M. 'sapientum'*, Singapore. T.S. root.

G. Outline ($\times 2$). H. Stele ($\times 9$); phloem—solid black; xylem—open circles. I. Phloem island from centre of stele ($\times 160$).

J–O. *M. 'sapientum'*, W. Africa. Perforated end walls of vessel elements from a single root, showing range of variation ($\times 66$, except J, $\times 30$). Only in O is pitting on lateral walls represented.

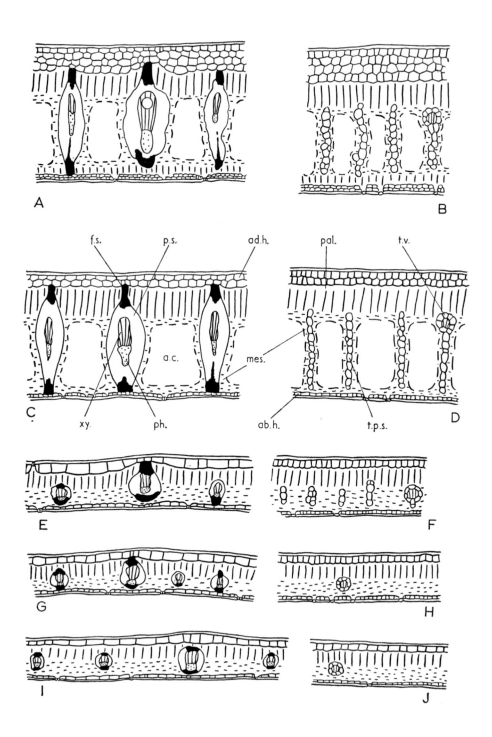

A

B

f.s.   p.s.   ad.h.   pal.   t.v.

a.c.   mes.

C   D

xy.   ph.   ab.h.   t.p.s.

E   F

G   H

I   J

FIG. 69. MUSACEAE AND HELICONIACEAE. Lamina (×70) in diagrammatic T.S. and L.S.

A, B. *Musa textilis*. A. T.S. B. L.S.

C, D. *Musa acuminata* subsp. *banksii*. C. T.S. D. L.S.

E, F. *Musa ornata*. E. T.S. F. L.S.

G, H. *Musa coccinea*. G. T.S. H. L.S.

I, J. *Heliconia* sp. for comparison. I. T.S. J. L.S.

ab. h.—abaxial hypodermis; ad. h.—adaxial hypodermis; a.c.—air-canal; f.s.—fibrous part of bundle sheath; mes.—abaxial mesophyll; pal.—palisade; p.s.—parenchymatous part of bundle sheath; ph.—phloem; t.p.s.—transverse parenchymatous septum; t.v.—transverse vein; xy.—xylem. Cells of epidermis not drawn.

peekelii. Abaxial epidermis papillose in *M. acuminata* subsp. *malaccensis*, *M. balbisiana*, *basjoo*, *flaviflora*, *sanguinea*.

Stomata always less frequent on adaxial than on abaxial surface, rather frequent adaxially in *M. acuminata* subsp. *burmannica* and *M. laterita*; restricted to indistinct files in abaxial intercostal regions. Terminal subsidiary cells short, never papillose but otherwise not markedly different from other epidermal cells (Fig. 67. C); lateral subsidiary cells usually narrower and much deeper than other epidermal cells (Fig. 67. D) although peculiarly flattened in *M. sanguinea*. Stomata never markedly sunken, guard cells with 2 equally thickened ledges (Fig. 67. D), except for guard cells with outer ledge much thicker than inner in *M. sanguinea*. Guard cells mostly 23–27 μm long but up to 30–33 μm long in *M. peekelii* and *sanguinea*, only 19–21 μm long in *M. textilis*; guard cells of adaxial surface always significantly longer than those of abaxial surface.

Hypodermis of enlarged, colourless cells conspicuous beneath each surface (Fig. 67. E–G) but deepest close to midrib, shallowest near to margin, although fairly constant in depth throughout greater part of lamina. Mostly 2-layered adaxially, 1-layered abaxially (Fig. 67. E) but 1-layered below each surface in *M. angustigemma*, *beccarii*, *laterita*, *sanguinea*, *velutina*, *violascens*; 2- or more-layered adaxially, 2-layered abaxially in *M. balbisiana*, *flaviflora*, *lolodensis*, *maclayi*, *textilis*. Outermost adaxial cells of multiseriate hypodermis smaller than inner. Adaxial cells mostly hexagonal and transversely extended in surface view, but more nearly cubical in *M. acuminata* (all subspp.), *itinerans*, *maclayi*, *schizocarpa*, *textilis*. Abaxial cells always smaller than adaxial cells, longitudinally extended in costal regions but intercostal cells irregular, usually with 4 L-shaped cells arranged around each substomatal chamber.

Mesophyll including a distinct adaxial palisade of 2–4 layers; abaxial mesophyll largely replaced by longitudinal **air-canals** lined by and occasionally traversed by small chlorenchymatous cells (Fig. 67. F); lowest mesophyll layer somewhat palisade-like in *M. textilis*. Air-canals segmented at regular and frequent intervals by complete **transverse septa** extending from palisade to uppermost abaxial mesophyll layer. Septa usually consisting of a single layer of closely fitting, tabular, colourless cells (Fig. 67. H); infrequently containing narrow transverse vascular commissures. Septa including somewhat thick-walled cells in *M. acuminata* subsp. *microcarpa*, *M. beccarii*, *flaviflora*, *itinerans*, *sanguinea*. Longitudinal veins sheathed by cells forming buttresses extending to each hypodermis (Figs. 67. E–G), outermost sheathing cells parenchymatous, cubical, usually 2–3-layered but only 1-layered in *M. sanguinea*. Abaxial and adaxial part of buttress partly or wholly fibrous but fibres little developed in *M. acuminata* subsp. *burmannica*. Largest veins often separated from abaxial hypodermis by a small mesophyll layer; smallest veins sometimes not attached to adaxial hypodermis, as in *M. angustigemma*, *flaviflora*, *peekelii*. **Transverse veins** situated in transverse parenchymatous septa and connecting longitudinal veins at intervals.

Long articulated **laticifers,** containing brown mucilage, commonly associated with longitudinal veins. **Expansion cells** present in association with each of main veins of lamina as enlarged portions of adaxial hypodermis. Diurnal movements of lamina effected by a 'pulvinar band' (Skutch 1927) at junction between lamina and midrib, air-canals being absent from this position. This region including numerous vb's with thick, sclerotic sheaths; enlarged abaxial hypodermis; adaxial cuticle attached to epidermis by pegs.

(b) *Musa ornata* and *M. coccinea*

Differing from spp. described under (a) and from each other in the following important ways.

Musa ornata (Fig. 69. E–F). Hypodermis 1-layered below each surface at all levels. Air-canals *absent* from mesophyll; abaxial mesophyll occupied by loose, spongy cells. Smallest longitudinal veins not buttressed to adaxial hypodermis. Transverse veins mostly attached to abaxial hypodermis but vascularized septa often incomplete above stomata.

Musa coccinea (Fig. 69. G–H). Hypodermis 1-layered below each surface. Palisade 1-layered. Air-canals *absent*; abaxial mesophyll composed of loose, much-lobed cells. Transverse parenchymatous septa *absent*. Transverse veins few, each sheathed by a single layer of parenchymatous cells and *not buttressed to abaxial hypodermis*. Longitudinal veins often not attached to adaxial hypodermis; outer parenchymatous sheath at level of metaxylem *often only 1-layered*.

(ii) *Leaf axis*

Leaf sheath eligulate, long; opposite margins not overwrapping. Base of lamina acuminate and in *Musa* with a distinct grooved petiole. Small depressions or pits sometimes present in adaxial surface of sheath; stomata sometimes present in the pits but not restricted to them (Skutch 1927). Abaxial hypodermis of outermost sheaths of pseudostem commonly becoming sclerotic, apparently due to influence of light, sclerosis occurring first in the cells around the substomatal chambers. **Chlorenchyma** forming a band close to adaxial surface of midrib and petiole. **Air-canals** present in a single arc at all levels (Fig. 68. A–E), separated from each other by narrow, longitudinal partitions of ground tissue; the canals traversed at frequent intervals by transverse diaphragms one or more cells thick, each diaphragm commonly consisting of a single layer of stellate cells or of a single layer of rounded cells sandwiched between 2 layers of stellate cells. Single arc of main **veins (I)** situated adaxial to and pectinating with air-canals but often difficult to distinguish from large bundles of abaxial system. Abaxial system (II) including many large and small vb's between air-canals and in abaxial ground tissue. Most abaxial vb's with well-developed fibrous sheaths, pectinating with **fibrous strands.** Small adaxial system of subsidiary vascular and fibrous bundles (III) present at all levels.

B. Ensete

This differs in leaf morphology from *Musa* in that the lamina is decurrent on the leaf axis so that a clearly defined petiole cannot be recognized (Cheesman 1947). Anatomically there is no fundamental difference in leaf structure between the 2 genera.

STEM

(Based on description by Skutch, 1932; for developmental details see Barker and Steward 1962; Fahn *et al.* 1963.) Vegetative axis consisting of a massive, underground **corm** with congested internodes, the apex eventually developing into a long peduncle. Axillary suckers developed only in *Musa*. **Periderm** sometimes arising in outer cortex. Inner limit of narrow cortex represented by an **endodermis.** Periphery of central cylinder including a plexus of irregular vb's. Course of vb's v. irregular but, according to Skutch, with a distinct cortical system. Vb's of central cylinder, unlike those of cortex, without fibrous sheaths. Leaf traces sometimes amphiphloic for part of their course.

ROOT

Periderm sometimes arising in outer cortex. Radial **air-canals** (Fig. 68. G), of lysigenous origin, conspicuous in inner cortex. **Stele** anomalous, including wide vessels and irregular **phloem islands** scattered throughout central, thick-walled ground tissue (Fig. 68. H), each phloem strand including several large sieve-tubes (Fig. 68. I). For detailed account see Riopel and Steeves (1964).

SECRETORY, STORAGE, AND CONDUCTING ELEMENTS

Crystals of calcium oxalate present as rhombohedral bodies, sometimes forming a coarse sand. Raphide-sacs common in all parts.

Silica common in **stegmata** in longitudinal files adjacent to fibrous part of bundle sheath in lamina and less commonly in leaf axis and stem. Silica-bodies of stegmata more or less rectangular in surface view, 'trough-like' owing to a shallow central depression (Fig. 67. K), part of silica-body near fibre often spinous with spines projecting into pits in thickened part of wall of silica-cell (Fig. 67. J). Silica also present as irregularly spherical bodies, each situated in unthickened cells of parenchymatous sheath of transverse veins in stem and leaf and sometimes in transverse septa of lamina (Fig. 67. I).

Tannin common in unspecialized, somewhat enlarged cells or in tannin-cells in palisade of lamina.

Articulated laticifers associated with vb's of all parts except root, their mucilaginous contents exuding at cut surfaces and darkening on exposure to air. Schizogenous mucilage cavities, apparently containing same material as laticifers, recorded in phloem of *Musa* by Skutch (1932).

Starch abundant in corm; grains flattened and eccentric (Fig. 68. F).

Xylem. Vessels confined to metaxylem of root, end walls often v. variable in a single root (Riopel and Steeves 1964); either with simple perforation plates on transverse end walls (Fig. 68. M, O), or with scalariform perforation plates on slightly oblique or oblique end walls (Fig. 68. J); elements sometimes with reticulate perforation plates on transverse end walls (Fig. 68. K, L, N).

Phloem. Sieve-tubes of isolated phloem strands in root with simple (rarely compound) sieve-plates on transverse end walls (Riopel and Steeves 1964).

ECONOMIC USES

The banana is the berry-like, seedless, parthenocarpic fruit of *Musa* '*sapientum*' which is a complex hybrid whose parents probably include

M. acuminata Colla and *M. balbisiana* Colla (Simmonds 1959, 1962). Many varieties are known, some of them by distinct specific names, as is *M. cavendishii*. One of the most distinctive varieties is the plantain, *M. 'paradisiaca'*, whose fruit is starchy and is cooked before being eaten. Both the banana and the plantain are cultivated extensively in tropical countries for local use whilst the banana is grown for export on a vast scale in West Africa, the West Indies and Central America, and the Canary Islands, the chief markets being in Europe and America. Manilla hemp, used in the manufacture of ropes and coarse string, is the fibre from the leaf sheath of *Musa textilis* Nee, the cultivation of which is carried out extensively in the Philippines. *Ensete ventricosum* is of local importance in Abyssinia and East Africa for its edible peduncle and fibrous leaf sheaths.

TAXONOMIC NOTES

In a detailed anatomical comparison between *Musa* and related genera (Tomlinson 1959) it has been shown that *Musa* (together with *Ensete*) is very distinct anatomically, supporting the modern tendency to regard it as forming a monotypic family, the Musaceae *sensu stricto*. *Ensete* is considered by some authors to be a generic entity separate from *Musa*. Despite distinct morphological differences only small, and probably inconstant, anatomical differences have been observed between the two genera. This present account is based on the earlier descriptions by Skutch (1927) and Tomlinson (1959) together with the examination of the lamina of 18 species obtained from the collection at the Regional Research Centre, Department of Agriculture, University of the West Indies, Trinidad. This later survey suggested that there were no diagnostic anatomical features in the lamina at the subgeneric level but was of interest in revealing that 1 species, *M. coccinea*, differed from other species of *Musa* in ways which recalled *Heliconia*, whilst *M. ornata* was intermediate between this exceptional and the normal type of lamina structure. This relationship is illustrated diagrammatically in Fig. 69.

GENERA AND SPECIES REPORTED ON IN THE LITERATURE

(For a discussion of the problems of nomenclature in the cultivated bananas see Simmonds 1962)

Barker and Steward (1962) *Musa acuminata* cv. Gros Michel, *M. balbisiana*; development.

Claverie (1909) *Musa* (now *Ensete*) *perrieri* Clav.; all parts, with notes on *M. ensete*, *M. sinensis*, *M. textilis*.

Fahn *et al.* (1963) *Musa* sp. cv. Dwarf Cavendish; development.

Lippitsch (1889) *Musa 'cavendishii'*, *M. ensete*, *M. 'paradisiaca'*; leaf.

Onken (1922) *Musa basjoo* Sieb., *M. 'cavendishii'* Lamb.; laticifers.

Petersen (1893) *Musa 'cavendishii'* Lamb., *M. 'sapientum'* Roxb. (according to Solereder and Meyer).

Pillai and Pillai (1961) *Musa 'paradisiaca'* L., *M. 'sapientum'* L.; root apex.

Pirotta and Marcatili (1886) *Musa discolor* Hort., *M. ensete* Bruce, *M. 'paradisiaca'* L., *M. rosacea* Jacq., *M. 'sapientum'* L., *M. sinensis* Sw., *M. speciosa* Un.; laticifers.

Riopel and Steeves (1964) *Musa acuminata* cv. Gros Michel; root.

Ross (1883) *Musa dacca* Hort.; root.
Saito (1900) *Musa 'sapientum'* L. var. *liukiuensis*; leaf.
Skutch (1927) *Musa 'sapientum'* L. var. Hort. Gros Michel; leaf.
Skutch (1930) *Musa 'sapientum'* subsp. *seminifera*; leaf.
Skutch (1932) *Musa 'sapientum'* subsp. *seminifera* var. Martini; cv. Gros Michel; stem.
Solereder and Meyer (1930) *Musa 'cavendishii'* Lamb.; all parts.
Tomlinson (1959) see Material Examined by the Author.
Trécul (1867) notes on numerous *Musa* spp.; laticifers.
Wittmack (1867–8) *Musa ensete*; all parts.

MATERIAL EXAMINED BY THE AUTHOR

The above description is based on the following material, which also served as the basis for a previous article (Tomlinson 1959).

Ensete arnoldianum (De Wild.) Cheesm.; Aburi, Ghana. Leaf, root.
E. gilletii (De Wild.) Cheesm.; Bamenda, Cameroons, W. Africa. Leaf, root.
E. ventricosum (Welw.) Cheesm.; material cultivated at Kew. Leaf.
Musa basjoo Sieb.; material cultivated at Kew. Lamina.
M. malaccensis Ridl.; Botanic Gardens, Singapore. Leaf.
M. 'paradisiaca'; Kibi, Ghana. All parts.
M. 'sapientum'; (i) material cultivated at Kew. Lamina. (ii) Botany Dept., University of Malaya. All parts. (iii) Botanic Gardens, University of Ghana. All parts.
M. sumatrana Becc.; Botanic Gardens, Singapore. Leaf.
M. textilis Nee; Botany Dept., University of Malaya. Leaf.
M. violascens Ridl.; Botany Dept., University of Malaya. Leaf.

In addition to this material, leaf samples from the following spp. cultivated at the University of the West Indies, Trinidad, have been examined. This material is preserved at Kew.

M. acuminata Colla subsp. *banksii* (F. Muell.) Simmonds; *M. acuminata* Colla subsp. *burmannica* Simmonds; *M. acuminata* Colla subsp. *malaccensis* (Ridl.) Simmonds; *M. acuminata* Colla subsp. *microcarpa* (Becc.) Simmonds; *M. acuminata* Colla subsp. *siamea* Simmonds; *M. balbisiana* Colla; *M. basjoo* Sieb.; *M. beccarii* Simmonds; *M. coccinea* Andrews; *M. flaviflora* Simmonds; *M. itinerans* Cheesm.; *M. laterita* Cheesm.; *M. lolodensis* Cheesm.; *M. maclayi* F. Muell.; *M. ornata* Roxb.; *M. peekelii* Lauterb.; *M. sanguinea* Hook. f.; *M. schizocarpa* Simmonds; *M. textilis* Nee; *M. velutina* Wendl. & Dr.; *M. violascens* Ridl.; *Musa* sp. (undetermined—from Sumatra).

BIBLIOGRAPHY FOR MUSACEAE

BARKER, W. G., and STEWARD, F. C. (1962) Growth and development of the banana plant I. The growing regions of the vegetative shoot. II. The transition from the vegetative to the floral shoot in *Musa acuminata* cv. 'Gros Michel'. *Ann. Bot.* **26**, 389–411, 413–23.
CHEESMAN, E. E. (1947) Classification of the bananas. I. The genus *Ensete* Horan. *Kew Bull.* **2**, 97–106.

CLAVERIE, P. (1909) Contribution à l'étude anatomique et histologique des plantes textiles exotiques (Passiflorées, Musacées, Palmiers, Aroïdées, Cypéracées). *Annls Mus. colon. Marseille* sér. 2, **7**, 11–207.

FAHN, A., STOLER, S., and FIRST, T. (1963) Vegetative shoot apex in banana and zonal changes as it becomes reproductive. *Bot. Gaz.* **124**, 246–50.

HÄRDTL, H. (1935) Das Blatt der Banane in baumechanischer Betrachtung. *Bot. Arch.* **37**, 75–79.

LANE, I. E. (1955) Genera and generic relationships in Musaceae. *Mitt. bot. StSamml., Münch.* **13**, 114–41.

LIPPITSCH, C. (1889) Ueber das Einreissen der Laubblätter der Musaceen und einiger verwandter Pflanzen. *Öst bot. Z.* **39**, 206–10, 259–63.

ONKEN, A. (1922) Ueber die Bedeutung des Milch- und Schleimsaftes für die Beseitigung des überschüssigen Calziums, ein Beitrag zur Exkretphysiologie der höheren Pflanzen. *Bot. Arch.* **2**, 281–333.

PETERSEN, O. G. (1893) Bidrag til Scitamineernes Anatomi. *K. danske vidensk. Selsk. Skr.* (6) **8**, 337–418; see *Just's bot. Jber.* **21** (1) 14, no. 111 (1893)—original not seen.

PILLAI, S. K., and PILLAI, A. (1961) Root apical organization in monocotyledons—Musaceae. *J. Indian bot. Soc.* **40**, 444–55.

PIROTTA, R., and MARCATILI, L. (1886) Ancora sui rapporti tra i vasi laticiferi ed il sistema assimilatore. *Atti. R. Ist. bot. Roma* **2**, 156–9.

RIOPEL, J. L., and STEEVES, T. A. (1964) Studies on the roots of *Musa acuminata* cv. Gros Michel. 1. The anatomy and development of main roots. *Ann. Bot.* **28**, 475–90.

ROSS, H. (1883) Beiträge zur Anatomie abnormer Monocotylenwurzeln (Musaceen, Bambusaceen). *Ber. dt. bot. Ges.* **1**, 331–8.

SAITO, K. (1900) Anatomische Studien über wichtige Faserpflanzen Japans mit besonderer Berücksichtigung der Bastzellen. *J. Coll. Sci. imp. Univ. Tokyo* **15**, 395–458.

SCHUMANN, K. (1900) Musaceae in Engler's *Das Pflanzenreich* **4**, 1–42.

SIMMONDS, N. W. (1959) *Bananas*. London. pp. 466.

—— (1962) *The evolution of the bananas*. London. pp. 170.

SKUTCH, A. F. (1927) Anatomy of the leaf of the banana, *Musa sapienium* L. var. Hort. Gros Michel. *Bot. Gaz.* **84**, 337–91.

—— (1930) Unrolling of leaves of *Musa sapientum* and some related plants and their reactions to environmental aridity. Ibid. **90**, 337–65.

—— (1932) Anatomy of the axis of the banana. Ibid. **93**, 233–58.

SOLEREDER, H., and MEYER, F. J. (1930) Musaceae in *Systematische Anatomie der Monokotyledonen*, Heft VI, 1–26.

TOMLINSON, P. B. (1959) An anatomical approach to the classification of the Musaceae. *J. Linn. Soc.* (Bot.) **55**, 779–809.

TRÉCUL, A. (1867) Des vaisseaux propres et du tannin dans les Musacées. *Annls Sci. nat.* Bot. sér. 5, **8**, 283–300.

WITTMACK, L. (1867–8) *Musa ensete.* Ein Beitrag zur Kenntniss der Bananen. *Linnaea* **35**, 209–90.

HELICONIACEAE
(Figs. 70–71)

Summary

A SMALL family consisting of some 120 species belonging to the single genus
Heliconia. It is largely restricted to South and Central America but there are
a few spp. in the South Pacific. The family is very uniform in its morphology,
all its members being herbaceous perennials with sympodially branched
rhizomes bearing distichous scale leaves. The erect leafy shoots are commonly
tall and bear alternate leaves, the overlapping bases of which form a pseudostem more conspicuous than the true aerial stem, which is always unbranched. The inflorescences are terminal on leafy shoots. Each leaf has a
long, eligulate, open sheath with opposite, over-wrapping margins. A long
terete petiole is usually present below the leaf blade, into which it extends as
the lamina midrib.

Lamina characterized by epidermal cells with sinuous anticlinal walls as
seen in surface view. Single-layered colourless **hypodermis** present below each
surface of lamina. **Air-canals** present throughout greater part of leaf axis,
with usually two distinct series of canals in middle part. Rigid peripheral zone
of fibrous tissue in petiole and below abaxial surface in leaf sheath and midrib. Stem showing no clear differentiation into cortex and central cylinder.
Endodermoid layer present in rhizome. Root commonly including cortical
air-canals; stele occasionally with phloem islands. **Silica** present in all spp.
in the form of rectangular silica-bodies, each with a deep central hollow and
situated in an unevenly thickened cell; these cells (**stegmata**) arranged in files
adjacent to fibrous tissues. **Raphide-sacs** abundant. **Vessels** confined to roots.

LEAF

(i) *Lamina*

Rolled in bud. Dorsiventral. **Hairs** usually absent, but branched, uniseriate,
candelabra-like hairs occasional on leaf axis, e.g. in *H. distans* and *H. illustris*.
Epidermis with cells never markedly thick-walled; narrow costal bands common on abaxial surface, but costal bands less frequently differentiated above
larger veins. Epidermal cells, in surface view, with sinuous walls (Fig. 70. A,
B) but non-sinuous on adaxial surface in *H. rostrata*; undulations only
visible at a high level of focus in *H. angustifolia*. Cells between veins more or
less isodiametric in outline; those over veins elongated, narrow. Adaxial
epidermis always much more uniform than abaxial. Papillae often conspicuous on adaxial surface in *H. metallica* (Fig. 70. E), *pulverulenta*, and to a
lesser extent in *H. cathartica* and *rostrata*.

Stomata usually more or less restricted to abaxial intercostal regions, sometimes absent below transverse veins and so restricted to distinct rectangular
areas as in *H. bihai* (Fig. 70. B). Stomata not usually in distinct files, but occasionally restricted to files of short, wide cells, each stomatal file alternating
with one or more files of long-cells as in *H. humilis*. Each stoma (Fig. 70. C)

with 2 narrow, deep, lateral subsidiary cells without sinuous walls. Two terminal subsidiary cells commonly present as well. Other cells, smaller in size than their neighbours, sometimes present near stomata. Guard cells not sunken, each with 2 equal ledges (Fig. 70. G); walls thickened beneath ledges except at thin-walled poles. **Hypodermis** of colourless, thin-walled cells 1-layered beneath each surface, adaxial always deeper than abaxial hypodermis (Fig. 70. D, F). Adaxial cells transversely extended and more or less hexagonal in surface view, arranged in distinct longitudinal files. Abaxial cells v. irregular, not uniformly arranged around substomatal chambers.

Chlorenchyma usually including a distinct 2–3-layered adaxial palisade; abaxial mesophyll usually rather loose and composed of lobed cells (Fig. 70. F). Cells beneath transverse and longitudinal veins usually more compact than those elsewhere. Independent fibrous strands always absent, except in *H. illustris* according to Solereder and Meyer. **Vascular bundles** usually independent of surface layers (Fig. 70. D), small vb's sometimes in contact with abaxial hypodermis, largest veins always remote from abaxial surface, but sometimes attached to adaxial hypodermis. Vb's usually sheathed by fibres both above and below, the sheath completed laterally by 1–2-layered parenchyma (Fig. 70. F). Smallest vb's sometimes without adaxial fibres. Largest veins including a single file of wide tracheal elements and extended protoxylem. **Transverse veins** situated at same level as longitudinal veins, independent of surface layers and sheathed by thin-walled, colourless cells. **Expansion cells** formed by enlargement of hypodermal cells above main veins.

(ii) *Leaf axis*

Cells of **epidermis** without distinctly sinuous walls. A 1-layered colourless **hypodermis** always present below abaxial surface in midrib and leaf sheath (Fig. 71. G), and below whole surface of terete petiole; hypodermal cells surrounding substomatal chambers of leaf sheath often becoming sclerotic. Petiole and midrib rarely including an abaxial band of thin-walled 'oblique-cells' similar to those of *Canna*, as in *H. hirsuta* and *H. humilis*. **Air-canals** present throughout leaf sheath and petiole and extending well into midrib (Fig. 71. A–E); in leaf sheath forming a single arc (Fig. 71. E), but in midrib (Fig. 71. A), petiole (Fig. 71. B, C), and distal part of leaf sheath (Fig. 71. D) supplemented by adaxial air-canals above main vascular arc. Each canal segmented at intervals by transverse **septa**, the septa composed either of a single layer of stellate cells (Fig. 71. H) or of one or more layers of rounded cells sandwiched between 2 layers of stellate cells, these multi-layered septa often including transverse veins.

Chlorenchyma in midrib forming a distinct adaxial band continuous with that of lamina; in sheath present as an abaxial layer; in petiole forming a complete subhypodermal layer. **Fibrous strands** well developed close to abaxial surface (Fig. 71. G), sometimes forming an almost continuous layer, especially in petiole. Fibrous layer also present below adaxial chlorenchyma in midrib of many spp. Additional mechanical layers sometimes produced by sclerosis of adaxial ground parenchyma cells (Fig. 71. F). Distribution of fibrous and sclerotic elements in leaf axis rather variable and possibly of specific diagnostic value. **Veins** arranged in 3 main systems (e.g. Fig. 71. D). Small adaxial system

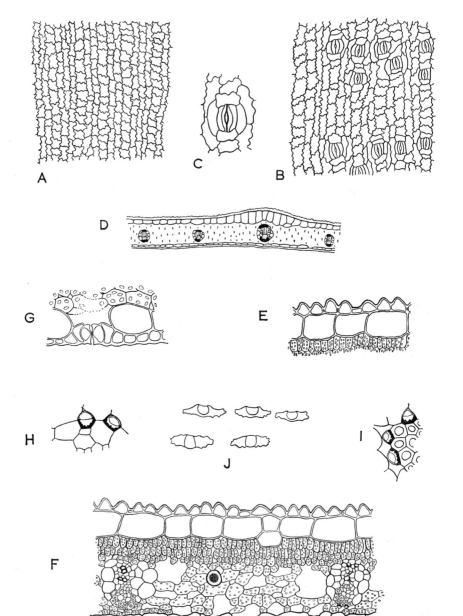

FIG. 70. HELICONIACEAE. Lamina of *Heliconia* (after Tomlin-son 1959).

A–C. *H. bihai.*

A. Adaxial epidermis, surface view ($\times 115$). B. Abaxial epidermis, surface view ($\times 115$). C. Stoma, surface view, abaxial epidermis ($\times 300$).

D–F. *H. metallica.* T.S. lamina.

D. ($\times 28$); assimilating tissue—short lines; mechanical tissue—solid black; xylem—hatched; phloem—stippled; epidermal cells not drawn. E. Adaxial surface layers ($\times 135$). F. ($\times$ 115).

G. *H. spectabilis.* T.S. stoma, abaxial surface ($\times 300$).

H–J. *H. metallica.* Stegmata ($\times 480$).

H, I. T.S. lamina. H. Next to bundle sheath parenchyma. I. Next to bundle sheath fibres. J. Isolated silica-bodies from lamina.

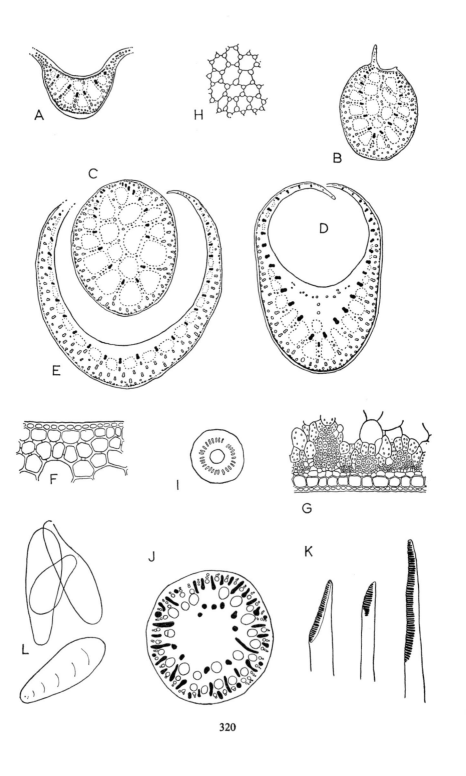

Fɪɢ. 71. HELICONIACEAE. *Heliconia* (after Tomlinson 1959).

A–E. *H. bihai*. T.S. leaf axis at successively lower levels (×3).

A. Midrib half-way between base and apex. B. Petiole just below insertion of lamina. C. Middle of petiole. D. Distal part of leaf sheath. E. Leaf sheath. Main arc (I) bundles—solid black.

F, G. Enlargements of parts of D (×115).

F. Adaxial; sclerotic hypodermis. G. Abaxial; hypodermis and abaxial fibres.

H. *H. metallica*. Stellate parenchyma of transverse diaphragm in air-canal of petiole (×65).

I, J. *H. bihai*. T.S. root.

I. Outline (×3). J. Stele (×30); phloem—solid black; xylem—open circles.

K. Perforated end walls of vessel elements from root (*H. aurantiaca* and *H. psittacorum*) (×70).

L. *H. bihai*. Starch grains from rhizome (×500).

of vascular and fibrous bundles (III) present above main vascular arc (I), in distal part of leaf axis, or sometimes restricted to petiole as in *H. hirsuta*. Abaxial vb's (II) forming a well-developed system of large and small pectinating bundles, some situated in the tissue between air-canals, the most abaxial bundles pectinating with the abaxial fibrous strands. Individual bundles resembling those of other scitaminean families (cf. Zingiberaceae).

AERIAL STEM

Inconspicuous and mostly enclosed within a pseudostem formed from overwrapping leaf sheaths. No distinction between cortex and central cylinder. Peripheral vb's somewhat congested and with well-developed fibrous sheaths forming a peripheral mechanical layer. Central bundles more diffuse and without fibrous sheaths. Each vb with 1 file of wide metaxylem elements and a single phloem strand, some central bundles including extended protoxylem.

RHIZOME

Periderm divisions sometimes observed in old rhizomes. **Cortex** separated from central cylinder by a distinct **endodermoid layer** and a narrow plexus of vascular strands. Cortical vb's each with a well-developed fibrous sheath next to phloem. Cortical **fibrous strands** common. Ground parenchyma of cortex rarely becoming somewhat aerenchymatous as in *H. psittacorum*. Vb's of **central cylinder** either without fibrous sheaths or each with a continuous but narrow fibrous sheath.

ROOT

Exodermis present as a compact layer of thin-walled, suberized cells immediately within piliferous layer. Inner **cortex** often including radial **air-canals** (Fig. 71. I). **Stele** with normal polyarch monocotyledonous construction except for irregular, often radially extended **phloem strands** sometimes cut off as phloem islands towards centre of stele, as in *H. bihai* (Fig. 71. J).

SECRETORY, STORAGE, AND CONDUCTING ELEMENTS

Crystals of calcium oxalate common in all parts, sometimes forming a coarse crystal sand. Raphide-sacs common in all parts and especially conspicuous in transverse septa of air-canals of leaf.

Silica always present as small, rectangular bodies, each with a deep central depression often almost dividing the body into two (Fig. 70. J); each silica-body situated in a cell with unevenly thickened walls; small protrusions from silica-body penetrating into pits or depressions in thickened wall of cell (Fig. 70. H, I). Such silica-cells or **stegmata** arranged in longitudinal files adjacent to sheathing fibres of vb's in all parts except root. Rarely also adjacent to transverse veins of lamina as in *H. acuminata* and *H. humilis*. Stegmata in rhizome often rather thin-walled and including an irregular silica-body. Scattered spherical silica-bodies also observed in palisade cells of *H. hirsuta*.

Tannin common in all parts in unspecialized cells.

Starch present as cylindrical or ellipsoidal but never flattened grains (Fig. 71. L); most abundant in storage rhizomes.

Xylem. Vessels apparently restricted to metaxylem of root, the elements with long scalariform perforation plates on oblique or v. oblique end walls (Fig. 71. K).

TAXONOMIC NOTES

Heliconia is here treated for convenience as a distinct family corresponding to the Heliconiaceae of Nakai (1941), since it has a distinctive combination of anatomical features by which it can be distinguished from related families. However, the family is probably most closely related to the Musaceae in the strict sense, since some spp. of *Musa* are very much like *Heliconia* in their leaf anatomy (cf. Musaceae and Fig. 69). There is little anatomical evidence for including *Heliconia* in the Strelitziaceae as Hutchinson does.

SPECIES REPORTED ON IN THE LITERATURE

For most earlier literature see Solereder and Meyer (1930).

Petersen (1893) *Heliconia bihai* L., *H. brasiliensis* Hook. f., *H. cannoidea* Rich. (*H. hirsuta* L. f. var. *cannoidea* Bak.), *H. 'martinicensis'*, *H. metallica* Planch. et Lind., *H. psittacorum* L. f. (according to Solereder and Meyer).
Pillai and Pillai (1961) *Heliconia illustris* Ker.-Gawl.; root apex.
Ross (1883) *Heliconia pulverulenta* Lindl.; root.
Skutch (1930) *Heliconia bihai* L.; leaf.
Solereder and Meyer (1930) *Heliconia illustris* Hort. Bull. f. *rubricaulis*; all parts.
Tomlinson (1959) see Material Examined by the Author.

MATERIAL EXAMINED BY THE AUTHOR

The above description is based partly on the following material, which also served as the basis for a previous article (Tomlinson 1959).

Heliconia aurantiaca Ghiesb.; Botanic Gardens, Singapore. All parts.
H. bihai L.; Botanic Gardens, Singapore. All parts.
H. metallica Planch. and Lind.; Botanic Gardens, Singapore. All parts.
H. psittacorum L. f.; Singapore. All parts.
H. rostrata Ruiz and Pav.; material cultivated at Kew. Leaf.
H. spectabilis Lindl. and Rodigas.; Botanic Gardens, Singapore. All parts.

In addition to this material, leaves of the following Brazilian spp. have since been examined (pickled material preserved at Kew).

Heliconia acuminata Rich., *H. angustifolia* Hook., *H. brasiliensis* Hook. var. *flava*, *H. cathartica* Lam., *H. distans* Grig., *H. humilis* Jacq.

BIBLIOGRAPHY FOR HELICONIACEAE

NAKAI, T. (1941) Notulae ad plantas Asiae orientalis (XVI). *J. Jap. Bot.* **17,** 189–210.
PETERSEN, O. G. (1893) Bidrag til Scitamineernes Anatomi. *K. danske vidensk. Selsk. Skr.* (6) **8,** 337–418; see *Just's bot. Jber.* **21** (1), 14, no. 111 (1893)—original not seen.
PILLAI, S. K., and PILLAI, A. (1961) Root apical organization in Monocotyledons— Musaceae. *J. Indian bot. Soc.* **40,** 444–55.

Ross, H. (1883) Beiträge zur Anatomie abnormer Monocotylenwurzeln (Musaceen, Bambusaceen). *Ber. dt. bot. Ges.* **1,** 331–8.

Skutch, A. F. (1930) Unrolling of leaves of *Musa sapientum* and some related plants and their reactions to environmental aridity. *Bot. Gaz.* **90,** 337–65.

Solereder, H., and Meyer, F. J. (1930) Musaceae. In *Systematische Anatomie der Monokotyledonen*, Heft VI, 1–26.

Tomlinson, P. B. (1959) An anatomical approach to the classification of the Musaceae. *J. Linn. Soc.* (Bot.) **55,** 779–809.

STRELITZIACEAE[1]
(Figs. 72–73)

SUMMARY

A FAMILY of 3 genera with very different distributions. *Ravenala* restricted to Madagascar, *Phenakospermum* to Brazil and the Guianas, and *Strelitzia* to South Africa. Commonly small **trees** of a palm-like habit with erect, woody, caespitose trunks but several species of *Strelitzia* rhizomatous. Leaves often v. large and always arranged distichously on stem. Inflorescence lateral except in *Phenakospermum*. Lamina characterized by well-developed **hypodermis** of several adaxial colourless layers; abaxial hypodermis 1–2-layered. Substomatal chambers each surrounded by an annulus of one or more hypodermal cells. Veins all buttressed to both surfaces; buttresses made up of 1–2 lateral layers of parenchyma completed above and below by well-developed, often massive fibrous strands. Transverse septa in mesophyll between longitudinal veins formed by vertical extensions of sheath of transverse veins. Petiole including many arcs of wide air-lacunae segmented by multiseriate diaphragms. *Ravenala* and *Strelitzia* differing from *Phenakospermum* in being without adaxial vascular system in leaf axis. Woody aerial **stem** with narrow cortex and peripheral mechanical zone of congested vb's each with a massive fibrous sheath. Underground portions of **root** characterized by an anomalous stele filled with wide metaxylem vessels and scattered **phloem islands,** each phloem strand including a single wide sieve-tube. **Silica** present in all organs except root, either as stellate, druse-like bodies in thin-walled cells adjacent to vb's or as spherical bodies in epidermal **stegmata** with unevenly thickened walls. Starch grains flattened only in *Ravenala*. **Raphide-sacs** common.

LEAF

(i) *Lamina*

Rolled in bud. Dorsiventral. **Hairs** absent. **Epidermis** sometimes wholly cutinized as in *Ravenala*. Thick layer of wax usually developed; in *Strelitzia* waxy layer consisting of erect, rod-like particles. Epidermal cells usually with only outer wall thickened, but in *Phenakospermum* inner walls of abaxial epidermal cells much thicker than the thinner, wholly cutinized outer walls. Anticlinal walls of epidermal cells in *Phenakospermum* markedly sinuous (Fig. 73. G, H). Adaxial epidermis v. uniform (Fig. 72. A), cells more or less isodiametric in surface view, or somewhat longitudinally extended. Abaxial epidermis (Fig. 72. B) differentiated into narrow costal and wide intercostal bands; costal cells narrow, elongated; intercostal cells isodiametric, wide but v. irregular.

Stomata mostly restricted to abaxial intercostal regions, usually absent

---

[1] This corresponds to Hutchinson's Strelitziaceae without *Heliconia*, which is regarded as a separate family (p. 316).

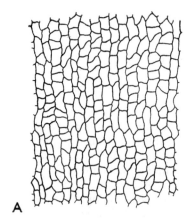

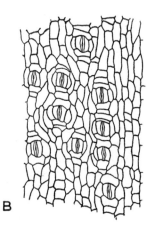

A

B

C

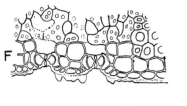

F

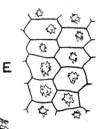

E

D

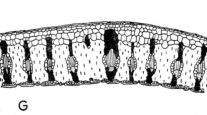

G

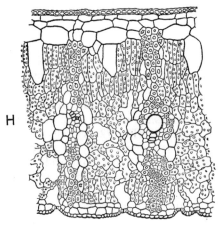

H

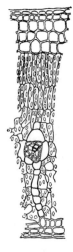

I

Fig. 72. STRELITZIACEAE. *Strelitzia* and *Ravenala*. Lamina (after Tomlinson 1959).

A–E. *Strelitzia.*

A–C. *S. reginae.* A. Adaxial epidermis, surface view (×130). B. Abaxial epidermis, surface view (×130). C. Silica-cells next to fibrous buttress in T.S. (×480). D. *S. nicolai.* Young plant. T.S. adaxial surface layers with hypodermal silica-bodies (hypodermis 1-layered) (×400). E. *S. reginae.* Silica-bodies in adaxial hypodermis, surface view of costal region (×480).

F–I. *Ravenala madagascariensis.* Lamina.

F. T.S. abaxial surface layers (×300). G. T.S. (×28); assimilating tissue—short lines; mechanical tissues—solid black; xylem—hatched; phloem—stippled. Epidermal cells not drawn. H. T.S. (×120); including a large vein. I. L.S. (×120); showing transverse commissure in T.S.

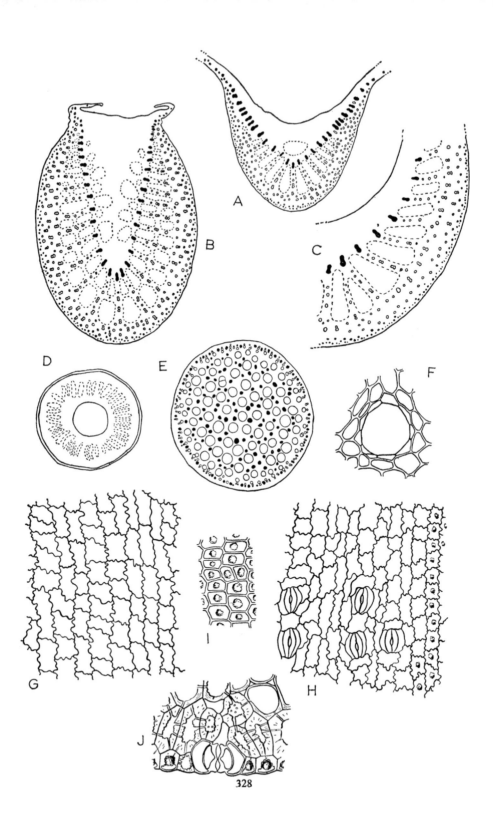

328

A–C. *Strelitzia nicolai.* T.S. leaf axis at successively lower levels ($\times 2\frac{1}{2}$).

A. Midrib, half-way between base and apex of lamina. B. Petiole, just below insertion of lamina. C. Part of leaf sheath. Main arc (I) bundles —solid black.

D–F. *Ravenala madagascariensis.* T.S. root.

D. Outline ($\times 2$). E. Stele ($\times 8$); phloem—solid black; xylem—open circles. F. Phloem island from centre of stele ($\times 150$).

G–J. *Phenakospermum guianense.*

G–H. Epidermis of lamina, surface view ($\times 300$). G. Adaxial. H. Abaxial, including part of a costal band. I, J. Abaxial epidermis of leaf base. I. Surface view ($\times 300$). J. T.S., including a stoma ($\times 430$).

below transverse as well as longitudinal veins and so confined to small rect-angular areas. Stomata not arranged in v. distinct files but in 3–5 series within each intercostal band; epidermal cells in same files as stomata sometimes wider than those elsewhere. Short terminal as well as deep lateral subsidiary cells usually present around each stoma, often associated with other small epidermal cells. Guard cells often sunken in *Ravenala* and *Strelitzia*, each with 2 equal ledges (Fig. 72. F). **Hypodermis** always more than 1-layered adaxially, up to 6 cells deep; on abaxial surface usually inconspicuous and 1-layered, but 2-layered in *Ravenala* (Fig. 72. G). Adaxial hypodermal cells usually somewhat transversely extended, but cells of innermost layers large, cubical or even anticlinally extended (Fig. 72. H). Abaxial hypodermis always shallow and small-celled; including an annulus of 1 or more cells around each substomatal chamber.

Chlorenchyma including a 2–3-layered adaxial palisade; abaxial mesophyll composed of loose, lobed cells and divided into rectangular compartments by transverse septa. **Longitudinal veins** congested, consisting of several orders of veins of differing size, all veins extended towards each surface via vertical and mostly fibrous buttresses (Fig. 72. G, H). Parenchyma at sides of veins 1–2-layered. Extended protoxylem present only in largest veins. **Transverse veins** provided with vertical extensions either to each hypodermis as in *Strelitzia*, or from abaxial hypodermis usually only as far as adaxial palisade in *Ravenala* (Fig. 72. I) and *Phenakospermum*, forming transverse septa. Abaxial elements of septa in *Phenakospermum* prosenchymatous or even fibrous. **Expansion cells** formed by enlargement of adaxial hypodermal cells above main veins to produce conspicuous bands of inflated cells, but not forming such a distinct 'pulvinar band' at junction of midrib and lamina as in *Musa*.

(ii) *Leaf axis*

Leaf sheath always short and indistinct, not forming a long tubular organ. Petiole always well developed and terete. **Epidermis** sometimes differentiated into costal and intercostal bands; cells often with slightly sinuous anticlinal walls in *Phenakospermum*. Inner wall of epidermal cells in petiole often becoming markedly thickened, the wall of each cell enveloping a silica-body, especially in *Phenakospermum* (Fig. 73. I, J). **Stomata** frequent, subsidiary cells sometimes becoming sclerotic in *Phenakospermum*. **Hypodermis** of one or more layers usually differentiated from ground parenchyma, often becoming sclerotic, especially in *Phenakospermum* and *Ravenala*.

Chlorenchyma present as a distinct abaxial band in all parts. **Air-canals** conspicuous and arranged in several series, some adaxial to the main vascular arc in distal part of leaf axis (Fig. 73. A, B). Abaxial canals always arranged in several arcs in petiole but usually consisting of a single arc at base of leaf sheath in *Phenakospermum* and *Strelitzia* (Fig. 73. C). Air-lacunae segmented at frequent intervals by thick transverse septa, often including transverse veins. Each septum consisting of 2–3 layers of small, stellate cells, their arms enclosing wide intercellular spaces or, less commonly, septa consisting of compact, rounded cells. Abaxial **fibrous strands** abundant in all parts of leaf axis and often, together with sclerotic hypodermis, forming a rigid peripheral mechanical zone. **Longitudinal veins** consisting of a main arc (I) of large, scitaminean-type vb's but sometimes in massive leaf axes difficult to distinguish from (II) and (III). Abaxial system (II) of many large and small vb's constituting most of vascular system of leaf axis (Fig. 73. A–C), the bundles mostly in walls of air-lacunae and often inverted but outermost vb's somewhat congested, with reduced vascular tissues, pectinating with fibrous strands to form part of peripheral mechanical zone. Adaxial system (III) of few small vascular and fibrous bundles present only in *Phenakospermum*.

STEM

(i) *Erect woody stems of* Phenakospermum, Ravenala, *and* Strelitzia *spp.*

Epidermis like that of abaxial surface of leaf sheath, in *Phenakospermum* made up of files of silica-cells with unevenly thickened walls. **Periderm** recorded for stem of *Strelitzia*. Hypodermal layers becoming sclerotic in *Phenakospermum* and *Ravenala*. **Cortex** narrow, including several series of large inner and small peripheral vb's; fibrous strands absent. Cortical vb's each with a well-developed fibrous phloem sheath; xylem sheathed only by parenchyma and including a single file of wide tracheal elements. **Endodermoid layer** absent.

Central cylinder including a wide peripheral zone of congested vb's embedded in sclerotic ground tissue. Each vb with a massive fibrous sheath and reduced vascular tissue. Transition from peripheral congested zone to central region with more diffuse vb's fairly abrupt. Largest of inner vb's (apparently recently entered leaf traces) each including many wide metaxylem elements, conspicuously extended protoxylem and inconspicuous fibrous sheath; other vb's (apparently leaf traces well below their insertion) each with a single file of wide metaxylem elements, no extended protoxylem and a complete fibrous sheath. Sheaths of central vb's not fibrous in *Strelitzia*. **Ground parenchyma** cells becoming enlarged, lobed or stellate to form wide intercellular lacunae in *Phenakospermum* and especially in *Ravenala*.

(ii) *Rhizome of* Strelitzia *spp. and stolons of* Phenakospermum

Cortex wide and well vasculated. **Endodermoid layer** well developed at inner limit of cortex. Vb's of central cylinder distributed v. irregularly.

ROOT

Usually wide; thick and fleshy in rhizomatous spp. of *Strelitzia*. **Periderm** divisions occasionally observed. Outer cortical cells forming an indistinct **exodermis** of compact, often suberized cells. Middle cortex of *Ravenala* including conspicuous radially extended **air-lacunae** (Fig. 73, D). **Endodermis**; cells developing U-shaped wall thickenings in mature roots. **Pericycle** commonly more than 1-layered, especially in *Strelitzia*. **Stele** of subterranean roots anomalous and including wide vessels scattered uniformly throughout the thick-walled ground tissue, together with scattered **phloem islands** (Fig. 73. E), each central phloem strand including a single wide sieve-tube (Fig. 73. F). Normal polyarch root structure recorded for aerial roots of *Phenakospermum* and *Ravenala*.

SECRETORY, STORAGE, AND CONDUCTING ELEMENTS

Crystals of calcium oxalate common, especially in transverse septa of air-canals in leaf axis. Raphide-sacs common, especially in stem.

Silica present as stellate, druse-like bodies, each in a thin-walled cell, silica-cells arranged in longitudinal files adjacent to vb's of all organs except root (Fig. 72. C–E); never situated in epidermis. Common in transverse septa of lamina and adjacent to transverse veins of leaf axis. Sometimes accompanied by silica sand. True **stegmata,** as epidermal cells with unevenly thickened walls, each cell including a spherical silica-body, developed only in *Phenakospermum* (Fig. 73. I–J) but possibly occurring in the other genera.

Tannin common in structurally unmodified cells.

Starch abundant in ground parenchyma of woody stem; also in rhizome and roots of *Strelitzia* spp. Grains markedly flattened only in *Ravenala*, more ellipsoidal or even spherical in *Strelitzia* and *Phenakospermum*.

Xylem. Vessels present in root of all spp. and in woody stem of *Phenako-spermum* and *Strelitzia* but not of *Ravenala*. Elements usually with scalariform perforation plates on oblique or v. oblique end walls, but perforation plates sometimes simple in roots of *Phenakospermum*. Vessel elements least special-ized in stem of *Strelitzia*.

Phloem. Sieve-tubes in phloem islands in root with compound sieve-plates on long end walls, but sieve-tubes probably with simple sieve-plates in stem and leaf.

ECONOMIC USES

Apart from the common use of *Ravenala madagascariensis* Gmel. and *Strelitzia reginae* Banks as ornamentals in tropical countries, these plants have no commercial value.

TAXONOMIC NOTES

This account is based on the description of the anatomy of *Ravenala* and *Strelitzia* by Tomlinson (1959) and of *Phenakospermum* by Tomlinson (1960). In the latter of these 2 articles their interrelationships are discussed in detail. These 3 genera resemble each other very closely and it is evident that they form a very distinct unit (cf. Lane 1955, Nakai 1948). There is no anatomical evidence, and apparently no sound morphological evidence, for including *Heliconia* with these 3 genera, as Hutchinson does.

GENERA AND SPECIES REPORTED ON IN THE LITERATURE

For most earlier literature see Solereder and Meyer (1930).

Lippitsch (1889) *Ravenala madagascariensis, Strelitzia alba, S. farinosa, S. reginae;* leaf.

Petersen (1893) *Ravenala madagascariensis* Sonn., *Strelitzia nicolai* Rge. et Kcke., *S. reginae* Banks (according to Solereder and Meyer).

Pillai and Pillai (1961) *Ravenala madagascariensis* Sonn.; root apex.

Ross (1883) *Ravenala madagascariensis* Sonn., *Strelitzia augusta* Thunb., *S. farinosa* Dry., *S. humilis* Hort., *S. nicolai* Rgl. and Kor., *S. reginae* Ait.; root.

Solereder and Meyer (1930) *Ravenala madagascariensis* Sonn., *Strelitzia reginae* Banks; all parts.

Tomlinson (1959, 1960) see Material Examined by the Author.

MATERIAL EXAMINED BY THE AUTHOR

The above description is based on the following material which also served as the basis for two previous articles (Tomlinson 1959, 1960).

Phenakospermum guianense (L. C. Rich.) Miq.; P. Campos-Porto; Botanic Gardens, Rio de Janeiro. All parts.

Ravenala madagascariensis Sonn.; (i) Botanic Gardens, Singapore. All parts. (ii) Material cultivated at Kew. Leaf. (iii) Botanic Gardens, University of Ghana. Leaf.

Strelitzia augusta Thunb.; material cultivated at Kew. Leaf, root.

S. nicolai Regel and Koch; (i) material cultivated at Kew. All parts. (ii) Botanic Gardens, Singapore. Young plant, leaf.

S. parvifolia Dryand.; material cultivated at Kew. Leaf, root.

S. reginae Banks; (i) Botanic Gardens, University of Ghana. Leaf, root. (ii) Material cultivated at Kew. Rhizome.

Strelitzia sp.; Rhodesia. Stem.

BIBLIOGRAPHY FOR STRELITZIACEAE

LANE, I. E. (1955) Genera and generic relationships in Musaceae. *Mitt. bot. StSamml., Münch.* **13**, 114–41.

LIPPITSCH, C. (1889) Ueber das Einreissen der Laubblätter der Musaceen und einiger verwandter Pflanzen. *Öst. bot. Z.* **39**, 206–10, 259–63.

NAKAI, T. (1948) A new attempt to the classification of the Strelitziaceae. *Bull. Tokyo Sci. Mus.* **22**, 19–24.

PETERSEN, O. G. (1893) Bidrag til Scitamineernes Anatomi. *K. danske vidensk. Selsk. Skr.* (6) **8**, 337–418; see *Just's bot. Jber.* **21** (1), 14, no. 111 (1893)—original not seen.

PILLAI, S. K., and PILLAI, A. (1961) Root apical organization in monocotyledons—Musaceae. *J. Indian bot. Soc.* **40**, 444–55.

ROSS, H. (1883) Beiträge zur Anatomie abnormer Monocotylenwurzeln (Musaceen, Bambusaceen). *Ber. dt. bot. Ges.* **1**, 331–8.

SOLEREDER, H., and MEYER, F. J. (1930) Musaceae. In *Systematische Anatomie der Monokotyledonen*, Heft VI, 1–26.

TOMLINSON, P. B. (1959) An anatomical approach to the classification of the Musaceae. *J. Linn. Soc.* (Bot.) **55**, 779–809.

—— (1960) The anatomy of *Phenakospermum* (Musaceae). *J. Arnold Arbor.* **41**, 287–97.

LOWIACEAE
(Figs. 74–75)

SUMMARY

AN isolated family of perhaps 5 species all belonging to the genus *Orchidantha*,[1] found in Malaya and Borneo in the lowest layer of the primary forest. Small herbs with erect rhizomes; the leaves arranged distichously on the leafy shoots, which have no well-developed stem but terminate in the inflorescence. Anatomical features of the lamina include: **chlorenchyma** without a palisade but consisting of an irregular mixture of large and small cells; frequent isolated **fibres** or small fibrous strands; transverse veins with a sheath of thick-walled cells. Leaf axis including 2 distinct systems of narrow air-canals, one above and the other below the main arc of vb's, the abaxial system including 2 separate arcs of canals. **Silica** present as 'hat-shaped' bodies, each situated in an unevenly thickened cell, these stegmata situated in longitudinal files adjacent to the vb's. Starch grains small, angular, and isodiametric. **Raphide-sacs** common.

LEAF

(i) *Lamina*

Rolled in bud. Main lateral veins diverging fron midrib at a narrow angle, connected by a dense system of transverse veins. Dorsiventral. **Hairs** absent. Cuticle thin. **Epidermis** consisting of thin-walled, shallow cells and not differentiated into distinct regions above and below veins. Adaxial cells rectangular or isodiametric in surface view (Fig. 74. A); abaxial cells more irregular (Fig. 74. B); the anticlinal walls often curved but never sinuous; cells arranged in short, longitudinal files. **Stomata** infrequent on adaxial surface, uniformly but diffusely scattered on abaxial surface. Lateral subsidiary cells deeper than other epidermal cells; terminal subsidiary cells not differentiated (Fig. 74. E). Guard cells (Fig. 74. F) not sunken, each with outer ledge much more conspicuous than inner ledge, the cell lumen almost occluded by wall thickenings in median part but not at thin-walled poles. **Hypodermis** (Fig. 74. C, D, G) consisting of a single layer of colourless cells beneath each surface but not well differentiated from assimilating tissue. Hypodermal cells usually slightly transversely extended; usually 4 hypodermal cells surrounding each substomatal chamber and sometimes containing chloroplasts. Isolated **fibres** and small fibrous strands frequent in most spp. near each surface, either next to hypodermis or separated from it by a single mesophyll layer (Fig. 74. C, D); occasionally next to epidermis.

Chlorenchyma without a palisade; including an irregular mixture of large and small cells (Fig. 74. I), both types of cell including equal numbers of chloroplasts but large cells often appearing empty in thin sections (Fig. 74. G). **Longitudinal veins** diffuse, situated in adaxial mesophyll remote from abaxial hypodermis and often attached to adaxial hypodermis or epidermis (Fig. 74.

---

[1] The earlier name *Lowia*, on which the Lowiaceae are based, has lapsed into synonymy.

C, G). Parenchymatous sheath of veins always 1-layered; sheath fibrous above and below, the adaxial fibres sometimes forming a buttress. **Transverse veins** frequent, rather congested; situated in abaxial mesophyll and often extending below longitudinal veins, each vein wide and with a well-developed sheath of one or more layers of thick-walled cells (Fig. 74. H). **Expansion cells** not developed.

(ii) *Leaf axis*

Midrib, petiole, and leaf sheath gradually confluent, not articulate, eligulate. **Hypodermis** not differentiated from rest of ground parenchyma and not sclerotic. Narrow **air-canals** present in several indistinct arcs but in distal part of leaf axis consisting of a system above as well as below main veins (Fig. 75. A–D). Abaxial air-canals arranged in 2 distinct arcs at most levels. Air-canals segmented at intervals by transverse diaphragms, 1 or more cells thick, the diaphragms including short-armed, stellate cells. Chloroplasts diffusely distributed and not restricted to a distinct chlorenchymatous band. **Main veins** distinct at all levels as a compact arc (I). Adaxial (III) and abaxial (II) vascular systems well developed at all levels and including several series of large and small vb's (e.g. Fig. 75. C). Fibrous strands common close to both adaxial and abaxial surfaces.

RHIZOME

Short, narrow, often erect. **Periderm** arising by division of outermost cells in old rhizomes. Fibrous strands common in outer cortex, except in *O. maxillarioides*. Inner limit of cortex represented by a distinct **endodermoid layer**; periphery of central cylinder including a vascular plexus. Cortical vb's each with a well-developed fibrous sheath. Central vb's without a fibrous sheath and with irregularly arranged vascular tissues, sometimes almost amphivasal.

ROOT

Sometimes with localized **tubers** formed by enlargement of cortex. **Exodermis** of compact, thin-walled, ligno-suberized cells always present. Air-lacunae present in inner cortex but often rather small (Fig. 75. E). **Stele** with normal polyarch vascular arrangement although phloem strands often extended radially inwards (Fig. 75. F) and occasionally isolated as phloem islands in *O. longiflora*.

SECRETORY, STORAGE, AND CONDUCTING ELEMENTS

Crystals of calcium oxalate common in all parts. Crystal sand abundant in rhizome. Raphide-sacs common, especially in rhizome.

Silica common as 'hat-shaped' bodies in unevenly thickened cells or stegmata (Fig. 74. K). Stegmata forming longitudinal files adjacent to vb's in all parts except root. Wall of stegmata adjacent to fibres of vb thickened and pitted (Fig. 74. J).

Tannin common only in rhizome.

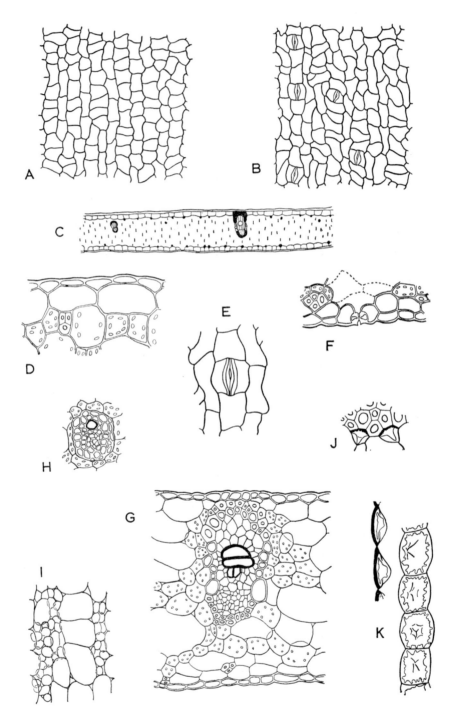

Fig. 74. LOWIACEAE. Leaf of *Orchidantha longiflora* (after Tomlinson 1959).

A, B. Epidermis of lamina, surface view (× 135).

A. Adaxial. B. Abaxial.

C, D. T.S. lamina.

C. (× 50) Assimilating tissue—short lines; mechanical tissues—solid black; xylem—hatched; phoem—stippled. Epidermal cells not drawn. D. Adaxial surface layers (× 270).

E, F. Stoma from abaxial surface (× 270).

E. Surface view. F. T.S.

G. T.S. main vein of lamina (× 220).

H. T.S. transverse commissure (× 180), from L.S. lamina.

I. Mesophyll of lamina in paradermal view (× 130).

J, K. Stegmata.

J. Next to bundle-sheath fibres of vb in petiole (× 270) K. In lamina, in surface and lateral view (× 480).

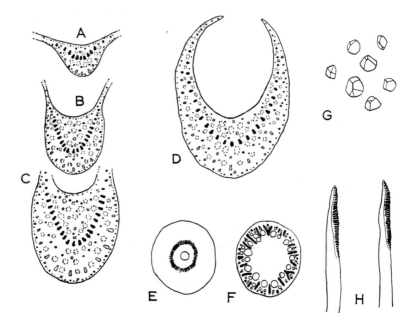

Fig. 75. LOWIACEAE. *Orchidantha longiflora* (after Tomlinson 1959).

A–D. T.S. leaf axis at successively lower levels (×4).

A. Midrib of lamina half-way between base and apex. B. Transition region between midrib and petiole. C. Distal part of leaf sheath. D. Leaf sheath. Main arc (I) bundles—solid black.

E, F. T.S. root.

E. Outline (×3). F. stele (×30); phloem—solid black; xylem—open circles.

G. Starch grains from rhizome (×500).

H. End walls of vessel elements from root (×66).

Starch common in leaf axis, but most abundant in rhizome; grains small, angular, and more or less isodiametric (Fig. 75. G).

Xylem. Vessels confined to metaxylem of root, elements 24–43 μm in diameter, up to 3000 μm long, closely resembling tracheids but with long scalariform perforation plates in v. oblique end walls (Fig. 75. H).

TAXONOMIC NOTES

This account is based upon that in Tomlinson (1959). Anatomically *Orchidantha* is very different from other members of the Scitamineae, a fact that supports its isolation as a monotypic family.

SPECIES REPORTED ON IN THE LITERATURE

For most earlier literature see Solereder and Meyer (1930).

Fahn (1954) '*Lowia meleagris*'; tracheal elements.
Solereder and Meyer (1930) *Orchidantha maxillarioides* K. Schum.; all parts.
Tomlinson (1959) see Material Examined by the Author.

MATERIAL EXAMINED BY THE AUTHOR

The above description is based on the following material, which also served as the basis for a previous article (Tomlinson 1959).

Orchidantha calcarea Henders.; Botanic Gardens, Singapore. Leaf.
O. longiflora Ridl.; Botanic Gardens, Singapore. All parts.
O. maxillarioides K. Schum.; Botanic Gardens, Singapore. All parts.
'*Lowia meleagris*'; material cultivated at Kew. All parts.

BIBLIOGRAPHY FOR LOWIACEAE

FAHN, A. (1954) Metaxylem elements in some families of the Monocotyledoneae. *New Phytol.* **53**, 530–40.
SOLEREDER, H., and MEYER, F. J. (1930) Musaceae. In *Systematische Anatomie der Monokotyledonen*, Heft VI, 1–26.
TOMLINSON, P. B. (1959) An anatomical approach to the classification of the Musaceae. *J. Linn. Soc.* (Bot.) **55**, 779–809.

ZINGIBERACEAE[1]

(Figs. 76–80)

SUMMARY

A LARGE tropical family with its centre of distribution in the Indo-Malayan region but extending through tropical Africa to Central and South America. Species mostly occupying shady habitat of primary forest floor. Herbaceous perennials, usually with thick, fleshy, sympodially branched rhizomes covered with distichous scale leaves. Aerial leafy shoots at ends of renewal buds usually terminating in an inflorescence or, less commonly, inflorescence and foliage leaves on separate shoots. Erect vegetative stems always unbranched and usually inconspicuous, aerial shoots mainly formed by overwrapping leaf bases constituting a pseudostem. Plane of insertion of distichous leaves significant taxonomically (Weisse 1932, 1933). Isodiametric **oil-cells** with suberized walls characteristic of family; contents of oil-cells imparting aromatic properties to all organs. **Hairs** almost invariably unicellular and rarely branched. Aerial stem typically separated into cortex and central cylinder by peripheral **fibrous cylinder**. **Silica** commonly restricted to epidermis of lamina, either as silica sand, or, in the tribe Alpinieae, as solitary spherical bodies in epidermal cells above and below veins. Starch grains frequently flattened.

HAIRS

Aerial parts not often conspicuously pubescent, but microscopic hairs quite common. Hairs on lamina sometimes restricted either to leaf margin, to abaxial surface, or to costal or intercostal regions (e.g. Fig. 77. C). Hairs always unicellular (Fig. 76. N), except for 2-celled hairs on rhizome of *Curcuma* (Fig. 80. J); usually unbranched except for forked or rarely stellate cells in *Renealmia* and occasionally in *Aframomum*. Walls of hairs commonly thick and lignified, cell lumen sometimes irregularly occluded. Hair bases sometimes constricted at leaf surface (Fig. 76. M), but bases more commonly swollen and pitted, especially in hairs at leaf margin (Fig. 76. J); base deeply sunken in spp. of *Hornstedtia* (Fig. 76. I) and *Renealmia*. Hairs commonly rather short and pointed, longer hairs most common on leaf axis as in *Hornstedtia* and *Renealmia*. In *Boesenbergia*, *Kaempferia*, *Scaphochlamys*, and *Zingiber*, hairs long, delicate, thin-walled and often ephemeral except for persistent, thick-walled bases becoming almost occluded by enlargement of neighbouring cells (Fig. 76. K–M).

LEAF

(i) *Lamina*

Entire, usually lanceolate, rolled in bud. Always dorsiventral. **Cuticle** thin, sometimes minutely papillose. **Epidermis** often with distinct costal bands of small cells above, but most commonly below veins; otherwise epidermis v. uniform, as in *Scaphochlamys*. Epidermal cells usually somewhat transversely

[1] This corresponds to Zingiberaceae of Hutchinson without Costeae, regarded by him merely as a tribe and here described as a separate family (p. 360).

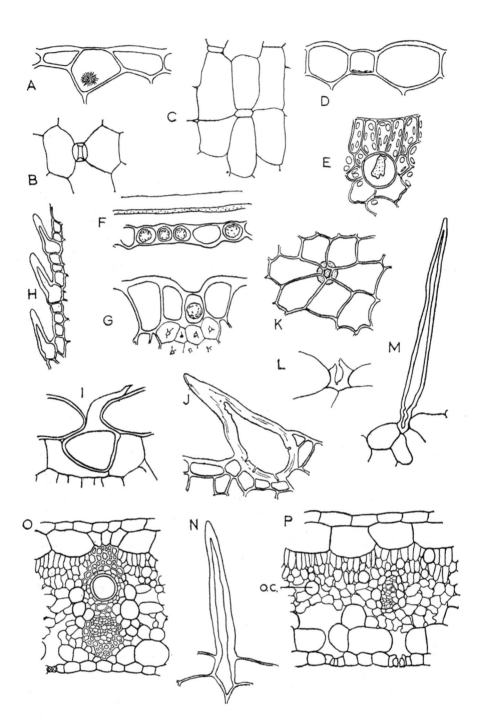

FIG. 76. ZINGIBERACEAE (after Tomlinson 1956).

A–E. Oil-cells.

A. *Alpinia speciosa.* T.S. petiole, epidermis (×477). B. *Burbidgea schizocheila.* Abaxial epidermis of lamina, surface view (×173). C. *Elettaria cardamomum.* L.S. root, ground parenchyma of cortex (×153). D. *Roscoea humeana.* L.S. lamina, epidermis (×317). E. *Hedychium gardnerianum.* L.S. lamina, junction of palisade and spongy mesophyll (×383).

F, G. *Alpinia javanica.* Stegmata (×460).

F. L.S. lamina, next to abaxial fibres of a bundle sheath; lumen of fibre stippled. G. T.S. lamina, next to fibres of a bundle sheath.

H–N. Hairs.

H. *Globba bulbifera.* Hairs on margin of leaf (×153). I. *Hornstedtia conica.* T.S. lamina, sunken hair in adaxial surface (×383). J. *Aframomum* sp. Hair from margin of leaf (×210). K–M. *Zingiber officinale.* K. Hair base from abaxial epidermis of lamina in surface view (×270). L. T.S. petiole, base of detached hair (×383). M. T.S. petiole, attached hair (×270). N. *Elettaria cardamomum.* T.S. midrib of lamina, hair from abaxial surface (×383).

O, P. *Hedychium gardnerianum.* T.S. lamina (×153).

O. Vb of first order. P. Vb. of third order. o.c. -oil-cell.

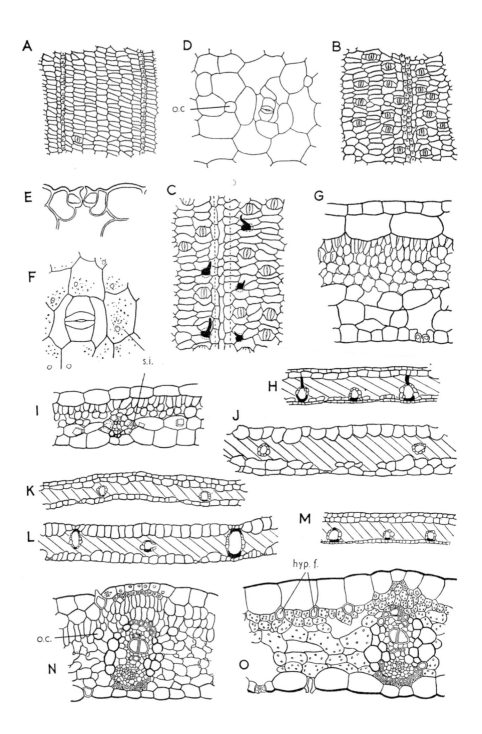

Fɪɢ. 77. ZINGIBERACEAE. Lamina (after Tomlinson 1956).

A, B. *Catimbium latilabre*. Epidermis, surface view (×70).

   A. Adaxial. B. Abaxial.

C. *Hornstedtia conica*. Abaxial epidermis, surface view (×117).

D–F. Stomata.

   D. *Camptandra ovata*. Abaxial epidermis, including oil cells (o.c.) (×103). E. *Hedychium gardnerianum*. T.S. adaxial epidermis (×377). F. *Alpinia speciosa*. Adaxial epidermis (×327).

G–O. T.S. lamina.

   G. *Brachychilum horsfieldii* (×153). H. *Geostachys taipingensis* (×48). I. *Globba bulbifera* (×147). J. *Camptandra ovata* (×48). K. *Kaempferia gilberti* (×48). L. *Kaempferia kirkii* (×48). M. *Alpinia sanderae* (×48). N. *Renealmia* sp. Vb of first order (×117). O. *Elettariopsis curtisii*) ×117).

   Assimilating tissue—hatched; fibrous tissue—solid black in H, J–M; o.c.—oil-cell; s.i.—silica; hyp. f.—hypodermal fibres.

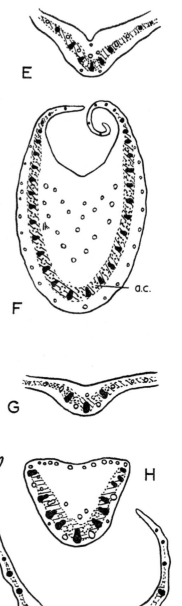

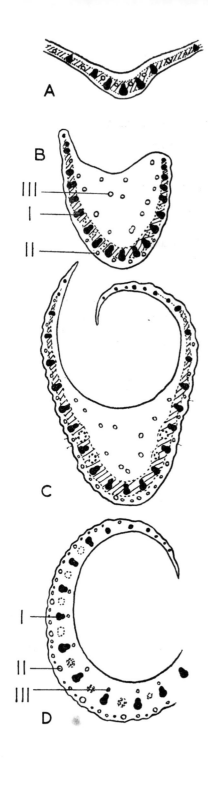

F<small>IG</small>. 78. ZINGIBERACEAE. T.S. leaf axis (after Tomlinson 1956).

A–D. *Elettaria cardamomum* (×7).

A. Midrib of lamina. B. Petiole. C. Upper part of leaf sheath. D. Lower part of leaf sheath.

E, F. *Kaempferia rotunda* (×7).

E. Midrib of lamina. F. Petiole.

G–I. *Globba winniti* (×13).

G. Midrib of lamina. H. Petiole. I. Upper part of leaf sheath.

a.c.—air-canal; I–III—bundle arcs (I—solid black); assimilating tissue—hatched.

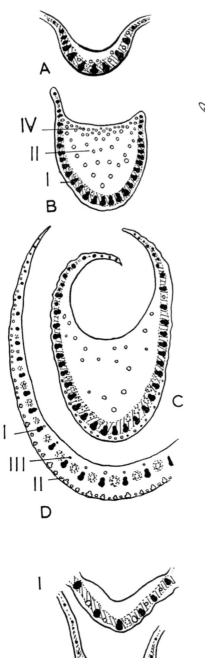

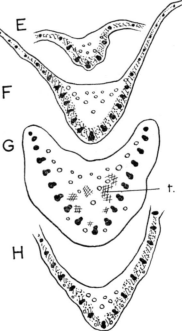

348

Fɪɢ. 79. ZINGIBERACEAE. T.S. leaf axis (after Tomlinson 1956).

A–D. *Alpinia javanica* (×13).

A. Midrib of lamina. B. Petiole. C. Upper part of leaf sheath. D. Lower part of leaf sheath.

E–H. *Zingiber officinale* (×7).

E. Midrib of lamina. F. Basal part of midrib. G. 'Pulvinus'. H. Upper part of leaf sheath.

I–K. *Roscoea* (×7).

I. *R. humeana*. Midrib of lamina. J. *R. purpurea*. Petiole. K. *R. purpurea*. Upper part of leaf sheath.

t.—tannin; I–IV—bundle arcs (I—solid black); assimilating tissue —hatched.

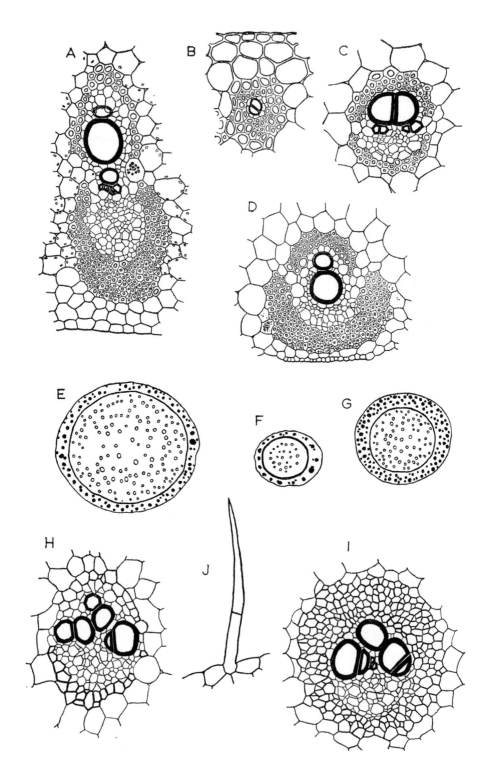

FIG. 80. ZINGIBERACEAE (after Tomlinson 1956).

A–D. *Alpinia speciosa.* T.S. vb's from petiole (×153).

A. Main arc I. B. Upper arc IV. C. Centre arc III. D. Lower arc II.

E–I. T.S. aerial stem.

E. *Hedychium gardnerianum* (×5). F. *Camptandra ovata* (×5). G. *Alpinia sanderae* (×5). H, I. *Alpinia speciosa* (×153). H. Bundle from central cylinder. I. Cortical bundle.

J. *Curcuma* sp. T.S. rhizome, 2-celled hair (×270).

extended and hexagonal (Fig. 77. A, B), otherwise more or less isodiametric and polygonal as in *Boesenbergia, Camptandra,* and *Scaphochlamys*; cells always most irregular in abaxial intercostal regions. Papillose epidermis rarely developed, except on adaxial surface of *Globba variabilis* and *Kaempferia rotunda.* Epidermal cells commonly v. large, especially in absence of colourless hypodermis as in *Camptandra, Elettariopsis* (Fig. 77. O), and *Kaempferia* (Fig. 77. L); walls never markedly thickened although outer wall usually thicker than remaining walls; anticlinal walls never markedly sinuous in surface view.

Stomata usually infrequent in adaxial surface and more or less restricted to abaxial intercostal regions. Each stoma (Fig. 77. F) with a pair of lateral subsidiary cells and often with a pair of terminal subsidiary cells. Other modified epidermal cells adjacent to stoma rare, except in *Boesenbergia* and *Camptandra* (Fig. 77. D), with subsidiary cells all shallower than deep epidermal cells. Guard cells never sunken, not symmetrical in T.S. because outer ledge always much larger than inconspicuous inner ledge, or inner ledge absent (Fig. 77. E).

Hypodermis of large, thin-walled, colourless cells common below one or both surfaces but varying in development in different parts of a single leaf; usually most well developed at lamina base and near midrib, least well developed at lamina apex and leaf margin. At a standard level, half-way between leaf base and apex and between midrib and margin, hypodermis either absent as in spp. of *Alpinia* and *Kaempferia* (Fig. 77. L); 1-layered beneath each surface as in *Aframomum, Geostachys* (Fig. 77. H), *Hedychium,* and *Renealmia*; present below adaxial surface only as in *Alpinia* (Fig. 77. M), *Hornstedtia,* and *Kaempferia* spp. (Fig. 77. K); present below abaxial surface only as in *Camptandra* (Fig. 77. J), *Globba* (Fig. 77. I), and *Zingiber*; or more than 1-layered below either surface as in *Brachychilum* (Fig. 77. G), *Hedychium,* and *Scaphochlamys.* Hypodermal cells in surface view either cubical or more usually transversely extended and hexagonal, except in costal regions; least regular in abaxial intercostal regions and not uniformly arranged around substomatal chambers. **Expansion cells,** causing unrolling of young leaf, developed by enlargement of hypodermal cells, either on each side of midrib as in *Alpinia javanica,* within midrib itself as in *A. exaltata* (Skutch 1930), or most commonly above larger veins of lamina. Isolated **fibres** or fibrous strands rarely present, but thin-walled fibres below adaxial epidermis recorded in *Elettariopsis,* short strands of adaxial hypodermal fibres observed in *Aframomum* and fibrous strands observed above, but not in contact with, main veins in *Renealmia* (Fig. 77. N).

Chlorenchyma usually including a 1–3-layered palisade of compact, anticlinally extended cells, but palisade indistinct and consisting of a single layer of short, conical cells, e.g. in spp. of *Camptandra* inhabiting dense shade. Abaxial mesophyll cells usually much lobed and producing a v. loose tissue. Longitudinal **veins** often rather distant, never v. congested, arranged in several orders of different sizes. Veins rarely independent of surface layers as in *Boesenbergia, Burbidgea, Camptandra* (Fig. 77. J), and *Scaphochlamys*; usually all vb's except smallest attached to abaxial surface and largest attached to both surfaces. In *Kaempferia* vb's mostly attached to adaxial surface only.

Bundle sheaths; O.S. parenchymatous 1(–2)-layered, complete around smallest veins independent of surface layers (Fig. 76. P), usually interrupted either below or both above and below larger veins (Fig. 76. O). Cells of O.S. always thin-walled, usually colourless and often elongated parallel to veins; sometimes including starch or silica. I.S. fibrous, sometimes thin-walled or even absent, as in *Boesenbergia* and *Camptandra* (Fig. 77. J); usually present above and below larger veins but present only below smaller veins; rarely forming narrow adaxial fibrous buttresses as in *Geostachys* (Fig. 77. H) and *Hornstedtia*. In *Renealmia* and occasionally in *Aframomum* larger veins often situated immediately below an independent strand of hypodermal fibres (Fig. 77. N). Vascular tissues including a single file of wide tracheal elements and several smaller abaxial late metaxylem elements; extended protoxylem present only in largest veins. Phloem strand always undivided. **Transverse veins** infrequent, narrow, independent of surface layers; each sheathed by a single layer of thin-walled cells.

(ii) *Leaf axis*

Leaf sheath always open although opposite margins overwrapping; always ending distally in a distinct **ligule,** the sheath either extending into a distinct petiole or else gradually confluent with lamina. Petiole in *Zingiber* short, fleshy and resembling a pulvinus. Thickened midrib, including several veins, usually extending to lamina apex, but sometimes veins all diverging into lamina at its base, the midrib region then not thickened and including only a single vein, as in *Burbidgea, Camptandra*. Outer surface of sheath often fluted owing to presence of ribs above peripheral bundles; epidermis of costal regions then often different from that of intercostal regions. Stomata and hairs often restricted to intercostal bands. Leaf axis including a single arc of abaxial **air-canals** extending from leaf insertion often well into midrib. Air-canals segmented at intervals by irregular transverse diaphragms of stellate cells or including a loose network of lobed cells, together with multi-layered diaphragms of both stellate and rounded cells, these thick septa including transverse veins. Air-canals pectinating with main veins and embedded in a distinct abaxial band of **chlorenchyma**; chlorenchyma of midrib continuous with that of lamina.

Vascular bundles arranged in 3 or 4 systems but not all systems equally developed at different levels. Main vb's (I) forming a single, conspicuous abaxial arc in all parts of leaf axis, pectinating with air-canals and embedded in chlorenchyma. Abaxial system (II) consisting of several arcs of vb's of different sizes, often pectinating with abaxial fibrous strands close to or in contact with abaxial surface, this layer, when well developed, forming a rigid peripheral zone as in *Alpinia, Hornstedtia,* and *Renealmia*. Abaxial bundles usually most well developed in leaf sheath, often absent from midrib and petiole, as in *Aframomum, Alpinia* (Fig. 79. A, B), and *Catimbium*; absent from leaf sheath in *Roscoea* (Fig. 79. K); present in distal part of leaf axis in *Brachychilum, Curcuma, Globba* (Fig. 78. H, I), *Hedychium,* and spp. of *Kaempferia*. Adaxial system (III) sometimes divisible into 2 separate systems (III and IV) as in petiole of *Alpinia* (Fig. 79. B), *Globba, Hedychium,* and *Hornstedtia*; usually well developed only in petiole and distal part of sheath; if

A a

present in leaf base usually visible only as a single arc of bundles, each bundle adaxial to a main arc bundle, as in *Alpinia* (Fig. 79. D) and *Elettaria* (Fig. 78 D). Adaxial system extending into midrib in *Alpinia, Elettaria, Globba, Hedychium*, and *Kaempferia*. Vb's of main and subsidiary arcs rarely at same level and pectinating, as in *Elettaria* (Fig. 78. A) and *Roscoea*. Main vb's (Fig. 80. A) each with a massive fibrous sheath above xylem and below phloem, a single file of wide tracheal elements, extended protoxylem, small late metaxylem elements and a single phloem strand. Phloem parenchyma cells often becoming sclerotic in *Hornstedtia*. Vb's of subsidiary arcs with reduced vascular tissues and usually without extended protoxylem. Abaxial bundles often with massive, almost complete fibrous sheaths (Fig. 80. D) or becoming purely fibrous strands before their blind endings. Adaxial bundles (Fig. 80. B, C) with or without well-developed fibrous sheaths and often with inverted vascular tissues. Bundle sheath cells collenchymatous in short, fleshy petiole of *Zingiber*; thin-walled in *Kaempferia*. Ground parenchyma cells usually v. uniform, but becoming v. sclerotic near abaxial surface in spp. of *Alpinia* and *Hornstedtia*.

Aerial Stem

(i) *Internode*

Cortex and central cylinder always distinct, usually separated from each other by a narrow fibrous cylinder (Fig. 80. E–G), except in *Globba*. **Cortex** fairly wide, including one (e.g. *Camptandra* (Fig. 80. F), *Globba*) or more (e.g. *Alpinia, Hedychium* (Fig. 80. E, G)) rings of vb's. Each cortical bundle (Fig. 80. I) with a complete, often massive fibrous sheath, usually widest next to phloem, but not in *Brachychilum*. Vascular tissues rarely inverted, including one or more files of wide tracheal elements and a single phloem strand. Cortical bundles somewhat congested in *Hornstedtia* to form a rigid mechanical zone. **Central cylinder** including many scattered vb's, each bundle without a well-developed fibrous sheath (Fig. 80. H).

(ii) *Node*

Main leaf traces entering stem gradually and not forming a vascular plexus, fibrous cylinder not markedly interrupted. Axillary buds present.

Rhizome

Segments usually quite short and fleshy, never fibrous or markedly stoloniferous, often v. short as in spp. of *Globba* and *Kaempferia*, the roots then becoming chief storage organs. Surface layers commonly suberized; suberization sometimes occurring only after formation of a kind of **periderm** by cell division in one or more layers; divisions rarely occurring in several cell layers separated by undivided, unsuberized layers. Rhizome differentiated into a wide **cortex** and a **central cylinder,** both regions including vb's with v. irregular distribution, their structure similar to that of vb's of aerial stem. Inner limit of cortex marked by a suberized but usually thin-walled **endodermoid layer.** Central cylinder with a peripheral plexus of irregular, congested vb's, the root traces inserted in this plexus. Central vb's sometimes congested but mechanical tissues usually poorly developed.

Root

Roots fleshy and tuberous in spp. of *Globba*, *Kaempferia*, and *Roscoea*; bearing localized tubers in *Curcuma*. **Exodermis** present as one or more layers of compact, suberized, but always thin-walled cells immediately below piliferous layer in mature roots. Superficial zone rarely with dividing cell layers resembling those in rhizome, as in *Globba* and *Kaempferia* spp. Narrow cylinder of thin-walled **fibres** sometimes differentiated immediately within exodermis as in *Elettaria* and especially in stout prop roots of some genera, e.g. *Hornstedtia*. Middle cortex rarely including conspicuous, radially-extended air-lacunae. Inner limit of cortex marked by a 1-layered **endodermis,** endodermal cells usually developing U-shaped thickenings in old roots. **Stele** including a thin-walled, 1-layered pericycle and a polyarch arrangement of vascular tissues. Phloem strands in some spp. often extended radially inwards, sometimes forming phloem islands as in *Hedychium*, *Hornstedtia*, and *Renealmia*. Peripheral ground tissues of stele usually fibrous; parenchymatous medulla commonly occupying central stele. Tuberous roots in *Globba*, *Kaempferia*, and *Roscoea* with a wide, starch-filled cortex but stele of same diameter as in non-tuberous roots.

Secretory, Storage, and Conducting Elements

Crystals of calcium oxalate common as prismatic, rhombohedral or tubular bodies associated with assimilating tissues and also common in colourless ground tissue cells, especially hypodermis of lamina. Crystalline material sometimes in the form of coarse sand as in *Roscoea*; sometimes in the form of large, solitary bodies as in hypodermal cells of lamina in *Globba*.

Silica common, either as sand or small, irregularly spherical bodies (Fig. 76. F, G), sometimes both together in a single cell. Silica-bodies nearly always in unmodified epidermal cells above and below main veins and almost restricted to tribe Alpinieae; internal silica-bodies observed only in *Kaempferia* spp. and in *Hornstedtia conica*. Silica-cells containing solitary silica-bodies, rarely with unevenly thickened walls and resembling true stegmata of related families. Silica sand in lamina usually in epidermal cells but not in cells of stomatal apparatus (Fig. 77. F), rarely internal, as in mesophyll of *Renealmia* and vein sheath of *Globba*. Sand not uncommon in other organs in ground parenchyma cells adjacent to vb's, but always absent from root.

Tannin common, mostly in cells of ground parenchyma in all parts; tannin-cells in lamina often larger than normal mesophyll cells. In *Zingiber*, elongated tannin-cells in files, resembling articulated laticifers, adjacent to vb's of stem and leaf. Tannin occasionally deposited in intercellular spaces.

Oil-cells abundant in ground parenchyma of all organs, common in epidermis of leaf, especially in lamina (Figs. 76. A, B, D 77. D;). Oil-cells small, more or less isodiametric (Fig. 76. C) and easily distinguishable from elongated ground parenchyma cells (Fig. 76. C); with suberized walls; each including a refractive body. Oil-cells recognizable close to apical meristems because differentiation completed v. early. In lamina, oil-cells most common in abaxial epidermis, uncommon in adaxial epidermis in *Kaempferia* spp. Cells resembling oil-cells, but with non-suberized walls, previously mistaken for aborted stomata.

Starch most abundant in rhizome and tuberous roots but common in stem and leaf axis near main vb's. Grains nearly always simple, often flattened as in *Globba, Hedychium,* and *Kaempferia,* rather irregular in outline; hilum often eccentric or situated in a projecting beak. Grains otherwise not flattened; spherical or ellipsoidal as in *Elettaria.*

Xylem. Vessels chiefly restricted to root and only recorded in stem of one sp.; elements with scalariform, oblique or v. oblique perforation plates, rarely with simple, transverse perforation plates, as in *Catimbium, Elettaria,* and *Elettariopsis.*

Phloem. Sieve-tubes probably always with simple sieve-plates, those in root situated on the most inclined end walls.

ECONOMIC USES

Ginger is the preserved rhizome of *Zingiber officinale* Rosc. and some other *Zingiber* spp. A yellow colouring matter, turmeric, and some kinds of curry powder are obtained from *Curcuma.* The seeds of *Elettaria cardamomum* Maton., known as cardamoms, are an important spice in India and the East. Those of some *Aframomum* spp. (Guinea grains) were once equally important. Members of the family find considerable local use in tropical countries as food (starchy rhizomes), spices, perfumes, and condiments (aromatic properties), dyes (coloured pigments), fibres (fibrous leaves), and even paper (flattened stems and sheaths). They are of some ornamental value and a few have found their way into the greenhouses of temperate countries.

TAXONOMIC NOTES

Elsewhere the anatomy of the Zingiberaceae (sens. lat.) has been described in greater detail (Tomlinson 1956) and there it is indicated that the two original subfamilies, Zingiberoideae and Costoideae, differ considerably in morphological, cytological, and palynological features, as well as in their anatomy. In comparison with other scitaminean families, the evidence for treating them also as two separate families is overwhelming (Tomlinson 1962).

Within the Zingiberaceae in this new narrow sense, the tribes cannot be recognized on an anatomical basis alone, although they do differ to some extent in the abundance of silica (Tomlinson 1956). It has been suggested in this earlier account that certain genera may possess diagnostic anatomical features. These include the arrangement of the vascular bundles in the leaf axis, the position and number of colourless hypodermal layers in the lamina, and the shape of the hairs.

GENERA AND SPECIES REPORTED ON IN THE LITERATURE

For most earlier literature see Solereder and Meyer (1930).

Barthelat (1893) *Alpinia calcarata, A. galanga, A. nutans, Amomum cardamomum, A. granum-paradisi, Curcuma leucorrhiza, C. longa, C. zedoaria, Hedychium coronarium, H. gardnerianum, Zingiber officinale*; all parts.

Becker (1931) *Brachychilum horsfieldii*; oil-cells.

Biermann (1898) *Curcuma zedoaria, Hedychium gardnerianum, Zingiber officinale*; oil cells.

Chakraverti (1939) *Curcuma longa* L.; rhizome.

Falkenberg (1876) *Hedychium gardnerianum*; stem.

Futterer (1896) *Alpinia nutans* Rosc., *Brachychilum horsfieldii* R. Br., *Curcuma amada* Roxb., *Globba humilis* Hort., *Hedychium coccineum* Buch.-Ham., *H. gardnerianum* Wall., *H. spicatum* Sm., *Kaempferia galanga* L., *K. gilberti* Hort., *Roscoea purpurea* Sm., *Zingiber casumunar* Roxb., *Z. officinale* Hortor. (ob Rosc. ?); all parts.

Lippitsch (1889) *Alpinia* sp., *Hedychium gardnerianum*; leaf.

Macfarlane (1892) *Hedychium* × *sadlerianum* and parents, *H. coronarium, H. gardnerianum*; leaf, starch.

Meyer (1881) *Alpinia calcarata, Curcuma longa* L., *C. zedoaria* Rosc., *Zingiber officinale* Rosc.; rhizome.

Petersen (1893) studied spp. of *Alpinia, Brachychilum, Cautleya, Elettaria, Globba, Hedychium, Kaempferia, Renealmia, Zingiber* (according to Solereder and Meyer).

Philipp (1923) *Alpinia calcarata, Curcuma longa, Zingiber officinale*.

Pillai *et al.* (1961) *Alpinia calcarata* Rosc., *Curcuma aromatica* Salisb., *C. longa* L., *Elettaria cardamomum* Salisb., *Hedychium coronarium* Koen., *Kaempferia galanga* L., *K. rotunda* L., *Zingiber officinale* Rosc., *Z. zerumbet* Rosc.; root apex.

Saito (1900) *Alpinia nutans* Rosc.; leaf.

Schlesinger (1895) studied lamina in spp. of *Alpinia, Amomum, Cautleya, Curcuma, Globba, Hedychium, Kaempferia, Renealmia, Roscoea, Zingiber* (according to Solereder and Meyer).

Skutch (1930) *Alpinia exaltata* (L.) R. and S.; leaf.

Solereder and Meyer (1930) *Alpinia allughas* Rosc., *A. japonica* Miq., *A. speciosa* K. Sch., *Donacodes pininga* Bl. (?*Hornstedtia* sp.), *Elettaria cardamomum* Maton, *Globba bulbifera* Roxb., *Hedychium gardnerianum* Rosc., *Kaempferia rotunda* L., *Phaeomeria magnifica* K. Sch., *Renealmia exaltata* L.f., *R. silvestris* Horan., *Zingiber casumunar* Roxb.; leaf.

Staudermann (1924) *Amomum pulchellum* Thwait., *Curcuma longa* L., *Globba marantina* L., *Hedychium coronarium* Koen., *Kaempferia rotunda* L., *Renealmia occidentalis* Gris., *Zingiber cylindricum* Moon; hairs.

Tomlinson (1956) see Material Examined by the Author.

Weber (1958) *Curcuma longa* L.; root.

Zacharias (1879) *Curcuma zedoaria, Globba marantinoides, Hedychium gardnerianum*; oil-cells.

MATERIAL EXAMINED BY THE AUTHOR

The above description is based on the following material, which also served as the basis for a previous article (Tomlinson 1956).

The main source of material was the greenhouses of the Royal Botanic Gardens, Kew, supplemented by pickled material of wild plants from Malaya, supplied by Dr. R. E. Holttum. Only the aerial parts of some spp. were available.

Aframomum sp.; *Alpinia javanica* Bl.; *A. sanderae* Hort.; *A. speciosa* K. Sch.; *Brachychilum horsfieldii* O. G. Peters.; *Burbidgea schizocheila* Hort.; *Camptandra ovata* Ridl.; *Catimbium latilabre* (Ridl.) Holtt.; *C. speciosum* (Wendl.) Holtt.; *Cautleya spicata* Bak.; *Curcuma domestica* Valet.; *Curcuma* sp.;

Elettaria cardamomum Maton.; *Elettariopsis curtisii* Bak.; *Geostachys taipingensis* Holtt.; *Globba bulbifera* Roxb.; *G. winniti* C. H. Wright; *Hedychium coccineum* Buch.-Ham. ex Sm. var. *angustifolium*; *H. elatum* R. Br.; *H. gardnerianum* Rosc.; *H. malayanum* Ridl.; *Hornstedtia conica* Ridl.; *H. scyphifera* (Koen.) Steud.; *Kaempferia angustifolia* Rosc.; *K. gilberti* Hort.; *K. kirkii* (Hook.) Witt. et Per.; *K. rotunda* L.; *Renealmia* sp.; *Roscoea cautleoides* Gagnep. var. *grandiflorum*; *R. humeana* Balf. et Sm.; *R. purpurea* Sm.; *Scaphochlamys breviscapa* Holtt.; *S. erecta* Holtt.; *S. rubromaculata* Holtt.; *Zingiber officinale* Rosc.

In addition to this material, the following spp. have been examined more recently (pickled material preserved at Kew).

Alpinia conchigera Griff.; collected by P. B. Tomlinson.
Boesenbergia prainiana (Bak.) Schlts.; Bukit-Timah, Singapore.
Camptandra parvula (King) Ridl.; collected by P. B. Tomlinson.
Globba leucantha Miq.; Bukit-Timah, Singapore.
G. variabilis Ridl.; Bukit-Timah, Singapore.
Hornstedtia scyphifera (Koen.) Steud.; Bukit-Timah, Singapore.
Kaempferia aethiopica Ridl.; collected by P. B. Tomlinson.
K. nigerica Hutch.; Enugu, Nigeria.
Renealmia exaltata L.; C. R. Metcalfe; West Indies.
Zingiber puberulum Ridl.; Singapore.

BIBLIOGRAPHY FOR ZINGIBERACEAE

BARTHELAT, G. J. (1893) *Contribution à l'étude histologique des Zingibéracées.* Ecol. sup. Pharmac. Paris. Thesis. pp. 86.

BECKER, R. (1931) Der Bau und die Entwicklungsgeschichte der Ölzellen und ihres Inhaltes, vornehmlich bei *Peperomia. Bot. Arch.* **33,** 48–81.

BIERMANN, R. (1898) *Ueber Bau und Entwicklung der Oelzellen und die Oelbildung in ihnen.* Diss. Bern. pp. 80; see *Arch. Pharm., Berl.* **236,** 74 (1898) and *Just's bot. Jber.* **26** (2), 14, no. 43 (1898)—original not seen.

CHAKRAVERTI, D. N. (1939) The occurrence of fugaceous cambium in the rhizome of *Curcuma longa* Linn. *Philipp. J. Sci.* **69,** 191–5.

FALKENBERG, P. (1876) *Vergleichende Untersuchungen über den Bau der Vegetationsorgane der Monocotyledonen.* Stuttgart. pp. 202.

FUTTERER, W. (1896) Beiträge zur Anatomie und Entwicklungsgeschichte der Zingiberaceae. *Bot. Zbl.* **68,** 241–8, 273–9, 346–56, 393–400, 416–31; **69,** 3–7, 35–46.

LIPPITSCH, C. (1889) Ueber das Einreißen der Laubblätter der Musaceen und einiger verwandter Pflanzen. *Öst. bot. Z.* **39,** 206–10, 259–63.

MACFARLANE, J. M. (1892) A comparison of the minute structure of plant hybrids with that of their parents and its bearing on biological problems. *Trans. R. Soc. Edinb.* **37,** 203–86.

MEYER, A. (1881) Beiträge zur Kenntniss pharmaceutisch wichtiger Gewächse. 2. Ueber die Rhizome der officinellen Zingiberaceen, *Curcuma longa* L., *C. Zedoaria* Roscoe, *Zingiber officinale* Roscoe, *Alpinia officinarum* Hance. *Arch. Pharm., Berl.* ser. 6, **15,** 401–29; see *Just's bot. Jber.* **9** (1), sec. 3, no. 68 (1881)—original not seen.

PETERSEN, O. G. (1893) Bidrag til Scitamineernes Anatomi. *K. danske vidensk. Selsk. Skr.* (6) **8,** 337–418; see *Just's bot. Jber.* **21** (1), 14, no. 111 (1893)—original not seen.

PHILIPP, M. (1923) Über die verkorkten Abschlußgewebe der Monokotylen. *Bibl. bot., Stuttgart* **23** (92), 1–30.

PILLAI, S. K., PILLAI, A., and SACHDEVA, S. (1961) Root apical organization in monocotyledons—Zingiberaceae. *Proc. Indian Acad. Sci.* B **53,** 240–56.

SAITO, K. (1900) Anatomische Studien über wichtige Faserpflanzen Japans mit besonderer Berücksichtigung der Bastzellen. *J. Coll. Sci. imp. Univ. Tokyo* **15**, 395–458.

SCHLESINGER, K. (1895) *Vergleichende Anatomie des Blattes der Marantaceen und Zingiberaceen.* Diss. Erlangen. pp. 74—original not seen.

SKUTCH, A. F. (1930) Unrolling of leaves of *Musa sapientum* and some related plants and their reactions to environmental aridity. *Bot. Gaz.* **90**, 337–65.

SOLEREDER, H., and MEYER, F. J. (1930) Zingiberaceae. In *Systematische Anatomie der Monokotyledonen*, Heft VI, 27–56.

STAUDERMANN, W. (1924) Die Haare der Monokotylen. *Bot. Arch.* **8**, 105–84.

TOMLINSON, P. B. (1956) Studies in the systematic anatomy of the Zingiberaceae. *J. Linn. Soc.* (Bot.) **55**, 547–92.

—— (1962) Phylogeny of the Scitamineae—morphological and anatomical considerations. *Evolution* **16**, 192–213.

WEBER, H. (1958) Die Wurzelverdickungen von *Calathea macrosepala* Schum. und von einigen anderen monocotylen Pflanzen. *Beitr. biol. Pfl.* **34**, 177–93.

WEISSE, A. (1932) Zur Kenntnis der Blattstellungsverhältnisse bei den Zingiberaceen. *Ber. dt. bot. Ges.* **50A**, 327–66.

—— (1933) Die Art der Distichie an den Achselsprossen von *Zingiber*. *Ber. dt. bot. Ges.* **51**, 13–20.

ZACHARIAS, E. (1879) Ueber Secret-Behälter mit verkorkten Membranen. *Bot. Ztg.* **39**, 617–28, 633–45.

COSTACEAE
(Fig. 81)

SUMMARY

A FORMER subfamily of Zingiberaceae, treated by Hutchinson merely as a tribe but which merits separate family status. It consists of 4 genera centred in South and Central America. *Costus* has a pan-tropical distribution although most of its species are American. *Tapeinochilus* is restricted to Ceram, Aru, New Guinea, and Queensland. *Monocostus* and *Dimerocostus* are American. All genera are markedly different in their vegetative morphology from the Zingiberaceae and a considerable range of life forms exists.

Aerial shoots often well developed, with distinct, rigid and commonly branched stems. Leaves inserted in a low spiral with divergences of the order of 1/5, 1/6, 1/7, etc., unlike any other flowering plants (Smith 1941, von Veh 1930). Leaf sheaths always tubular. Plants not aromatic. Some spp. of *Costus* with v. reduced aerial shoots. *Costus englerianus* outstanding because of absence of rhizome; creeping stems bearing scale leaves and a single terminal foliage leaf at any one time. The chief anatomical differences from Zingiberaceae are as follows: absence of oil-cells; frequent occurrence of uniseriate, multicellular hairs; different arrangement of vb's in stem and leaf; virtual absence of air-canals; stellate, druse-like silica-bodies restricted to internal cells next to vb's and never present in the epidermis. These differences amplified in the following brief notes.

LEAF

(i) *Lamina*

Hairs never sunken, sometimes short; either pointed, unicellular and thick-walled (Fig. 81. P), or commonly uniseriate, multicellular, long and rather thin-walled, as in *Costus malortieanus* (Fig. 81. Q, R) and at the leaf margin of *C. lucanusianus*. **Epidermis** without distinct costal bands above and below veins; always relatively shallow; longitudinal cell files not easily recognizable. Cells isodiametric, square or polygonal in surface view and never markedly elongated. **Stomata** (Fig. 81. D) often with several irregularly arranged subsidiary cells in addition to terminal and lateral subsidiary cells, as in *Costus englerianus*. **Hypodermis** always well developed below each surface, either as a single layer of v. large cells as in *Costus afer* (Fig. 81. A) or most commonly more than 1-layered below each surface (Fig. 81. B, C). **Chlorenchyma** always shallow (Fig. 81. C) but including a 1–2-layered palisade; in *Costus englerianus* including numerous large, colourless, slightly thick-walled starch-storage cells. **Veins** independent of surface layers. **Transverse veins** usually numerous, often with thin-walled fibres forming abaxial part of sheath.

(ii) *Leaf axis* (Fig. 81. E–K)

Sheath tubular (Fig. 81. H), extending into a short annular ligule; sometimes splitting by growth of axillant branch. Petiole, except in *Costus engle-*

rianus, always present, short, fleshy and articulated to sheath. Main vascular arc (I) embedded in chlorenchyma, in adaxial position in petiole (Fig. 81. F, J); subsidiary bundles (II) abaxial to main arc in petiole (Fig. 81 J.) and midrib and sometimes represented by a single vb. No adaxial subsidiary system present. Subsidiary vb's in leaf sheath pectinating with main bundles to form a single arc (Fig. 81. G). Air-canals absent from petiole and midrib, occasionally v. feebly developed at base of leaf sheath. Bundle sheaths of vb's in petiole usually composed of **collenchyma** (Fig. 81. K) but fibrous elsewhere. Hypodermal ground parenchyma cells of sheath always colourless, often enlarged, and simulating hypodermis of lamina.

AERIAL STEM

(i) *Internode* (Fig. 81. L, M)

Cortex v. narrow, sometimes only 2–3 cells wide; not including a discrete vascular system; sometimes including a layer of chlorenchyma. **Fibrous cylinder** usually sinuous in outline in T.S. Peripheral vb's mostly embedded in fibrous cylinder, each with a well-developed, complete fibrous sheath confluent with fibres of fibrous cylinder. Central vb's with poorly developed fibrous sheaths. Mechanical tissues collenchymatous in *Costus englerianus*.

(ii) *Node*

Nodal plexus of vascular tissues developed as a result of horizontal insertion of many leaf trace bundles and irregular anastomoses between them. Axillary buds usually developed.

RHIZOME AND ROOT

As in Zingiberaceae, see p. 354-5, but without oil-cells.

SECRETORY, STORAGE, AND CONDUCTING ELEMENTS

Silica present as solitary, stellate, or druse-like bodies (Fig. 81. N–O); silica-cells never epidermal. Silica-cells next to vb's in all parts except root, especially abundant in stem and rhizome and often forming an almost complete layer around each bundle; sometimes next to transverse veins, as in *Costus cylindricus* and *Tapeinochilus ananassae*; sometimes with unequal wall thickenings and then resembling true stegmata. Silica sand occasional.

Oil-cells absent.

Starch grains not flattened, often large and irregular, usually restricted to rhizome. In *Costus englerianus* starch found only in mesophyll of leaf and restricted to large colourless starch-storage cells.

Xylem. Vessels restricted to root.

TAXONOMIC NOTES

Reasons for treating the Costaceae as a separate family from the Zingiberaceae have already been presented (see p. 299). The subject is also discussed in two of the author's earlier papers (Tomlinson 1956, 1962). The Costaceae were first raised to the rank of a family by Nakai (1941).

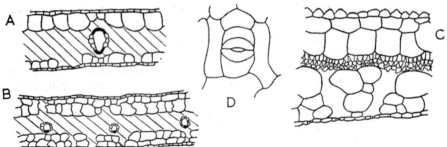

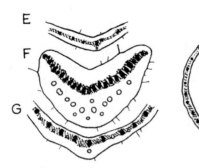

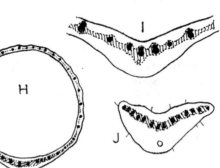

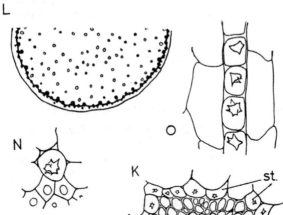

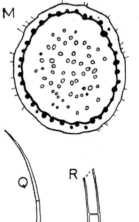

Fig. 81. COSTACEAE. *Costus* (after Tomlinson 1956).

A–C. T.S. lamina.

A. *C. afer* ($\times$ 57). B. *C. rumphianus* ($\times$ 48). C. *C. malortieanus* ($\times$ 57).

D. *C. lucanusianus*. Stoma, abaxial epidermis, surface view ($\times$ 327).

E–K. T.S. leaf axis; main arc (I) bundles—solid black.

E–H. *C. malortieanus* ($\times$ 5). E. Midrib of lamina. F. Petiole. G. Median sector of leaf sheath. H. Leaf sheath. I. *C. afer*. Midrib of lamina ($\times$ 10). J. *C. lucanusianus*. Petiole ($\times$ 10). K. *C. malortieanus*. Petiole, vb of abaxial arc ($\times$ 153); with well-developed collenchyma.

L, M. T.S. stem ($\times$ 5).

L. *C. lucanusianus*. Lower part of aerial stem. M. *C. malortieanus*. Upper part of aerial stem.

N, O. *C. lucanusianus*. Stegmata from aerial stem.

N. T.S. ($\times$ 417), fibres of cortical bundle. O. L.S. ($\times$ 317).

P–R. Hairs.

P. *C. lucanusianus*. Unicellular hair from abaxial epidermis of lamina, in surface view ($\times$ 383). Q, R. *C. malortieanus*. Q. Multicellular hair from lower epidermis of lamina ($\times$ 95). R. Basal part of hair from T.S. lower part of sheath ($\times$ 383).

In A and B assimilating tissue hatched; fibrous tissue—solid black.

In K, st.—stegmata.

GENERA AND SPECIES REPORTED ON IN THE LITERATURE

For most earlier literature see Solereder and Meyer (1930).

Barthelat (1893) *Costus villosus*; all parts.
Futterer (1896) *Costus malortieanus* H. Wendl.; all parts.
Petersen (1893) *Costus* (according to Solereder and Meyer).
Pillai *et al.* (1961) *Costus speciosus* Sm.; root apex.
Schlesinger (1895) lamina of *Costus* (according to Solereder and Meyer).
Smith (1941) *Costus elegans* Hort. ex Peters., *C. tappenbeckianus* J. Braun and K. Schum.; shoot apex.
Solereder and Meyer (1930) *Costus speciosus* Sm. var. *sericea* K. Schum.; lamina.
Staudermann (1924) *Costus glabratus* Sw., *Tapeinochilus hollrungii* K. Schum.; hairs.
Tomlinson (1956) see Material Examined by the Author.

MATERIAL EXAMINED BY THE AUTHOR

The above description is based partly on the following material, which also served as the basis for a previous article (Tomlinson 1956).

The main source of material was the greenhouses of the Royal Botanic Gardens, Kew. Only the aerial parts of some spp. were available.

Costus afer Ker.-Gawl.; *C. discolor* Rosc.; *C. lucanusianus* J. Braun and K. Schum.; *C. malortieanus* Wendl.; *C. rumphianus* Valet. ex Heyne; *C. tappenbeckianus* J. Braun and K. Schum.

In addition to this material, the following spp. have been examined more recently (pickled material preserved at Kew).

Costus cylindricus Rosc.; C. R. Metcalfe s.n.; West Indies.
C. englerianus K. Schum.; P. B. Tomlinson s.n.; Ghana.
C. speciosus (Koen.) Sm.; Hort. Kew.
Tapeinochilus ananassae K. Schum.; Hort. Kew.

BIBLIOGRAPHY FOR COSTACEAE

BARTHELAT, G. J. (1893) *Contribution à l'étude histologique des Zingibéracées.* Ecol. sup. Pharmac. Paris. Thesis. pp. 86.
FUTTERER, W. (1896) Beiträge zur Anatomie und Entwicklungsgeschichte der Zingiberaceae. *Bot. Zbl.* **68**, 241–8, 273–9, 346–56, 393–400, 416–31; **69**, 3–7, 35–46.
NAKAI, T. (1941) Notulae ad plantas Asiae orientalis (XVI). *J. Jap. Bot.* **17**, 189–210.
PETERSEN, O. G. (1893) Bidrag til Scitamineernes Anatomi. *K. danske vidensk. Selsk. Skr.* (6) **8**, 337–418; see *Just's bot. Jber.* **21** (1), 14, no. 111 (1893)—original not seen.
PILLAI, S. K., PILLAI, A., and SACHDEVA, S. (1961) Root apical organization in monocotyledons—Zingiberaceae. *Proc. Indian Acad. Sci.* B **53**, 240–56.
SCHLESINGER, K. (1895) *Vergleichende Anatomie des Blattes der Marantaceen und Zingiberaceen.* Diss. Erlangen. pp. 74—original not seen.
SMITH, B. M. (1941) The phyllotaxis of *Costus* from the standpoint of development. *Proc. Leeds phil. lit. Soc.* **4**, 42–63.
SOLEREDER, H., and MEYER, F. J. (1930) Zingiberaceae. In *Systematische Anatomie der Monokotyledonen,* Heft VI, 27–56.
STAUDERMANN, W. (1924) Die Haare der Monokotylen. *Bot. Arch.* **8**, 105–84.
TOMLINSON, P. B. (1956) Studies in the systematic anatomy of the Zingiberaceae. *J. Linn. Soc.* (Bot.) **55**, 547–92.
—— (1962) Phylogeny of the Scitamineae—morphological and anatomical considerations. *Evolution* **16**, 192–213.
VEH, R. VON (1930) Untersuchungen und Betrachtungen zum Blattstellungsproblem. *Flora, Jena* **125**, 83–154.

CANNACEAE
(Figs. 82–83)

Summary

A MONOTYPIC family originating in America, the one genus *Canna* including about 50 species, some now widely distributed throughout the tropics and many hybrids cultivated in more temperate countries. The habit is very uniform, with a fleshy, underground, sympodially branched rhizome bearing distichous scale leaves, each rhizome segment ending in a leafy shoot. Each aerial shoot has a well-developed stem with a distichous arrangement of leaves, those at the base of the stem being represented by bladeless sheaths but with a transition to the distal foliage leaves. The inflorescence is terminal on the leafy shoot.

Anatomical features characteristic of the family include the absence of hairs, an epidermis composed of alternating files of wide and narrow cells, a colourless hypodermal layer beneath each surface of the lamina, a layer of **'oblique-cells'** commonly developed in the petiole and midrib. Aerial stem without clear boundary between cortex and central cylinder. Stem and rhizome with conspicuous **mucilage canals** or cavities. Starch grains flattened and **silica** present in the form of stellate or druse-like silica-bodies in thin-walled cells adjacent to vb's.

Leaf

(i) *Lamina*

Rolled in bud. Usually dorsiventral but sometimes almost isolateral. **Hairs** absent from all the material so far examined. **Cuticle** v. thin and inconspicuous. **Epidermis** with infrequent costal bands of small cells above the largest veins, costal bands more frequent abaxially, below the veins. Wide intercostal regions (Fig. 82. A, B) including rather irregular bands of 1–2 files of narrow, rectangular longitudinally extended cells alternating with single or less commonly double files of wide, transversely extended cells visible in T.S. as alternate wide and narrow cells. Anticlinal walls of epidermal cells not sinuous.

Stomata often abundant on adaxial surface but usually most frequent on abaxial surface, always restricted to files of wide cells in intercostal regions. Each stoma with a pair of narrow lateral subsidiary cells but no distinct terminal subsidiary cells; guard cells each with 2 prominent cutinized ledges (Fig. 82. D), outer not usually significantly larger than inner ledge. **Hypodermis** of colourless, thin-walled cells, 1-layered below each surface (Fig. 82. C, E, F); cells transversely extended and usually hexagonal in surface view, those of adaxial hypodermis most regular. Substomatal chambers not surrounded by constant arrangement of hypodermal cells.

Chlorenchyma always with a distinct adaxial palisade, less commonly with a palisade-like layer adjacent to abaxial hypodermis, as recorded for *C. orientalis*. Spongy mesophyll cells v. loose, much lobed, and often extending

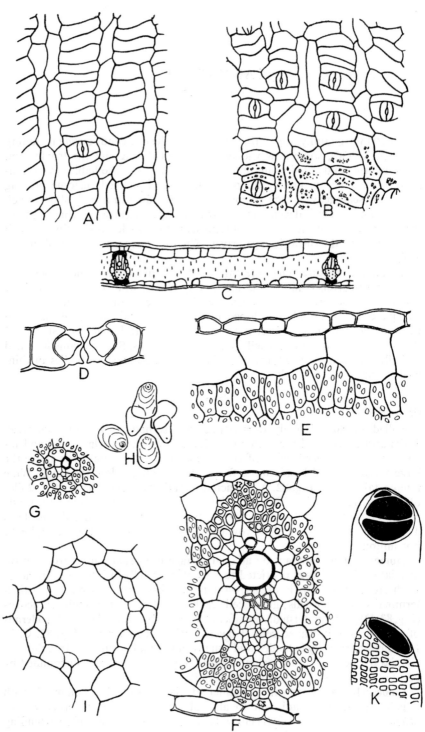

366

Fig. 82. CANNACEAE (after Tomlinson 1961).

A–G. Lamina of *Canna* sp.

A–B. Epidermis, surface view (×150). A. Adaxial. B. Abaxial; crystal sand drawn only in a few cells. C–F. T.S. C. (×60). Assimilating tissue—short lines; epidermal cells not drawn. D. Stoma from abaxial surface (×660). E. Adaxial surface layers (×250). F. Main vein (×150). G. T.S. transverse commissure from L.S. of lamina (×250).

H. Starch grains from rhizome (×120).

I. T.S. mucilage canal from internode of aerial stem (×250).

J, K. Vessel elements from root (×150).

J. Perforation plate with 2 thickening bars. K. Simple perforation plate.

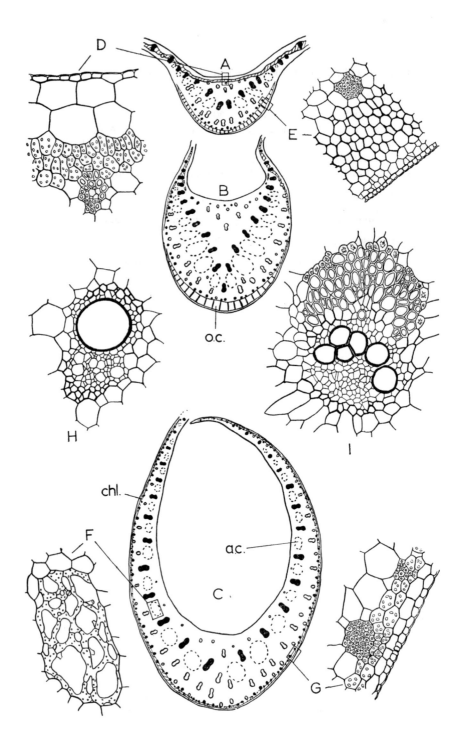

O.C.

chl.

a.c.

F<small>IG</small>. 83. CANNACEAE (after Tomlinson 1961).

A–C. Leaf axis in T.S. at successively lower levels (×6). Main arc (I) bundles—solid black.

A. Midrib half-way between base and apex of lamina. B. Petiole just below insertion of lamina. C. Sheathing leaf base.

D–G. Details of A and C (×120).

D. Adaxial part of midrib. E. Abaxial part of midrib. F. Air-canal from leaf sheath. G. Abaxial part of leaf sheath.

H. T.S. central vb from internode of aerial stem (×120).

I. T.S. vb from centre of rhizome (×120); starch grains omitted.

o.c.—oblique-cells; a.c.—air-canal; chl.—chlorenchyma.

across suostomatal chambers. **Longitudinal veins** rather diffuse, arranged in several orders of differing size. Largest veins (Fig. 82. F) attached to each surface by conspicuous fibrous buttresses, smallest veins independent of surface layers, other veins attached either to each surface or to abaxial surface only, veins never in contact with epidermis although often separated from it only by small silica-cells. Smallest veins completely sheathed by colourless parenchyma, other veins with only a partial, lateral parenchyma sheath. Inner fibrous sheath usually well developed above and below largest veins but less conspicuous and often present only below smaller veins, absent from smallest veins. Largest veins with extended protoxylem, a single file of wide metaxylem elements and narrow late metaxylem elements together with a single phloem strand. **Transverse veins** numerous, equidistant from and independent of each surface, sheathed by parenchyma (Fig. 82. G). Leaf expansion from bud described by Löv (1926) and Skutch (1930).

(ii) *Leaf axis*

Midrib, petiole, and leaf sheath distinct but gradually confluent and not articulated; ligule absent. **Epidermis** of rectangular, elongated cells including occasional stomata but no hairs. **Oblique-cells** present in most species as elongated cells with rounded ends, more or less hexagonal in T.S., arranged obliquely to the long axis and forming an abaxial hypodermal tissue in the midrib (Fig. 83. E) but ending somewhat abruptly in the petiole. **Air-lacunae** (Fig. 83. A–C) arranged in a single arc extending from the leaf base to the distal part of the midrib. Each canal traversed at long intervals by multiseriate diaphragms of isodiametric cells enclosing large intercellular spaces, the diaphragms often including transverse veins. Canals also plugged at more frequent intervals by a v. loose tissue of irregularly stellate cells forming indistinct septa, the septa connected by vertically extended cells. The cells of both of these types of tissue often containing small chloroplasts (Fig. 83. F).

Longitudinal veins arranged in three distinct systems. A main system (I) in the form of a single arc of large vb's pectinating with but adaxial to the air-canals. A subsidiary abaxial system (II) of several pectinating arcs of large and small vb's, the largest, most adaxial vb's v. similar to those of the main arc. A small adaxial system (III), often of inverted vb's, most conspicuous in the petiole. Structure of main and subsidiary vb's resembling that of the vb's of the Zingiberaceae. Small bundles, nearest to abaxial surface, often completely sheathed by fibres and pectinating with a system of large or small **fibrous strands** still closer to the abaxial surface (Fig. 83. C). Bundle sheaths often collenchymatous near leaf insertion. **Chlorenchyma** in midrib present as an adaxial band continuous with that of lamina (Fig. 83. D), but in leaf sheath represented by an abaxial band separated from epidermis by a single colourless hypodermal layer and frequently including fibrous strands.

AERIAL STEM

(i) *Internode*

Epidermis similar to that of abaxial surface of leaf axis. Boundary between cortex and central cylinder not differentiated. **Chlorenchyma** present as a narrow layer of small cells separated from epidermis by 1–2 layers of colourless hypodermal cells. Peripheral vb's with well-developed fibrous sheaths, pectinating with **fibrous strands** to form a weak mechanical zone. Largest peripheral vb's like those of the main arc (I) of the leaf, but smaller and with reduced vascular tissues. **Central vascular bundles** (Fig. 83. H) irregularly scattered, either without sheathing fibres or at the most with a little thick-walled prosenchyma adjacent to xylem and phloem; each vb provided with a single file of wide metaxylem elements; only the largest vb's with extended protoxylem. Ground tissue including numerous **mucilage canals** (Fig. 82. I).

(ii) *Node*

Slightly constricted, including a vascular plexus of many horizontal, girdling and anastomosing bundles. Main leaf traces entering the stem abruptly and said by Falkenberg (1876) to exhibit the 'palm-type' of distribution in the stem. Large **mucilage cavities** abundant and continuous with mucilage canals of the internode.

Rhizome

Epidermis not cutinized. **Cortex** narrow, including scattered vb's; fibrous sheaths of cortical bundles well developed next to xylem and still more so next to phloem. Fibrous strands sometimes present in outer cortex as in *C. edulis*. Cortical vb's of rhizome said by Guillaud (1878) to be independent of vascular system of central cylinder. **Central cylinder** delimited from cortex by an indistinct **endodermoid layer** surrounding a narrow zone of small cells with girdling and anastomosing vascular strands embedded in it. Central vb's (Fig. 83. I) each with several files of tracheal elements. Fibrous bundle sheaths well developed only around the phloem. **Mucilage canals** common, especially near periphery of central cylinder, but larger and more irregular than those of aerial stem.

Root

Cortex including a compact peripheral **exodermis** of small, slightly suberized cells but no fibres. Innermost cortical cells v. regularly arranged and sometimes thick-walled. **Endodermis** becoming conspicuously thick-walled only in old roots. Pericycle 1-layered. **Stele** with typical polyarch arrangement of vascular tissues; not including a central parenchymatous medulla.

Secretory, Storage, and Conducting Elements

Crystals of calcium oxalate common in ground tissues of all organs as rhombohedral bodies, sometimes forming a coarse sand, as recorded for *C. coccinea*.

Albuminous crystals recorded in chloroplasts of *C. gigantea* and leucoplasts of *C. warscewiczii* by Solereder and Meyer (1930).

Silica common as druse-like, stellate bodies in all parts except root, each in a small thin-walled cell; silica-cells in long, continuous files adjacent to fibres of bundle sheaths; in lamina commonly in a hypodermal position but never in epidermis.

Tannin common in structurally unmodified parenchyma cells in all organs, but most frequent in stem.

Starch abundant in ground parenchyma of rhizome; grains (Fig. 82. H) flattened, ellipsoidal, eccentric, and often striated; 60–70 μm long, but up to 130 μm long in *C. edulis* and *C. indica*.

Anthocyanin in vacuoles of epidermal cells imparting a reddish colour to aerial parts of some spp.

Mucilage, said to include crystalline material, exuding at cut surfaces from mucilage canals in aerial stem and rhizome. Canals in aerial stem (Fig. 82. I) long, unbranched, anastomosing, and widening into cavities at nodes; in rhizome canals wider and more irregular. Each canal with a central mucilage-filled cavity surrounded by small secretory cells, the cavity originating either lysigenously (Lutz 1897) or possibly also schizogenously (Leblois 1887).

Xylem. Vessels present in root, usually with simple perforation plates on transverse or slightly oblique end walls (Fig. 82. K), or occasionally with scalariform perforation plates having few thickening bars (Fig. 82. J). Elements in stem perforated, but end walls scarcely different from those of imperforate tracheids.

ECONOMIC USES

Canna edulis Ker.-Gawl. (Queensland Arrowroot) is a native of the West Indies but is cultivated in Australia, the Pacific Islands, and parts of Asia for its starchy rhizomes, which are either consumed as a vegetable or used in starch extraction. The starch is easily digested, as is that of the true Arrow-root (*Maranta arundinacea*; see Marantaceae on p. 386). *Canna indica* L. has a similar use. Many hybrids, mostly originating from *C. indica*, are widely cultivated as ornamentals, even at quite high latitudes. Some spp. tend to grow as weeds.

TAXONOMIC NOTES

The anatomy of the family has been briefly discussed in relation to its systematic position by Tomlinson (1961). The chief single structural feature in which the Cannaceae differ from other families of the Scitamineae is in the presence of wide mucilage canals in the stem and rhizome, but *Canna* can also be distinguished by a unique combination of anatomical characters. Some of these individual diagnostic features are also found distributed at random in the remaining scitaminean families but not in a way to indicate any close relationship between any one of these families and the Cannaceae.

SPECIES REPORTED ON IN THE LITERATURE

For most earlier literature see Solereder and Meyer (1930).

Falkenberg (1876) *Canna indica*; stem.
Guillaud (1878) *Canna indica* L.; stem.
Leblois (1887) *Canna sanguinea, C. zebrina*; stem.
Lippitsch (1889) *Canna indica, C. iridiflora*; leaf.
Löv (1926) *Canna flaccida*; leaf.
Lutz (1897) *Canna* sp.; stem.

Petersen (1893) numerous *Canna* spp. (according to Solereder and Meyer).
Skutch (1930) *Canna* sp.; leaf.
Solereder and Meyer (1930) *Canna indica* L.; all parts.
Tomlinson (1961) see Material Examined by the Author.

MATERIAL EXAMINED BY THE AUTHOR

The above description is based partly on the following material, which also served as the basis for a previous article (Tomlinson 1961). Material cultivated at Achimota, Ghana (all parts).

Canna coccinea Mill.; *C. indica* L.; *C. orientalis* Rosc.; *Canna* hybrid (unnamed).

In addition to this material, *C. edulis* Ker.-Gawl.; T. G. Walker s.n.; Ceylon, was examined (pickled material preserved at Kew).

BIBLIOGRAPHY FOR CANNACEAE

FALKENBERG, P. (1876) *Vergleichende Untersuchungen über den Bau der Vegetationsorgane der Monocotyledonen.* Stuttgart. pp. 202.

GUILLAUD, A. (1878) Recherches sur l'anatomie comparée et le développement des tissus de la tige dans les monocotylédones. *Ann. Sci. nat.* Bot. sér. 6, **5**, 5–176.

LEBLOIS, A. (1887) Recherches sur l'origine et le développement des canaux sécréteurs et des poches sécrétrices. *Ann. sci. nat.* Bot. sér. 7, **6**, 247–330.

LIPPITSCH, C. (1889) Ueber das Einreißen der Laubblätter der Musaceen und einiger verwandter Pflanzen. *Öst. bot. Z.* **39**, 206–10, 259–63.

LÖV, L. (1926) Zur Kenntnis der Entfaltungszellen monokotyler Blätter. *Flora, Jena* **120**, 283–343.

LUTZ, L. (1897) Gomme de *Canna. Bull. Soc. bot. Fr.* **44**, xlviii–li.

PETERSEN, O. G. (1893) Bidrag til Scitamineernes Anatomi. *K. danske vidensk. Selsk. Skr.* (6) **8**, 337–418; see *Just's bot. Jber.* **21** (1), 14, no. 111 (1893)—original not seen.

SKUTCH, A. F. (1930) Unrolling of leaves of *Musa sapientum* and some related plants and their reactions to environmental aridity. *Bot. Gaz.* **90**, 337–65.

SOLEREDER, H., and MEYER, F. J. (1930) Cannaceae. In *Systematische Anatomie der Monokotyledonen*, Heft VI, 56–62.

TOMLINSON, P. B. (1961) The anatomy of *Canna. J. Linn. Soc.* (Bot.) **56**, 467–73.

MARANTACEAE

(Figs. 84–86)

SUMMARY

A TROPICAL family of some 30 genera and 800 species with centres of distribution in America (tribe Maranteae) and in the Old World (tribe Calatheae). Members of the family are common in the undergrowth of primary forest, but also occur in secondary vegetation. The family is herbaceous and the species perennate by means of sympodially branched rhizomes which bear the erect shoots. These commonly branch in a very complex but always well-ordered fashion, and in some species have a scrambling or semi-scandent, bamboo-like habit, as in *Hypselodelphis*, *Ischnosiphon*, and *Trachyphrynium*. On the other hand, many species of *Calathea* and *Maranta* have reduced aerial shoots without conspicuous stems. In spite of this wide range of habit forms in the Marantaceae, the branch units have a very constant arrangement of parts (Schumann 1902, Tomlinson 1961). Aerial shoots are seldom dimorphic, with separate leafy and flowering shoots, as in species of *Calathea* and *Stachyphrynium*. Leafy shoots are of two kinds according to whether the shoot bears either only one or two kinds of leaf, the type of shoot being constant for each species. The two kinds of leaf differ in whether one-half of the blade is rolled innermost or outermost in bud, there often being a corresponding asymmetry of the fully expanded blade. Shoots may then be *homotropous* when they bear only 1 kind of leaf, or *antitropous* when 2 kinds of leaf occur. Members of this family can easily be recognized in the vegetative state because of a characteristic callus or **pulvinus** of swollen tissue at the distal end of the petiole, just below the insertion of the lamina. Variegated leaf blades are common.

Hairs common, unicellular, unbranched, distinctive because of base surrounded by a cushion of inflated epidermal cells. **Epidermis**: cells in surface view characteristically with sinuous anticlinal walls and often papillose. **Hypodermis** of a single layer of colourless cells always developed below each surface of the lamina. **Transverse veins** in lamina numerous and v. congested and always partly sheathed by thin-walled fibres. Leaf axis including an arc of **air-canals** and typically a peripheral mechanical zone. Pulvinus always including a wide subhypodermal tissue of 'oblique-cells'; mechanical tissues weakly developed. **Stem** with a peripheral mechanical zone similar to that of leaf axis, but otherwise without a distinction between cortex and central cylinder. Rhizome characterized by **endodermoid layer** between cortex and central cylinder. Root often including cortical air-lacunae; **phloem islands** not uncommon in stele. **Silica** commonly present in all parts except root, either as hat-shaped bodies in cells with unevenly thickened walls, i.e. **stegmata,** adjacent to vb's but never in epidermis; or as thin-walled, often large and usually colourless, isodiametric and idioblastic cells in mesophyll of lamina. Starch grains ellipsoidal and slightly eccentric, rarely flattened or angular.

HAIRS

Often absent, e.g. in *Halopegia, Megaphrynium, Stromanthe, Thalia, Thaumatococcus*, and *Trachyphrynium*; sometimes restricted to leaf margins or midrib; common on leaf sheath and abaxial surface of lamina and sometimes restricted to costal regions. Hairs also common on rhizome and rhizome scales. Individual hairs (Fig. 84. E, F) almost always unicellular, simple, acicular, and somewhat thick-walled but usually short; base constricted at leaf surface and characteristically embedded in a cushion of swollen epidermal cells, the swelling of these cells apparently causing erection of hairs otherwise adpressed in immature leaves. Hairs rarely septate as in *Monotagma* and rhizome of *Megaphrynium* and *Sarcophrynium*. Hairs on pulvinus sometimes conspicuously different from those elsewhere, as in *Monotagma spicatum* (Fig. 85. H).

LEAF

(i) *Lamina*

Rolled in bud. Dorsiventral. **Epidermis** consisting of costal bands of small cells above and below veins, separated by wide intercostal bands. Cells irregular in surface view because of markedly sinuous anticlinal walls (Fig. 84. A, B), but usually more or less rectangular and either longitudinally or transversely extended; sometimes isodiametric (Fig. 84. K) as in spp. of *Calathea* and *Maranta*. Epidermal cells commonly papillose (Fig. 84. J), especially on abaxial surface. In *Monotagma spicatum* lumen of epidermal cells commonly occluded by massive wall thickenings. **Stomata** infrequent in adaxial surface and mostly restricted to abaxial intercostal bands. Stomata not sunken but sometimes provided with a distinct outer chamber surrounded by epidermal papillae. Lateral subsidiary cells always present as 2 deep narrow cells with non-sinuous walls (Fig. 84. G). Guard cells (Fig. 84. H) each with a well-developed outer ledge; inner ledge usually inconspicuous, except in *Monotagma, Ischnosiphon*, and *Thalia*; ledges equal in *Thalia welwitschii* (Fig. 84. I). Lumina of guard cells constricted by wall thickenings except at thin-walled poles.

Hypodermis of a single, thin-walled layer of colourless cells always present beneath each surface; adaxial usually more conspicuous than abaxial hypodermis, except in some *Calathea* spp. Cells usually hexagonal and transversely extended in surface view, but often almost cubical in *Calathea*; abaxial cells least regular, not uniformly arranged around substomatal chambers. Hypodermal cells at junction of lamina and midrib and above largest veins functioning as **expansion cells,** the hypodermis sometimes 2-layered in these regions (Skutch 1930).

Chlorenchyma usually occupying one-half of total depth of lamina but often v. reduced in shade-dwelling spp., as in *Calathea*. Palisade of 1–3 layers, often of conical cells, usually differentiated from abaxial spongy mesophyll. **Longitudinal veins** v. uniformly and distantly spaced, not easily divisible into different orders on the basis of size except for main veins each with a well-developed fibrous sheath and extended protoxylem. Veins almost always attached to each hypodermis by fibres (Fig. 84. D); largest veins separated from epidermis only by inconspicuous silica-cells; smallest veins sometimes

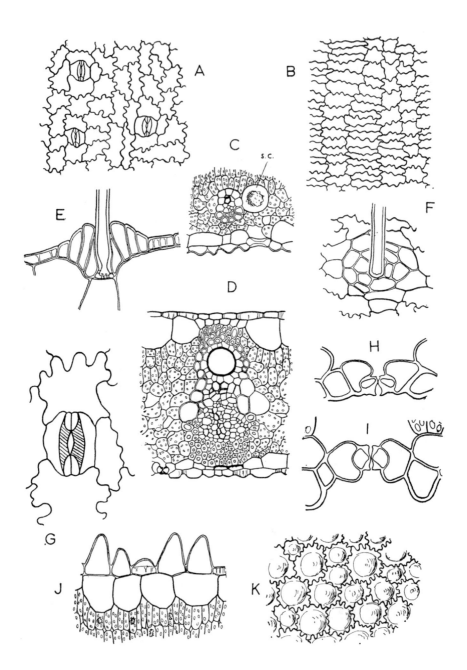

FIG. 84. MARANTACEAE. Leaf (after Tomlinson 1961).

A, B. *Ischnosiphon aruma.* Epidermis of lamina in surface view
($\times$ 220).

A. Abaxial. B. Adaxial.

C, D. *Marantochloa mannii.*

C. L.S. lamina, transverse vein in T.S. with associated silica-cell
($\times$220). D. T.S. longitudinal vein of lamina ($\times$280).

E, F. *Maranta arundinacea.* Hairs ($\times$220).

E. T.S. adaxial surface of lamina with hair base. F. Adaxial surface
view of lamina.

G, H. *Sarcophrynium brachystachyum.* Stoma from lamina ($\times$760).

G. Adaxial surface view. H. T.S. abaxial surface.

I. *Thalia welwitschii.* T.S. stoma from abaxial surface of lamina ($\times$760).

J, K. *Calathea zebrina.* Adaxial surface of lamina ($\times$220).

J. T.S. K. Surface view.

s.c.—silica-cell.

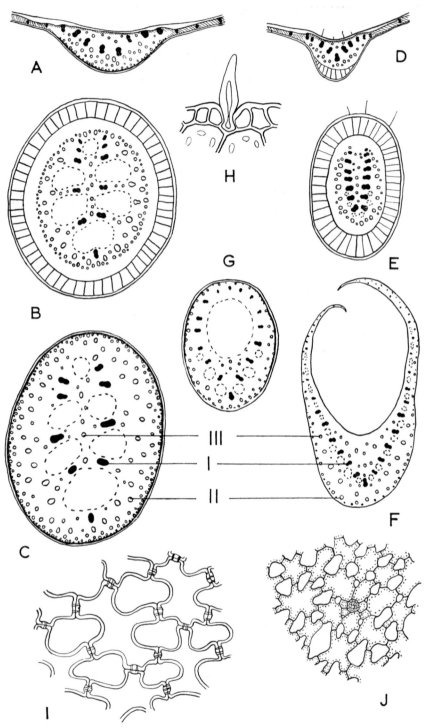

Fɪɢ. 85. MARANTACEAE. Leaf (after Tomlinson 1961).

A–G. T.S. leaf axis at different levels; main arc (I) bundles—solid black (×7½).

A–C. *Thaumatococcus daniellii*. A. Midrib of lamina. B. Pulvinus. C. Petiole. D–F. *Calathea zebrina*. D. Midrib of lamina. E. Pulvinus. F. Leaf sheath. G. *Halopegia azurea*. Petiole.

H. *Monotagma spicatum*. T.S. hair from adaxial surface of pulvinus (×550).

I, J. Diaphragm cells as seen in T.S. leaf axis (×280).

I. *Calathea lutea*. T.S. petiole, thick-walled cells. J. *Thalia welwitschii*. T.S. leaf sheath, thin-walled cells and fibrous strand.

I–III—vb arcs (see text); chlorenchyma hatched in A and D; oblique cells as radiating lines in B, D, and E.

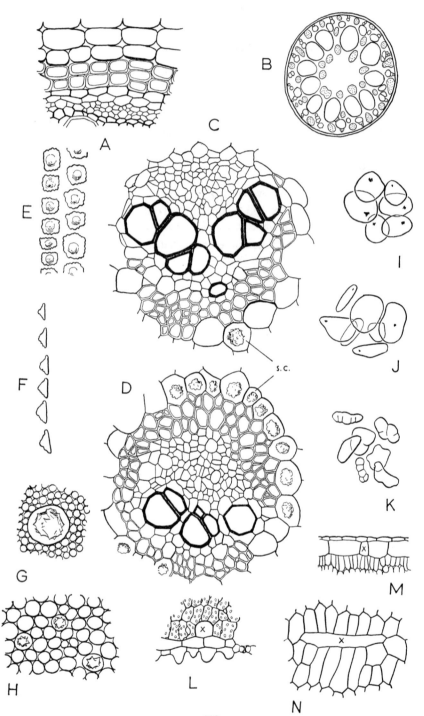

s.c.

FIG. 86. MARANTACEAE (after Tomlinson 1961).

A, B. T.S. root.

A. *Megaphrynium macrostachyum.* Innermost cortical layers and periphery of stele (× 280). B. *Thaumatococcus daniellii.* Stele; vessels out-lined, phloem stippled (× 50).

C, D. *Sarcophrynium brachystachyum.* T.S. vb's from rhizome (× 220).

C. Central cylinder. D. Cortex.

E–H. Silica.

E. *Marantochloa mannii.* Silica-bodies in surface view from a file of stegmata below a longitudinal vein of lamina (× 440). F. *Donax grandis.* Silica-bodies in optical section from a file of stegmata adjacent to a transverse vein of lamina (× 440). G. *Hypselodelphis violacea.* Silica-cell in palisade of lamina seen in paradermal view (× 280). H. *Calathea lutea.* Silica-bodies in palisade cells of lamina seen in paradermal view (× 280).

I-K. Starch grains from rhizome (× 280).

I. *Maranta arundinacea.* J. *Calathea lietzei.* K. *Thaumatococcus daniellii.*

L–N. Secretory cells (× 220).

L. *Thalia welwitschii.* T.S. abaxial surface layers of lamina. M–N. *Hypselodelphis violacea.* Adaxial hypodermis of lamina. M. T.S. N. Paradermal view.

s.c.—silica-cell.

separated from adaxial hypodermis by chlorenchyma, as in *Megaphrynium*. Sheathing fibres well developed above and below veins, but rarely forming distinct adaxial buttresses except in *Marantochloa cuspidata*. **Transverse veins** v. congested and numerous, usually only 120–150 μm and never more than 200 μm apart, situated in abaxial mesophyll but never in contact with hypodermis. Each vein sheathed by adaxial parenchyma and abaxial, thin-walled, septate fibres (Fig. 84. C).

Variegated leaves common (Möbius 1918), either blotched or striped. The colour variation in variegated leaves is due to one or more of the following causes (see summary by Tomlinson 1961). The causes are structural and include variation in number of chloroplasts in mesophyll cells; local absence of chlorophyll or its replacement by xanthophyll; differences in shape of palisade cells; development of an abnormally large, air-filled intercellular system; variation in thickness of lamina and size of hypodermal cells, frequently associated with loss of palisade mesophyll. These differences are often emphasized still further by localized development of epidermal papillae and anthocyanin pigments in epidermis.

(ii) *Leaf axis, excluding pulvinus*

Leaf sheath long, open; opposite margins usually overwrapping. Upper limit of sheath rarely marked by a ligule formed by fusion of opposite margins. Petiole commonly developed; long, terete. **Epidermis** of petiole and abaxial part of leaf sheath usually with sinuous anticlinal cell walls, but adaxial epidermis of leaf sheath composed of rectangular cells with non-sinuous walls. **Stomata** frequent, in sheath usually restricted to abaxial surface. **Hypodermis** of 1–2 layers of colourless cells always differentiated below adaxial surface of midrib and sometimes becoming sclerotic; a similar hypodermis often developed in petiole and abaxial surface of leaf sheath.

Chlorenchyma in midrib restricted to a conspicuous adaxial band continuous with that of lamina, but in petiole and sheath usually restricted to a narrow subhypodermal abaxial layer. **Fibrous zone** commonly differentiated, except in spp. of *Calathea, Ctenanthe*, and *Halopegia*; sometimes restricted to distal or abaxial part of leaf axis, as in spp. of *Maranta, Monotagma*, and *Thalia*; terminating abruptly in the pulvinus but sometimes recurring in abaxial part of mid ribas in *Haumania, Hypselodelphis, Megaphrynium, Sarcophrynium,* and *Trachyphrynium*. Fibrous zone composed either of a continuous fibrous layer with included vascular strands or more commonly of congested but discrete fibrous strands together with vb's sheathed by numerous fibres; strands often separated from each other by sclerotic ground parenchyma. Outermost strands of fibrous zone situated in chlorenchymatous layer, rarely next to epidermis as in *Maranta* and *Thalia*.

Air-lacunae present in a single arc, extending from leaf base to midrib (Figs. 85. A–F), but often constricted or even absent from pulvinus, often v. narrow in spp. of *Calathea* and absent from leaf sheath of *C. insignis*. Additional, large adaxial air-lacuna present in *Halopegia* (Fig. 85. G) and some *Thalia* spp. in petiole and distal part of leaf sheath. *Haumania* differing from all other genera in having a single wide air-lacuna at centre of sheath, becoming irregularly subdivided by longitudinal partitions in petiole. Canals rarely including an almost continuous network of stellate cells as in spp. of *Ischnosiphon* and *Thalia*. Canals more commonly segmented by transverse septa of 2 kinds: (*a*) uniseriate diaphragms, never including vascular tissue, composed of a single layer of stellate, rarely thick-walled cells (Fig. 85. I, J); (*b*) multiseriate diaphragms, often including transverse veins, composed of 1–3 central layers of rounded cells sandwiched between 2 limiting layers of stellate cells.

Longitudinal veins arranged in 3 main systems (Fig. 85. C). Main arc (I) of large vb's forming a V or U in T.S., alternating with and adaxial to air-canals; each vb including extended protoxylem. Abaxial subsidiary system (II) of many arcs of large and small vb's; frequently associated with fibrous strands; often situated in longitudinal partitions between air-canals; outermost vb's with massive fibrous sheaths usually forming part of peripheral fibrous zone. Adaxial subsidiary system (III) of inconspicuous, often inverted, bundles with reduced vascular tissues or even represented by strands of fibres, the vb's situated between the arms of the V of the main arc. Adaxial system sometimes absent, as from distal part of leaf sheath of *Maranta bicolor*, but usually most conspicuous in this region. Longitudinal veins connected at irregular intervals by narrow transverse commissures, the commissures not sheathed by fibres as in lamina. Narrow **fibrous strands** common in ground parenchyma of lower part of leaf sheath as in spp. of *Calathea*, *Ctenanthe*, *Maranta*, *Marantochloa*, *Megaphrynium*, and *Thalia*; sometimes within air-canals and supported by transverse diaphragms.

(iii) *Pulvinus*

Always present as a distinct swelling at base of midrib; articulated to petiole, but articulated to midrib only on adaxial surface, except in *Hypselodelphis* with pulvinus articulated to midrib on both surfaces. **Epidermis** and indumentum often conspicuously different from those of leaf axis. **Stomata** often v. abundant, especially on abaxial surface, and of significance in leaf movement according to Hermann (1916). Peripheral 1–4 hypodermal layers differentiated as indistinct **chlorenchyma**, sometimes including patches or a reticulum of colourless cells. Most of periphery of pulvinus occupied by a complete cylinder of 1, or more rarely 2, layers of **'oblique-cells'**, the individual cells usually at an oblique angle to long axis of pulvinus, each v. long but with rounded ends, the walls slightly thickened with v. inconspicuous slit-like pits on side walls and more conspicuous rounded pits on end walls. This tissue commonly continuing into midrib on its abaxial surface except in *Hypselodelphis*. Ground tissue immediately within layer of oblique-cells differentiated as a usually thick, non-vasculated layer of compact, tangentially-extended cells, usually hexagonal in T.S. **Longitudinal veins** arranged as in petiole but more congested and with an almost complete radial symmetry (Fig. 85. B, E). Mechanical tissues not well developed and not forming a peripheral sclerotic layer. **Air-canals** sometimes continuous with those in petiole and midrib, but often represented by a loose spongy tissue. Function of pulvinus, in orientating leaf, much investigated (e.g. by Debski 1895, Hermann 1916, Schwendener 1896).

(i) *Internode*

Internode below first foliage leaf on each branch unit commonly v. long in spp. with well-developed, much-branched aerial shoots. Subsequent internodes usually short. Internodes in spp. without well-developed aerial stems short and congested, the shoot then partly consisting of a pseudostem of overlapping leaf bases. **Epidermis** often composed of cells with distinctly sinuous anticlinal walls. Superficial tissues of long internodes usually differentiated, like those of abaxial surface of leaf axis, into a colourless, sometimes thickwalled **hypodermis**, a narrow band of **chlorenchyma,** and a **fibrous zone** of congested vascular and fibrous bundles.

Cortex and central cylinder not distinguishable. Central **vascular bundles** diffuse, often arranged in several distinct cylinders, the vb's of each cylinder with a characteristic appearance in T.S. largely due to variation in amount and distribution of sheathing fibres (Bertrand 1958). Main entrant vb's recognizable by conspicuous extended protoxylem, remaining vb's usually including a single file of wide tracheal elements. *Haumania* differing from all other genera in possessing a ring of inverted vb's close to peripheral fibrous zone. Ground tissue in *Megaphrynium* and *Sarcophrynium* often including a distinct sclerotic layer towards centre of stem. Narrow **fibrous strands** abundant in ground parenchyma of lower internodes in *Donax*, *Marantochloa* spp., *Stromanthe*, and *Thalia*.

(ii) *Node*

Peripheral vb's of leaf sheath not passing into centre of stem but remaining as part of peripheral mechanical zone of stem. Nodal plexus often developed, apparently in association with development of branch trace, as in *Hypselodelphis*. Peripheral ground tissue of node often enlarged to form a conspicuous, non-vasculated **callus** of necrosed and suberized cells; vascular tissues within callus sometimes enclosed by a common endodermis. Fibrous tissues reduced and often replaced by collenchyma. Air-lacunae of leaf axis usually ending abruptly at node.

Never markedly stoloniferous, commonly fibrous or woody, sometimes swollen and fleshy as in *Maranta arundinacea*. Surface layers often becoming suberized, lignified, or tanniniferous but never forming a distinct periderm. Peripheral layers sometimes remaining starch-free and thus conspicuous to the naked eye at a cut surface as in *Maranta arundinacea*. **Cortex** including numerous peripheral fibrous strands; in *Thalia* fibrous strands also common in inner cortex. Cortical vb's infrequently with a complete fibrous sheath as in *Hypselodelphis*, *Ischnosiphon*, *Sarcophrynium* (Fig. 86. D), and *Trachyphrynium*, more usually with fibres well developed only next to phloem; vascular tissues usually including several files of tracheids. **Central cylinder** delimited from cortex by a distinct **endodermoid layer.** Periphery of central cylinder marked by a plexus of congested, irregular vascular strands. Central vb's usually more congested than those of cortex, otherwise similar except for well-developed fibrous sheath at xylem pole only (Fig. 86. C); rarely absent as in *Halopegia*. Ground parenchyma somewhat spongy or lacunose in spp. of *Calathea, Thalia,* and *Trachyphrynium.*

ROOT

Swollen root **tubers** developed in spp. of *Calathea* and *Maranta,* either by enlargement of cortex alone, as in *Maranta bicolor* and *kerchoveana,* or by enlargement of both cortex and parenchymatous stele as in *Calathea macrosepala* (Weber 1958) and *C. rotundifolia.* Piliferous layer of large cells conspicuous and persistent in old roots. Branched root-hairs recorded by Solereder and Meyer in *Ctenanthe luschnathiana.* **Exodermis** of one to many layers of compact, suberized or lignified cells present in all spp. except those of *Halopegia*; rarely with unevenly thickened walls as in *Monotagma rhodantha.* Peripheral **fibrous zone** almost always present immediately within exodermis. **Cortex** often including radial **air-lacunae,** especially in spp. from moist habitats. Innermost cortical layers v. regular, often with widely U-shaped wall thickenings simulating a multiseriate endodermis (Fig. 86. A). Cells of true **endodermis** also often with U-shaped wall thickenings but sometimes persistently thinner-walled than innermost cortical cells. Pericycle 1-layered, sometimes becoming thick-walled. **Stele** with polyarch vascular arrangement, sometimes with innermost wide metaxylem elements remote from and unconnected with protoxylem poles. **Phloem islands,** situated at level of innermost xylem vessels and remote from peripheral phloem strands, observed in roots of *Hypselodelphis, Megaphrynium, Monotagma, Sarcophrynium, Thaumatococcus* (Fig. 86. B), and *Trachyphrynium.* Ground tissue of stele usually wholly fibrous, but with a parenchymatous medulla in *Hypselodelphis* and *Megaphrynium.*

SECRETORY, STORAGE, AND CONDUCTING ELEMENTS

Crystals. Calcium oxalate crystals common and often abundant in ground parenchyma of all parts except root as rhombohedral, rod-like, or even acicular bodies; sometimes in clusters or forming a coarse sand; most conspicuous in hypodermis of lamina.

Silica common in all parts except root as small silica-bodies included either in thin-walled cells or more usually in cells with unevenly thickened walls to form **stegmata.** Silica-cells never situated in epidermis. Silica-cells of lamina clearly divisible into the following 4 main types (*a*)–(*d*), sometimes all occurring together in a single leaf as observed in *Donax, Hypselodelphis, Megaphrynium,* and spp. of *Marantochloa* but distribution varying considerably, even in a single individual. (*a*) Large stegmata in longitudinal files adjacent to sheathing fibres of longitudinal veins, each cell with the wall adjacent to the fibre markedly thickened and enveloping a 'hat-shaped' silica-body with a flattened, spinulose base and a central papilla (Fig. 86. E). (*b*) Similar but usually much smaller stegmata adjacent to fibres of transverse veins (Fig. 86. F), observed in all spp. except *Marantochloa cuspidata, oligantha, Saranthe urceolata,* and *Thalia welwitschii.* (*c*) Large, thin-walled, colourless cells up to 35 μm in diameter, each including a large, stellate or druse-like silica-body (Fig. 86.

G); silica-cells of this type situated in mesophyll just below palisade and commonly adjacent to transverse veins or even restricted to this position. Silica-cells of type (*c*) often associated with much smaller cells or exhibiting a wide range of sizes within a single leaf. (*d*) Small silica-bodies, mostly spherical and druse-like, or rarely more irregular or elongated, usually 3–5 μm in diameter, but diameter up to 20 μm in *Ctenanthe*, situated in normal mesophyll cells, especially those of palisade (Fig. 86. H).

Stegmata comparable to types (*a*) and (*b*) above, but with more irregular silica-bodies also present in leaf axis and stem; always situated next to vb's. Silica-cells in rhizome often rather thin-walled and commonly forming almost complete sheaths around vb's. Silica sand recorded in lamina of *Donax* and *Saranthe*.

Tannin common in unmodified cells of ground parenchyma of all parts. In lamina sometimes restricted to specialized, enlarged mesophyll cells, e.g. in *Calathea*.

Secretory cells with colourless, mucilaginous contents recorded in *Hypselodelphis* in hypodermis of lamina and ground parenchyma of other parts (Fig. 86. M, N). Similar but much longer mucilage cells, arranged in longitudinal files adjacent to abaxial hypodermis of lamina, observed in *Thalia welwitschii* (Fig. 86. L). Secretory cells with suberized walls recorded in hypodermis of lamina of *Saranthe urceolata*.

Starch usually abundant in ground parenchyma of rhizome but not uncommon in aerial stem and in central ground parenchyma of leaf axis. Grains usually simple, smoothly spherical or ellipsoidal and slightly eccentric, rarely flattened as in *Calathea lietzei* (Fig. 86. J) and *C. vittata*. Starch grains angular or even compound in spp. of *Maranta* (Fig. 86. I), *Marantochloa, Megaphrynium, Sarcophrynium,* and *Trachyphrynium*; v. irregular in *Thaumatococcus* (Fig. 86. K).

Xylem. Vessels present in root in all spp. examined; with simple, more or less transverse perforation plates in *Donax, Halopegia, Hypselodelphis, Ischnosiphon, Marantochloa, Megaphrynium,* and *Thaumatococcus*; otherwise with scalariform perforation plates on oblique end walls. Vessels also present in axis of many spp. with well-developed aerial stems, the elements having scalariform, oblique perforation plates, as in *Marantochloa, Sarcophrynium, Thalia,* and *Thaumatococcus*, but in *Hypselodelphis* often with simple perforation plates.

Phloem. Sieve-tubes in root with long, compound sieve-plates in oblique or v. oblique end walls; sieve-tubes in aerial parts with more specialized, often simple sieve-plates in less oblique end walls.

ECONOMIC USES

West Indian Arrowroot (*Maranta arundinacea* L.) is a source of a very easily digested starch which is used in the preparation of infant and invalid foods. The starch is extracted from the rhizomes which are too fibrous to be used as a vegetable. The rhizomes also serve to propagate the plant. The cultivation of this crop was one of the main industries of St. Vincent in the West Indies and the crop is still extensively cultivated there. *Calathea alluia* Lindl. has a similar but much more local use, the starch being found in root tubers which, being non-fibrous, are eaten as a vegetable. The split or unsplit canes of some of the larger members of this family, e.g. spp. of *Donax* and *Ischnosiphon*, sometimes have considerable use in mat and basket making. Many of the smaller spp., mostly belonging to the genera *Calathea* and *Maranta*, are common indoor plants of temperate regions, valued for their variegated foliage.

Taxonomic Notes

This description is based upon the author's earlier account of the Marantaceae (Tomlinson 1961) in which both morphological and anatomical features are summarized. A detailed survey of a limited number of spp. is given by Bertrand (1958). It is noted in the first of these papers that there is no consistent combination of anatomical features by which members of the two tribes Maranteae and Calatheae can be distinguished from one another. A few of the genera show characteristic anatomical features but these are not often easy to define. It is surprising that the anatomy of this family is so uniform when the external morphology of the plants is so diverse compared with that of other families of the Scitamineae. Taking the taxonomic distribution of different types of tracheal elements in the Marantaceae as a criterion, it is suggested that during the evolution of the family there has been a trend from simple to more elaborate habit forms (Tomlinson 1961).

Genera and Species reported on in the Literature

For most early literature see Solereder and Meyer (1930).

Bertrand (1958) leaf, stem of all spp. *Ataenidia conferta* (Benth.) Milne-Redhead, *Halopegia azurea* (K. Schum.) K. Schum., *Haumania danckelmaniana* (J. Braun and K. Schum.) Milne-Redhead, *H. liebrachtsiana* (De Wild. and Th. Dur.) J. Léonard, *Hypselodelphis poggeana* (K. Schum.) Milne-Redhead, *H. scandens* Louis and Mullenders, *H. violacea* (Ridl.) Milne-Redhead, *Marantochloa congensis* (K. Schum.) J. Léonard and Mullenders, *M. congensis* var. *pubescens* J. Léonard and Mullenders, *M. congensis* var. *nitida* J. Léonard and Mullenders, *M. leucantha* (K. Schum.) Milne-Redhead, *M. mannii* (Benth.) Milne-Redhead, *M. oligantha* (K. Schum.) Milne-Redhead, *M. purpurea* (Ridl.) Milne-Redhead, *Megaphrynium macrostachyum* (Benth.) Milne-Redhead, *Sarcophrynium leiogonium* (K. Schum.) K. Schum., *S. prionogonium* (K. Schum.) var. *puberulifolium* Schnell., *S. schweinfurthianum* (O. Kuntze) Milne-Redhead, *Trachyphrynium braunianum* (K. Schum.) Bak.

Debski (1895) studied 4 spp. (according to Solereder and Meyer); pulvinus.

Hassack (1886) *Calathea vittata, Maranta eximia, M. massangeana, M. sanguinea*; leaf.

Hermann (1916) *Calathea backerniana* E. Morr., *C. flavescens* Lindl., *C. lietzei* E. Morr., *C. oppenheimiana* E. Morr., *Ctenanthe setosa* Eichl., *C. steudneri* Eichl., *Maranta arundinacea* L., *M. bicolor* Ker., *M. guyana* Hort., *M. kerchoveana* (*leuconeura*) E. Morr., *M. lindeni* E. Morr.; pulvinus.

Higbee and Sievers (1945) *Calathea lutea*; wax.

Holm (1927) *Maranta arundinacea* L.; leaf.

Lippitsch (1889) *Maranta arundinacea*; leaf.

Meyer (1930) *Maranta kerchoveana* Morr.; root.

Möbius (1918) *Calathea chantrieri, C. lietzei, C. lindenii, C. makoyana, C. massangeana, C. oppenheimiana, C. veitchiana, C. wiotiana*; variegated leaves.

Petersen (1893) studied spp. of *Calathea, Ctenanthe, Donax* (*Phrynium*), *Maranta, Monotagma* (*Ischnosiphon*), *Myrosma* (*Saranthe*), *Phrynium, Pleiostachya* (*Ischnosiphon*), *Saranthe, Stromanthe, Thalia*; all parts (according to Solereder and Meyer).

Pillai and Pillai (1961) *Calathea zebrina* Lindl., *Maranta arundinacea* L., *M. major, M. variegata* Lodd., *M. zebrina* Sims., *Phrynium capitatum* Willd., *Stromanthe sanguinea* Sond.; root apex.

Pray (1957) *Maranta bicolor* Ker.; leaf margin.

Renner (1908) *Ctenanthe setosa*; hairs.

Schittengruber (1954) *Maranta leuconeura*; leaf.

Schlesinger (1895) studied spp. of *Calathea, Ctenanthe, Donax* (*Clinogyne*), *Ischnosiphon, Maranta, Monotagma* (as *Ischnosiphon laxus* Koern. and *I. secundus* Peters.), *Myrosma* (as *Saranthe moritziana* Eichl.), *Phrynium, Saranthe, Sarcophrynium* (*Phrynium oxycarpum* Bak., *P. prionogonium* Bak.), *Stachyphrynium* (*Phrynium spicatum* Roxb.), *Stromanthe, Thalia, Trachyphrynium* (according to Solereder and Meyer).

Schwendener (1896) *Calathea albicans* A. Brongn., *C. argyraea* Koern., *C. flavescens* Lindl., *C. jagoriana* Regel, *C. lietzei* E. Morr., *C. longibracteata* Lindl., *C. ornata* Koern. var. *regalis, C. princeps* Regel, *C. pulchella* Koern., *C. rotundifolia* Koern., *C. rufibarba* Fenzl., *C. smaragdina* Linden, *C. variegata* Koern., *C. zebrina* Lindl., *Ctenanthe kummeriana* Eichl., *C. setosa* Eichl., *Maranta arundinacea* L., *M. bicolor* Koern., *M. eximia* Regel, *M. kerchoveana* E. Morr., *M. noctiflora* Regel and Koern., *M. oblongifolia* Regel, *Stromanthe porteana* Gris.; pulvinus.

Skutch (1930) *Calathea magnifica* Morton and Skutch; leaf.

Solereder and Meyer (1930) *Calathea zebrina* Lindl., *Ctenanthe setosa* Eichl., *Maranta arundinacea* L., *M. bicolor* Hort. (*M. leuconeura* E. Morr.), *Saranthe eichleri* Peters., *S. urceolata* Peters.; all parts.

Tomlinson (1961) see Material Examined by the Author.

Weber (1958) *Calathea macrosepala* Schum.; root.

MATERIAL EXAMINED BY THE AUTHOR

The above description is based on the following material, which also served as the basis for a previous article (Tomlinson 1961).

(i) Living material from West Africa.

Ataenidia conferta (Benth.) Milne-Redhead; *Halopegia azurea* (K. Schum.) K. Schum.; *Hypselodelphis violacea* (K. Schum.) Milne-Redhead; *Marantochloa congensis* Léonard and Mullenders var. *pubescens; M. cuspidata* (Rosc.) Milne-Redhead; *M. mannii* (Benth.) Milne-Redhead; *M. oligantha* (K. Schum.) Milne-Redhead; *M. purpurea* (Ridl.) Milne-Redhead; *Megaphrynium macrostachyum* (Benth.) Milne-Redhead; *Sarcophrynium brachystachyum* K. Schum.; *Thalia welwitschii* Ridl.; *Thaumatococcus daniellii* (Benn.) Benth.; *Trachyphrynium braunianum* (K. Schum.) Bak.

(ii) Pickled material, from Kew unless otherwise stated.

Calathea angustifolia Koern.; *C. argyrophylla* Hort.; *C. insignis* Peters.; *C. lietzei* E. Morr.; *C. lutea* Mey. (West Indies); *C. rotundifolia* Koern. var. *fasciata; C. rufibarba* Fenzl.; *C. trinitensis* Britton (West Indies); *C. vittata* Koern.; *C. wiotiana* Makoy; *C. zebrina* Lindl.; *Ctenanthe oppenheimiana*

Schum.; *Donax grandis* (Miq.) Ridl. (Malaya); *Ischnosiphon aruma* Koern. West) Indies); *Maranta arundinacea* L. (West Indies); *M. bicolor* Ker.; *Marantochloa leucantha* (K. Schum.) Milne-Redhead; *Monotagma rhodantha* Mann and Wendl. (West Indies); *M. spicatum* (Aubl.) Macbride (West Indies); *Phrynium capitatum* Willd. (Malaya); *Stromanthe lutea* Eichl. (West Indies); *S. sanguinea* Sond. (West Indies); *S. tonckat* Eichl. (West Indies); *Thalia geniculata* L. (Florida).

BIBLIOGRAPHY FOR MARANTACEAE

BERTRAND, L. (1958) Contributions à l'étude anatomique des Marantacées africaines. *Bull. Inst. Étud. centrafr.* **15-16,** 99–144.

DEBSKI, B. (1895) Über Bau und Bewegungsmechanismus der Blätter der Marantaceae. *Anz. Akad. Wiss. Krakau.* 244–50—original not seen.

HASSACK, C. (1886) Untersuchungen über den anatomischen Bau bunter Laubblätter, nebst einigen Bemerkungen, betreffenden die physiologische Bedeutung der Buntfärbung derselben. *Bot. Zbl.* **28,** 84–85, 116–21, 150–4, 181–6, 211–15, 243–6, 276–9, 308–12, 337–41, 373–5, 385–8.

HERMANN, W. (1916) Die Blattbewegungen der Marantaceen und ihre Beziehung zur Transpiration. *Flora, Jena* **109,** 69–96.

HIGBEE, E. C., and SIEVERS, A. F. (1945) Note on the wax from *Calathea lutea. Jl N.Y. bot. Gdn* **46,** 192–6.

HOLM, T. (1927) Sciaphilous plant-types. *Beih. bot. Zbl.* **44,** 1–89.

LIPPITSCH, C. (1889) Über das Einreißen der Laubblätter der Musaceen und einiger verwandter Pflanzen. *Öst. bot. Z.* **39,** 206–10, 259–63.

MEYER, F. J. (1930) Die Leitbündel der Radices filipendulae (Wurzelanschwellungen) von *Maranta kerchoveana* Morr. *Ber. dt. bot. Ges.* **48,** 51–57.

MÖBIUS, M. (1918) Merkwürdige Zeichnungen auf Marantaceenblättern. *Ber. dt. bot. Ges.* **36,** 263–70, 323–31.

PETERSEN, O. G. (1893) Bidrag til Scitamineernes Anatomi. *K. danske vidensk. Selsk. Skr.* (6) **8,** 337–418; see *Just's bot. Jber.* **21** (1), sec. 14, no. 111 (1893)—original not seen.

PILLAI, S. K., and PILLAI, A. (1961) Root apical organization in monocotyledons—Marantaceae. *Proc. Indian Acad. Sci.* B **53,** 302–17.

PRAY, T. R. (1957) Marginal growth of leaves in monocotyledons: *Hosta, Maranta* and *Philodendron. Phytomorphology* **7,** 381–7.

RENNER, O. (1908) Zur Morphologie und Ökologie der pflanzlichen Behaarung. *Flora, Jena* **99,** 125–55.

SCHITTENGRUBER, B. (1954) Stomata fehlen den Blattflecken von *Maranta leuconeura. Protoplasma* **43,** 115–19—original not seen.

SCHLESINGER, K. (1895) *Vergleichende Anatomie des Blattes der Marantaceen und Zingiberaceen.* Diss. Erlangen. pp. 74—original not seen.

SCHUMANN, K. (1902) Marantaceae in Engler's *Das Pflanzenreich* (4) **48,** 1–184.

SCHWENDENER, S. (1896) Das Wassergewebe in Gelenkpolster der Marantaceen. *Sber. preuß. Akad. Wiss.* **4,** 535–46.

SKUTCH, A. F. (1930) Unrolling of leaves of *Musa sapientum* and some related plants and their reactions to environmental aridity. *Bot. Gaz.* **90,** 337–65.

SOLEREDER, H., and MEYER, F. J. (1930) Marantaceae. In *Systematische Anatomie der Monokotyledonen,* Heft VI, 62–84.

TOMLINSON, P. B. (1961) Morphological and anatomical characteristics of the Marantaceae. *J. Linn. Soc.* (Bot.) **58,** 55–78.

WEBER, H. (1958) Die Wurzelverdickungen von *Calathea macrosepala* Schum. und von einigen anderen monocotylen Pflanzen. *Beitr. biol. Pfl.* **34,** 177–93.

A NOTE ABOUT STOMATA

STOMATAL ontogeny in many plants is known to involve a well-organized sequence of divisions. This sequence is usually constant throughout different parts of a single individual and also appears to be constant throughout large groups. Thus there is a belief that stomatal development can be used as a key feature to indicate the affinities between large taxonomic groups. It has been used extensively in this way in discussing the relationships between the major groups of gymnosperms, notably by Florin (1931). Evolutionists believe that similar extensive application of information about stomatal ontogeny will throw light on the interrelationships between groups of angiosperms. The situation has been surveyed in monocotyledons by Stebbins and Khush (1961) but in a way that requires comment because their interpretations are very misleading when considered in the light of their observations. Although certain features of stomatal structure are listed in the Appendix (p. 404) and described in further detail throughout the text, I have made no studies of stomatal development except in Commelinaceae (q.v., p. 33). For this and other reasons I am not prepared to draw lengthy conclusions, in the manner of the above authors. This attitude may be explained further.

Descriptive terms have been proposed for different types of mature stomata. In monocotyledons stomata with 2 lateral subsidiary cells parallel to the guard cells (e.g. Fig. 32. C) have been referred to as *paracytic*, those with 4 subsidiary cells (e.g. Fig. 7. G, I) as *tetracytic*, those without subsidiary cells as *anomocytic* (Metcalfe 1961). This by no means encompasses the range of types and the terms could be multiplied. The great value of these terms in description cannot be denied but it must be emphasized that they refer to the surface appearance of the stomatal complex when fully differentiated. However, it is false to assume that because stomata in two monocotyledonous families superficially appear similar, they must necessarily have had the same developmental pathway and, further, that this must indicate genetic affinity for the two families concerned. Nevertheless this seems to be the basis for the conclusions of Stebbins and Khush.

If *development* is to be the basis for comparison, as distinct from *construction*, then development should be known. Stebbins and Khush themselves make developmental observations on only two species of monocotyledons (*Juncus effusus* and *Sagittaria montevidensis*) and draw attention to information about stomatal development in Commelinaceae and Gramineae which is available in the literature. (They appear to have overlooked other relevant literature, e.g. Pfitzer 1870.) Apart from this limited information all other conclusions about stomatal development by these two authors are arrived at by *inference*. This seems a very inadequate basis for the wide conclusions that are drawn.

The fact is we know virtually nothing about stomatal development in monocotyledons. There is no way of inspecting the mature stomatal complex and deciding which of the adjacent epidermal cells have a special developmental relation to the guard cells and which have not. The grasses are a much-cited example of how the mature stoma gives an entirely misleading impression of developmental pathways. Subsidiary cells are, by definition, *structurally* modified cells surrounding and often in contact with guard cells. Some subsidiary cells are related to guard cells in a precise developmental way, others are not. Cells which bear a special developmental relation to the guard cells may be indistinguishable from other epidermal cells at maturity. By definition these are not subsidiary cells.

Of the families described in this volume detailed information about stomatal development is available only for the Commelinaceae. This is summarized on p. 33 and shows that around the guard mother cell 2, 4, or 6 subsidiary cells may be cut off. In the remaining families stomatal development has been studied in *Ananas* of Bromeliaceae. Here no less than 9 divisions are involved in stomatal development subsequent to the appearance of the guard mother cell. However, anatomists might describe stomata in Bromeliaceae as 'paracytic' because at maturity 2 thin-walled lateral subsidiary cells are characteristically present; the remaining cells involved in development are not usually specially differentiated. The mature stoma therefore gives little indication of its lengthy developmental history. In this context, although not entirely relevant, it may be mentioned that in the Pandanaceae yet another method of producing 'paracytic' stomata is available, involving 6 divisions subsequent to the appearance of the guard mother cell (Pfitzer 1870, Tomlinson 1965). Otherwise the more familiar paracytic stomata in Gramineae, and according to Hamann (1963) in Centrolepidaceae, require only 2 such divisions.

On this basis one begins to appreciate that stomatal ontogeny in monocotyledons is a much more complex problem than Stebbins and Khush would indicate. Only by careful and lengthy studies will the information we need become available. When this information has been gathered we may be in a position to make worth-while suggestions about the interrelationships of monocotyledonous families, but not before. It is a matter of regret that evolutionists seem to lack the patient regard for accurate detail which the descriptive anatomist finds necessary.

LITERATURE CITED

FLORIN, R. (1931) Untersuchungen zur Stammesgeschichte der Coniferales und Cordaitales. I. Morphologie und Epidermisstruktur der Assimilationsorgane bei den rezenten Koniferen. *K. svensk. Vet. Akad. Handl.* ser. 3, **10**, 588.

HAMANN, U. (1963) Über die Entwicklung und den Bau des Spaltöffnungsapparats der Centrolepidaceae. *Bot. Jb.* **82**, 316–20.

METCALFE, C. R. (1961) The anatomical approach to systematics. General introduction with special reference to recent work on monocotyledons. pp. 146–50 in *Recent Advances in Botany*. Toronto.

PFITZER, E. (1870) Beiträge zur Kenntnis der Hautgewebe der Pflanzen. *Jb. wiss. Bot.* **7**, 532–87.

STEBBINS, G. L., and KHUSH, G. S. (1961) Variation in the organization of the stomatal complex in the leaf epidermis of monocotyledons and its bearing on their phylogeny. *Am. J. Bot.* **48**, 51–59.

TOMLINSON, P. B. (1965) A study of stomatal structure in Pandanaceae. *Pacif. Sci.* **19**, 38–54.

COMMENTS ON 'A NOTE ABOUT STOMATA'

By C. R. METCALFE

Dr. Tomlinson's thesis that quite different ontogenetic pathways can give rise to types of stomatal apparatus that look alike in mature leaves is quite correct. He has therefore performed a useful service in reminding us that the paracytic stomata in the Bromeliaceae are not ontogenetically equivalent to the paracytic stomata of, for example, the Gramineae and Centrolepidaceae. This being so it is quite true that it would be incorrect to conclude that because paracytic stomata occur in these 3 families they are closely related to one another.

On the other hand, it is just as important to remember that even if all paracytic stomata are not ontogenetically equivalent, the fact that they occur in the mature leaves of some plants and not in others enables them to be used as reliable diagnostic characters. Indeed this has been done quite regularly for many years by pharmacognosists when identifying and maintaining an acceptable standard of purity for crude drugs. This applies also to other microscopical characters that are of proved *diagnostic* value, but we cannot necessarily accept them as indicators of natural taxonomic affinity. We should do well to remember that characters which are diagnostically valid are not consequently equally valid as evidence of close genetical relationship between the plants in which they are exemplified.

It takes a long time to study the ontogeny of plant structures histologically by using our present techniques. It is not, therefore, a practical proposition for a taxonomist or systematic anatomist who has to examine a great many specimens every day to undertake ontogenetic studies on all of them. It would often be very rewarding and make for greater taxonomic accuracy if ontogenetic studies at the histological level could be undertaken more readily and frequently, but it would only waste time to attempt what is impractical. It is for reasons of this kind that taxonomy must remain at least partly subjective since we have to use our taxonomic intuition in deciding on the value and significance of the characters we use. It is surprising and perhaps refreshing to remember how successful we have been in classifying plants in spite of the fact that we have had to rely on our intuitive powers.

A NOTE ABOUT CONDUCTING ELEMENTS

Xylem

No special studies of tracheal elements have been undertaken. Incidental observations, however, support the conclusion of Cheadle (1943–55) regarding evolutionary trends in tracheal elements of monocotyledons. Information about xylem elements is noted in individual family descriptions and further summarized very briefly in the Appendix (p. 413). This list also incorporates additional information from Cheadle's papers together with that given by Fahn (1954) and Carlquist (1966). Cheadle's conclusions about phylogenetic specialization in tracheal elements and the way in which these conclusions apply to the families included in this volume may be summarized.

(i) *Vessel elements have evolved from tracheids.* This follows from the observations by Cheadle (1943*a*) that the least specialized types of vessel elements are most like tracheids. In some monocotyledons it is not easy to decide whether tracheal elements are imperforate or not. In the Mayacaceae, for example, Cheadle records vessels in the leaf whereas I have not. This may only be a difference of interpretation. Elsewhere in *Mayaca*, vessels are unspecialized with long, scalariform, indistinctly perforate end walls. Where my results elsewhere differ from Cheadle's, a similar difference of interpretation might be involved.

(ii) *Vessels appeared first in the late metaxylem.* This was decided by Cheadle (1944) from the observation that the most specialized elements always occur in the metaxylem. I have examined this topic only incidentally but find no evidence to contradict it.

(iii) *Vessels appeared first in the roots and later in the stem and leaf.* This is concluded by Cheadle (1943*b*) from the observation that the most specialized tracheal elements always occur in the xylem of the root, with elements of decreasing specialization in the stem and leaf. The distribution of vessels in the families I have studied fully supports this since they may be (*a*) restricted to the root, (*b*) restricted to root and stem, (*c*) present in all parts. No other types of distribution have been found. These families differ greatly in the degree of specialization of their tracheal elements. Families with vessels in the roots only and which are therefore least specialized include Cannaceae, Heliconiaceae, Lowiaceae, and Musaceae. Other families, such as Commelinaceae, Eriocaulaceae, and Xyridaceae, are highly specialized in this respect because they include vessels in all parts. The remaining families occupy a somewhat intermediate position, notably the Rapateaceae in which vessels always occur in stem and root, but not leaf (Carlquist 1966). The Bromeliaceae are of especial interest because of their wide range. Specialized, unspecialized, and intermediate categories occur in this one family (Cheadle 1955). It would be of value to know how the degree of specialization of tracheal elements in Bromeliaceae is correlated with life form which is equally diverse, since both aspects are capable of reasonable phylogenetic interpretation. We still lack enough detailed knowledge to do this.

No studies of wall sculpturing in tracheal elements have been attempted despite the wide range of features known to exist (Bierhorst and Zamora 1965).

Phloem

No special study of sieve-tube elements has been made and available information is far too scanty to permit worthwhile comment.

LITERATURE CITED

BIERHORST, D. W., and ZAMORA, P. M. (1965) Primary xylem elements and element associations of angiosperms. *Am. J. Bot.* **52,** 675–710.

CARLQUIST, S. (1966) Anatomy of Rapateaceae—roots and stems. *Phytomorphology* **16,** 17–38.

CHEADLE, V. I. (1943a) The origin and certain trends of specialization of the vessel in the Monocotyledoneae. *Am. J. Bot.* **30,** 11–17.

—— (1943b) Vessel specialization in the late metaxylem of the various organs in the Monocotyledoneae. *Am. J. Bot.* **30,** 484–90.

—— (1944) Specialization of vessels within the xylem of each organ in the Monocotyledoneae. *Am. J. Bot.* **31,** 81–92.

—— (1953) Independent origin of vessels in the monocotyledons and dicotyledons. *Phytomorphology* **3,** 23–44.

—— (1955) Conducting elements in the xylem of Bromeliaceae. *Bull. Bromel. Soc.* **5** (1), pp. 4.

FAHN, A. (1954) Metaxylem elements in some families of the Monocotyledoneae. *New Phytol.* **53,** 530–40.

APPENDIX

Distribution of some important diagnostic characters of morphology and anatomy in the 16 families dealt with in this volume

INDEX TO TABLES OF DIAGNOSTIC CHARACTERS

WHERE a name is recorded in **bold type** the feature is regarded as either universally present in the family (sometimes genus or subfamily) or so common that its diagnostic value can be emphasized.

I. HABITAT

Some families encompass a wide range of ecological tolerance. The following list merely emphasizes predominant tendencies.

A. MESOPHYTIC (commonly also forest-dwelling)

Bromeliaceae	Flagellariaceae	Musaceae
Cannaceae	(*Flagellaria*)	Strelitziaceae
Cartonemataceae	Heliconiaceae	(*Ravenala*)
Commelinaceae	Lowiaceae	Zingiberaceae
Costaceae	Marantaceae	

B. HELOPHYTIC (commonly swamp-dwelling)

Commelinaceae	**Mayacaceae**	Xyridaceae
Eriocaulaceae	Rapateaceae	
Flagellariaceae	Strelitziaceae	
(*Hanguana,*	(*Phenakospermum*)	
Joinvillea)		

C. XEROPHYTIC

Bromeliaceae	Rapateaceae	Strelitziaceae
Commelinaceae		(*Strelitzia*)

D. EPIPHYTIC

Bromeliaceae	Commelinaceae	Zingiberaceae
	(rare)	(rare)

II. STEM MORPHOLOGY

The general habit and method of growth of the families described in this volume is often not well understood. Until a much fuller investigation of construction and development of shoots has been carried out systematic anatomical comparisons have a limited value. The following notes claim neither complete nor accurate knowledge of growth form and other features. They are more likely to indicate areas where accurate morphological observation is greatly needed.

A. REPRODUCTIVE AXIS

1. Flowering process terminating shoot growth (shoot *hapaxanthic*)

Bromeliaceae	Eriocaulaceae (some)	Musaceae
Cannaceae	Flagellariaceae	Rapateaceae
Cartonemataceae	Heliconiaceae	Strelitziaceae
Commelinaceae (some)	Lowiaceae	(*Phenakospermum*)
Costaceae	Marantaceae	Xyridaceae (most)
	Mayacaceae	Zingiberaceae

(The reproductive axis is usually obvious and the 'inflorescence' is described as terminal. Where shoot growth is sympodial and eviction of terminal inflorescences is rapid they may become pseudolateral, e.g. in some Bromeliaceae and especially in the Mayacaceae. Careful examination may be necessary to distinguish pseudolateral inflorescences from truly lateral partial inflorescences.)

2. Flowering process not terminating shoot growth (shoot *pleonanthic*)

Bromeliaceae (few)	Strelitziaceae	Xyridaceae
Commelinaceae (some)	(*Ravenala*,	
Eriocaulaceae (some)	*Strelitzia*)	

(The 'inflorescence' is lateral.)

3. Inflorescence often on a *separate shoot without foliage leaves*

Costaceae	Marantaceae	Zingiberaceae
Heliconiaceae?		

4. Inflorescence axis including a long, more or less naked *scape*

Eriocaulaceae   **Rapateaceae**   **Xyridaceae**

B. VEGETATIVE AXIS

1. *Aerial axis* (usually arising from an underground axis)

(*a*) Aerial axis woody, *arborescent*

Bromeliaceae (few, e.g. *Puya* spp.)   **Strelitziaceae** (most)

(*b*) Aerial axis *herbaceous* but erect, well developed, usually with elongated internodes

Commelinaceae	Flagellariaceae	Marantaceae
Costaceae	(*Flagellaria*,	(often somewhat woody)
Eriocaulaceae	*Joinvillea*)	
(e.g. *Paepalanthus*		
spp.)		

(c) Aerial axis more or less *scandent*

| Bromeliaceae (few) | Commelinaceae (few) | Flagellariaceae (*Flagellaria*) |

(d) Aerial axis *decumbent*, often submerged

| Commelinaceae | Eriocaulaceae (some) | **Mayacaceae** |

(e) Aerial axis short, with congested internodes (predominantly *rosette-plants*)

Bromeliaceae	Flagellariaceae	Xyridaceae
Commelinaceae	(*Hanguana*)	(*Xyris*)
Eriocaulaceae	Lowiaceae	
(e.g. most		
Eriocaulon spp.)		

(f) Aerial axis largely enclosed by overwrapping and overlapping *leaf sheaths*

| Cannaceae | Marantaceae (some) | Zingiberaceae |
| Heliconiaceae | **Musaceae** | |

(g) Vegetative aerial axis often much-branched (this is largely correlated with the development of a nodal plexus, see e.g. p. 361)

| Commelinaceae | Costaceae | Marantaceae |

2. *Underground axis*

The diverse morphology of underground axes in monocotyledons is largely concealed by the few rigidly defined textbook terms which are available. This is not an appropriate place to go into a detailed discussion. It may be noted, however, that 'rhizomes' as horizontal underground axes may bear either scale-leaves or (very rarely in the families under consideration here) foliage leaves. 'Corm', as a short, erect, enlarged but underground axis, is a useful term. However, the 'corm' in Musaceae is morphologically equivalent to the lowest (juvenile) part of a woody axis, as in *Ravenala*, whereas the 'corm' in other monocotyledons may simply be an erect rhizome-segment. Nevertheless, used in general description without precise morphological intention, the terms are useful.

(a) *Rhizome* (usually branched sympodially); more or less fleshy unless otherwise stated

Cannaceae	Heliconiaceae	Strelitziaceae
Commelinaceae	(rarely woody)	(*Strelitzia* spp.)
(rarely woody)	Marantaceae	Zingiberaceae
Costaceae	(sometimes woody)	

(b) *Corm*

| Bromeliaceae (rare) | Lowiaceae | Musaceae |
| Commelinaceae (rare) | | |

(c) *Bulbs* are not developed in any of these families except in a few *Cyanotis* spp. (Commelinaceae).

III. LEAF ARRANGEMENT AND MORPHOLOGY

A. LEAF ARRANGEMENT

1. Leaves *distichous* (alternate)

Bromeliaceae[1]	Heliconiaceae	Xyridaceae
(rarely)	Lowiaceae	(*Xyris*)
Cannaceae	Marantaceae	Zingiberaceae
Commelinaceae[1]	Strelitziaceae	
(some)		

2. Leaves *polystichous* (spirally arranged)

Bromeliaceae	Eriocaulaceae	Xyridaceae
Cartonemataceae	Flagellariaceae?	(*Abolboda*,
Commelinaceae[1]	Mayacaceae	*Orectanthe*)
(some)		

3. Leaves *spiromonostichous* (arranged in a low spiral)

Costaceae

B. LEAVES IN BUD

1. In the following families the leaf is linear and apparently neither folded nor markedly rolled in bud

Bromeliaceae	Eriocaulaceae	Rapateaceae?
Flagellariaceae?	Mayacaceae	Xyridaceae
(*Flagellaria*,		
Hanguana)		

The following special types of vernation may also be noted:

2. Leaf *plicate* in bud

Flagellariaceae (***Joinvillea***)

3. Leaf *rolled* in bud

(*a*) Lamina halves rolled separately, adaxial side innermost, each half folded above midrib

Commelinaceae

(Condition in Cartonemataceae is not known.)

(*b*) Lamina rolled with one half completely encircling the other

All families of **Zingiberales**

C. LEAF DIFFERENTIATION

1. Leaf *tendrillous*

Flagellariaceae (***Flagellaria***)

2. Leaf *equitant* (*Iris*-like)

Rapateaceae?[2]   Xyridaceae (*Achlyphila, Xyris*)

---

[1] Even in plants in which a spiral leaf arrangement is typical, *seedling leaves* and the *first leaves on branches* are almost invariably distichously arranged (with the possible exception of the Eriocaulaceae). This 'juvenile' distichous condition may be retained permanently as in Bromeliaceae, but especially in the Commelinaceae (q.v.).

[2] For special morphology of leaf in Rapateaceae see p. 130.

3. Leaves with marginal *spines*

Bromeliaceae (**Bromelioideae, Pitcairnioideae** only)

4. Leaf *undifferentiated* into distinct blade and sheath

Bromeliaceae (most)	Flagellariaceae	Xyridaceae
Eriocaulaceae	(*Hanguana*)	(*Abolboda,*
	Mayacaceae	*Orectanthe*)

In the remaining families the blade is more or less distinct from the sheathing base.

5. *Petiole* developed as a distinct organ between blade and sheath

Bromeliaceae (few)	Heliconiaceae	Rapateaceae[1]
Commelinaceae (few)	Marantaceae	Strelitziaceae
Costaceae (petiole	Musaceae	Zingiberaceae
short)	(*Musa*)	(few, e.g. *Zingiber*)
Flagellariaceae		
(*Flagellaria*)		

6. *Pulvinus* at base of blade

Marantaceae

In Costaceae and rarely in Zingiberaceae (e.g. *Zingiber*) the short fleshy petiole may serve a pulvinar function in secondarily orientating the blade.

7. Leaf sheath *ligulate* (ligule is an extension of the mouth of the sheath above insertion of the blade or petiole)

Costaceae[2]	Xyridaceae	**Zingiberaceae**
Flagellariaceae[2]	(some *Xyris* spp.)	
(*Joinvillea*)		

In Commelinaceae the mouth of the sheath is commonly very hairy but a true ligule never develops.

8. Leaf sheath, where differentiated, closed or open

(*a*) Sheathing base a *closed* tube, not split vertically down one side

Cartonemataceae	Costaceae	Flagellariaceae
Commelinaceae		(*Flagellaria*)

In Commelinaceae tubular sheath commonly has a vertical line of micro-hairs down ventral side.

(*b*) Sheathing base an *open* tube, split vertically down ventral side, opposite margins overwrapping

Bromeliaceae	Heliconiaceae	Rapateaceae
Cannaceae	Lowiaceae	Strelitziaceae
Flagellariaceae	Marantaceae	Xyridaceae
(*Hanguana,*	Musaceae	Zingiberaceae
Joinvillea)		(rarely closed)

In some spp. (e.g. of *Tillandsia* in Bromeliaceae) opposite margins of the sheath may be closely adpressed and it is not immediately obvious that the tube is open.

[1] For special morphology of leaf in Rapateaceae see p. 130.

[2] Ligule is more or less annular.

IV. HAIRS

The following lists refer largely to hairs on the lamina. A number of different categories is recognized. These categories are unavoidably arbitrary, and it may sometimes happen that, in different families, hairs belonging to any one category may also possess other characteristics by which they can be readily distinguished. For example it is easy to distinguish the 3-celled glandular hairs of Commelinaceae from those in Eriocaulaceae.

DISTRIBUTION AND MODE OF ATTACHMENT OF HAIRS

1. Hairs apparently *absent* from vegetative parts

Cannaceae	Lowiaceae	Xyridaceae
Flagellariaceae	Musaceae	(*Abolboda,*
(*Flagellaria*)	Strelitziaceae	*Achlyphila,*
Heliconiaceae		*Orectanthe*)

2. Hairs *sunken*

Bromeliaceae	Flagellariaceae	Marantaceae[1]
(stalk of scales)	(*Hanguana*)	Zingiberaceae

3. Hairs *superficial* (base of glandular hairs much shallower than rest of epidermis, e.g. Figs. 1. A, p. 16; 30. E–F, p. 150)

Commelinaceae Eriocaulaceae

4. Hairs abundant in or restricted to *leaf axils*

Eriocaulaceae	Rapateaceae	Xyridaceae (*Xyris*)
Mayacaceae		

A. HAIRS UNBRANCHED, UNICELLULAR

1. Large *papillae*, transitional to true hairs (e.g. Fig. 3. A, p. 20)

Commelinaceae Xyridaceae

(These are usually localized and are not readily confused with a uniformly papillose epidermis—see epidermis, p. 403.)

2. Unicellular *prickle-hairs* (short, pointed hairs with an inflated base, e.g. Figs. 15. B, C, p. 72; 76. J, p. 342)

Flagellariaceae (*Joinvillea*) Zingiberaceae

3. Unicellular *filamentous* or rigid hairs (e.g. Fig. 76. M)

Marantaceae Xyridaceae (*Xyris*) Zingiberaceae

In Marantaceae and Zingiberaceae hairs are almost *exclusively unicellular* (rarely septate).

B. HAIRS UNBRANCHED, 2-CELLED

1. Two-celled *prickle-hairs*, short with an inflated base (e.g. Fig. 3. B)

Commelinaceae

[1] In Marantaceae hairs are typically embedded in a basal cushion of inflated epidermal cells (e.g. Fig. 84. E, p. 376).

2. Two-celled *hook-hairs* (apex pointed, recurved, e.g. Fig. 3. K–M)

Commelinaceae

C. HAIRS UNBRANCHED, 3-CELLED

1. *Glandular hairs* (micro-hairs); basal cell usually superficial (Figs. 1, 2, pp. 16–19; 32. G–I, p. 154)

Commelinaceae   **Eriocaulaceae**

In Commelinaceae the middle cell is never very short, in Eriocaulaceae the middle cell is short and often thickened as a special 'collar-cell'.

D. HAIRS UNBRANCHED, MULTICELLULAR

1. Two–6-celled, probably *slime-secreting hairs* (restricted to leaf axils, e.g. Fig. 20. G, p. 98)

Rapateaceae   Xyridaceae (*Xyris*)

Hairs in Rapateaceae are described as 'non-glandular' but 'slime-producing'; in *Xyris* as 'glandular'. It is possible that axillary hairs in Eriocaulaceae and Mayacaceae also secrete slime or mucilage. Bromeliaceae sometimes accumulate axillary mucilage but it is not known if this comes from hairs.

2. Uniseriate *filamentous* hairs (e.g. Figs. 33. E, p. 156; 81. Q, p. 362)

Bromeliaceae   Commelinaceae   Mayacaceae
(*Navia,*   Costaceae   Rapateaceae?
Cottendorfia)   Eriocaulaceae

3. *Flagelliform* hairs (Fig. 4. A–E, p. 22)

Commelinaceae (*Belosynapsis, Cyanotis*)

4. *Capitate* hairs (uniseriate multicellular hairs with an inflated terminal cell, or cells, e.g. Fig. 4. I)

Bromeliaceae   Commelinaceae   Eriocaulaceae
(*Navia* only)   (*Triceratella,*   (mostly on
Cartonemataceae   rare elsewhere)   reproductive parts)

5. *Rugose* hairs (Fig. 4. K)

Commelinaceae (*Palisota*)

E. HAIRS BRANCHED, MULTICELLULAR

1. *T-shaped hairs* (e.g. Fig. 30. L, M, p. 150)

Eriocaulaceae

2. *Irregularly* branched hairs (e.g. Figs. 4. L; 15. D, p. 72)

Commelinaceae   Flagellariaceae
(*Palisota*)   (*Hanguana, Joinvillea*)

F. PELTATE SCALES

Bromeliaceae (Figs. 41–47, pp. 200–214)

D d

V (i). LEAF ANATOMY (*Lamina*) (as opposed to leaf axis; see p. 407).

A. SYMMETRY

1. Lamina *dorsiventral*; in all families except those under 2

2. Lamina *isolateral*

Flagellariaceae	Mayacaceae	Xyridaceae
(*Joinvillea*)	(somewhat	(*Achlyphila, Xyris*)
	dorsiventral)	

In *Xyris* lamina is flattened *laterally* (e.g. Fig. 21. A, p. 100). In Rapateaceae lamina is dorsiventral with a tendency towards isolateral construction.

B. CUTICLE

1. Minutely *papillose* (see also papillose epidermis, C 2 (*e*), p. 403

Commelinaceae (some) Zingiberaceae (some)

2. Longitudinally or reticulately *striate* (e.g. Fig. 9. M–U, p. 38)

Commelinaceae Eriocaulaceae
(sometimes reticulate)

3. Cuticle extruding erect, *rod-like* particles

Musaceae Strelitziaceae

C. EPIDERMIS

1. *Size of epidermal cells.* In most families epidermis is shallow in proportion to total depth of lamina and usually with smaller cells above and below veins differentiated as distinct costal bands. The following exceptions may be noted:

(*a*) Epidermis often *deep* in proportion to total thickness of lamina, or uniformly enlarged as a 'water-storage' tissue (e.g. Figs. 10. B, p. 40; 33. J, p. 156; 77. J, p. 344)

Commelinaceae Eriocaulaceae Zingiberaceae

(*b*) Epidermal cells above and below veins often *larger* than those elsewhere
Eriocaulaceae

(*c*) Epidermal cells with localized *inward protrusions*
Eriocaulaceae (some *Paepalanthus* spp.)

(*d*) Files of epidermal cells locally enlarged as '*expansion cells*'
Flagellariaceae (plicate leaf of *Joinvillea*)

(*e*) Costal bands of epidermal cells *not* usually differentiated
Bromeliaceae

2. *Shape of epidermal cells.* In most families epidermal cells are predominantly longitudinally extended, the walls not sinuous in surface view. The following exceptions may be noted:

(*a*) Epidermal cells often *isodiametric, irregularly polygonal or transversely extended* in surface view (e.g. Fig. 5. L–M, p. 28)

Commelinaceae	Lowiaceae	Zingiberaceae
Costaceae		

(*b*) Epidermis clearly differentiated into *files of longitudinally and files of transversely extended* cells (Fig. 82. A, B, p. 366)

Cannaceae

(*c*) Epidermis differentiated into *long- and short-cells* (cf. Gramineae in vol. i)

Flagellariaceae (*Joinvillea*)

(An apparently similar differentiation may develop as an artefact in Eriocaulaceae owing to superficial hairs which become detached from their basal cell, e.g. Fig. 30. A, B, p. 150.)

(*d*) Epidermal cells with *sinuous* outline in surface view (e.g. Fig. 70. A, p. 318)

Bromeliaceae	**Heliconiaceae**	Rapateaceae
Eriocaulaceae	**Marantaceae**	(slight in some spp.)
(slight in some spp.)	Musaceae	Strelitziaceae
Flagellariaceae	(rarely)	(**Phenakospermum**)
(**Joinvillea**)		

(*e*) Epidermis sometimes *papillose* (e.g. Fig. 18. I–J, p. 94) (see also papillose cuticle, B. 1, p. 402)

Costaceae	Musaceae	Xyridaceae
Marantaceae		(some *Xyris* spp.)

3. *Thickness of epidermal cell walls.* Cell walls of epidermis in most groups slightly thickened with somewhat greater thickening of outer wall. Otherwise wall thickness varies widely, often within a single group, in ways which are difficult to categorize. The following more significant generalizations may be made:

(*a*) Epidermal cells typically *thin-walled* (e.g. Fig. 32. E, p. 154)

Cartonemataceae	Costaceae	Mayacaceae
Commelinaceae	Eriocaulaceae	Zingiberaceae
	(some)	

(*b*) Epidermal cells uniformly *thick-walled* (e.g. Fig. 31. A–C, p. 152)

Eriocaulaceae (some)	Xyridaceae (*Achlyphila*, some *Xyris* spp.)

(Thickness of epidermal wall in *Xyris* varying in ways which are said to be specifically diagnostic.)

(*c*) Epidermal cells with inner walls *thicker than outer* (e.g. Fig. 53. F, p. 232)

Bromeliaceae	Rapateaceae	Xyridaceae
Flagellariaceae	Strelitziaceae	(*Orectanthe*)
(slight in *Flagellaria*)	(*Phenakospermum*)	

D. STOMATA

1. *Subsidiary cells.* All families described in this volume have a stomatal apparatus including 2 thin-walled lateral subsidiary cells clearly differentiated from other epidermal cells. Lateral subsidiary cells may be deeper or shallower than normal epidermal cells depending on the height of the epidermal cells. In some families no other specialized subsidiary cells occur, in others there are additional subsidiary cells which can be recognized structurally (and in some instances developmentally). For a discussion of the diagnostic value of the stomatal apparatus see p. 390.

(a) Subsidiary cells 2, lateral (e.g. Fig. 32. C–D), i.e. stomata paracytic

Bromeliaceae	Eriocaulaceae	Marantaceae
Cannaceae	Flagellariaceae	Mayacaceae
Commelinaceae[1]	(*Hanguana*,	Rapateaceae
(*Cuthbertia*,	*Joinvillea*)	Xyridaceae
Triceratella)	Lowiaceae	Zingiberaceae

(b) Subsidiary cells 4, 2 lateral thin-walled, 2 terminal (e.g. Fig. 7. I, p. 34), i.e. stomata tetracytic

Cartonemataceae	Costaceae	Musaceae
Commelinaceae[1]	Heliconiaceae	Strelitziaceae
(part)		

(c) Subsidiary cells 6, 2 lateral pairs, 1 pair thin-walled, 2 terminal (e.g. Fig. 7. F)

Commelinaceae[1] (part)

(d) Subsidiary cells (in addition to lateral thin-walled pair) *several*, indefinite and poorly differentiated (e.g. Fig. 81. D, p. 362)

Costaceae	Musaceae?	Strelitziaceae?

(e) Stomata often surrounded by modified epidermal cells (e.g. Fig. 57. D–F, p. 240)

Bromeliaceae (many)   Marantaceae (few)
(See details on pp. 224–45.)

2. *Guard cells.* Guard cells in the families studied are either relatively thin-walled or with varying amounts of wall thickening, which is always least well developed at the poles. Each guard cell may include two equal cutinized ledges so that the stomata are symmetrical in T.S., otherwise they are asymmetrical in varying degrees when the inner ledge is less or much less well developed than the outer.

(a) Guard cells *symmetrical* in T.S. (e.g. Fig. 84. I, p. 376)

Cannaceae (most)	Heliconiaceae	Mayacaceae
Flagellariaceae	Marantaceae	Musaceae
(*Hanguana*)	(few)	Strelitziaceae

(b) Guard cells *slightly asymmetrical* in T.S. (e.g. Fig. 84. H)

Cannaceae	Flagellariaceae	Marantaceae (most)
Cartonemataceae	(*Flagellaria*,	Xyridaceae (*Abolboda*,
Commelinaceae	*Joinvillea*)	*Xyris*)
Costaceae	Lowiaceae	Zingiberaceae

[1] For distribution of different stomatal types in Commelinaceae, including special case of *Geogenanthus*, see p. 32.

(c) Guard cells *markedly asymmetrical* in T.S. (e.g. Figs. 32. D, p. 154; 52. A–H, p. 230)

Bromeliaceae   **Eriocaulaceae**

(d) Guard cells *sunken* (e.g. Fig. 55. F–K, p. 236)

Bromeliaceae (many)   Strelitziaceae (*Ravenala, Strelitzia*)

(e) Guard cells thick-walled with dumb-bell-shaped lumina (*grass-like*)

Flagellariaceae (*Flagellaria,*   Rapateaceae
   Joinvillea)

E. Hypodermis

1. Colourless hypodermal layers *absent*

Commelinaceae (some) Mayacaceae   Zingiberaceae (some)
Flagellariaceae   Xyridaceae
  (*Joinvillea*)   (*Achlyphila, Xyris*)

In Commelinaceae and Zingiberaceae where a colourless hypodermis is absent it is often replaced by an enlarged epidermis (e.g. Fig. 10. B, p. 40).

2. Colourless hypodermis discontinuous, as discrete *bands*

Commelinaceae (some)   Eriocaulaceae

In Eriocaulaceae hypodermal bands usually continuous with bundle-sheath extensions (e.g. Fig. 32. E).

3. Colourless hypodermis more or less *continuous* below one or both surfaces (e.g. Fig. 70. F, p. 318)

Bromeliaceae   Flagellariaceae[1]   Rapateaceae
Cannaceae[1]   (*Flagellaria,*   Strelitziaceae
Cartonemataceae   *Hanguana*)   Xyridaceae
Commelinaceae (some) Heliconiaceae[1]   (*Abolboda,*
Costaceae   Marantaceae[1]   *Orectanthe*)
Eriocaulaceae (few)   Musaceae   Zingiberaceae (many)

4. Adaxial (sometimes also abaxial) hypodermis *multiseriate* (e.g. Fig. 8. E, p. 36)

Bromeliaceae   Musaceae (most)   Xyridaceae (some *Abol-*
Commelinaceae (few)   **Strelitziaceae**   *boda, Orectanthe* spp.)
Costaceae   Zingiberaceae (some)

5. Hypodermis consisting of more or less continuous *sclerotic* layers (e.g. Fig. 60. A, B, p. 248)

Bromeliaceae   Rapateaceae (some)

F. Fibres

1. Fibres or fibrous strands in mesophyll *isolated*

Bromeliaceae   Rapateaceae   Zingiberaceae (rare)
Lowiaceae

(Fibres in Lowiaceae and Zingiberaceae mostly solitary and next to hypodermis (e.g. Fig. 74. C, D, p. 336), fibres in Bromeliaceae usually in large aggregates not associated with surface layers, e.g. Fig. 62. H, I, p. 252.)

[1] Usually 1-layered below each surface.

G. Mesophyll

1. One or more distinct *palisade* layers are differentiated in most families (e.g. Fig. 70. F, p. 318) except as follows:

2. Palisade *not* or scarcely differentiated

Bromeliaceae (some)	Flagellariaceae	Xyridaceae
Cartonemataceae	Mayacaceae	(many *Abolboda* and
Eriocaulaceae (many)		some *Xyris* spp.)

3. Chlorenchyma cells elongated, somewhat *radiately arranged* around veins in T.S. (observed in herbarium material)

Cartonemataceae

4. Chlorenchyma consisting of *mixed* large and small cells (Fig. 74. I, p. 336)

Lowiaceae

5. Chlorenchyma cells specialized:

   (*a*) palisade cells irregularly *lobed*, V- or W-shaped in T.S. (e.g. Fig. 8. M, p. 36)
   Commelinaceae (especially in *Palisota*)

   (*b*) palisade cells *invaginated* (e.g. Fig. 27. B, p. 128)
   Rapateaceae

   (*c*) mesophyll including elongated '*peg-parenchyma*' cells (e.g. Fig. 19. H, p. 96)
   Xyridaceae (some *Xyris* spp.)

6. Mesophyll including *colourless* central cells, sometimes collapsing at maturity (e.g. Fig. 14. E, p. 70)

Flagellariaceae	Rapateaceae	Xyridaceae (***Achlyphila***,
(***Joinvillea***)		occasional in *Xyris*)

7. Mesophyll including distinct or indistinct *air-lacunae* (e.g. Figs. 16. F, p. 84; 33. L, p. 156; 67. F, p. 304)

Bromeliaceae	**Mayacaceae**	Musaceae
Eriocaulaceae	(lacunae septate)	Xyridaceae (*Abolboda*)

8. Mesophyll including well-developed *transverse parenchymatous buttresses* (e.g. Fig. 67. H)

Musaceae   **Strelitziaceae**

Vestiges of these may occur in Heliconiaceae. In Rapateaceae mesophyll sometimes includes indistinct transverse plates of compact cells.

H. Veins

1. Veins few to numerous in a single series in all families except the following:

2. *Single* median vein in leaf (Fig. 16. F)

Mayacaceae

3. Veins in two (rarely more) *distinct series* (e.g. Fig. 22. D–F, p. 102)

Flagellariaceae (*Hanguana*)   Xyridaceae (*Achlyphila, Xyris* spp.)

For distribution of different vein arrangements in *Xyris* see pp. 105–110.

4. Veins more or less wholly *independent* of surface layers (e.g. Fig. 63, p. 256)

Bromeliaceae	Costaceae	Zingiberaceae (few)
Cartonemataceae	Heliconiaceae	
Commelinaceae	Xyridaceae (*Xyris*)	

5. Largest or most veins *attached* to one or both surfaces by well-developed bundle-sheath extensions. Extensions may be largely parenchymatous (from O.S., e.g. Fig. 32. E, p. 154) or fibrous (from I.S., e.g. Fig. 14. G, p. 70), referred to as pa. and fi. respectively.

Cannaceae (fi.)	Marantaceae (fi.)	Rapateaceae (fi.)
Eriocaulaceae (pa.)	**Musaceae** (pa.)	**Strelitziaceae** (pa.)
Flagellariaceae (fi.)		Zingiberaceae (fi.)
(*Flagellaria,*		
Joinvillea)		

In Zingiberaceae veins are attached mostly to abaxial surface.

6. Veins attached mostly to *adaxial* surface (Fig. 74. C, p. 336)

Lowiaceae

7. Veins *compound* (including 2 or more vb's, e.g. Fig. 20. A, p. 98)

Xyridaceae (many *Xyris* spp., see p. 107; rare in *Abolboda*)

I. TRANSVERSE VEINS

1. Forming a *dense* system, often conspicuous to the naked eye, veins partly or wholly sheathed by thick-walled cells (e.g. Fig. 84. C, p. 376)

Commelinaceae	Flagellariaceae	Lowiaceae
Costaceae	(*Hanguana*)	Marantaceae

V (ii). LEAF ANATOMY (*Leaf axis*) (as opposed to lamina; see p. 402)

In the **Zingiberales** a combination of anatomical features of the leaf axis is more or less diagnostic for each family. This is indicated in the following tables. The data refer to sections taken at an approximately standard level of the leaf axis close beneath the level of insertion of the blade (but excluding the pulvinus in Marantaceae) unless otherwise stated. The pulvinus of Marantaceae is distinguished by its peripheral *oblique-cells*. Elsewhere somewhat similar cells are developed only in Cannaceae.

1. *Main assimilatory tissue*

   (*a*) *Abaxial*

Cannaceae (sheath)	Musaceae	Strelitziaceae
Marantaceae (sheath)		

   (*b*) *Adaxial*

Cannaceae (midrib)	Heliconiaceae	Marantaceae (midrib)

   (*c*) *Diffusely* distributed

Lowiaceae

   (*d*) Associated with *main veins*

Costaceae	Zingiberaceae

2. *Air-lacunae*

(*a*) *Not* or only feebly developed

Costaceae

(*b*) In *one* series, *abaxial* to main veins

Cannaceae   Marantaceae   Musaceae

(*c*) In *one* series, *alternating* with main veins in a pectinate manner

Zingiberaceae

(*d*) In *two* series, one adaxial and the other abaxial to main veins

Heliconiaceae

(*e*) In *several* series, both adaxial and abaxial to main veins

Lowiaceae   Strelitziaceae

3. *Vascular bundles* with same basic construction in all families, arranged in 1 main and usually 1 or more subsidiary arcs as seen in T.S. The main bundle arc is equidistant from each surface with the following exceptions:

(*a*) Main vascular system *adaxial*

Costaceae   Lowiaceae (slightly)   Musaceae (slightly)

(*b*) Main vascular system *abaxial*

Zingiberaceae

For the diagnostic value of the arrangement of the subsidiary vascular systems see separate family descriptions.

VI. STEM ANATOMY

A. RHIZOME

Erect underground stems and to a large extent congested above-ground stems have a basically similar construction in different families, being differentiated into a wide cortex and central cylinder with intervening endodermoid layer surrounding a narrow vascular plexus which represents the region of insertion of root-traces. Vascular bundles, usually collateral, occur in both cortex and central cylinder. The following exceptions may be noted:

1. Endodermoid layer absent, usually replaced by a layer of *sclerenchyma*

Eriocaulaceae (few)   Xyridaceae

2. Vascular bundles often *amphivasal*

Eriocaulaceae   Rapateaceae   Xyridaceae

B. AERIAL STEM

1. Erect axis often *intermediate* in anatomical structure between typical aerial stem and typical rhizome (largely because of continuous development of roots)

Bromeliaceae   Flagellariaceae   Rapateaceae
Eriocaulaceae   (*Hanguana*)

2. Axis with well-developed *vascular-plexus* at each node

Cannaceae	**Costaceae**	Marantaceae
Commelinaceae		

3. Stems *hollow*

Flagellariaceae (*Joinvillea*)

4. *Cortex* clearly differentiated from central cylinder

(*a*) By a layer of sclerenchyma[1] (sometimes accompanied by an 'endodermoid' layer). Peripheral vb's in contact with or included within sclerenchyma except in Zingiberaceae.

Bromeliaceae	Costaceae	Rapateaceae
Cartonemataceae	Eriocaulaceae	Zingiberaceae
Commelinaceae	(e.g. *Paepalanthus*)	

(*b*) By peripheral *congested* vb's in outer part of central cylinder.

Flagellariaceae (*Flagellaria*)   Strelitziaceae

(*c*) By an *endodermoid layer*.

Flagellariaceae (*Hanguana*)   Mayacaceae

5. Cortex including an *independent* vascular system (e.g. Fig. 80. E–G, p. 350)

Bromeliaceae	Musaceae	Zingiberaceae
Cartonemataceae	Strelitziaceae	

6. Cortex including peripheral *collenchymatous strands* (Fig. 12. B, C, p. 46)

Commelinaceae

7. Cortex *not* differentiated from central cylinder (peripheral vb's usually somewhat congested and with well-developed fibrous sheaths)

Cannaceae	Heliconiaceae	Marantaceae

8. Vascular bundles reduced to a *single series*

Eriocaulaceae (few, e.g. *Tonina*)   Mayacaceae

(This is the normal condition in the scape of Eriocaulaceae and many Xyridaceae (*Xyris*).)

9. Vascular bundles often *amphivasal* (e.g. Fig. 34. C, p. 164)

Eriocaulaceae   Rapateaceae

VII. ROOT MORPHOLOGY AND ANATOMY

A. Root Morphology

1. Roots *tuberous*

(*a*) *wholly* tuberous

Strelitziaceae (some)   Zingiberaceae (some)

(*b*) *locally* tuberous

Commelinaceae	Lowiaceae	Marantaceae

[1] Similar arrangement occurs in the scape of some Eriocaulaceae and Xyridaceae.

2. Roots *intracauline* through several internodes
Bromeliaceae

B. ROOT ANATOMY

1. *Root epidermis*

Root-hairs from paired or clustered *short*-cells (e.g. Fig. 36. A–H, p. 176)
Eriocaulaceae

2. *Root cortex*. Diagnostic features of anatomy of root cortex which have been noted but investigated very incompletely except in Rapateaceae include: extent and distribution of peripheral sclerotic and suberized layers (*exodermis*), extent and distribution of *air-lacunae* in middle cortex, distribution of *tannin* (see especially Rapateaceae), distribution of *sclerenchyma* in inner cortex. The following special features are noteworthy.

(*a*) Middle cortex differentiated into *long- and short-parenchyma* cells (e.g. Fig. 39. H, p. 182)

Eriocaulaceae	Rapateaceae	Xyridaceae
Mayacaceae		

(*b*) Short-cells in horizontal plates, alternating with a plate of long-cells

Eriocaulaceae	Rapateaceae	Xyridaceae
(*Eriocaulon* spp.)	(Rapateoideae)	(*Xyris*)

3. *Root stele*. Diagnostic features in the anatomy of the stele which have been noted but incompletely investigated except in Rapateaceae include: size and number of *endodermal* layers, distribution of *wall thickening* in endodermal cells, size and number of *pericyclic* layers, distribution of *sclerenchyma* in ground tissue, size of *metaphloem* sieve-tubes (see especially Rapateaceae). The following special features may be noted:

(*a*) Stele including both *medullary vessels and sieve-tubes* (e.g. Fig. 68. H, p. 306)

Musaceae   Strelitziaceae

(*b*) Stele including *medullary vessels* (e.g. Fig. 37. C, p. 178)

Eriocaulaceae (few)   Rapateaceae (few)

(*c*) Stele including a *single wide central metaxylem vessel* (only a few spp. in each family, e.g. Fig. 38. J, p. 180)

Commelinaceae	Eriocaulaceae	Xyridaceae

(*d*) Protoxylem elements situated in pericycle, *next to endodermis* (e.g. Fig. 38. I)

Eriocaulaceae	Mayacaceae	Xyridaceae

(This condition may be generally common in finer branch roots.)

VIII. CELL INCLUSIONS, SECRETORY AND CONDUCTING ELEMENTS

A. SILICA

1. *Silica distribution*; refers largely to distribution of silica in *lamina*.

(*a*) Silica *absent*

Cartonemataceae	Mayacaceae	Xyridaceae
Eriocaulaceae		

(*b*) Silica present in a *minority* of genera

Commelinaceae

(*c*) Silica more or less restricted to *epidermis*

Bromeliaceae   Rapateaceae   Zingiberaceae
Commelinaceae

In Rapateaceae and Zingiberaceae silica is more or less restricted to costal regions.

(*d*) Silica more or less restricted to *internal tissues* (usually in cells next to vb's)

Costaceae	Heliconiaceae	Strelitziaceae
Flagellariaceae	Lowiaceae	(*Ravenala*,
(*Flagellaria*,	Marantaceae	*Phenakospermum*)
Hanguana)	Musaceae	

(*e*) Silica more or less *equally distributed* in both epidermal and internal tissues

Bromeliaceae	Strelitziaceae	Zingiberaceae
(rarely)	(*Phenakospermum*)	(rarely)
Flagellariaceae		
(*Joinvillea*)		

(*f*) Silica-cells *idioblastic*, not restricted to epidermal or vascular tissues

Heliconiaceae (rarely)   **Marantaceae**

(*g*) Silica-cells of 2 or more distinct types in the same leaf

(i) *2 types*

Heliconiaceae (rarely)   Musaceae (rarely)

(ii) *4 types*

Marantaceae

In Commelinaceae 2 dissimilar types of silica-cell occur, 1 in one group of genera, the other in another group.

(*h*) Silica-cells differentiated as *stegmata* (small cells with unevenly thickened walls enveloping a silica-body, e.g. Fig. 70. H, I, p. 318)

Costaceae (rarely)	**Lowiaceae**	Strelitziaceae
Flagellariaceae	Marantaceae	(*Phenakospermum*)
(*Joinvillea*)	**Musaceae**	Zingiberaceae
Heliconiaceae		(Alpinieae)

2. *Types of silica-bodies*

(*a*) Silica-bodies usually solitary, except as in (*b*)

(*b*) Silica-bodies either as *coarse aggregates* or finer accumulations (*silica sand*) within each cell (e.g. Figs. 5. A, B, p. 28; 77. F, I, p. 344)

Bromeliaceae	Flagellariaceae	Rapateaceae
Commelinaceae	(*Hanguana*)	(*Saxofridericioideae*)
		Zingiberaceae

Silica sand may occur sporadically in families where silica is otherwise deposited as solitary bodies.

(*c*) Solitary bodies *cubical*

Flagellariaceae (*Joinvillea*)

(*d*) Solitary bodies irregularly *spherical*, surface rugose (e.g. Fig. 27. A, p. 128)

Bromeliaceae   Musaceae (rare)   Zingiberaceae
Heliconiaceae (rare)   **Rapateaceae**

Aggregated silica-bodies of Commelinaceae and Rapateaceae (Saxofridericioideae) are also spherical.

(*e*) Solitary bodies '*hat-shaped*' (e.g. Figs. 74. J, K, p. 336; 86. E–H, p. 380)

Lowiaceae   **Marantaceae**

(*f*) Solitary bodies stellately-spherical or *druse-like* (e.g. Fig. 72. E, p. 326)

Cannaceae   Marantaceae   Strelitziaceae
Costaceae

(*g*) Solitary bodies '*trough-shaped*' (e.g. Fig. 67. K, p. 304)

Heliconiaceae   **Musaceae**

(Silica-bodies in these 2 families, though very similar, can be distinguished by the depth of the central depression.)

B. Calcium Oxalate

Often widely and abundantly distributed, the following special types should be noted.

1. *Raphide-sacs*

   Bromeliaceae   **Lowiaceae**   **Strelitziaceae**
   Heliconiaceae   **Musaceae**

2. *Raphide-canals* (see p. 54)

                          Commelinaceae

Triceratella is distinguished by raphide-canals next to veins, unlike all other genera in the Commelinaceae.

C. Mucilage

1. Idioblastic *mucilage cells* (Fig. 86. L–N, p. 380)

                          Marantaceae (occasional)

2. Mucilage secreted in *slime-cavities* or canals

   Bromeliaceae   **Cannaceae**   **Rapateaceae**

   (For slime- or mucilage-secreting hairs, see p. 401.)

D. Laticifers

Musaceae   Zingiberaceae (rare)

E. Oil-Cells

Zingiberaceae

F. VESSELS

1. Vessels restricted to *roots*

Bromeliaceae	**Heliconiaceae**	**Musaceae**[1]
Cannaceae	**Lowiaceae**	Strelitziaceae
Costaceae	Marantaceae	Zingiberaceae
Flagellariaceae		
(*Hanguana*?)		

2. Vessels restricted to *root and stem*

Bromeliaceae	Mayacaceae	Strelitziaceae
Marantaceae	**Rapateaceae**	Zingiberaceae

3. Vessels in *all parts*

Bromeliaceae	Flagellariaceae	Marantaceae
Commelinaceae	(*Flagellaria*?	Mayacaceae[2]
Eriocaulaceae	*Joinvillea*?)	**Xyridaceae**

[1] Cheadle records vessels in the inflorescence axis of *Musa*.
[2] Cheadle records vessels in the leaf of *Mayaca*.

POSTSCRIPT AND COMMENTARY

By C. R. METCALFE

INTRODUCTION

IT is not possible, at the stage which has been reached in the investigations on which *Anatomy of the Monocotyledons* is based, to make a detailed anatomical comparison between the families described in this volume and all of the other families of monocotyledons. Nevertheless it is possible to direct attention to some points of general interest, and it is with this object in mind that this postscript to, and commentary on, Dr. Tomlinson's work has been written. Attention is directed particularly to plants belonging to other families which have already been studied or are still being investigated by the team of botanists who are engaged in preparing *Anatomy of the Monocotyledons*.

RELATIONSHIP OF MONOCOTYLEDONS TO DICOTYLEDONS

The general elementary introduction to the anatomy of monocotyledons that is given to students no doubt gives an over-simplified picture of the subject. This is partly because the strongest emphasis is generally placed on the well-known anatomical differences between the monocotyledons, on the one hand, and the dicotyledons, on the other. The lack of a cambium in the monocotyledons is particularly stressed, although it is conceded that the occasional radial alignment of cells between the xylem and phloem of monocotyledons may provide evidence of previous cambial activity now almost lost in the evolutionary history. This question is most frequently referred to by those botanists who seek to prove that the monocotyledons are derived from dicotyledons. It is doubtful if there is any truth in this argument. It must also be pointed out that many monocotyledons, particularly the palms, have achieved arboreal proportions without having a cambium, whilst monocotyledons such as *Dracaena* and those belonging to a few other related genera have a cambium-like zone of dividing cells in the ground tissue of the outer part of the stem which provides a mechanism for increasing the girth of the stem whilst adding additional vascular bundles at the same time. Dr. Tomlinson has reminded us in Volume II of this series (p. 19) that the growth in thickness of palms is achieved through the activity of a primary thickening meristem 'which is continuous beneath successive leaf-bases and in which cell-division is largely in a tangential plane'. Internodal elongation begins only when the activity of this thickening meristem has ceased, so that, in effect, the trunk has often already attained considerable thickness at only a short distance below the apical meristem. An additional increase in girth in some palm stems is subsequently achieved by the division and further enlargement of cells which take place over a wide area, particularly in the parenchymatous ground tissue of the central cylinder.

The method by which a palm stem increases in girth seems at first sight to be something rather anomalous amongst the monocotyledons as a whole, until we remember, as Dr. Tomlinson has pointed out, that fugaceous thickening meristems occur in other monocotyledons with thick fleshy axes, notably in the Zingiberaceae and Musaceae, both of which families are included in this volume.

We may then perhaps ask ourselves whether the mechanism, by variations of which the stems of monocotyledons increase in thickness, may not be more significant in the evolutionary history of monocotyledons than the possession of a somewhat dubious relic of a true cambium. It might be argued that the non-cambial methods of increasing in girth have arisen in monocotyledons after their capacity to grow in thickness by a normal cambium had been lost. When we remember, however, that palm-like stems have been found a long way back in the geological record it seems hard to believe that they are derived from dicotyledons which have lost their cambium and developed a new mechanism by which the arboreal habit has been achieved. Although we have no positive proof, it seems on the face of things more plausible to believe that monocotyledons have followed their own line of evolutionary development independently of that of dicotyledons, at least for a very long period of geological time. It is particularly hard to picture any monocotyledonous families as we know them today as having had any immediate derivation from the existing families of dicotyledons. There are objections even to the derivation of the Alismataceae and their allies from a ranalian stock (Metcalfe 1963). This is because of differences in the structure of stomata and in the nature of the aerenchymatous ground tissue in the 2 families. Besides, vessels in the Alismataceae are confined to the roots, but in the Ranunculaceae they occur throughout the plant.

HISTOLOGICAL SIMILARITIES AND DIVERSITIES WITHIN THE MONOCOTYLEDONS

(i) The significance of size of the plant body

It may at this point be useful to refer briefly to the over-all size of monocotyledonous plants, for the size is clearly related to the possession of a method of providing the necessary mechanical support and the vasculature that is needed to maintain a plant body of large proportions. It is often emphasized that monocotyledons are mainly herbaceous plants, and it is implied that this is so because their lack of cambium makes it impossible for them to produce woody trunks. Attention has, however, already been drawn to the fact that palms may attain the dimensions of quite large trees. Then we can remind ourselves that even the grasses can be arboreal as exemplified by the bamboos which in some areas form bamboo 'forests' when the larger species grow together in great masses.

It is true that few, if any, of the plants described in this volume attain such a large stature as the palms and bamboos or even as the screw pines (Pandanaceae), but nevertheless some of them such as the bananas and Heliconias with their pseudostems (see also Editor's Preface on p. vii), although herbaceous, are of exceptionally large size compared with most herbs in temperate regions. These large monocotyledons are all natives of the warmer parts of the world, and it will be noticed that although small and large monocotyledons occur together in these tropical and sub-tropical regions, as one proceeds northwards and southwards to the temperate zones the large monocotyledons disappear and only those that are relatively small in size are still to be found. From this we may perhaps conclude that the mechanisms by which monocotyledons are able to attain large dimensions are successful in warm countries, but less so where it is colder. There is a similar tendency for arboreal dicotyledons to be more numerous in the tropics, but nevertheless there are also many dicotyledonous trees and shrubs in temperate regions. Dr. Tomlinson believes, however, that large monocotyledons with perennial above-ground parts fail to exist in cool temperate regions because they have no dormancy mechanism rather than because they have no cambium.

(ii) *Vascular bundles*

It is not unusual to speak of vascular bundles in monocotyledons as if there were but one type. It is true that they are all alike in showing no convincing evidence of a cambium and, in transverse sections, their distribution is often apparently scattered. On the other hand, for example in the culms of many grasses, they are restricted to only a few rings or even to a single circle. Similar bundles occur also in a few dicotyledonous families such as Amaranthaceae, Chenopodiaceae, and Piperaceae. Then again transverse sections of the dicotyledonous Nymphaeaceae show widely dispersed vascular bundles recalling those in the aquatic monocotyledons belonging to Hutchinson's Calyciferae. The occurrence of apparently scattered vascular bundles can therefore serve as a useful diagnostic character among dicotyledons and monocotyledons because of its relatively restricted taxonomic distribution. We must not, however, take this one character as evidence of close relationship unless the ontogeny and 3-dimensional arrangement of the vascular bundles is also alike in the families concerned. Current research shows that, in those monocotyledons which have been studied in detail, there is a regular pattern underlying the apparently scattered arrangement of the bundles in transverse section (Zimmermann and Tomlinson 1968). The further outcome of these investigations is keenly awaited.

Those who speak of monocotyledonous vascular bundles as if they were all alike generally picture them as resembling the large 'basic-type' in grasses with 1–2 conspicuously large lateral metaxylem elements (Fig. XX, 3, p.194 of Vol. I). Dr. Tomlinson has already confirmed in the palms that transverse sections of a single vascular bundle taken at different levels have a cross-sectional appearance that is far from uniform. We must, therefore, be on our guard when making use of variations in the structure of bundles for taxonomic purposes. However, with careful safeguards to ensure that comparisons are drawn only between sections taken at the corresponding level in the plants under examination, the variations in bundle structure can be very useful. The range of bundle structure in the grasses themselves provides some good examples (Vol. I, p. xxxiv). Differences in the bundle structure in the palms have to be treated much more circumspectly because their appearance changes so much at different levels. The very peculiar bundles in the yam family (Dioscoreaceae), to which attention has been briefly directed (Metcalfe 1963), will be discussed much more fully by Dr. E. Ayensu in a forthcoming volume in this series. We have also been reminded (Stant 1964, 1967) that the conducting tissue is greatly reduced in the aquatic plants belonging to the

Alismataceae and Butomaceae. Here, no doubt, less mechanical support and less well-developed vascular bundles are needed than in monocotyledons that occur on dry land. We must remember, however, by way of contrast, that although the Common Reed (*Phragmites communis*) grows at the margins of rivers, ponds, and lakes, it is provided with well-developed vascular bundles and mechanical tissue. Reeds, however, are not buoyed up by the water in the same way as members of the Alismataceae and Butomaceae, and their tall culms would collapse and their leaves would wilt when exposed to strong winds were it not for the mechanical support within them.

(iii) *Hairs*

Hairs are, on the whole, less frequent and of fewer types in monocotyledons than in dicotyledons. It is true that there are some families of dicotyledons in which hairs are infrequent or from which they are perhaps absent. On the other hand, there are some families of monocotyledons in which hairs are numerous and of diverse types. Of the families described in this volume the Bromeliaceae, Commelinaceae, and Eriocaulaceae stand out because of the numerous and diverse hairs which they exhibit. The hairs, or more strictly scales, of the Bromeliaceae are particularly interesting, especially from the ecological standpoint, because of their capacity to absorb water. This is of special significance for the epiphytic species as Dr. Tomlinson has reminded us. So far as we are aware precisely similar scales are not known to occur in other families of monocotyledons, although from statements in the literature it is clear that water-absorbing hairs occur in certain dicotyledons (Haberlandt 1914). The superficial similarity of the scales in some of the Bromeliaceae to those that occur in certain sections of the genus *Rhododendron* is very striking, although there are notable points of difference in the detailed structure of the scales. Cowan (1950) points out that the scales of rhododendrons, like those of Bromeliaceae, serve to reduce transpiration but he also states that the scales in both families, at least in some circumstances, serve to absorb water as well. More precisely Cowan (1950, p. 103) in making a comparison between the scales in the 2 families says that 'The Rhododendron scale appears to function in an homologous but somewhat different manner'. For further details the reader is referred to Cowan's book. Attention should also be directed to one of the categories of trichome in the Commelinaceae to which Dr. Tomlinson refers as 3-celled glandular micro-hairs. These are of special interest because, in some respects, they recall the micro-hairs of the Gramineae, which, although usually 2-celled, are similar in form although much smaller. This may have taxonomic significance and supports the opinion held by some botanists that the Gramineae are related to, although more specialized than, the Commelinaceae. Similar hairs have been noted only occasionally amongst the Cyperaceae, e.g. in *Lagenocarpus* (Metcalfe 1963).

(iv) *Chlorenchyma in lamina*

In spite of the very great diversity of external form which is to be found in the leaves of the plants described in this volume, the leaf blade (lamina) is very frequently dorsiventral in structure. That is to say the mesophyll is differentiated in such a way that the cells in the adaxial and abaxial parts of

E e

the chlorenchyma are not alike. This is generally made apparent by the differentiation of the adaxial chlorenchyma into palisade cells, although their palisade-like character is not necessarily very pronounced. Although leaves with adaxial palisade cells occur in families such as the Gramineae and Cyperaceae, this is not really characteristic of these last 2 families. Then again among the plants described in this present volume isobilateral leaves are uncommon, and this applies also to the Cyperaceae as well as to the Juncaceae in which isobilateral structure is still more rare. Isobilateral structure occurs also in other families of monocotyledons that have not yet been described in *Anatomy of the Monocotyledons*, and it is probably most familiar in temperate regions among the cultivated Bearded Irises. It should be noted, however, that various types of elaboration of the isobilateral leaf are to be found amongst the Cyperaceae (Metcalfe and Gregory 1964), of which a more complete account will appear in a forthcoming volume.

(v) *Hypodermis in lamina*

The development of one or more histologically distinctive hypodermal cell layers is characteristic of many of the plants described in this volume. These cells are most commonly present beneath the adaxial epidermis. Usually the hypodermis consists of thin-walled, often inflated, translucent cells, and the layers of these cells may be continuous or discontinuous. In a few species the hypodermal layers are sclerotic. These useful diagnostic characters are also to be seen in other families of monocotyledons such as the Cyperaceae and to a smaller extent the Gramineae and they likewise occur amongst the palms. The presence of a hypodermis tends to be taxonomically sporadic in all of the families, and it serves therefore as a character of diagnostic value rather than one that provides reliable evidence of affinity between the plants in which a hypodermis is known to occur.

(vi) *Air-canals and cavities*

Air-canals or cavities occur in the axis and blade of the leaf as well as in stems and roots. They may be either enlarged intercellular spaces or arise by the breakdown of translucent cells. In some genera and species the cells that become disorganized are polygonal or rounded and in others stellate. When the cells break down, transverse septa sometimes remain, and may provide support for vascular bundles running transversely to the long axis of the organs in which they occur. The transverse bundles frequently, but not invariably, serve as commissures interconnecting the longitudinal bundles. Air-canals are prevalent in, but by no means confined to, aquatic plants and those that occur in marshes. Among monocotyledons they are especially well-developed in such families as the Alismataceae and Butomaceae. They also occur in plants such as the Heliconias, which reach their maximum development in regions where the atmospheric humidity is high. Their distribution in the grasses is of interest for here they are to be found not only in aquatic species but also in the roots of species from dry as well as from wet localities. They occur widely in the leaves and culms of members of the Cyperaceae, but there are numerous members of the family in which they are not present. One has only to examine transverse sections of the lamina of almost any of our common *Carex* species to find them. Air-canals similar to those of the Cyperaceae are also highly characteristic of the Juncaceae.

From what has just been said it is evident that the common belief that air-canals and aerenchyma are of ecological significance because they occur so widely in aquatic and marsh plants may be misleading. The facts suggest that the tendency for them to develop is more inherent in some taxa than in others and that their ecological significance is secondary. To look at it in another way, when a species has an inherent capacity to develop air-canals or aerenchyma, this characteristic may give the species an advantage when it is in competition with others that grow in water or marshes. However this may be, air-canals are known to occur not only in a number of apparently unrelated monocotyledonous families but also in certain dicotyledons belonging to families between which there are no close affinities. From this we may conclude that the inherent tendency to produce canals may well have originated more than once in the course of evolution.

(vii) *Stomata*

The dominant type of stoma amongst the families described in this volume is paracytic. This again brings the families described here into line with the Gramineae and Cyperaceae, on the one hand, and with the Alismataceae and Butomaceae, on the other. Dr. Tomlinson notes the occurrence of tetracytic stomata in a few families and of stomata with higher numbers of subsidiary cells in others (see p. 404). Tetracytic stomata also occur occasionally in Cyperaceae, e.g. in *Lagenocarpus* (Metcalfe 1963) and in many Palmae (see Vol. II of this series).

Overarching of stomata by cuticular papillae occurs sporadically not only amongst the families described in this volume but also amongst those included in the Glumiflorae.

(viii) *Leaf bases*

It is noteworthy that so many of the plants described in this volume have sheathing leaf bases which may be open or closed. This applies also to the Gramineae, Cyperaceae, and Juncaceae. It may also be significant that in some of the Cyperaceae and Juncaceae, which are commonly regarded as specialized families, the leaf may be reduced so that only the sheathing base remains, carbon assimilation then being taken over by the photosynthetic stem.

(ix) *The ligule*

The ligule is an outgrowth from the upper end of the leaf base and it is situated close to the position in which the lower end of the lamina and the upper end of the sheathing base are joined. The ligule is highly characteristic of grass leaves, in some of which it is represented by a flap of tissue and in others by hairs. Ligules occur also in a few of the plants described in this volume, particularly in the Costaceae and Zingiberaceae, as well as in *Joinvillea* amongst the Flagellariaceae. The presence of a ligule in *Joinvillea* will interest those who believe that this genus may be related to the grasses. Other anatomical characters likewise afford evidence in support of this putative relationship. Those who also feel that there is some evidence in favour of a relationship between the Commelinaceae and Gramineae will be interested to note Dr. Tomlinson's comment that in the Commelinaceae the mouth of the sheath is commonly very hairy, although a true ligule never develops.

(x) *Silica*

Many of the plants described in this volume are characterized by the deposition of silica, usually as bodies of which the shape is constant in and characteristic of the species in which they are exemplified. In spite of speculations concerning the possible function of silica deposits in plants, we are still far from certain what determines their occurrence or what part they play in the economy of the plant. Silica-bodies are to be seen in quite a number of dicotyledonous families but, on the whole, they are much more common in and characteristic of monocotyledons.

The restricted and varied location of silica-bodies within the plant strikes us as very remarkable if we stop to think about it. To begin with it may be noted that it is relatively unusual for silica-bodies to be completely lacking in the families described in this volume. When present, the bodies may be (i) confined to the epidermis; (ii) restricted to internal tissues where they are to be seen especially in cells next to the vascular bundles; (iii) present in the epidermis and next to the vascular bundles; (iv) present in scattered idioblasts without any special locations; (v) restricted to specialized cells with unevenly thickened walls, known as stegmata. In shape they may be spherical, cubical, hat-shaped, druse-like, or trough-shaped.

Some of the above types of silica-bodies and stegmata are common also in the palms. One of the more interesting points to note, however, is that although silica-bodies are very common in the Gramineae, the shapes of the bodies are for the most part quite different from those described in this volume. Furthermore they are to be found chiefly, but not exclusively, in epidermal cells. In some grasses they are restricted to epidermal cells situated above bundles of fibres, but in others they occur in cells between as well as in those above the veins. Furthermore, when present both between and over the veins the shapes of the bodies are often quite different in these 2 types of location within an individual leaf. There is no need to expand this topic any further for it has already received fuller attention throughout Vol. I.

Passing on from the Gramineae to the Cyperaceae we again find silica-bodies in nearly all of them, but here also the shape of the bodies is quite different from that in the Gramineae, the dominant type for the family being conical, although there are many interesting exceptions (Metcalfe and Gregory 1964). The conical bodies of the Cyperaceae are perhaps most similar to those which in this volume are described as hat-shaped, a type which, together with others, is to be found amongst the palms. The nodular bodies of the Cyperaceae also recall those which are here described as druse-like. Then again, although it is generally believed that the Cyperaceae are related to the Juncaceae, silica-bodies are not known to occur in this last family.

The reader may well ask himself what all this means in terms of taxonomy, phylogeny, ecology, and physiology. It is clear that we have still much to learn about the significance of silica not only in the families mentioned in this discussion, but in other monocotyledons in which it is also to be found. The fact that there are many other monocotyledons in which there are no silica-bodies is also a matter for wonder. It should be noted that the occurrence of silica does not appear to be confined to plants from any particular ecological niche. When present they are to be found alike both in species from the tropical jungle as well as in plants exposed to many types of ecological rigour in many different parts of the world. The morphology of silica-bodies must, almost certainly, be genetically controlled, because the shapes of the bodies are constant in and characteristic of the species in which they occur, and there is also clearly a correlation between the types of body and the taxonomic affinities of plants containing them.

CONCLUSION

In concluding this postscript the writer cannot refrain from referring once again to the histological diversity that is being emphasized by the investigations on which these volumes are based. If, for the moment, we ignore the internal structure and consider only the external form of plants we cannot fail to be impressed by the range of morphological variation that we encounter. We are unable to appreciate the full extent of this diversity by laboratory work alone, and it is necessary for us to proceed, as Dr. Tomlinson has done, to parts of the world where botanical exploration is still incomplete. Only then will we learn how much there is about external form that will repay intensive observation in the field. When we reflect that diversity of form is an outward expression of many different arrangements of cells and tissues within the plant body we can hardly fail to realize the magnitude of the task before us in attempting to understand how these numerous cellular patterns develop. The problem of discovering to what extent cellular organization is determined by the demands of environment or is inherent in the plants themselves is also one that will continue to make great demands on research workers for a long time to come. It is to be hoped that these pages will contribute towards these endeavours by presenting facts on which conclusions can be based. Our most immediate purpose is, however, to present classified histological data so that they can be used as an integral part of taxonomy. Readers will no doubt find themselves greatly indebted to Dr. Tomlinson for having brought together so many details that will assist in this direction.

LITERATURE CITED

COWAN, J. M. (1950) *The Rhododendron leaf. A study in epidermal appendages.* Oliver and Boyd, Edinburgh and London. pp. vi+116.

HABERLANDT, G. (1914) *Physiological plant anatomy*, translated from the fourth German edition by Montagu Drummond. Macmillan, London. pp. xv+777.

METCALFE, C. R. (1963) Comparative anatomy as a modern botanical discipline. *Adv. bot. Res.* (ed. R. D. Preston) **1**, 101–47.

—— and GREGORY, M. (1964) Comparative anatomy of monocotyledons. Some new descriptive terms for Cyperaceae, with a discussion of variations in leaf form noted in the family. *Notes from the Jodrell Laboratory*, i, pp. 13.

STANT, M. Y. (1964) Anatomy of the Alismataceae. *J. Linn. Soc.* (Bot.) **59**, 1–42.

—— (1967) Anatomy of the Butomaceae. Ibid. **60**, 31–60.

ZIMMERMANN, M. H. & TOMLINSON, P. B. (1968) Vascular construction and development in the aerial stem of *Prionium* (Juncaceae). *Am. J. Bot.* **55**, in press.

AUTHOR INDEX

SUBJECT INDEX

Note: *Where families have been specially studied, the page numbers are given in bold type. Italic page numbers are references to figures.*

F f

PRINTED IN GREAT BRITAIN
AT THE UNIVERSITY PRESS, OXFORD
BY VIVIAN RIDLER
PRINTER TO THE UNIVERSITY